# astronomy

*through space and time*

# astronomy
*through space and time*

s u n e   e n g e l b r e k t s o n
*p a c e   u n i v e r s i t y*

**WCB**
**Wm. C. Brown Publishers**
Dubuque, Iowa•Melbourne, Australia•Oxford, England

**Book Team**

Project Editor  Jane Ducham
Production Editor  Carol M. Besler
Designer  Eric Engelby
Art Editor  Rachel Imsland
Photo Editor  Carrie Burger
Permissions Coordinator  Karen L. Storlie
Visuals/Design Developmental Consultant  Donna Slade

## Wm. C. Brown Publishers
A Division of Wm. C. Brown Communications, Inc.

Vice President and General Manager  Beverly Kolz
Vice President, Publisher  Earl McPeek
Executive Editor  Jeffrey L. Hahn
Vice President, Director of Sales and Marketing  Virginia S. Moffat
National Sales Manager  Douglas J. DiNardo
Marketing Manager  Christopher T. Johnson
Advertising Manager  Janelle Keeffer
Director of Production  Colleen A. Yonda
Publishing Services Manager  Karen J. Slaght
Permissions/Records Manager  Connie Allendorf

## Wm. C. Brown Communications, Inc.

President and Chief Executive Officer  G. Franklin Lewis
Corporate Senior Vice President, President of WCB Manufacturing  Roger Meyer
Corporate Senior Vice President and Chief Financial Officer  Robert Chesterman

Cover photos: Background: © Hans Neleman; Insets: Top: NASA;
Middle and Bottom: Courtesy ROE/Anglo-Australian Observatory

Copyedited by Jim Clark

Photo Research by Toni Michaels

The credits section for this book begins on page 437 and is considered an
extension of the copyright page.

# topics
# overview

▲

# c o n t e n t s

▲

s
contents

vii

## 4

## A Universe of Matter, Force, and Radiation 59

page 91

## 5

## Optical, Radio, and High-Energy Astronomy 75

## 6

## An Overview of the Solar System 95

contents

**page 123**

7

# The Earth and Moon System 113

8

# The Terrestrial Planets: Mercury, Venus, and Mars 137

9

# The Giant Planets: Jupiter and Saturn 161

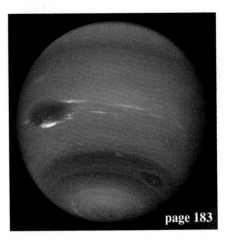

**page 183**

10

# The Outer Worlds: Uranus, Neptune, and Pluto 183

contents

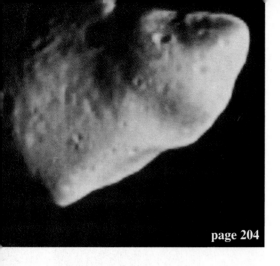

contents

page 350

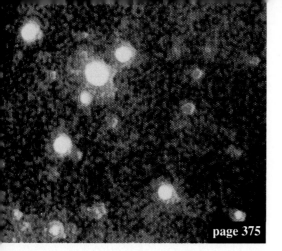

page 375

contents

# preface

*Astronomy: Through Space and Time* is designed to provide an introduction to astronomy for undergraduate students who take science courses as elective subjects. These are liberal arts students as well as business, education, science, and mathematics majors. This textbook makes no assumptions about students' preparations in science and mathematics when treating principles of astrophysics, celestial mechanics, or spherical astronomy. The purpose of this book is to stimulate thinking, develop scientific attitudes and observational skills, and encourage students to pursue astronomy as an avocational activity.

The reasons for astronomy's increased involvement in the educational process are numerous: the fascination of the sky, the historical development of astronomy as a science, recent discoveries of black-hole candidates and exotic active galaxies, and advances in our understanding of the origin and structure of the universe. Such topics promote useful classroom and observational experiences that provide scientific literacy to a larger segment of the population. Astronomy contributes some of the scientific and mathematical skills required by an advanced technical society. Thus, astronomy serves as an important tool to help prepare students to face the economic, social, and political experiences in the years ahead.

One concern confronting educators today is how science—and in particular, astronomy—can serve the public and keep our institutions competitive into the next century. A report on the positive influence of astronomy was published in 1990 by the Space Telescope Science Institute, operated by the Association of Universities for Research in Astronomy. The report entitled "An Education Initiative in Astronomy" states that "in the 1990s, the foremost educational problem for astronomers is *in the population at large.* The youth of America are failing to learn adequate science and math skills. The shortfall undermines our economy, which depends on advanced technology and industrial innovation. The group also felt that "astronomy has a significant role to play in improving the science literacy of the public and in attracting more minorities into scientific and technical careers."

## About the Book

*Astronomy: Through Space and Time* contains subject matter suitable for a one-semester course at universities, colleges, and state community colleges that offer introductory courses in astronomy. Topics are grouped into four sections. The first contains related material that provides a foundation for topics treated in later chapters. The remaining three sections deal with the solar system, stars, and galaxies.

"Foundations" (chapters 1 through 5) introduces the sky as seen from the Earth. Coordinates are generated on the celestial sphere to locate and measure the positions of celestial objects; time is treated as a means to record astronomical events and to compute position. This section focuses on the forces of nature that interact with matter; on the nature of radiant energy; and on the detection of electromagnetic radiation by means of ground-based telescopes, orbiting observatories, and other instruments. In addition, this section focuses on the historical development of astronomy.

"The Solar System" (chapters 6 through 11) begins with an overview of the solar system. Chapter 7 follows with a discussion of the Earth and Moon. In the following chapters I have grouped Mercury, Venus, and Mars as rocky terrestrial planets; Jupiter and Saturn as liquid and solid hydrogen giant planets; and Uranus and Neptune as distant icy planets. Pluto is described as a tiny, distant planet that resembles the major satellites of Uranus and Neptune. Following this I discuss satellites with their respective planets. And lastly, asteroids, comets, and meteoric fragments are grouped as minor members of the solar system.

In "Our Sun and Other Stars" (chapters 12 through 16), the Sun serves as a bridge between the solar system and the distant stars. A general discussion of the stars includes topics such as stellar distance measurement; magnitudes; classification; and the aggregation of stars into binary systems, clusters, and associations. Stellar evolution is described from the birth of stars in diffuse dust and gas to later stages of energy production. Terminal stages as white dwarfs, neutron stars, and black holes complete the section.

"Our Milky Way and Other Galaxies of the Universe" (chapters 17 through 20) begins with a description of the Milky Way Galaxy in which the Sun is located. The Milky Way system represents one of many galaxies that populate the universe. The galaxies are classified according to their physical appearances. Most are found in galaxy clusters, which in turn form superclusters. Some galaxies have active nuclei: radio galaxies, Seyfert galaxies, and quasars. The enormous energy emitted by active galaxies may be produced by a central black hole. This section ends with the question of the structure, origin, and development of the observable universe from a burst of energy to the stars and galaxies observed today.

## To the Instructor

In *Astronomy: Through Space and Time,* our objective is to provide more than a flow of astronomical "facts." There are three categories of activities: subject matter understandings, habits of thinking, and skills. All textbooks provide the necessary subject matter, but this should not be the only purpose of a text designed for an introductory course in astronomy. Subject matter must serve as a method of procedure to instill habits of thinking and to develop skills. Habits of thinking requires the selection of problems involving analysis of data, accurate observation of phenomena, development of conclusions based on data relevant to a problem, analysis of evidence, and establishment of causes on the basis of observed effects.

In a laboratory, students are exposed to specific skills in the preparation of demonstrations and experiments. The laboratory as well as observational exercises in astronomy should be an integral part of the program of studies. Therefore, in *Astronomy: Through Space and Time,* exercises are provided in each chapter in Sky Watchers boxes, which are designed to motivate students to engage in outdoor observations. Planetarium instruction can be a worthy laboratory supplement to actual observations.

Moreover, mathematical skills have not been overlooked nor deemphasized but remain an integral part of the learning process. A large part of the physics and mathematics instruction has been treated separately in each chapter's Methods and Understandings boxes. This arrangement provides each instructor the opportunity to determine which topics are applicable to a given situation. Treat the Methods and Understandings topics as resource unit material that can be used at the discretion of the instructor. Both the Sky Watchers and Methods and Understandings boxes are designed to stimulate critical thinking and to follow a conceptual approach in reaching the objective set forth in this book.

## Ancillary Materials

*Astronomy: Through Space and Time* is accompanied by several supporting materials designed to give instructors and students a more productive experience with introductory astronomy. Among these supports are:

*WCB Test Generation Software:* Software for the Mac, IBM, or Apple environments. This software will allow instructors to prepare tests, exams, and quizzes using a bank of prepared questions. Instructors will also be able to manipulate the questions provided as well as create and save their own testing material.

*Instructor's Manual:* A printed resource for instructors, including transparency masters, lecture objectives, a list of transparencies and slides provided by the publisher, the printed contents of the WCB test generation software, and

related teaching suggestions.

*Transparencies:* A collection of 100 full-color illustrations taken from the textbook for overhead use in the classroom.

*Slides:* A collection of 100 full-color photos taken from the textbook for a closer look in the classroom.

For more information on the above supports and for information on additional software, video, and videodisc support in astronomy, please contact your local WCB Representative, or call the WCB Educational Services Department at 1–800–228–0459.

You may also direct your questions and comments to:

Wm. C. Brown Publishers
2460 Kerper Boulevard
Dubuque, IA 52001
Attention: Physics/Astronomy Editorial Department

## Acknowledgments

Grateful appreciation is expressed to many educators and scientists for their help and inspiration. I acknowledge the observations from the AAVSO international data base sent to me by AAVSO Director Janet A. Mattei. I wish to thank my colleagues, the staff, and the students at Pace University for their assistance, especially James A. Cannon, Dmeter Yablonsky, Agnes Sarlo, Robert Loomis, Joan Botknecht, Matthew Ganis, and Maheen Yunus. My appreciation also goes to Sandi Kitt, librarian at the American Museum-Hayden Planetarium, who gave assistance with their extensive library of research books and materials.

Special thanks and appreciation to all those who reviewed all or part of the manuscript:

**Keung L. Luke**
California State University, Long Beach

**Thomas W. Noonan**
Brockport State College

**Michael Stewart**
San Antonio College

**Dennis Hibbert**
North Seattle Community College

**Bill E. Burnley**
Murray State University

**Bruce D. Dod**
Mercer University

**Charles D. Teague**
Eastern Kentucky University

**David Curott**
University of North Alabama

**John Pye**
Maui Community College

**Steve Danford**
University of North Carolina at Greensboro

**Norman A. Higginbotham**
Southeastern Louisiana University

preface

In addition, I would like to express my sincere appreciation for the invaluable aid provided by all staff members of Wm. C. Brown Communications, Inc., in the preparation of this work from an initial manuscript to an attractive book. A special acknowledgment to Jeffery Hahn, Executive Editor; Jane Ducham, Project Editor; Bob Fenchel, Developmental Editor; Carol Besler, Production Editor; Carrie Burger, Photo Editor; Karen Storlie, Permissions Editor; Rachel Imsland, Art Editor; Eric Engelby, Designer; and Susie Kotz, Senior Secretary.

Finally, I am deeply indebted to my wife, Grace Victoria, and to members of our family for providing helpful suggestions, stimulating conversation, and much encouragement.

The title of this text, *Astronomy: Through Space and Time*, may remind the reader of a book by the English astronomer Sir James Jeans. As an author of popular books over a generation ago, Sir James Jeans inspired many young people, including this author, to pursue a lifelong interest in astronomy. In recognition, the title of one of his books was adapted and used as part of the title of the present work.

preface

A Babylonian astrological stone from about 1200 B.C. showing
symbols representing the Sun, Moon, and stars.

Long before the beginning of written history, people observed the Sun, Moon, planets, and stars. Then, as now, the sky served as a timekeeper and calendar for planting and harvesting crops, dating festivals, and predicting solar and lunar eclipses.

Early sky watchers did not practice astronomy as a science. Instead, they based their astronomical practices on mythology and mysticism. Their observations did not lead to general laws, nor were they subject to verification. As a science, astronomy is a method of studying the heavens; the motions, magnitudes, distances, and physical nature of celestial bodies.

## Sumerian – Babylonian Astronomy

An early civilization established by the Sumerians flourished between the Tigris and Euphrates Rivers in about the third millenium B.C. These people, and later the Babylonians, worshipped celestial divinities: the sky (Anu), the Sun (Shamash), the Moon (Sin), the brightest planet Venus (Ishtar), and the constellation Orion (Ningirsu). They were convinced that knowledge of the motions of the Sun, Moon, and planets was needed to predict future events on Earth (fig. 1.1). Early worshippers practiced *astrology* and tried to document the alleged influence of the stars on the affairs and destinies of people. This superstition was passed down to the Greeks, and through them to other Europeans, eventually influencing astronomers as late as the Renaissance.

The Babylonians developed tables showing the calculated positions of the Sun, Moon, and planets (fig 1.1). They grouped the stars into **constellations** that portrayed the various people and animals in legend and mythology. The Babylonians also divided some of the fixed stars into twelve constellations of the **zodiac,** which served as a background for the moving Sun, Moon, and planets.

**figure 1.1**

The planet Venus and the early crescent Moon in conjunction. Babylonian astrologers believed that configurations of the Moon, planets, and stars influenced future events.

Early astronomers determined the position of the Sun at the beginning of each season by measuring the length of the noon shadow cast by an upright pillar called a *gnomon* (fig. 1.2). Measuring the position of the Sun was especially important on the first day of spring because that day was the start of the new year. In those days, spring began when the Sun was in the constellation Taurus, the bull, a powerful deity early Babylonians believed responsible for rejuvenation of the Earth.

The Babylonians also developed a lunar calendar and predicted eclipses. The lunar calendar is based on the time re-

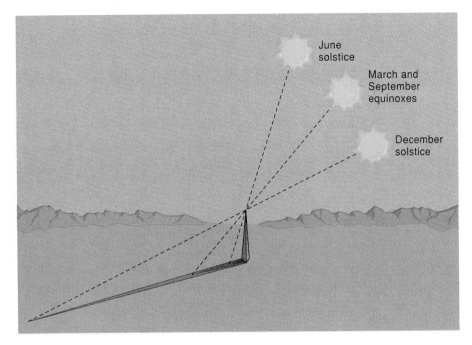

**figure 1.2**
Ancient people measured the length of the shadow cast by a gnomon to determine the altitude of the Sun. The gnomon provided a way to calculate the length of the day and the year, the beginning of each season, and the inclination of the Earth's axis.

▲ a. Total lunar eclipse

b. Total solar eclipse ▼

**figure 1.3**
*a.* A lunar eclipse occurs when the full Moon enters the shadow cast by the Earth. *b.* A solar eclipse happens when the new Moon passes between the Earth and Sun.

quired for the Moon to pass through its phases. Once the Babylonians established tables for the Sun and Moon, they could predict **lunar eclipses.** A lunar eclipse occurs when the full Moon enters the shadow cast by the Earth (fig 1.3a). An eclipse is a rare event because the full Moon is usually either above or below the Earth's shadow.

**Solar eclipses** are more difficult to predict because they can be observed only from a narrow path made by the Moon's shadow across the surface of the Earth. A solar eclipse occurs when the Moon passes between the Earth and the Sun (fig. 1.3b). When the Greek historian Callisthenes reached Babylon during Alexander the Great's conquest of the city, he sent Aristotle a table of eclipse predictions dating back about two thousand years.

## Classical Greek Astronomy

Greek science began with Thales (640–546 B.C.), who learned geometry in Egypt, then gave that knowledge to the Greeks. He was the first to provide abstract proofs of geometrical theorems. This innovation provided astronomers with a way to express mathematically the positions and motions of the celestial bodies.

Thales proposed a universe of earth, air, water, and fire, with water as the basic element. He reasoned that water condensed into solids and evaporated to produce air that in turn generated fire. Thales placed a flat Earth in the center of a universe of air, supported by water. The Sun and stars served as celestial fires, and celestial objects moved in circular paths around a central Earth. Here we see the origin of the **geocentric world system** that was finally challenged in the sixteenth century by the **heliocentric world system** of Copernicus.

Eudoxus of Cnidus (408–355 B.C.), a student of Plato, developed the first mathematical **model** describing the motions of celestial bodies. Astronomers consider his scheme of concentric spheres around a stationary Earth to be the beginning of astronomy as a science. His model explained the phenomenon rather than abstractly resembling the physical system. Thus Eudoxus accounted for the motions of the Sun, Moon, planets, and stars.

Aristotle (384–322 B.C.) proposed a new way to study nature. Using the observational method, he developed the principle of planetary motion described by Eudoxus. Aristotle modified the Eudoxian model by adding more spheres, bringing the total to 55. The outer stellar sphere served as the Prime Mover that transmitted its motion through the additional spheres down to the inner sphere of the Moon.

Aristotle's observations were significant contributions to astronomy. He found evidence for the shape of the Earth, and the reason for the Moon's phases and eclipses; and he calculated the relative distances between celestial objects. Aristotle confirmed that the Earth is a sphere by observing the change in altitude of stars when seen from different latitudes, and the curvature of the Earth's shadow on the Moon during a lunar eclipse. He turned to the stars for further proof of the Earth's curvature, concluding that Earth must be small when compared with the celestial sphere because a small change in the observer's position north or south will cause a substantial change in the altitude of the stars. Although many of his interpretations were wrong, Aristotle's work remained the authority in astronomy for 2,000 years, until the heliocentric system was established during the Renaissance.

## Greek Measurements of Sizes and Distances

Astronomers from Aristotle to Ptolemy (ca. A.D. 100–178) measured the sizes and distances of the Earth, Moon, and Sun. Aristotle knew that the Sun is larger and more distant than the Moon. He reasoned that if the Moon passes between the Earth and the Sun during a solar eclipse and appears to be the same size as the Sun, the Moon must be the smaller body.

A more scientific approach was used by Aristarchus (310–230 B.C.) in his classical work *On the Sizes and Distances of the Sun and Moon*. Aristarchus observed

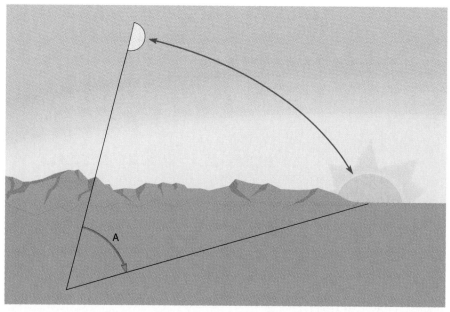

a.

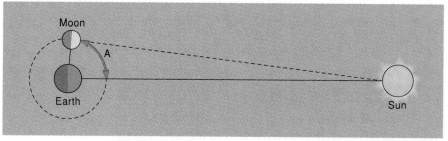

b.

**figure 1.4**

*a.* Aristarchus measured the angle between the Sun and first quarter Moon. *b.* Angle A provided Aristarchus with a way to calculate the relative distances of the Sun and Moon.

the angle between the quarter Moon and the Sun and found it to be 87° (fig. 1.4a). The actual value is 89° 50″ or almost a right angle. Aristarchus did not know the exact moment when the Moon reached quarter phase; if he had, the difference between his measurement and the actual value would be even smaller. Using 87° as the value for the angle, Aristarchus deduced that the Sun was 19 times more distant than the Moon (fig. 1.4b).

To determine the sizes of the Sun and Moon, Aristarchus compared the apparent diameter of the Moon to the Earth's shadow during a lunar eclipse (fig 1.5). He noted that during a solar eclipse, the Sun and Moon are within the cone of darkness. The Sun is in total eclipse for only a few minutes; thus the Sun and Moon must have the same angular dis-

placement. Aristarchus concluded that the diameter of the Sun is 19 times the diameter of the Moon. (The Sun is actually 400 times larger in diameter and 400 times the distance of the Moon.) Later Ptolemy used the same method with remarkable results, but improvements in the measurement of the Sun's diameter and distance were not achieved until the seventeenth century.

After 300 B.C., the intellectual center of Greek civilization shifted to Alexandria, which was the capital of Egypt at that time. Eratosthenes of Cyrene (ca. 275–195 B.C.) went to Alexandria as tutor to the royal household and administrator of the most famous library of antiquity. After Aristotle's time, scholars generally agreed that the Earth was a sphere, but its dimensions remained in

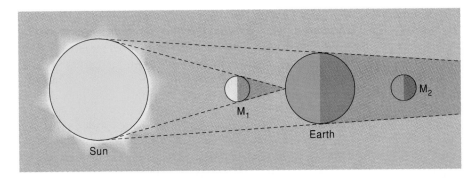

**figure 1.5**

The geometry of solar and lunar eclipses. During a solar eclipse, the shadow cone of the new Moon (M₁) strikes the Earth. During a lunar eclipse, the full Moon (M₂) is immersed in the shadow of the Earth.

The angle of the Sun at Alexandria was found with an instrument called a hemispherical gnomon or *skaphe*. This instrument is a hollow hemisphere with a vertical pin in its center. The shadow of the pin marks an angle equal to 1/50 of the meridian circle of 360°, indicating that the difference in latitude between Alexandria and Syene is 1/50 of the circumference of the Earth. The distance between the two points was 5,000 Egyptian stadia, making the circumference of the Earth 50 × 5,000 = 250,000 stadia. Later, the figure was revised to 252,000 stadia, which is conveniently divisible by 360. The Egyptian stadium is about 158 meters or 517 feet. The measured circumference of 39,670 kilometers (km) is very close to the present value of 40,030 km.

## The First Heliocentric Systems

Not all Greek astronomers supported the geocentric system of Eudoxus and Aristotle. Heraclides (388–312 B.C.) proposed a semi-heliocentric system that kept the Earth at the center but placed Mercury and Venus in concentric circles about the Sun. Aristarchus set forth a true heliocentric hypothesis with the Earth and other planets revolving around the Sun.

Heraclides was one of Plato's pupils, but he favored the doctrine of the Earth in motion. To explain the daily apparent motion of the sky, Heraclides simply gave the Earth an axial spin. Aristotle produced a number of arguments against rotation, pointing out that an object thrown into the air could not return to the point of release if the Earth rotated eastward. This fallacy introduced by Aristotle persisted for over fifteen hundred years, until the arrival of modern astronomy (chapter 3).

Supporters of the geocentric doctrine faced a more significant problem. The planets in their courses vary in brightness, thus they must vary in distance from the Earth. This variance is impossible in the Eudoxian system. Heraclides proposed that Mercury and Venus change brightness because they revolve around the Sun, which in turn moves in a circle about a stationary Earth.

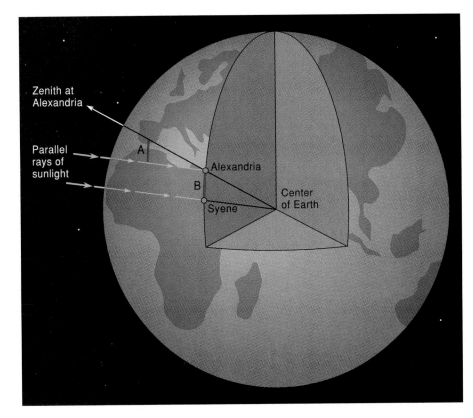

**figure 1.6**

Eratosthenes' measurements. The zenith angle of the Sun at Alexandria (A) is equal to the difference in latitude (B) between Alexandria and Syene. Since the distance between the two locations is known, the circumference of the Earth can be calculated.

doubt. Cleomedes, who lived in the first century A.D., described how Eratosthenes measured the circumference of the Earth to within a few hundred meters of its value (fig. 1.6).

Syene, near present-day Aswan, is south of Alexandria and almost at the latitude of the Tropic of Cancer. Here the noon Sun stands directly above the observer on the first day of the Northern Hemisphere's summer, on or about June 21. According to tradition, on June 21 at Syene, the Sun was reflected from the bottom of a vertical well. On the same day in Alexandria, the Sun's vertical angle equals the difference in latitude between Alexandria and Syene. The two places are almost due north and south of each other. These relative locations are required for proper comparative measurement.

Aristarchus believed that the Sun and the fixed stars were stationary in an infinite universe, and that the Earth revolved in a circle centered on the Sun. How did an advanced heliocentric system evolve at such an early time? Scholars have debated this question. The idea was possibly a natural outcome of the work of Heraclides. The Earth does move as Aristarchus described, but he failed to convince other Greek astronomers. They rejected the system as incapable of accounting for the "appearances of the heavens."

## The Zenith of Greek Astronomy: The Almagest

Hipparchus of Nicea, the greatest of all classical Greek astronomers, made his observations from Alexandria and Rhodes between 160 and 125 B.C. Only one of his works remains: a commentary on Eudoxus and Aratus. Fortunately, his significant contributions were recorded by Ptolemy in the greatest astronomical work of antiquity, the *Almagest.* Hipparchus discovered the Earth's **precession,** a gradual turning of the planet about an imaginary axis at right angles to the plane of its orbit around the Sun. He perfected the geocentric system using circles instead of spheres.

Hipparchus discovered precession by comparing his own observations of lunar eclipses with those made almost two centuries earlier. The position of the Moon during previous eclipse observations indicated that stars have a gradual angular displacement eastward parallel to the ecliptic (see Methods and Understandings 1.1). Hipparchus attributed the precessional cycle to the apparent rotation of the celestial sphere rather than motion of the Earth.

Hipparchus observed a "new star," one that appeared in the sky where no star was known to exist. Such a star reaches maximum brightness, then gradually fades from view. Hipparchus did not understand the nature of these stars. Today, astronomers call them **novae.** The word is Latin for new stars, but they are actually old stars that suddenly erupt and increase in brightness as much as 100,000 times (see chapter 16).

Hipparchus realized the need to record changes in the sky and compiled a *Star Catalogue,* listing over 800 stars. He carefully recorded the positions of the stars so that future generations could measure long-period changes in the sky.

Hipparchus was the first astronomer to classify stars according to brightness. He grouped stars in six **magnitudes** from the brightest (first magnitude) to the faintest (sixth magnitude) stars visible to the unaided eye. Today astronomers use a modified form of Hipparchus's magnitude scale.

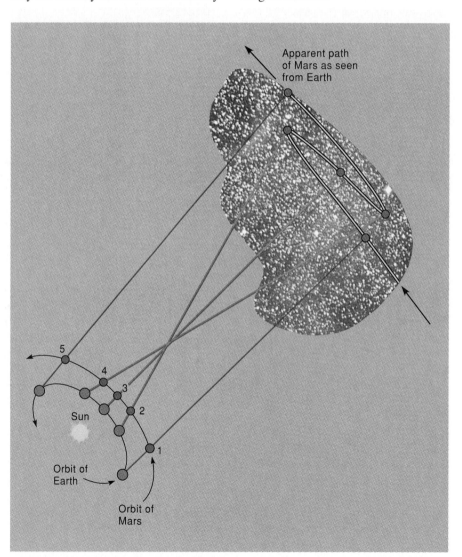

**figure 1.8**

The retrograde motion of Mars is caused by the revolution of the Earth and Mars around the Sun. Between positions 1 and 2, Mars appears to be moving to the east. At positions 2 and 4, Mars appears to be stationary; between positions 2 and 4, it appears to be moving to the west (retrograde motion). At position 3, the Sun, Earth, and Mars are in line. Between positions 4 and 5, Mars appears to be moving eastward once again.

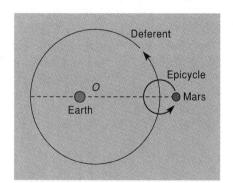

**figure 1.7**

The geocentric system of Ptolemy. Mars revolves in an epicycle centered on a deferent. The deferent is centered at *O,* which is eccentric to the Earth. The center of the epicycle moves uniformly around the deferent.

The *Almagest* of Ptolemy contains the writings of Hipparchus, Eudoxus, Heraclides, Apollonius, and Aristarchus. Without the *Almagest* their contributions might have been lost. Originally it was called the *Mathematical Treatise,* and the *Great Astronomer* when used as a textbook. Arabs called the work *al megiste,* the greatest, and that translated to the *Almagest.* The work is the most comprehensive collection of Greek astronomy.

The *Almagest* consists of thirteen sections called books that deal with the Earth as a sphere at the center of the universe; latitude and differences in the length of the longest day at various latitudes; the obliquity of the ecliptic; and the measurement of the year with respect to the Sun and stars. The main body deals with motions of the heavens according to Greek astronomy.

Ptolemy had to account for two variations in the motions of the planets. The first is a variation of the apparent motion that occurs as the distance between a planet and the Earth changes. He explained this variation by using an eccentric or **deferent** circle (fig. 1.7). In the heliocentric system, the problem is resolved by placing the planet in an elliptical orbit around the Sun.

The second variation refers to the apparent change in the motions of the planets relative to the stars. Ptolemy's model contained an **epicycle** centered on the deferent. Mars, for example, revolves in the epicycle as the center of the epicycle moves along the deferent. When seen in the plane of the epicycle (as from the Earth), Mars appears to move eastward in **direct motion** until it reaches a stationary point, then reverses direction and travels west in **retrograde motion.** The planet then stops again, reverses direction and once more proceeds toward the east. The retrograde motion of Mars is actually caused by Earth passing between Mars and the Sun, as shown in figure 1.8.

## Observing the Sky from the Earth

Let us view the sky as people did before the invention of the telescope. To an earthbound observer, the stars seem to

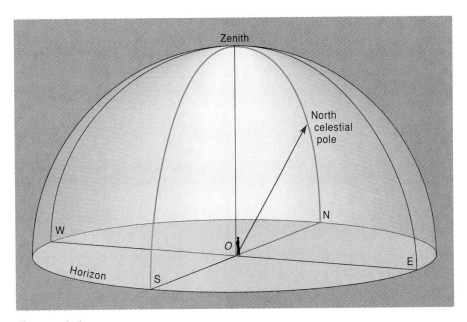

**figure 1.9**

The horizon marks the intersection of the plane of the observer (*O*), called the horizontal plane, with the celestial sphere.

be attached to the inner surface of an extensive vault that forms the sky. Astronomers find this illusion of an imaginary **celestial sphere** very useful; they divide the sky into a grid of intersecting circles and reference points to locate different celestial objects. Think of the celestial sphere as a coordinate system, as astronomers do, to become more familiar with the sky.

From Earth, only half of the celestial sphere can be seen at one time, and the small area of the Earth's surface around you appears as a flat plane (fig. 1.9). The intersection of this plane and the sky is called the **horizon,** the circle separating the visible celestial hemisphere from the invisible half below the horizontal plane. The **cardinal points** (directions)—north, east, south, and west—divide the horizon into four equal parts to provide direction on the Earth as well as in the sky.

## Rotation and Diurnal Motion

As the stars journey across the sky, you and the Earth seem to be stationary at the center of the celestial sphere. We know that the apparent movement of the sky is caused by the **rotation,** or spin, of the Earth around an imaginary axis passing through its center from pole to pole.

The Earth completes one rotation from west to east in about 24 hours, and the celestial sphere seems to complete an opposite **apparent diurnal motion** from east to west.

Picture the Earth at the center of the celestial sphere with its axis extended to the stars. Imagine the extended axis striking the celestial sphere at two opposite points called the north and south **celestial poles.** The celestial sphere appears to pivot on these points, causing the stars to drift in concentric circles around the celestial poles (fig. 1.10). A star located near one of the celestial poles will turn in a smaller **diurnal circle** than one located away from the poles. One star in particular, **Polaris,** the North Star, is almost at the north celestial pole. Its small diurnal circle cannot be detected by the unaided eye, so the star provides a very convenient way to find the north celestial pole.

The apparent diurnal motion of the stars does not look the same from every latitude around the world. If you observe the sky from the middle latitudes of the Northern Hemisphere, the north celestial pole lies between the **zenith** (the point on the celestial sphere directly above the observer) and the north point on the horizon. Your location on the Earth determines the elevation of the celestial

**figure 1.10**

Circumpolar star trails. Circumpolar stars are located between the north celestial pole and the north point on the horizon. The bright star trail near the center is made by Polaris, the North Star.

pole. For example, if your geographic latitude is 40° north, the north celestial pole is the same number of degrees (40) above the north point on the horizon.

Imagine facing north and looking toward the north celestial pole, in the direction of Polaris (fig. 1.11). The celestial sphere turns counterclockwise, carrying the stars around the pole in diurnal circles of increasing size. All the stars between the north celestial pole and the north point remain above the horizon during the entire period of rotation. These stars are **circumpolar stars.** All circumpolar stars are within a diurnal circle that is tangent to or just touching the horizon at the north point.

A star in a larger diurnal circle dips below the northern horizon, sets in the northwest, crosses the north point below the horizon, and rises in the northeast.

Stars farther from the celestial pole make increasingly larger diurnal arcs and spend a longer time below the northern horizon. These stars rise more to the east and set more to the west than stars closer to the pole. A star 90° from the celestial pole makes the largest diurnal arc, rising at the east point and setting at the west point on the horizon. Half of this star's diurnal circle is above the horizon, so the star is visible for half of the rotational period. Stars north of this diurnal circle spend more than 12 hours above the horizon.

The largest diurnal circle is also the **celestial equator** (fig 1.11). The celestial equator is the counterpart of the geographic equator around the Earth. To visualize the celestial equator, imagine a plane passing through the Earth at the geographic equator. The extension of this plane into the sky generates a great circle that bisects the celestial sphere midway between the celestial poles.

Imagine yourself facing south. East is to your left and west is to your right. Picture the celestial equator intersecting the horizon at the east point, reaching its greatest elevation on the celestial sphere above the south point, and intersecting the horizon again at the west point. The

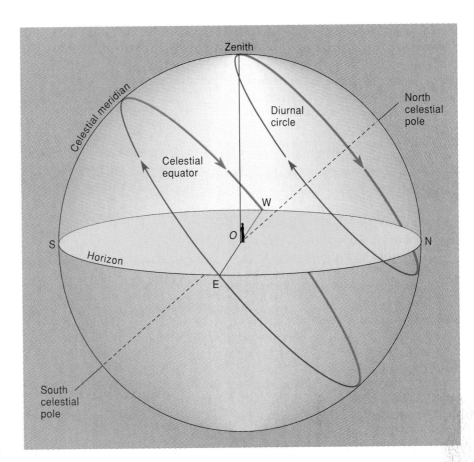

**figure 1.11**

The celestial sphere from 40° north latitude. Diurnal circles cross the sky parallel to the celestial equator.

# SKY WATCHERS 1.1

## estimating angular distance

The angular distance between stars is a basic measurement in astronomy. Angles on the celestial sphere can be estimated using a metric scale or rule divided into centimeters (cm) and millimeters (mm). At arm's length, one centimeter will equal about one degree. To test your accuracy, measure the diameter of the Moon (which is slightly more than 0.5°) by placing your thumbnail on the 5-mm mark and framing the Moon between your thumbnail and the zero point on the scale. The distance between your eye and the scale should equal 60 cm.

For your first project, find your latitude by measuring the angle between the horizon and the north celestial pole. The position of Polaris is a close approximation to the north celestial pole, so you can use Polaris in place of the actual pole. Face north and measure the angular distance to Polaris in 10-cm intervals from the horizon (fig.1.12). How does your estimate compare with the actual value of your latitude?

Another way of measuring angles on the celestial sphere is to keep a record of the angular separations between a few prominent stars. Locate the stars at the end of the bowl of the Big Dipper. They make an angle of 5.5°, or 5.5 cm on your scale. The angle from Polaris to a point midway between those stars is about 30° or one-third the distance between your zenith and horizon. Use these estimates when you measure large angles on the celestial sphere.

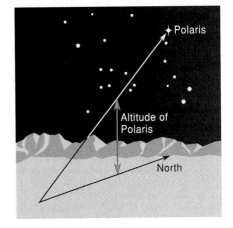

**figure 1.12**

The altitude of Polaris is almost equal to the observer's latitude.

stars south of the celestial equator rise in the southeast and set in the southwest, following diurnal circles that decrease in size toward the south point. More than half of their diurnal circles are obscured, so these stars remain above the horizon for less than 12 hours.

The stars surrounding the south celestial pole are never seen from the middle latitudes in the Earth's Northern Hemisphere. The south celestial pole is below the southern horizon by the same angle as the north celestial pole is elevated above the northern horizon at the middle latitudes. The stars between the south point on the horizon and the south celestial pole are within a circle hidden from your view.

You have observed the effects of the Earth's rotation on the stars seen from the middle latitudes. Now let's look at the sky from pole to pole. Imagine you are at the north geographic pole. The north celestial pole is at your zenith, directly overhead (fig 1.13). As the Earth rotates, the sky seems to turn as before, but now you are at the center of rotation. Thus the stars make circles parallel to the horizon, from left to right. All the stars are circumpolar and do not rise or set. The north celestial pole is overhead and 90° from the horizon, so the celestial equator and the horizon coincide. Only the stars north of the celestial equator are visible, and all stars south of the celestial equator remain obscured.

Now imagine you are standing on the geographic equator. The celestial equator arches overhead from the zenith to the east and west points (fig. 1.14). The celestial poles are at the north and south points. The Earth's axis of rotation lies in the plane of the horizon; thus every star rises and sets perpendicular to the horizon. All the stars from pole to pole remain above the horizon for half the rotational period.

If you are at the south geographic pole, the south celestial pole is overhead at the zenith, and the celestial equator coincides with the horizon. Once again, all

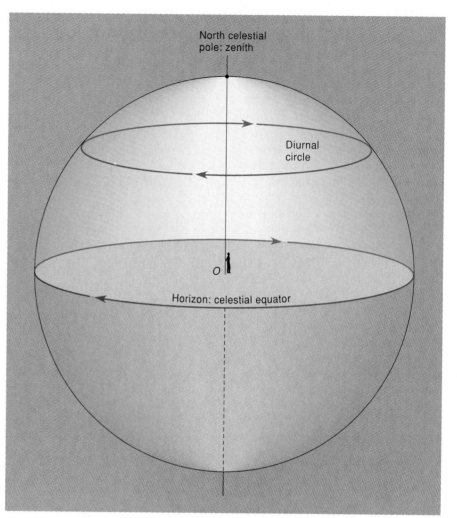

▲ figure 1.13

Celestial sphere showing diurnal circles of the stars as observed from the Earth's north pole. All stars are circumpolar and do not rise or set.

figure 1.14 ▶

Celestial sphere showing diurnal circles of the stars as observed from the Earth's equator. All stars rise and set perpendicular to the horizon.

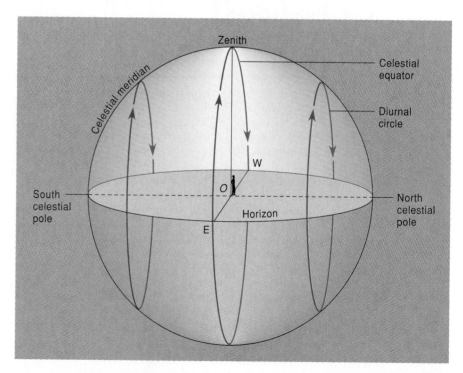

## Precession of the Equinoxes

The equinoxes and solstices do not remain fixed in the same position on the celestial sphere but slowly drift westward and return again among the same stars over a period of about 25,800 years. This apparent change is called the *precession of the equinoxes*. Precession was detected by Hipparchus in the first century B.C. He thought the effect was a motion of the sky, but we know it is the gradual turning of the Earth around an imaginary axis through its center and perpendicular to the plane of the ecliptic (fig. 1.15). This *ecliptic axis* intersects the celestial sphere at two points, the north and south ecliptic poles. As the Earth slowly turns on the ecliptic axis, its rotational axis revolves in a 23 1/2° angle around the ecliptic poles. The effect is similar to the movement you can see in the axis of a spinning toy top. The precessional motion causes the equinoxes and solstices to move westward, and the stars appear to drift eastward parallel to the ecliptic.

Precession is caused by the gravitational attraction of the Sun and Moon trying to bring the Earth's equatorial bulge in line with the ecliptic plane. The Earth counters this attraction by slowly turning its rotational axis clockwise around the ecliptic poles. As the rotational axis changes direction, Polaris will appear to drift away from the north celestial pole and eventually will be replaced by other stars (fig. 1.15 inset).

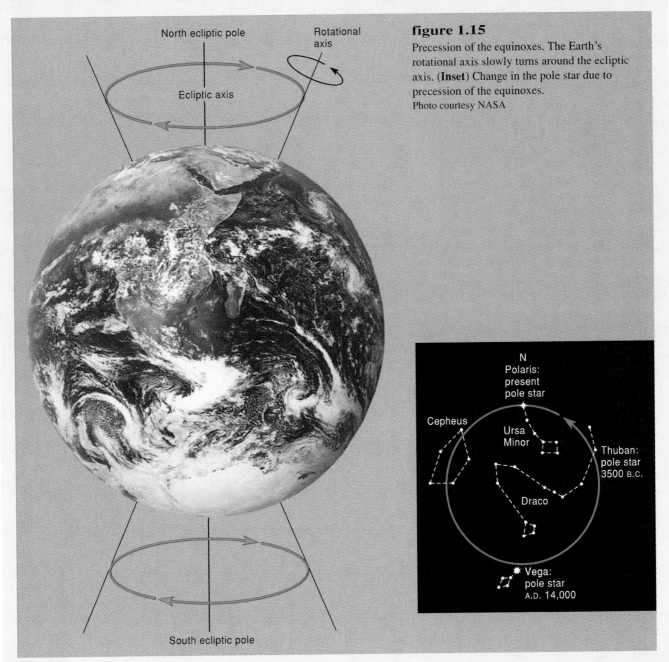

**figure 1.15**
Precession of the equinoxes. The Earth's rotational axis slowly turns around the ecliptic axis. (**Inset**) Change in the pole star due to precession of the equinoxes.
Photo courtesy NASA

the sky from earth

11

the stars move in circles parallel to the horizon, but now from right to left. Only stars south of the equator are visible; the northern sky is perpetually hidden from view.

## Revolution and Annual Motion

During one year the length of day and night changes, the Sun is high in summer and low in winter, and a slow annual westward drift of the stars changes the constellations seen each season. These variations are caused by the orbital motion of the Earth—its **revolution**—and the tilt or **inclination** of the Earth's axis with respect to its orbital plane. The year marks the **period of revolution,** the time in which the Earth completes one circuit around the Sun. The year is divided into four seasons that are determined by the location of the Earth in its orbit.

To better understand inclination, think of the Earth's orbit embedded in a plane passing through the centers of the Sun and the Earth. Half of the Sun and the Earth are above the orbital plane. The direct rays of sunlight that strike the Earth perpendicular to its surface are also in this plane. The Earth's rotational axis is inclined 23 1/2° to an imaginary line at right angles to the plane of the orbit. The Earth's equatorial plane is also inclined 23 1/2° to the plane of the orbit. During the year, the Earth's axis remains parallel, always pointing in the direction of the celestial poles. This parallelism of the axis combined with the inclination of the axis permit the direct rays of the Sun to reach 23 1/2° north and south of the equator, causing seasonal change (fig. 1.16).

The vertical rays of the Sun strike the equator on March 21; the Tropic of Cancer, 23 1/2° north latitude, on June 21; the equator again on September 23; and the Tropic of Capricorn, 23 1/2° south latitude, on December 22. Each of these dates marks the change in the seasons. (From year to year, these dates may vary by one day.)

The revolution of the Earth is reflected on the celestial sphere in the **annual motion** of the Sun. During the year, the Sun appears to drift eastward among the constellations of the zodiac. These constel-

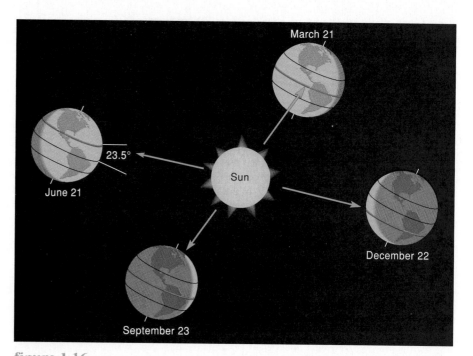

**figure 1.16**

The Earth at different seasons. The Earth's equatorial plane is inclined 23¹/₂° to the plane of the orbit.

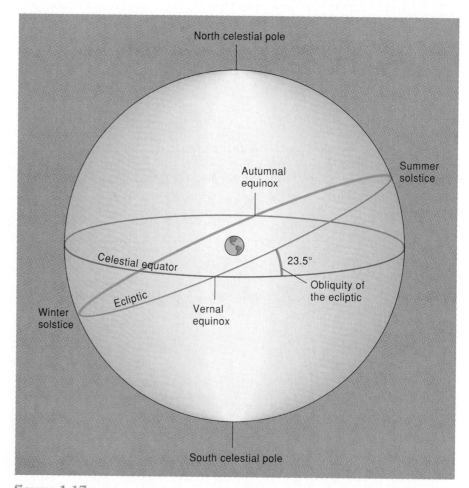

**figure 1.17**

The celestial equator and the ecliptic projected onto the celestial sphere. The solstices and equinoxes locate the position of the Sun on the dates of seasonal changes.

figure 1.18
The full Moon. Bright rays from prominent craters stretch across the surface. The flat lowlands are called marias, Latin for "seas."

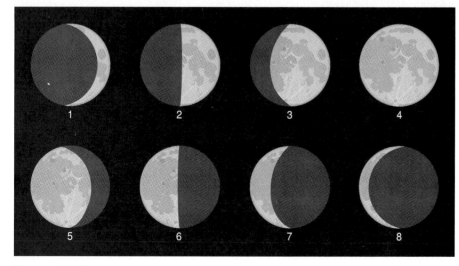

figure 1.19
The phases of the Moon: *1.* waxing crescent, *2.* first quarter, *3.* waxing gibbous, *4.* full, *5.* waning gibbous, *6.* last quarter, *7.* waning crescent, and *8.* late waning crescent prior to new-Moon phase.

lations are Aquarius, Pisces, Aries, Taurus, Gemini, Cancer, Leo, Virgo, Libra, Scorpius, Sagittarius, and Capricornus. There are 360° in a circle and 365 days in the year, so the Sun advances about one degree per day and returns to the same constellation in one revolution of the Earth.

The Earth's revolution causes the Sun to generate another apparent circle on the celestial sphere. In one year, the center of the Sun traces a path called the **ecliptic** among the stars of the zodiac (fig. 1.17). This circle is the projection of the plane of the Earth's orbit onto the celestial sphere. The geographic equator is inclined 23 1/2° to the orbit of the Earth, so the ecliptic is inclined to the celestial equator by an equal amount. This is known as the **obliquity of the ecliptic** (fig 1.17).

The ecliptic and the celestial equator intersect at two opposite points. The first is the **vernal equinox,** where the Sun is situated on the celestial sphere on or about March 21. The **autumnal equinox** marks the position of the Sun on or about September 23. Between the equinoxes are two points on the ecliptic called the **summer solstice** and **winter solstice** where the Sun is located on June 21 and December 22 respectively. The solstices are 23 1/2° north and south of the celestial equator. (Note that the seasons are reversed in the Southern Hemisphere; thus the equinoxes and solstices in this text apply to the Northern Hemisphere.)

## The Motion of the Moon

The changing Moon attracts more attention and admiration than any celestial body (see fig. 1.18). Long the subject of poetic expression, the Moon appears in twilight as a thin crescent enhanced by bright stars or a planet, or rising full with its face reddened by dust and water vapor in the atmosphere.

The Earth and Moon are constant companions in their journey around the Sun. The Moon's apparent orbit around the Earth is elliptical; thus its apparent or angular diameter changes from one month to another. A more conspicuous change is the shape of the Moon as it passes through its **phases**: new, first quarter, full, and last quarter (fig. 1.19). Each

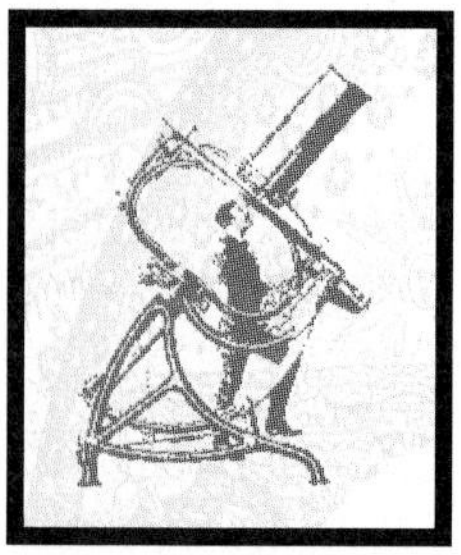

### finding the period of the Moon's revolution

The time required by the Moon to pass through its phases is not the same as its period of revolution on the celestial sphere. Why is there a difference between these time intervals? To find out, start by observing the Moon at first quarter, and mark its place, date, and time on a star map. On succeeding nights, repeat the observations and estimate the number of degrees per day the Moon advances in its orbit. Record the number of days required by the Moon to complete one revolution and return to its initial position among the stars. How many days elapsed since the previous first quarter? Did the Moon return to quarter phase again?

The Moon needs slightly over 27.3 days to complete one revolution with respect to the stars. How many degrees of arc does the Moon advance per day? You can calculate this amount as follows:

$$\text{Daily motion of the Moon} = \frac{360°}{27.3 \text{ days}}$$
$$= \text{about } 13° \text{ per day.}$$

The Moon takes 29.5 days to pass through its phases, so it requires an additional 2.2 days after completing one full revolution to complete one cycle of phases (see fig. 7.15).

cycle of phases is 29.53 days. The phase, or appearance of the illuminated lunar surface, is determined by the relative positions of the Sun and Moon with respect to the Earth. The Moon has an apparent motion eastward among the constellations of the zodiac of a little more than 13° per day. At this rate, it completes its circuit in a "moonth" of time, or a little less than one calendar month. Each month, the Moon catches up with and passes the Sun to start another cycle of phases.

## The Wandering "Stars"

Planets appear as bright starlike objects moving among the constellations of the zodiac (fig. 1.20). Usually they are distinguished by their steady light—they do not *scintillate,* or twinkle, as much as the **fixed stars.** Five visual planets, known to ancient people as the "wandering stars," were named after the gods: *Mercury, Venus, Mars, Jupiter,* and *Saturn.* Three telescopic planets, *Uranus, Neptune,* and *Pluto,* were discovered in modern times (Uranus can be seen with the naked eye under optimum sky conditions). These bodies and Earth total nine major planets that revolve around the Sun. With the exceptions of Mercury and Pluto, the orbits of the planets are inclined to the plane of the ecliptic by only a few degrees of arc. All the planets except Pluto remain within the boundaries of the zodiac. (The large inclination of Pluto's orbit carries the planet north and south of the zodiac.) How-

**figure 1.20**
The planet Venus and the Pleiades, a star cluster in the constellation Taurus.

ever, if you are familiar with the zodiac constellations, you can easily distinguish the visual planets from the bright stars.

Occasionally a planet can be seen after sunset in twilight as an *evening star* or before sunrise in the east as a *morning star.* They are usually Mercury and Venus, which occupy orbits between the Earth and Sun. Mercury is nearest to the Sun, thus difficult to see—by the time the sky is dark enough to make the planet visible, it usually has followed the sun below the western horizon. The remaining visual planets can also be morning and evening stars. But in this configura-

tion they lie beyond the Sun and are at their greatest distance from the Earth.

Mercury has the shortest period of revolution and was aptly named after the fleet-footed messenger of the gods. As Mercury revolves in its orbit, the planet seems to swing east and west of the Sun. The greatest angular distance on the celestial sphere between Mercury and the Sun does not exceed 28°. For this reason, the planet escapes detection by many observers.

Venus, the brightest planet, was named for the ancient goddess of beauty. Observers may see Venus for several

**figure 1.21**
Saturn and its rings.

hours after sunset and before sunrise. The planet revolves in a larger orbit than Mercury and can extend as much as 47° from the Sun. Venus appears as a faint, star-like object near the western horizon at sunset. As the days pass, the planet steadily increases in brightness and angular separation from the Sun, then reverses direction and reaches greatest brilliancy before disappearing in the twilight glow.

Venus returns as a morning object above the eastern horizon before sunrise. The planet increases in brightness and angular separation from the Sun. Greatest brilliancy occurs before Venus reaches its greatest angular distance from the Sun. The planet reverses direction and continues to fade and lose altitude until it is lost in the glare of the rising Sun.

Mars, the first planet beyond the Earth, has a distinctive orange-red color and so was named after the bloody god of war. The planet revolves more slowly in an orbit larger than the Earth's and consequently takes almost two years to go around the Sun. Through a telescope, Mars reveals as much surface detail as a naked-eye view of the full Moon. The planet's surface has polar ice caps, ocher-colored desert regions, and grey-green areas that are rocky in composition. The

greenish areas are more distinctive when the ice caps recede from the middle latitudes during spring and summer of the Martian year.

Jupiter is second to Venus in brightness and is distinguished as the brightest planet observable from dusk to dawn. It is white and appears quite distinctive against the background field stars. Jupiter is brightest when opposite the Sun in the sky and therefore at its closest approach to the Earth. The planet advances slowly in its orbit, so the Earth catches up to and passes Jupiter every 399 days. In that time, Jupiter advances to the next constellation of the zodiac. Jupiter completes one revolution in 11.9 years.

Saturn, more distant from the Sun than Jupiter, is opposite the Sun every 378 days. Named after the god of time, the planet slowly treads its way, taking almost 29.5 years to return to the same stars of the zodiac. Saturn was the most distant planet known until the invention of the telescope. The planet should be viewed through a telescope of moderate aperture (a 60 mm refractor, for example) to be fully appreciated. One of the most breathtaking sights in astronomy is the icy rings of Saturn at maximum inclination to the Earth (fig. 1.21).

Three more planets were discovered after the invention of the optical tele-

scope. Uranus was found by astronomer William Herschel in 1781. He first thought the planet was a comet, but its motion among the stars led him to conclude that the object was a new planet. More than twice as far from the Sun as Saturn, Uranus takes a little over 84 years to complete one circuit on the celestial sphere. Neptune was discovered by Johann G. Galle in 1846 in the same region predicted by John Couch Adams and Urbain Jean Leverrier. The location was determined by computations based upon the orbital motion of Uranus. Neptune is farther in space than Uranus and requires 165 years to complete one revolution. Pluto, the most distant planet, was discovered by Clyde Tombaugh at Lowell Observatory in 1930. This small and faint planet takes 248 years to pass through all the constellations of the zodiac.

## The Fixed Stars

Until now, we have treated the stars merely as a background for the motions of the Sun, Moon, and planets. The fixed stars seem to be attached to the celestial sphere, forming the familiar configurations we call constellations (fig 1.22). Today the constellations look about the same as they did when people named them. The stars are in motion, but the patterns seem stationary because of their vast distances from the Earth. We will examine these stars in terms of their brightness, color, and distribution.

Even a casual glance at the sky reveals differences in the brightness and colors of stars. Some of the bright red, orange, white, and blue stars are scattered across the sky as solitary beacons, while others are found in strikingly beautiful collections. The 20 brightest stars are first-magnitude stars, but the dimmest sixth-magnitude stars require perfect eyesight and an optimum sky. About 6,000 stars are visible to the unaided eye. Observers see a dramatic increase in number of visible stars when they use binoculars or a telescope.

## Stellar Systems

In 1610, Galileo described the **Milky Way** as a mass of innumerable stars in such abundance that their light gradually merged into a distant hazy glow. He was among the first to use the telescope and to observe stars fainter than sixth magnitude. Today, long-exposure photographs of the Milky Way show countless numbers of stars in clusters, and star clouds interspersed with bright and dark **nebulae** composed of dust particles and gases along its central plane. This narrow aggregation of stars and nebulae is an edge-on view of several spiral arms wrapped around the center of our stellar system, the **Galaxy.**

Photographs of the Milky Way show extensive star clouds in the direction of Sagittarius, the constellation between us and the center of the Galaxy. The center is hidden from our view by foreground stars and dark nebulae.

Astronomers once believed that the entire universe consisted of a flat disk of stars centered on the Sun. All the stars visible from the Earth occupy only a small portion of the Galaxy, and our Sun is only one star of many billion that make up this vast disk of stars. The size of the Galaxy can be better understood if we use the the speed of light as our standard of measure. At the rate of 300,000 km per second, light from a star at one edge of the Galaxy would take over 100,000 years to reach the opposite side. The Sun is located in one of the spiral arms about two-thirds of the way from the center toward the edge (fig. 1.23).

A telescope also reveals distant hazy, cloudlike patches far beyond the Galaxy. Long-exposure photographs resolve these formations into other systems of stars. The total number of galaxies is not known, but statistical studies attest to many billions. The galaxies form in clusters, some of which contain tens of thousands of star systems. Figure 1.24 shows the Perseus cluster of galaxies seen in the direction of the constellation Perseus. Light from this cluster requires approximately 250 million years to reach the Earth.

Our galaxy and all other galaxies represent the large-scale structure of an expanding universe. At the present time, the universe is believed to be about 15 to 20 billion years old. Initially, all matter and energy was contained in an extremely dense "primeval atom." The

**figure 1.22**

The constellation Orion. The Great Nebula, M42, appears as a slightly fuzzy glowing mass in the lower center of the photograph.

**figure 1.23**

Near-infrared image of the central region of our home galaxy, the Milky Way, taken from the Cosmic Background Explorer satellite.

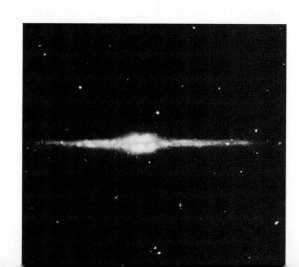

**figure 1.24**
A cluster of galaxies in the direction of the constellation Perseus.

atom exploded, giving this theory its popular name, the **big bang.** According to the big-bang theory, the lighter elements, mainly hydrogen and helium, were formed in a rapidly expanding universe. Later, huge clouds of hydrogen and helium condensed into clusters of galaxies. These clusters are moving away from each other and are observed as the expanding universe.

## Astronomy as a Science

Scientific investigation transformed astronomy from its roots in superstition to the model of an expanding universe of galaxies. Think of science as a method used to seek solutions to problems. Using **scientific method,** an investigator will define a problem and collect data pertaining to the problem. The investigator then makes a proposition, or provisional solution; a **hypothesis,** or tentative proposal to be tested. The hypothesis must be consistent with known data. Additional data is collected and the hypothesis is tested by observations, resulting in conclusions that strengthen or weaken the hypothesis. If the hypothesis survives this process, it becomes a **theory** derived from and supported by the established evidence. Mature theories are called **scientific laws.**

Investigators use **deductive** and **inductive reasoning** to arrive at scientific laws. With the deductive method, ideas are shaped from general principles or concepts already established. For example, let the law of universal gravitation be the general principle. Then the law of falling bodies or the motions of the planets around the Sun become applications of this general principle—that all bodies in the universe attract each other. The process is not without fault, because if the general premise is wrong, the conclusions based on new data will prove false.

With inductive reasoning, investigators arrive at generalizations and scientific laws after proof is obtained and verified through experimentation or observation. In the sixteenth century, the Danish astronomer Tycho Brahe showed that comets travel in elongated paths that cut across the orbits of the planets. This discovery, along with other observations, disproved the existence of Eudoxus's crystal spheres and contributed to our modern concept of the planets in motion around the Sun.

Scientific laws must not be interpreted as absolute truths incapable of change. Astronomers use laws to express the current knowledge or understanding of celestial bodies. In this process, explanations and interpretations may need revision. For example, Sir Isaac Newton defined gravity as an attractive force of the Earth on objects on or near its surface. To question the existence of this force might seem to be a lack of common sense. Albert Einstein, however, in his *General Theory of Relativity,* described a new law of gravitation that departs from Newtonian theory. Einstein proposed that the path of an object in a gravitational field produced by a body is determined by the curvature of the field, and not by the attractive force of the body. Astronomy must be thought of as an evolutionary and dynamic process subject to constant change as new discoveries add to our understanding of the cosmos.

Astronomers and other scientists often use a mathematical model, which is an *explanation,* not a small-scale replica of the original design. A model describing how the planets revolve around the Sun expresses apparent motions, but it should not be construed as absolute movement in space. On the cosmic scale, a model portraying receding galaxies expresses the behavior of matter and energy in a four-dimensional universe of space and time.

## SUMMARY

From the Earth, the sky appears as an infinitely large dome called the celestial sphere. The Earth seems to be at the center of this imaginary sphere, while the Sun, Moon, and planets move against the background stars of the zodiac.

The rotation, revolution, and precession of the Earth impart apparent motions to celestial bodies. As the Earth rotates from west to east, the sky seems to turn in diurnal motion from east to west. The Earth revolves counterclockwise in its orbit in a period of one year, giving an apparent annual motion to the Sun from west to east. Precession is a gradual swing of the Earth's rotational axis in a clockwise direction. Precession turns the rotational axis once around the ecliptic pole in 25,800 years.

Astronomers have generated circles and points on the celestial sphere to measure positions of celestial objects and to locate the observer on Earth. The horizon is a great circle formed by the intersection of the sky and the Earth where the observer stands. The cardinal points, north, east, south, and west, are on the horizon. The celestial equator is the circle cut by the plane of the Earth's equator projected onto the celestial sphere. Another circle, the ecliptic, is formed by the intersection of the Earth's orbital plane and the celestial sphere.

The Moon revolves in an apparent orbit around the Earth. In about one month, the Moon passes through phases: new, first quarter, full, and last quarter.

The planets occupy orbits at different distances from the Sun. Mercury and Venus are nearer to the Sun than the Earth. Mars, Jupiter, and Saturn are in orbits farther from the Sun than the Earth. Three far-distant planets, Uranus, Neptune, and Pluto, were discovered after the invention of the telescope.

The Sun and billions of other stars form a huge disk called the Milky Way Galaxy. Our star system represents one of billions of other galaxies that make up the universe. Galaxies appear to be moving away from each other as though the universe is in a state of expansion, which astronomers theorize results from an initial explosion of the cosmos billions of years ago.

Astronomers study the heavens scientifically. The results of their investigations must be consistent with known data and general laws. Hypotheses are tested by observations that provide the evidence needed for confirmation and explanation of a particular celestial event. The science of astronomy is a method of studying the heavens.

## KEY TERMS

| | |
|---|---|
| annual motion | lunar eclipse |
| apparent diurnal motion | magnitude |
| autumnal equinox | Milky Way |
| big bang | model |
| cardinal points | nebulae |
| celestial equator | novae |
| celestial poles | obliquity of the ecliptic |
| celestial sphere | |
| circumpolar stars | period of revolution |
| constellations | phases |
| deductive reasoning | Polaris |
| deferent | precession |
| direct motion | retrograde motion |
| diurnal circle | revolution |
| ecliptic | rotation |
| epicycle | scientific laws |
| fixed stars | scientific method |
| Galaxy (Milky Way) | solar eclipse |
| geocentric world system | summer solstice |
| heliocentric world system | theory |
| horizon | vernal equinox |
| hypothesis | winter solstice |
| inclination | zenith |
| inductive reasoning | zodiac |

## PROBLEMS

1. If you are located at 40° north latitude, is Polaris visible above your horizon? If so, at which cardinal point, and by how many degrees above the horizon?

2. If you travel due north from your location in problem 1 and change your latitude 10°, will Polaris increase or decrease in elevation? Why? By how many degrees?

3. You are at your home latitude observing three stars rising in the east. The first star is 23.5° north of the celestial equator; the second is on the celestial equator; the third is 23.5° south of the celestial equator. Which star will remain in the sky for the longest period of time? Why? How would the diurnal motions of these stars appear to an observer at the equator? At 40° south latitude?

4. Compare the diurnal arcs of the Sun on June 21, September 23, and December 21 with the stars in problem 3.

5. If you record the position of the Moon among the stars and repeat the operation after one lunation, will the Moon be in the same constellation? Explain. Hint: The revolution of the Earth causes the Sun to be displaced eastward along the ecliptic about 1° per day.

6. Explain why a lunar eclipse is visible to everyone on the night side of the Earth.

7. Venus has never been seen rising in the east at sunset. Why?

8. If the angular distance between a planet and the sun is 135°, does the planet occupy an orbit inside or outside the orbit of the Earth? Explain.

9. Which one of the following planets has the largest retrograde motion: Mars, Jupiter, or Saturn? Why?

10. Using a star atlas, locate the position of the Sun at the equinoxes and the solstices. Name the constellations in which the Sun is located at these times.

## REFERENCES

Aristotle. 1952. *Metaphysics.* Trans. E. W. Webster. Vol. I, book XII, chap. 8. Great Books of the Western World. Chicago: Encyclopedia Britannica Press.

Chauvenet, William. 1960. *A Manual of Spherical and Practical Astronomy.* 5th ed. Vol. I. New York: Dover Publications, Inc.

Heath, Thomas L. [1913] 1966. *Aristarchus of Samos.* Reprint. London: Oxford University Press.

Norton, Arthur P. 1986. *Norton's Star Atlas.* Edited by Gilbert E. Satterthwaite. Avon, Eng.: The Bath Press.

Ptolemy. 1952. *The Almagest.* Trans. R. Catesby Taliaferro. Great Books of the Western World. Chicago: Encyclopedia Britannica Press.

Smart, W. M. 1979. *Textbook on Spherical Astronomy.* 6th ed. Rev. by R. M. Green. Cambridge: Cambridge University Press.

Taton, Rene, ed. 1963. *Ancient and Medieval Science.* Trans. A. J. Pomerans. New York: Basic Books, Inc.

U.S. Naval Observatory. Nautical Almanac Office. *The Astronomical Almanac.* Washington, D.C.: U.S. Government Printing Office.

# 2

## time and place in the heavens

The Pleiades, M42, is an open cluster of stars in the constellation
Taurus. It is also known as the "Seven Sisters," for the brightest
stars that can be seen with the unaided eye. The nebulosity is made
bright by starlight reflecting off interstellar dust and gas.

One of the rewarding experiences in astronomy is a view of the stars on a clear, dark moonless night. At first, the sky seems to be a mass of sparkling confusion, but gradually distinct geometric patterns emerge and the **constellations** known to people throughout the world become clear. The beginnings of awareness of the constellations as such are lost in antiquity, but conspicuous star groups called **asterisms**, such as the Big Dipper and the Pleiades, have been found on rock carvings dating back to prehistoric times.

The familiar constellations of the northern sky, and some southern groups such as Centaurus and Ara within 40° of the south celestial pole, were recognized in classical times. The constellations of the zodiac received special attention since they form the background for the Sun, Moon, and planets. The stars within a constellation were given names identifying the various parts of the figure. For example, Spica, the brightest star in Virgo, in Latin means "the ear of grain" carried by the goddess for whom the constellation is named.

Altogether, 48 constellations were passed down from antiquity to the present time by Ptolemy in the *Almagest*. By the seventeenth century, astronomers began to produce maps of the heavens using constellation pictures to enclose the stars. Bayer, in 1603, and Hevelius, in 1690, produced maps with the stars shown in various sizes to represent differences in magnitude (fig. 2.1). The largest images on the maps were the brightest or first-magnitude stars.

Bayer also introduced a system in which the brightest stars of each constellation were identified by the small letters of the Greek alphabet. Usually, the brightest star is called alpha ($\alpha$), the second brightest beta ($\beta$), and so forth, followed by the possessive name of the constellation. In Bayer's system, Spica becomes $\alpha$ Virginis.

Over time, constellations were added and deleted from the list. The eighteenth-century astronomer Lacaille proposed

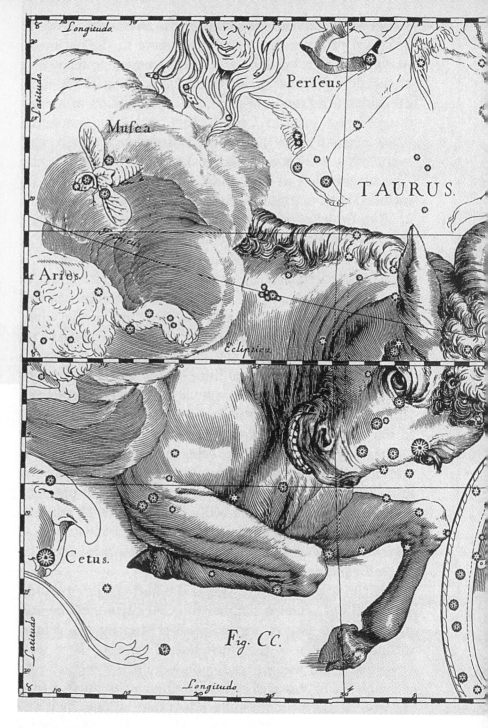

**figure 2.1**

Star maps published in the seventeenth century illustrated the constellations with ancient mythological figures. Forty-eight classical constellations were passed down from antiquity.

thirteen new ones to fill the spaces around the south celestial pole. He also divided a very large ancient southern constellation, Argo Navis, into Carina, Puppis, and Vela. A total of 88 constellations are recognized today.

In 1801, Bode used a spherical-coordinate or grid system to define the area occupied by each constellation. But Bode's divisions were not standardized

and, on maps drawn by others, some stars were placed in adjoining constellations. By 1930, the boundaries of the constellations were standardized by the International Astronomical Union, and today the ancient star patterns exist as defined areas on the celestial sphere.

Since the 1930s, the Earth's precession and the intrinsic motions of the stars have made slight changes in stellar pat-

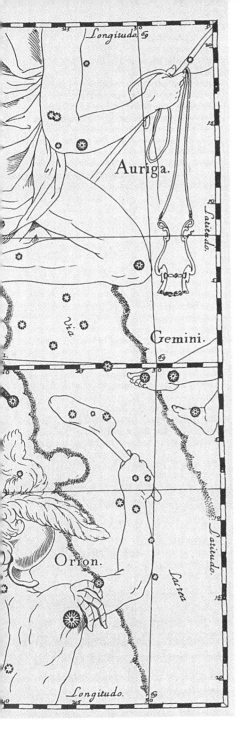

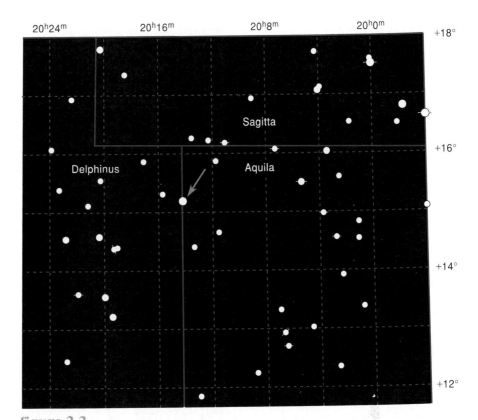

**figure 2.2**

Today, 88 constellations are recognized. Their boundaries are defined by two measurements—the right ascension and the declination of the area of the sky occupied by the constellation. The arrow shows the position of Rho (ρ) Aquilae on the boundary between the constellations Aquila and Delphinus.

terns within constellation boundaries. For example, the star Rho (ρ) Aquilae has moved from its location in Aquila to the adjacent constellation Delphinus (fig. 2.2 and Star Map II).

## Measurements of Position

Before we can study stars in detail, it is essential to learn how their positions are determined on the celestial sphere. Like the familiar meridians of longitude and circles of latitude on the Earth's surface, the celestial sphere is divided into a grid formed by two sets of circles at right angles to each other. The position of a star is measured by its angular distance from a reference circle selected from each set.

## The Geographic System of Coordinates

We define a position on the surface of the Earth by geographic coordinates. In this system, the north and south poles become points on the surface generated by the rotation of the Earth. A plane perpendicular to the polar axis passing through the center of the Earth intersects the surface of Earth along the **geographic equator.** From this reference circle to the poles, there is a set of smaller circles called **parallels.** A second set of great circles called **meridians** passes through the poles perpendicular to the parallels. By international agreement, the meridian through Greenwich, England, was selected as a meridian reference circle. It is called the **prime meridian.**

The coordinates of a given position are called **latitude** and **longitude** and are measured from the equator and the prime meridian respectively. Latitude is the angular distance north or south of the equator. It is measured along the meridian passing through the position, increasing from 0° at the equator to 90° at the poles. The position is marked N or S to indicate the direction north or south of the equator. Longitude is the angular distance from 0° at the prime meridian through 180° east and west. Longitude is measured along the equator or the parallel passing through the position and labeled E or W. The author's home is located using this system in fig. 2.3.

## The Horizon Coordinate System

To construct a coordinate system on the celestial sphere, we follow the same procedure as when using the geographic system on the Earth. First we select a point of origin or pole at 90° to a reference circle. To meet our requirements we select the horizon as our fundamental reference circle. Thus we have a **horizon coordinate system** that locates the positions of stars as seen from one point, our location on the Earth (fig. 2.4). In this system, your horizon is the intersection on the celestial sphere of an imaginary plane tangent to or touching the Earth at *your position*. Since every point on the globe has its own horizon, a set of coordinates constructed from this circle describes the sky for a single position at any given instant of time. The pole in this coordinate system is the **zenith,** the point on the celestial sphere directly above the observer at 90° to the horizon. A line extending from the zenith through your position to the center of the Earth and continued to the opposite side strikes the celestial sphere at the **nadir.** The horizon, your first reference circle, makes 90° angles with both the zenith and the nadir.

A set of progressively smaller circles drawn parallel to the horizon and extending to the zenith are called parallels of altitude. A set of great circles extending vertically from the zenith to the nadir and making right angles with the parallels of altitude are called vertical circles. A great circle connecting the north point on the horizon, the north celestial pole, the zenith, the south point on the horizon, the south celestial pole, and the nadir is the **celestial meridian,** the vertical reference circle.

The vertical coordinate or **altitude** of a star is its angle above the horizon measured along the vertical circle passing through the star. Altitude is equal to 0° at the horizon and 90° at the zenith. The horizontal coordinate or **azimuth** is the angular distance measured eastward along the horizon from the north point to the vertical circle passing through the star's position. Azimuth increases from 0° at the north point to 90° east, 180° south, 270° west, and 360° north to complete the circle.

Although measurements in the horizon system are made on the celestial sphere, the coordinates are attached to the observer and not the sky. As the Earth rotates, your zenith and horizon turn with

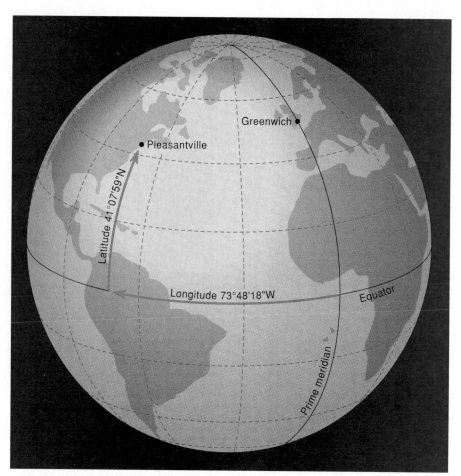

**figure 2.3**
The author's home is located using the geographic system of coordinates.

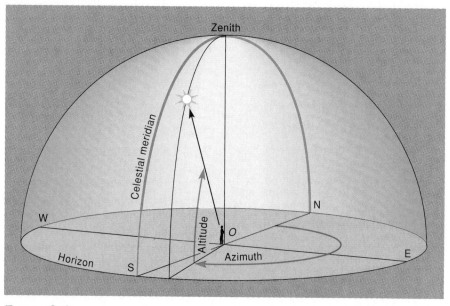

**figure 2.4**
Horizon coordinate system. The position of a body on the celestial sphere is determined by its azimuth and altitude.

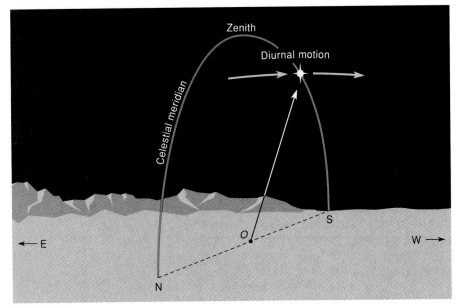

**figure 2.5**

Meridian transit of a star. The apparent diurnal motion of a star from east to west across an observer's meridian is caused by the Earth's rotation from west to east.

you, while the stars drift from east to west. The altitude and azimuth of a celestial body are therefore continuously changing as time passes. For this reason, the time of observation must be known. Later you will learn how time is kept by astronomers.

The coordinates of the horizon system are very useful in making observations relative to the observer's position on Earth. For instance, you may wish to know when and how high above the horizon a comet will be seen at your latitude; when and where on the horizon the Moon will rise and set; or when and where a particular object will pass, or transit, the celestial meridian (fig. 2.5). Since geographic latitude and longitude on the Earth are related to the altitude and azimuth of the Sun, Moon, planets, and stars, celestial navigation makes use of horizon coordinates to find positions at sea.

## The Equator Coordinate System

To relate one observer's data to the data of others, astronomers have devised several coordinate systems that are fixed to the celestial sphere and share the diurnal motion of the stars. In the system we shall be using, the **celestial equator** becomes the first reference circle and the **celestial poles** are the points of origin. In this **equator coordinate system** (fig. 2.6), the coordinates are independent of the observer and keep the same value for all positions on the Earth. There are small circles between the celestial equator and the celestial poles called parallels of declination. From the poles, twenty-four **hour circles** are drawn perpendicular to the celestial equator. The vertical coordinate called **declination** is the angle from the celestial equator measured along the hour circle passing through a star. Declination is marked positive (+) north and negative (−) south from 0° at the celestial equator through +90° at the north celestial pole and −90° at the south celestial pole. Declination is abbreviated **dec.**, or represented by the lowercase Greek letter delta ($\delta$). The declination of a star 10° north and another 10° south will be designated +10° and −10°, respectively. Parallels of declination run east and west, but they measure angular distances north and south from the celestial equator to the celestial poles.

Hour circles run north and south, but measure angular distances eastward from the vernal equinox, represented by the Aries symbol ($\Upsilon$). A vertical reference circle serves the same purpose in the sky as the prime meridian does in the geographic coordinate system. This hour circle connects the celestial poles with the vernal and autumnal equinoxes. Remember the equinoxes are the points where the celestial equator intersects the **ecliptic.** The vernal equinox is the zero point for the horizontal coordinate (fig. 2.7). **Right ascension** is the name given to the angular distance from the vernal equinox measured *eastward* along the celestial equator. An angle on the celestial equator can be expressed in time coordinates as well as degrees of arc. In about 24 hours, the celestial sphere completes 360° of diurnal motion. One hour of time is equivalent to 15°; 20 minutes of time, 20m = 05°; 04m = 01°. Right ascension is measured in hours, minutes, and seconds of time and is abbreviated **R.A.** or represented by the lowercase Greek letter alpha ($\alpha$). As the Earth rotates, a star on the same hour circle as the vernal equinox has an R.A.= 00h and will cross your celestial meridian at the same time as the vernal equinox. A star at R.A.= 01h is located on an hour circle 15° east of the vernal equinox, and will **transit** one hour later. In one rotational period, right ascension increases from 00h at the vernal equinox eastward through 24 hours.

To better visualize these coordinates, let us follow the Sun among the stars for one year, or one period of annual motion. You recall that the path of the Sun, the ecliptic, is inclined 23 1/2° to the celestial equator. On March 21, the Sun is at the vernal equinox, where the ecliptic and the equator intersect; the Sun's coordinates are R.A.= 00h, dec.= 00°. By June 21, the Sun has advanced to the summer solstice, R.A.= 06h, dec.= +23 1/2°. Continuing eastward along the ecliptic, by September 23 the Sun reaches the autumnal equinox, where once again the celestial equator and ecliptic intersect, R.A.= 12h, dec.= 00°. At the winter solstice, December 22, the Sun's coordinates are R.A.= 18h, dec.= −23 1/2°. Thus in one year, the Sun will return again to the vernal equinox with R.A.= 00h, dec.= 00°.

So far, we have treated the equator system coordinates as though they are rigidly attached to the celestial sphere. But the celestial poles and the celestial equator are merely extensions of their geographic counterparts and will therefore be affected by any change in the alignment of the Earth's axis. In chapter 1, we discussed precession of the Earth's axis, which causes the north and south celestial poles to sweep out circles centered on the ecliptic poles (fig. 1.15). As a result, the equinoxes and solstices slowly drift westward, bringing the intersection of the ecliptic and the celestial equator (our zero point in the coordinate system) to another constellation of the zodiac. Consequently, there is a gradual change in the right ascension and declination of the stars. Astronomers must take this motion into account when precise measurements are required.

## Seasons of the Stars

We have noted how the revolution of the Earth causes a westward drift of the constellations in the course of one year. As a result of this motion, each season has its own constellations dominating the night sky. Of course, in one night from dusk to dawn, the rotation of the Earth allows us to observe most of the stars visible from a given latitude. By seasonal stars we mean those that rise in the east at sunset and remain above the horizon almost the entire night.

Star Maps I–IV show the stars and constellations of the night sky in spring, summer, autumn, and winter.

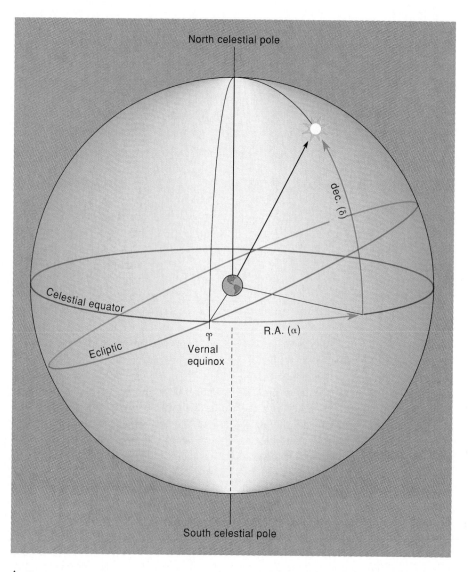

▲ **figure 2.6**

Equator system of coordinates. The position of a star on the celestial sphere is determined by its right ascension (R.A.) and its declination (dec.).

**figure 2.7** ▶

Right ascension and declination of the star Hamal, in the constellation Aries. Right ascension (R.A.) is measured eastward from the vernal equinox (♈) to the hour circle passing through the star. Declination (dec.) is the angular distance along the hour circle from the celestial equator to the star.

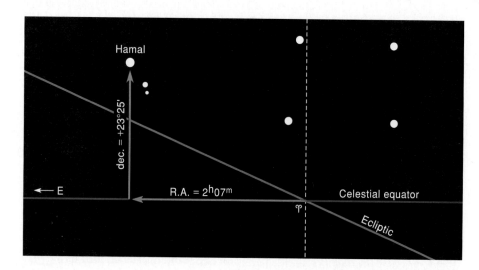

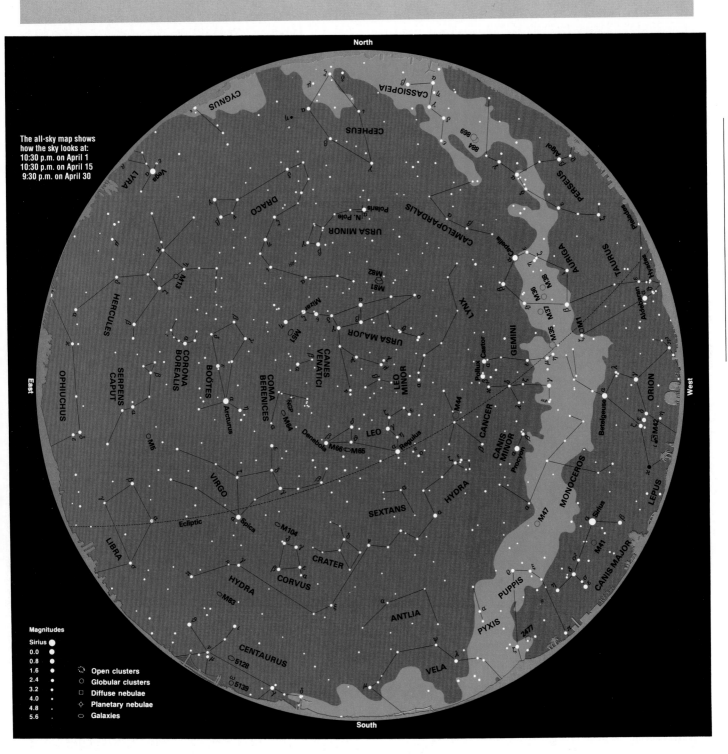

**star map I**

The stars in April, from 40° north latitude.

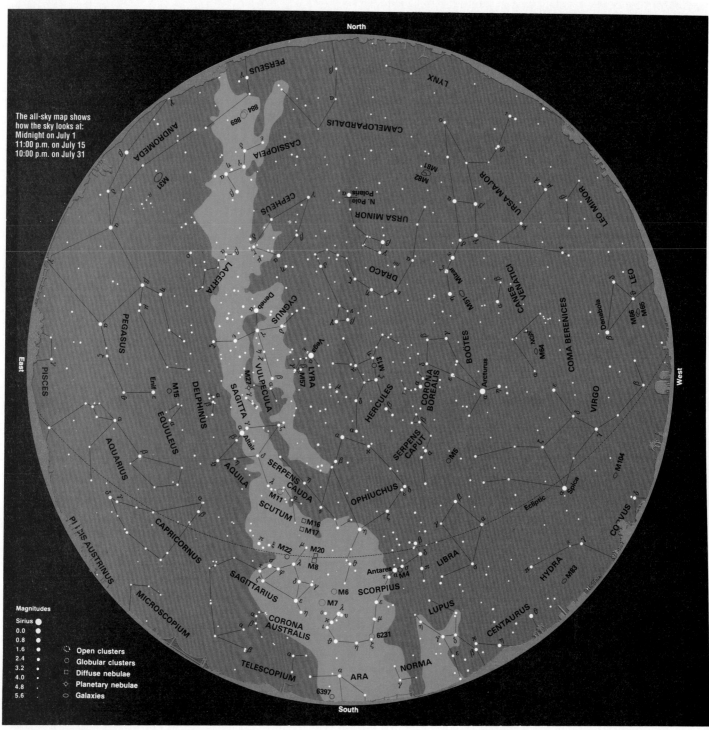

The all-sky map shows
how the sky looks at:
Midnight on July 1
11:00 p.m. on July 15
10:00 p.m. on July 31

North

South

East

West

PERSEUS

ANDROMEDA

M31

884
869

CASSIOPEIA

CEPHEUS

LACERTA

CYGNUS

Deneb

VULPECULA

M27

SAGITTA

DELPHINUS

M15

Enif

EQUULEUS

PEGASUS

PISCES

AQUARIUS

AQUILA

Altair

SERPENS
CAUDA

SCUTUM

M11

M16
M17

M22

M20

M8

SAGITTARIUS

CAPRICORNUS

MICROSCOPIUM

PISCIS AUSTRINUS

CORONA
AUSTRALIS

TELESCOPIUM

6397

ARA

M6

M7

SCORPIUS

Antares

M4

6231

LUPUS

NORMA

CENTAURUS

HYDRA

M83

LIBRA

OPHIUCHUS

SERPENS
CAPUT

M5

HERCULES

M13

LYRA

Vega

M57

CORONA
BOREALIS

BOÖTES

Arcturus

CANES VENATICI

NGC

M64

COMA BERENICES

VIRGO

Spica

Ecliptic

M104

CORVUS

LEO

Denebola

M66
M65

LEO MINOR

URSA MAJOR

M81
M82

Mizar

M51

CAMELOPARDALIS

LYNX

DRACO

URSA MINOR

N. Pole
Polaris

CAMELOPARDALIS

Magnitudes

Sirius
0.0
0.8
1.6
2.4
3.2
4.0
4.8
5.6

Open clusters
Globular clusters
Diffuse nebulae
Planetary nebulae
Galaxies

**star map II**

The stars in July, from 40° north latitude.

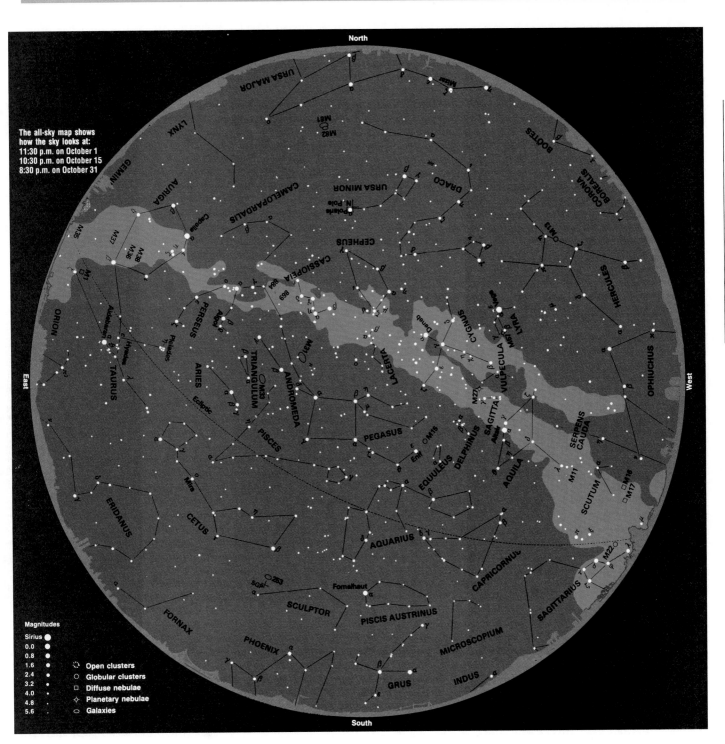

**star map III**

The stars in October, from 40° north latitude.

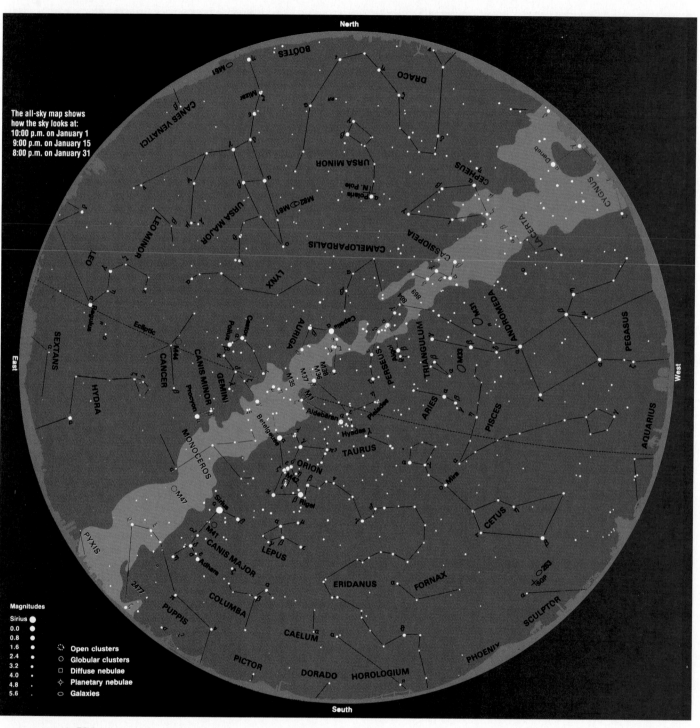

The all-sky map shows
how the sky looks at:
10:00 p.m. on January 1
9:00 p.m. on January 15
8:00 p.m. on January 31

North

East

West

South

Magnitudes

Sirius
0.0
0.8
1.6
2.4
3.2
4.0
4.8
5.6

Open clusters
Globular clusters
Diffuse nebulae
Planetary nebulae
Galaxies

**star map IV**

The stars in January, from 40° north latitude.

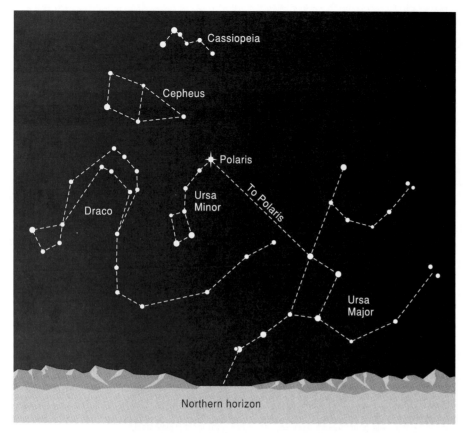

**figure 2.8**

The north circumpolar stars are located between the celestial pole and the north point on the horizon within a diurnal circle equal to the altitude of the pole.

## Northern Circumpolar Stars

We have defined the circumpolar stars as the stars that remain above the horizon for the entire diurnal period of 24 hours. These stars neither rise nor set because they pass between the celestial pole and the north point on the horizon. Figure 2.8 shows the sky as seen from 40° north latitude, where the stars with declinations +50° to +90° will be circumpolar. Within this region around the north celestial pole are some familiar configurations in the sky, including Ursa Major, Ursa Minor, Draco, Cassiopeia, and Cepheus.

## Stars of the Zodiac

The word zodiac means "circle of animals" and refers to the series of 12 constellations named after real and mythical figures found in a 16° belt centered on the ecliptic. In the middle latitudes of the Northern Hemisphere, the constellations of the zodiac cross the sky high overhead in winter and low above the southern horizon in summer. The reason for the difference in altitude during the year is the 23 1/2° inclination of the ecliptic to the celestial equator. At about midnight on June 21, the vernal and autumnal equinoxes are at the east and west points on the horizon. The winter solstice in the constellation Sagittarius (R.A.= 18h, dec.= −23 1/2°) will be on the meridian south of the celestial equator by an amount equal to its declination. At 40° north latitude, the celestial equator crosses the meridian at an altitude of 50°, which means that the winter solstice reaches a maximum altitude of only 26 1/2° above the south point. For this reason, you will need a south horizon free of trees or other obtructions in order to observe Sagittarius.

At the same time of night on September 23, the vernal equinox in the constellation Pisces (R.A.= 00h, dec.= 00°) will cross the meridian at the same elevation as the celestial equator, or 50° altitude. Now the winter solstice is just below the horizon in the southwest while

the summer solstice has climbed above the horizon in the northeast.

By midnight on December 21, the vernal equinox has advanced to the west bringing the autumnal equinox to the east point on the horizon. The summer solstice in Gemini (R.A.= 06h, dec.= +23 1/2°) is on the meridian only 16 1/2° from the zenith at 40° north latitude. On March 21, the autumnal equinox in the constellation Virgo (R.A.= 12h, dec.= 00°) will transit the meridian at about midnight.

## Stars of Spring

The Big Dipper in Ursa Major appears above the celestial pole and serves as a guide to early-evening spring stars (see Star Map I). The pointer stars at the end of the bowl lead north to Polaris in the handle of the Little Dipper and south to the bright star Regulus in Leo. The handle of the Big Dipper forms an arc to Arcturus in Boötes. The arc continues to Spica in Virgo and Gienah (γ) in Corvus.

The constellation Leo is recognized by an asterism in the shape of a sickle, or backward question mark, followed by a right triangle. The first-magnitude star Regulus is in the handle of the sickle. Hydra consists of faint stars stretched out from a point below Leo east to Libra, while the head of Hydra forms a keystone to the south and east of Regulus and northwest of Alphard (α), the "heart of Hydra."

With the exception of the first-magnitude star Spica, there are only faint third- and fourth-magnitude stars to outline Virgo. A line from Regulus to Zavijava (β) and Spica follows the ecliptic and intersects the equator at the autumnal equinox a few degrees east of Zavijava. Four second- and third-magnitude stars in Corvus form a distinctive sail-like asterism called "Spica's spanker."

Another faint constellation, Libra, contains four stars of third and fourth magnitudes in the form of a trapezium. Zubenelgenubi (α) helps locate the ecliptic through this part of the sky. The Arabian name of the star means the "southern claw" and alludes to one of the claws of Scorpius; the "northern claw,"

### deep-sky observing in spring

The bright stars in Boötes form a kite-shaped figure representing a herdsman behind a plow formed by the Big Dipper. The third brightest star in the sky, Arcturus, is distinguished by its orange color. When you are outdoors observing, compare this star with blue-white Spica in Virgo and the white star Regulus in Leo. The bright triangle formed by these stars dominates the spring sky.

The stars of Canes Venatici locate the legendary hunting dogs of Boötes pursuing the bear, Ursa Major. The constellation was devised by Hevelius in 1690 to fill the gap between the classical constellations Ursa Major and Boötes listed by Ptolemy. The brightest star, Cor Caroli (α), or "heart of Charles," was named in honor of Charles I of England.

Canes Venatici contains some interesting objects catalogued by Charles Messier in the eighteenth century. A bright globular cluster M3 (number 3 in Messier's catalogue; see appendix E.4) can be resolved as stars in a small telescope; a spiral galaxy, M63, is found between Cor Caroli and Alkaid (η), the end star in the handle of the Big Dipper. The notable spiral M51, the Whirlpool galaxy, is located below Alkaid. This galaxy is seen facing our direction in space with its spiral arms wrapped about its center (fig. 2.9).

Although Coma Berenices is mentioned by the Greeks, this constellation was not defined until the sixteenth century. No stars are brighter than fourth magnitude, but the region is rich in galaxies. No less than seven

**figure 2.9**
The Whirlpool galaxy, M51, in the constellation Canes Venatici, as photographed through a large telescope. The spiral arms contain luminous stars and nebulous clouds of gas and dust.

Messier objects are bright enough to be resolved with low-power optics. One of these is a globular cluster of stars, but the rest comprise an aggregation of tens of thousands of galaxies called the Coma cluster.

Coma Berenices lies on the celestial sphere at 90° from the Milky Way. More

galaxies are found in the direction of Coma Berenices and Virgo than in any other part of the sky because this region is as far as possible from obscuring nebulae found in the Milky Way.

---

Zubeneschamali (β), is the only green star of this magnitude visible without optical aid.

## Stars of Summer

Three first-magnitude stars, Vega, Deneb, and Altair, form the "summer triangle" that passes overhead during the summer nights in the middle latitudes (see Star Map II). The Milky Way adds to the beauty of the sky with its dark rifts, star clouds, and nebulae.

In the constellation Lyra, Vega and other bright stars form a tiny equilateral

triangle and parallelogram. The "northern cross" defines the ancient constellation Cygnus, which is especially rich in clusters and dark lanes of dust and gas. Long-exposure photographs reveal the gas clouds of the North America nebula made bright by the ultraviolet radiation of starlight (fig. 2.10). With a telescope,

**figure 2.10**  ▶

The North America nebula, in this photograph taken through a telescope, is a gaseous formation in the constellation Cygnus. The nebula's name comes from its resemblance to the North American continent.

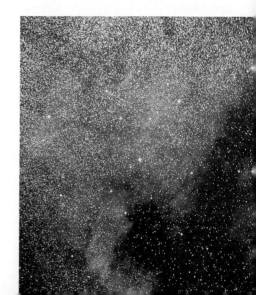

## deep-sky observing in summer

The summer triangle is one of the most rewarding regions to observe with the unaided eye, with binoculars, or with a small telescope. Sheliak (β) in the constellation Lyra is a binary system composed of two stars that eclipse each other in a period of about 13 days. When one star passes in front of the other, there is a one-magnitude loss in brightness that can be detected visually. Nearby Sulufat (γ) has the same magnitude as Sheliak and can be used as a comparison star when the variable is at minimum brightness. Between these stars is the famous Ring nebula, M57, a hazy oval "smoke ring" surrounding a blue central star (fig. 2.11).

The globular cluster in Hercules, M13, is regarded as the jewel of the summer sky (fig. 2.12). It can be found along the western side of the keystone one-third of the distance from η to ζ Herculi. Just barely visible to the eye, a moderate-sized telescope resolves the cluster into a ball of hundreds of thousands of stars.

Vulpecula occupies a faint region of the Milky Way south of Cygnus. The constellation contains M27, the Dumbbell nebula, a planetary nebula that resembles a hazy green cloud.

In the northern part of Ophiuchus near the celestial equator, there are three globular clusters, M10, M12, and M14, that are among the more than 100 clusters surrounding the center of the Galaxy. To the south, the constellation dips into the Milky Way below the ecliptic within the zodiac. Two more clusters, M9 and M19, are found on either side of the ecliptic. In Serpens, look for two clusters, M5 and M16. (Refer to appendix E.4, the Messier Catalogue.)

**figure 2.11**
A telescopic view of the Ring nebula, M57, a sphere of expanding gases that has the appearance of a ring surrounding a central star. M57 is located in the constellation Lyra.

**figure 2.12**
The Great Cluster in Hercules, M13, is the brightest globular cluster seen from the Northern Hemisphere. It appears as a faint hazy glow to the naked eye.

the double star Albireo (β), can be separated easily into blue and gold components.

The main attractions in Aquila are the bright stars Altair (α), Alshain (β), and Tarazed (γ) that point to Vega in Lyra and help locate the summer triangle. A line between Arcturus and Vega passes through two constellations that are easily recognized by their distinctive arrangement rather than the brightness of their stars. Corona Borealis, which was introduced in the spring sky, resembles a diadem or necklace of seven stars of second, third, and fourth magnitudes. The brightest star, named Alphecca (α), is also referred to as Gemma, the "gem of the crown."

Hercules lies east of the crown, appearing as a large letter H of third-magnitude stars. Four central stars of the H form the "keystone." Ophiuchus and Serpens are extensive constellations representing a large figure grasping a writhing serpent. Ophiuchus extends from Hercules to Scorpius no less than half the distance between the zenith and horizon. Serpens is divided into two separate regions; Serpens Caput, the head of the serpent to the west, and Serpens Cauda, the tail to the east. Serpens joins Ophiuchus at the stars called the Yeds (δ) and (ε) and Sabik (η).

The bright stars of Scorpius resemble a large fishhook and form the scorpion of ancient mythology. It is one of the few constellations that resembles the figure it is supposed to represent. The constellation's brightest star Antares, the "rival of Mars," shines with a distinctive red color.

The center of the Galaxy lies beyond the stars of Sagittarius, making this the sky's richest region of nebulae, star clouds, and clusters. The bright stars form an unusual asterism called "the teapot."

time and place in the heavens

chapter 2

astronomy: through space and time

## deep-sky observing in autumn

The most interesting attraction in Andromeda is the Great Galaxy, M31, the only visual spiral galaxy (fig. 2.13). To the eye, M31 appears as an elliptical hazy glow and gives little evidence of its size or distance. At over two million light-years from the Earth, the galaxy is the most distant object visible without optical aid. Find it north of Mirach about half as far as the distance between Mirach (β) and Alpheratz.

Continue to Mirfak and locate the constellation Perseus. Messier failed to catalog the famous double cluster found in the northern region of Perseus bordering on Cassiopeia.

Algol is an eclipsing binary star that is the prototype for this class of variable stars. Discovered to be variable by 20-year-old English astronomer John Goodricke in 1783, Algol varies in magnitude between 2.2 and 3.5 magnitudes in a period of 02d 20h 48m. The star is at the apex of a small triangle formed by third- and fourth-magnitude stars. When Algol reaches minimum, it is equal in brightness to the third-magnitude star in the triangle.

A line from Alpheratz and Algenib extended twice the distance between the stars leads to Cetus and the bright star Diphda (β). The remainder of the constellation extends northeast across the celestial equator

**figure 2.13**

The Great Galaxy in Andromeda, M31, is located more than two million light-years away and is the nearest spiral galaxy beyond the Milky Way. To the unaided eye it appears as a faint lens-shaped patch of light.

to Menkar (α), a second-magnitude star south of Hamal.

A distinguishing feature of Cetus is Mira, "the wonderful," a red supergiant pulsating star. For about 330 days, the star is about ninth magnitude and too faint to be seen without a telescope. Then the star expands in size and brightens to a third or fourth magnitude red ruby, remaining at maximum for about 10 days before fading out of sight.

### Stars of Autumn

The Great Square is formed by three bright stars in Pegasus—Markab (α), Sheat (β), and Algenib (γ)—along with Alpheratz (α), the brightest star in Andromeda (see Star Map III). This distinctive asterism is used as a guide to the constellations of the season. Between Polaris and the square is Cassiopeia, which contains five bright stars in the form of the letter *W*. From Polaris, extend a line to Caph (β) in Cassiopeia and continue along the eastern side of the square south to the vernal equinox in Pisces. The constellation contains an asterism called the circlet, the western fish, which can be used as a guide to the vernal equinox.

Located about 20 degrees north of Alrescha (α), in Pisces, the constellation

Aries forms a small obtuse triangle containing three bright stars: Hamal (α), Sheratan (β), and Mesartim (γ).

Andromeda extends in an arc from Alpheratz toward the northeast. A well known double, Almach (γ), has beautiful contrasting yellow and blue stars. Continue the curve of bright stars formed by Andromeda to Mirfak (α), the brightest star in Perseus, one of the most attractive constellations of the northern hemisphere of the sky.

### Stars of Winter

Of all the constellations, Orion is the most impressive, with its distinctive pattern of bright stars that form the outline of the giant hunter of mythology (see

Star Map IV). Four stars in a rectangular shape represent the shoulders and knees, while three more inside the rectangle identify the jewels in Orion's belt. Betelgeuse in the northeast corner of the rectangle is a cool red giant known to be larger than the orbit of Mars. To the southwest, the blue giant Rigel is more luminous than ten thousand Suns. The remaining stars in the rectangle, Bellatrix (γ) and Saiph (κ), as well as the belt stars Mintaka (δ), Alnilam (ε), and Alnitak (ζ), are also classified among the hottest and bluest stars.

The "winter triangle" is an almost perfect equilateral triangle made by three first-magnitude stars, Betelgeuse, Sirius, and Procyon. First find Sirius, the brightest star in the sky, by extending a line

deep-sky observing in winter

Orion is a breeding ground for stars that evolve from the surrounding nebulosity. Near Alnitak, the Horsehead nebula looms out of a dark bay of dust and gas (fig. 2.14). Shaped in the form of the head and neck of a horse, this nebula is merely a sector of a great mass of interstellar matter surrounding the entire constellation.

South of Alnitak in the region known as the sword of Orion, you will find the famous Great Nebula, M42, glowing in a pale greenish light (fig. 2.15). Embedded in the gaseous cloud are four components of a multiple star Theta Orionis called the Trapezium. The nebula is made bright by ultraviolet radiation emitted by nearby stars. Center the Trapezium in the telescope and observe the nebula with averted or peripheral vision.

The kite-shaped figure of Auriga is found north of Orion and El Nath (β) in Taurus. In the constellation, south of Capella, there is a small triangle of stars called the "the kids" (Capella means "goat"). The top star of the triangle, Epsilon Aurigae, is an eclipsing binary consisting of a yellow giant revolving around an even larger, cool object too faint to be seen. The presence of this mysterious source is known by the periodic dimming of the visible companion.

Auriga is also in the Milky Way and therefore possesses its share of interesting clusters and asterisms. Three open clusters, M36, M37, and M38, are between Capella and El Nath.

A few degrees west of Rigel, the fourth-magnitude star Lambda Eridani marks the beginning of Eridanus, the celestial river. From Lambda, its stars swing north to Cursa (β) and then meander west, east, and finally south below the horizon to the first-magnitude star Achernar.

▲ figure 2.14

Difficult to see even through a telescope, the Horsehead is a dark nebula located near the star Zeta Orionis. The Horsehead projects against a bright gaseous nebula in the background.

figure 2.15 ▶
The Great Nebula in Orion, M42 and M43, is a gaseous cloud located in Orion's "sword." It can be seen with the unaided eye as a faint patch of light.

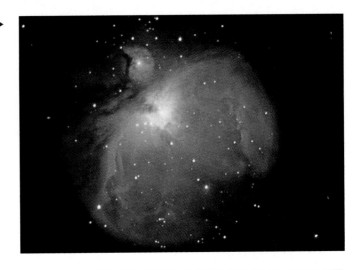

time and place in the heavens

southeast from the belt of Orion; then from Sirius continue northeast to Procyon.

Additional winter stars of all colors form a halo around Orion. Beginning at Procyon, follow an arc northeast of Orion to the bright stars Castor and Pollux in Gemini, where the summer solstice is located. Continue the arc to the first-magnitude star Capella, found north of Orion in Auriga, and south to the orange

star Aldebaran in Taurus. View the two prominent clusters, the Hyades and Pleiades ("seven sisters") using low-power optics.

## The Measurement of Time

From antiquity, people have found the need to measure the passage of time.

The oldest system was based upon the daily motion of the Sun and the change from day to night. Later, the phases of the Moon provided a convenient way to keep time by the month. Finally, the cycle of the seasons was used to measure time over a period of a year.

Today, accurate timekeeping is essential for commerce, industry, and the activites of our daily lives. In astronomy, the periods of eclipsing binaries and variable stars, the occurrence of eclipses and occultations, and the risings and settings of the Sun and Moon are a few of the many phenomena that must be timed to within a fraction of a second.

A time system is also necessary to keep a record of astronomical events of the past and to compute the future positions of celestial bodies. For instance, the dating of ancient eclipses has contributed to a better understanding of the rotation of the Earth. The precession of the Earth's axis was discovered by Hipparchus when he determined the time the Sun reached the equinox.

Before we investigate various time systems, it will be necessary for you to understand the meaning of time and how it is measured. Think of time as an interval between two events, such as the beginning and end of a vacation or any other activity that you might pursue. A unit of measure must be devised to determine how much time has elapsed. This unit or standard interval of time is established by means of a constantly recurring phenomenon. Since antiquity, the diurnal and annual motions of the Sun and revolution of the Moon have provided the required units of day, month, and year. When clocks were invented, the day was divided into hours, minutes, and seconds of time.

Several time systems are used in astronomy and daily life. These are **sidereal time, apparent solar time,** and **mean solar time.** The first, sidereal time, is based upon the daily motion of the stars due to the Earth's rotation. Apparent solar time, sometimes called sundial time, is determined by the actual daily motion of the Sun across the sky. Mean solar time uses the average motion of the Sun and thereby provides the constant unit required for timekeeping.

## Sidereal Time

As the Earth spins on its axis, every star makes a complete circuit through the sky in one rotational period. Sidereal time is the measure of the Earth's rotation; thus every hour of sidereal time is equal to 15° of angular motion (360° ÷ 24h). A star on your local meridian will have moved to 15° west one sidereal hour later

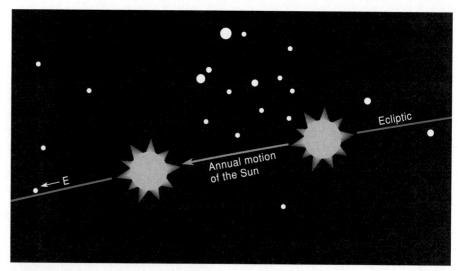

**figure 2.16**
The Sun is displaced eastward along the ecliptic by the revolution of the Earth in its orbit.

and will return to your meridian in 24 hours of sidereal time. There are small variations in the rotational period of the Earth that astronomers must take into account, but, for now, consider the period of rotation of the Earth to be constant.

In any measurement, a convenient point of origin is necessary; in the sidereal time system, the vernal equinox serves this purpose. A **sidereal day** is defined as the time between two successive meridian transits of the vernal equinox. For example, if the vernal equinox is on your meridian, your local sidereal time (LST) = 00h. In one hour, the vernal equinox will be 15° west and your LST = 01h.

Recall that right ascension is measured eastward along the celestial equator from the vernal equinox. Therefore, one hour after the transit of the vernal equinox, the hour circle designating R.A. = 01h will be on your meridian. A star transits when the local sidereal time and its right ascension are equal. Consider the brightest star Sirius with a R.A. = 06h 44m. Sirius will cross your meridian at LST = 06h 44m.

## Apparent Solar Time

The diurnal motion of the Sun along the ecliptic was the first natural repetitive event used to measure the passage of time (fig. 2.16). As the Sun crosses the

sky, the shadow cast by a sundial marks the changing angle of the Sun. This system of measurement is called apparent solar time. The **apparent solar day** is defined as the interval between two successive transits of the Sun. The apparent solar day is slightly longer in duration than the sidereal day (one rotation of the Earth). We have discussed how the Sun is displaced to the east along the ecliptic about 1° per day as the Earth revolves in its orbit. In order to bring the Sun to the meridian and complete the solar day, the Earth must rotate more than 360° relative to the stars.

The difference between the sidereal day and apparent solar day can be visualized if you picture the Sun and a star in conjunction at noon solar time on the meridian. In one sidereal day the Earth completes one rotation and brings the star back to the meridian. But the Sun has advanced about 1° east and will cross the meridian about four minutes later. The following day, the difference in meridian transit between the Sun and the star will accumulate to eight minutes. In six months, the difference is 12 hours, when the star crosses the meridian at midnight solar time. In one year, the Sun and the star will be in conjunction again.

In summary, an apparent solar day is almost four minutes longer than a sidereal day. Clocks in everyday use are geared to the solar day, so, by our time measurements, the sidereal day is equal

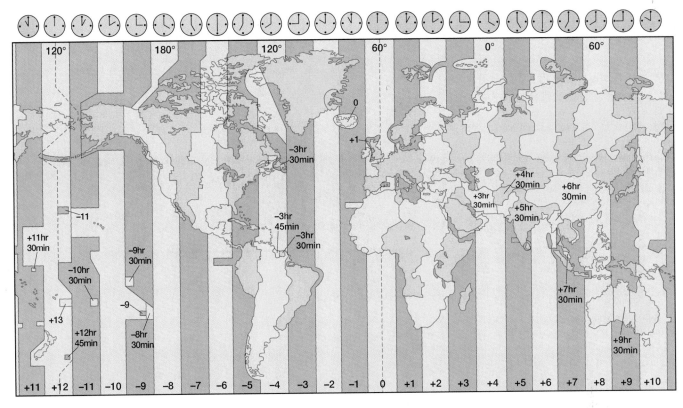

**figure 2.17**
Standard time zones begin at Greenwich and continue east and west every 15° longitude to the international date line at 180° longitude.

to 23h 56m 04s solar time compared to the solar day of 24h 00m 00s.

## Mean Solar Time

Like other planets, the Earth changes its speed and distance in orbit about the Sun. When the Earth is nearest to the Sun and revolving at its greatest speed, the Sun appears to move more rapidly eastward along the ecliptic. The opposite is true when the Earth is at its greatest distance from the Sun. These variations prevent the Sun from reaching the meridian in the same period of time every day. Moreover, the inclination of the Earth's axis causes an additional difference in the length of the solar day between the equinoxes and the solstices.

In order to eliminate the variations of apparent solar time and yet provide an interval of time based upon the rotation of the Earth, an imaginary sun was substituted for the real one in the sky. This fictitious sun moves with uniform speed along the celestial equator at the average rate of the actual Sun on the ecliptic, completing one circuit of the sky in the same period of time as the actual Sun. During the course of the year, the real Sun will alternately transit before and after this **mean sun.** Both cross the meridian at the same time on or about April 16, June 15, September 1, and December 26. Do not think of the fictitious or mean sun as the actual Sun brought to the celestial equator. The mean sun is a moving point that is located mathematically by its position in right ascension among the stars. Mean solar time is kept by our clocks for astronomical computations as well as our daily activities.

## Standard Time

The difference in local time between places was not a problem until the nineteenth century when railroads connected points over great distances. At first, every station kept its own local mean time, but schedules were confused until a uniform timekeeping method was devised. In 1883, the railroads adopted four time zones across the continental United States.

Every locale within each zone maintains the same clock time regardless of the local mean time. Zone time is called **standard time** with a name added to identify each zone: eastern standard, central standard, mountain standard, and Pacific standard. Today there are standard time zones around the world.

Starting with the prime meridian at Greenwich, 0° longitude, standard meridians were selected every 15° east and west to 180° longitude on the opposite side of the globe (fig. 2.17). The boundaries of the time zones were constructed approximately 7.5° on both sides of the standard meridians. Local adjustments were made in the boundaries between zones to avoid inconveniences or to follow rivers or state lines. In each zone, the time used generally corresponds to the local mean time of the standard meridian.

## The Length of the Year

Generally, the year is thought of as the 12-month **calendar year,** or the time required for the Earth to complete one revolution about the Sun. Astronomically, there are several kinds of years, each one of a different length depending on which point is used to measure the period of revolution. These include the **sidereal year,** the **tropical** or **solar year,** and the **lunar year** of 12 lunations totaling 354 days.

The sidereal year is the Earth's period of revolution with respect to the stars, or the time required for the Sun to return to the same point on the celestial sphere. The length of a sidereal year in mean solar days is 365d 06h 09m 10s.

The tropical year is the year of the seasons, and the time required by the Earth to make one revolution with respect to the equinoxes (fig. 2.18). Beginning at the vernal equinox, the Sun advances along the ecliptic and returns to the equinox in one tropical year. The civil calendar we use is based upon the tropical year of 365d 05h 48m 46s mean solar time. Due to precession, the equinox slowly drifts westward 50 arc seconds (50″) annually. Precession shortens the distance the Sun travels to return to the equinox and complete the tropical year. The 50″ on the celestial sphere is equivalent to 20m 24s of time of solar motion, or the difference in length of the sidereal year (the true period of the Earth) and the tropical year on which our calendar is based.

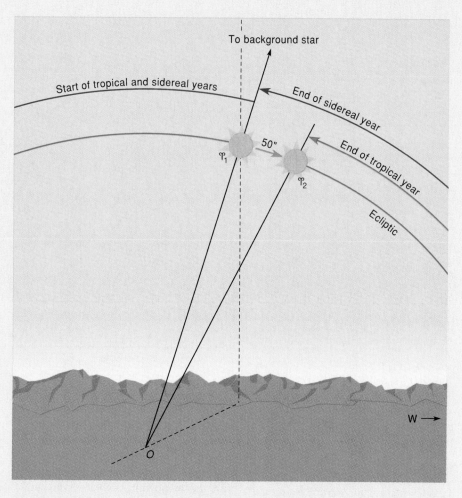

**figure 2.18**

The sidereal year is the Sun's period with respect to the stars. The tropical, or solar, year is the time for the Sun to return to the vernal equinox. The tropical year is shorter than the sidereal year because of precession of the equinox from ♈$_1$ to ♈$_2$.

### International Date Line

If you wish to fly around the globe in an easterly direction, it will be necessary for you to advance your clock one hour at every standard meridian. At the completion of your journey you will have gained 24 hours, one full day. If you decide to make the same trip flying westward and set your clock back, you will have lost one day on your return.

To avoid this problem of time difference, the 180° meridian was selected as the international date line where the date will change. The line follows the meridian except for a slight deviation between Siberia and Alaska and the region between Ellice Islands and New Zealand. At the international date line, the local mean time is the same but the western side is one day later than the eastern side. If you cross the line from east to west, the date is advanced one day. If a crossing is made from west to east, the date is changed back one day.

### Universal Time

Standard observational publications contain the computed positions of the celestial bodies for a year in advance. The

*Astronomical Almanac* issued by the United States Naval Observatory and the Royal Greenwich Observatory lists the times and coordinates of the Sun, Moon, planets, and stars, and phases of the Moon, occultations, eclipses, and risings and settings of the Sun and Moon. The places of these bodies are given for each day of the year and in some instances are timed in hours, minutes, and seconds of **universal time (UT)**. Universal time is a very close approximation of but not exactly equal to the mean diurnal motion of the Sun. Universal time is defined as **Greenwich mean time (GMT)** starting at midnight.

## The Calendar

The chronological division of the civil and religious years into days, weeks, and months is called a calendar. Days, months, and years are astronomical in origin and based upon the motions of the Earth and Moon. The week is not connected to any celestial event although each quarter phase of the Moon occurs in about seven days. Unfortunately, there is no way in which the solar year of 365.242199 days can be divided into synodic months containing 29.530589 days, so adjustments must be made to calendars by adding or subtracting days in order to conveniently stay in step with the seasons.

### The Julian Calendar

In 46 B.C., a new Roman calendar was established by Julius Caesar, aided by the Alexandrian astronomer Sosigenes. This so-called **Julian calendar** was based on the Egyptian solar calendar and adopted throughout the Roman Empire. It remained in use into the Christian era until the calendar reform of Pope Gregory XIII in 1582.

At the time of Caesar, the Mediterranean world except Egypt used lunar calendars based upon the phases of the Moon. Caesar was interested in correcting the Roman calendar to conform to the solar year, and also to bring the vernal equinox to March 25, which had been the original date for the first day of spring. In addition, Rome needed a uniform calendar to administer the provinces under its jurisdiction.

The Julian calendar divides the solar year into 12 months of almost equal length, alternating between 30 and 31 days. Since the lunar year contains 12 synodic months, each averaging 29.5 days, the extra days per month added to the Julian calendar compensated for the 11-day difference between the lunar and solar years.

Because the solar year is 365 1/4 days long, the Julian calendar has three successive years of 365 days and an intercalary or leap day added to the fourth year for a total of 366 days. Caesar lengthened the year 46 B.C. to 445 days, to bring the calendar in step with the seasons and the date of the vernal equinox to March 25. In the old Roman calendar, the year began in March, so the last month, February, needed only 28 days to complete the year. Caesar kept the month short and used it to insert the leap day every fourth year.

A century before Caesar, the date that Roman magistrates took office had been changed to January 1, and that date had become the official New Year's Day, although the people continued to celebrate the end of the year in February. The Julian calendar adopted January 1 as the start of the year and it continues as New Year's Day in the Gregorian calendar in use today.

Six centuries after the Julian calendar was adopted, the Christian era of timekeeping was introduced by an abbot named Dionysius Exiguus. Previously, the calendar years were based upon the traditional date of the founding of Rome. Dionysius attempted to correlate earlier Christian events with dates in the reign of the Roman emperors. He used the year 754 of the Roman calendar as A.D. 1, the beginning of the Christian era, which is preceded by 1 B.C., without a year zero. Arab numerals, which include zero, were not introduced to the western world until after the thirteenth century. Consequently, the first century ended in A.D. 100 and, contrary to popular belief, the twenty-first century begins on January 1, 2001, and not in the year 2000.

### The Gregorian Calendar

The addition of a full leap day every four years makes the Julian calendar 11 minutes and 14 seconds longer than the solar year. Therefore, the Sun reaches the vernal equinox and the first day of spring ahead of the previous calendar date by this amount of time. In A.D. 325, the Council of Nicea decreed that Easter would fall on the first Sunday after the full Moon after the vernal equinox. At that time, the first day of spring occurred on March 21, a gain of four days since the calendar was adopted in 45 B.C. If allowed to continue, Easter as well as other holidays eventually would be celebrated out of season.

Among the problems considered by the Council of Trent between the years 1545 and 1563 was how to correct the error in the Julian calendar. In 1582, Pope Gregory XIII recommended the **Gregorian calendar** to bring the vernal equinox back to March 21 as established by the Council of Nicea. Then a revision was made in the leap year rule to bring the calendar in closer agreement with the solar year. By omitting the leap day in century years not divisible by 400, the years 1700, 1800, and 1900 became regular years while 1600 and 2000 were retained as leap years. This modification keeps the Gregorian calendar in step with the seasons to within one day in 3300 years. No adjustment is necessary until A.D. 5000.

---

## SUMMARY

Most of the northern constellations originated in the mythology of the people of the Near East and the Mediterranean world. Altogether, 48 constellations were passed down from antiquity in various translations of the *Almagest*. Later, in the seventeenth and eighteenth centuries, 40 more constellations were added for a total of 88. Each defines the boundaries of specific areas on the celestial sphere.

The positions of the celestial bodies within the constellations are defined by astronomical coordinate systems, which divide the celestial sphere into a grid similar to the parallels of latitude and meridians of longitude projected onto the Earth. Places in the sky are designated by intersecting circles pertaining to each coordinate system.

The horizon system of coordinates gives the positions of objects in terms of an observer's geographic latitude and longitude. The zenith is defined as the point above the observer, and the horizon as the first reference circle. The celestial meridian serves as the second reference circle, connecting the north and south points on the horizon to the celestial poles and the zenith. Altitude is the angular distance between a celestial body and the horizon. Azimuth is the angular distance from the north point to the celestial body measured eastward along the horizon.

Other coordinate systems are fixed to the celestial sphere and share the diurnal motion of the sky. In the equator coordinate system, 24 hour circles are drawn perpendicular to the celestial equator, which is the first reference circle. The hour circle through the vernal equinox becomes the second reference circle. Declination is the angular distance north or south of the celestial equator. Right ascension is measured eastward from the vernal equinox along the celestial equator.

Various astronomical maps portray the celestial sphere and show the stars in different sizes to indicate their magnitudes. The boundaries between constellations are fixed along hour circles and parallels of declination as established by the International Astronomical Union. In addition to constellations, maps show the location of double stars, variable stars, clusters, nebulae, and galaxies.

A time system is necessary to record astronomical events as well as compute positions of celestial bodies. Several systems are in use. Sidereal time is the measure of the Earth's true rotational period with respect to the stars. The apparent solar day is defined as the interval between two successive transits of the Sun. Mean solar time eliminates the irregularities found in apparent time. Standard time or zone time is a uniform timekeeping method whereby every locale within each zone maintains the same clock time regardless of the local mean time. Standard observational publications contain the computed positions of celestial bodies, which are given in universal time, UT, or Greenwich mean time. 00h UT is equal to midnight GMT.

The calendar is the chronological division of the civil and religious years into days, weeks, and months. The Julian calendar divides the solar year into 12 months that alternate between 30 and 31 days. In 1582, Pope Gregory XIII established the Gregorian calendar, which is in closer agreement with the solar year.

# KEY TERMS

| | |
|---|---|
| altitude | azimuth |
| apparent solar day | calendar year |
| apparent solar time | celestial equator |
| asterism | celestial meridian |
| celestial pole | mean sun |
| constellation | meridians |
| declination (dec.,δ) | nadir |
| ecliptic | parallels |
| equator coordinate system | prime meridian |
| geographic equator | right ascension (R.A., α) |
| Greenwich mean time (GMT) | sidereal day |
| Gregorian calendar | sidereal time |
| horizon coordinate system | sidereal year |
| hour circles | standard time |
| Julian calendar | transit |
| latitude | tropical year |
| longitude | universal time (UT) |
| lunar year | zenith |
| mean solar time | |

# PROBLEMS

1. Make a list of the constellations that cross the meridian between 9:00 P.M. and midnight on March 21, June 21, September 23, and December 22.

2. At approximately what time will the constellations in problem 1 cross the meridian one month later? Explain.

3. Describe the position of the Big Dipper at midnight on the first day of each season.

4. Which circumpolar constellation is above the north celestial pole at 9:00 P.M on September 23? At midnight?

5. With a star map, locate the equinoxes and solstices. How would you use a star map to find the equinoxes and solstices in the actual sky?

6. Name the constellations and first-magnitude stars that are in the direction of full-moon phase if it occurs on December 22. Hint: The full Moon is opposite the Sun.

7. Describe the appearance of the Orion Nebula as seen through binoculars or small telescope.

8. At which latitude would a star in your zenith graze the northern horizon 12 hours later? Explain.

9. Name and describe the Messier objects visible between 9:00 P.M. and midnight, current date.

10. What are the right ascension and declination of the equinoxes and solstices?

11. At your home latitude, what are the coordinates in the horizon system of a star with 00° declination at the time of rising, meridian transit, and setting?

12. What are the altitude, right ascension, and declination of the Sun at noon on March 21, June 21, September 23, and December 22 at: (a) your latitude; (b) Tropic of Cancer; (c) Equator; and (d) Tropic of Capricorn.

13. In what part of the sky would you look to find stars with the following coordinates: (a) altitude = 60°, azimuth = 50°; (b) altitude = 00°, azimuth = 00°; (c) altitude = 40°, azimuth = 200°; and (d) R.A.= 00h, dec.= 00°; all at 9:00 P.M. on September 23?

14. In the middle latitudes of the Northern Hemisphere, at what time of the year will the full Moon reach its lowest meridian altitude? In which constellation will it be found?

# REFERENCES

Becvar, Antonin. 1974. *Atlas Borealis 1950. 0.* 2nd ed. Cambridge, Mass.: Sky Publishing Co.

———. 1974. *Atlas Eclipticalis.* 2d ed. Cambridge, Mass.: Sky Publishing Co.

Chauvenet, William. 1960. *A Manual of Spherical and Practical Astronomy.* 5th ed. Vol I. New York: Dover Publications, Inc.

Norton, Arthur P. 1986. *Norton's Star Atlas.* 17th ed. Revised and rewritten by Christopher R. Kitchen et.al. New York: John Wiley and Sons, Inc.

Smart, W. M. 1979. *Textbook on Spherical Astronomy.* 6th ed. Rev. by R. M. Green. Cambridge: Cambridge University Press.

Tirion, Wil, Barry Rappaport, and George Lovi. 1987. *Uranometria 2000.0.* Vol. I, *The Northern Hemisphere.* Richmond, Va.: Willmann-Bell, Inc.

U.S. Naval Observatory. Nautical Almanac Office. *The Astronomical Almanac.* Washington, D.C.: U.S. Government Printing Office.

Vorontsov-Vel 'yaminov, B. A.1969. *Astronomical Problems.* Trans. P.M. Rabbitt. Oxford: Pergamon Press.

time and place in the heavens

c h a p t e r

3

t h e   m a k i n g   o f   m o d e r n   a s t r o n o m y

Before invention of the telescope, astronomers used astrolabes to
measure the positions of the Moon and planets. Time was kept by
measuring the altitude of the Sun.

In the preceding chapters we discussed changes in the positions of the planets on the celestial sphere as seen by an observer on the Earth. Why do the planets behave this way? What action is responsible for their motion? The answers to these questions were given when the concept of gravitation as a universal force was developed in the seventeenth century. *Gravitation* is the first of four known forces of nature that govern the behavior of matter from the smallest elementary particles to the largest collection of galaxies. From it came a new branch of astronomy called *celestial mechanics,* which deals with the problems of mass and motion by the mathematical application of gravitational laws.

Prior to this time, Aristotle's belief in the existence of natural and violent or enforced motion was accepted without the benefit of experimental proof; all natural motion was due to an inclination to move in a preferred direction. So it was natural for the Earth to be at the center of the universe, and no force was necessary to cause objects to fall to its surface. To the Greeks, motion was the result of an applied push or pull that had to be maintained by a force. And in the heavens, planets moved effortlessly in uniform circular motion about the Earth at the center of the universe.

## Copernicus and the New World System

The period of European history called the Renaissance marked the rediscovery by scholars of the literary works of the classical Greeks. The *Almagest* and other writings had been brought to Europe by Islamic civilization. It was a time when the Ptolemaic geocentric system and the work of Aristotle were accepted as dogma. With few exceptions, astronomy consisted of translating texts and compiling tables of positions for the Moon and planets.

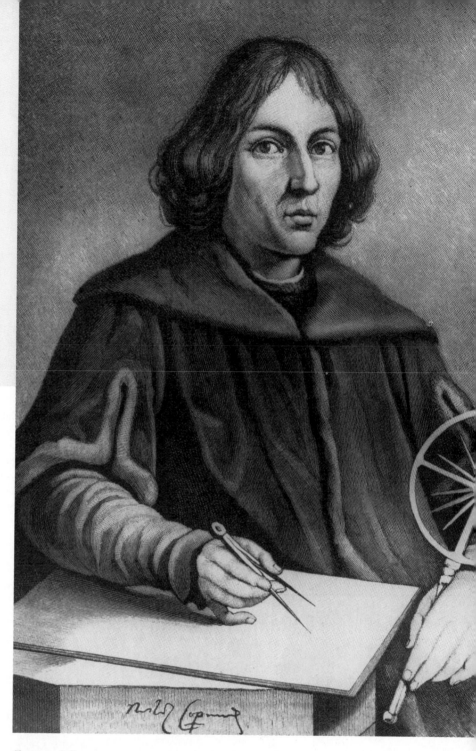

figure 3.1
Nicolaus Copernicus.

But the Renaissance brought more than a revival of interest in the classics. It was a period of transition that affected government and religion as well as the arts and sciences. The time was right to revolutionize thinking by displacing the Earth into an orbit about the Sun. Nicolaus Copernicus (1473–1543), in his ***De Revolutionibus Orbium Coelestium*** (*On the Revolutions of the Heavenly Spheres*), gave an argument for the heliocentric world system that marked the beginning of a new scientific age.

Copernicus (see fig. 3.1) was born in Torun, Poland, and attended the University of Cracow until 1494. In 1496, he traveled to Italy where he studied law at Bologna and theology and medicine at

Padua. We know he was introduced to astronomy and philosophy because, in 1500, he lectured in astronomy in Rome.

In 1506, Copernicus returned to Poland to assume his duties as canon of Frauenburg cathedral, a position he had obtained in 1497. In addition to his clerical duties, Copernicus established an observatory where he studied the motions of the planets for the next 20 years. During this time, he became convinced that the Ptolemaic system could not adequately explain planetary movements and proceeded to develop a new world system.

Copernicus was not prepared to publish his views, but his unwillingness must be judged in terms of the tumultuous times. The Reformation was underway and, as a clerical administrator, he was reluctant to add to the religious revolt. But Copernicus was urged on by his supporters and in 1530 he wrote the *Commentariolus,* a summary of his ideas which would later be expanded into *De Revolutionibus.* This preliminary work received favorable attention from scholars and ecclesiastics, including Pope Clement VII. Finally Copernicus agreed to publish, and *De Revolutionibus* was completed in 1543 and presented to its author on his deathbed.

Like so many other great scientific ideas, the heliocentric hypothesis had its share of criticism. Renaissance astronomers used the same argument as Aristotle to disprove the motions of the Earth. There were adherents among astronomers as well as the clergy but almost a century would pass before the superiority of the Copernican system was confirmed by the next generation of astronomers.

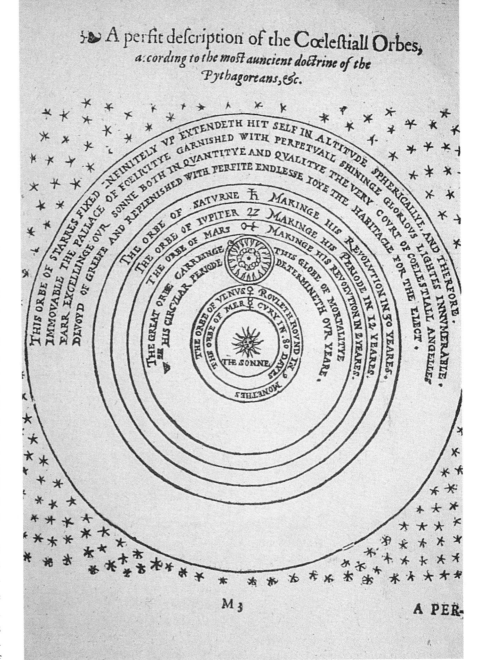

figure 3.2

An early drawing of the Copernican heliocentric system.

### De Revolutionibus

Copernicus presented his argument for the Earth in motion around a static Sun in a series of six documents or "books." They included topics that described the shape of the Earth and its motions, points, and circles, in particular the ecliptic, that are generated on the celestial sphere. He explained precession as a slow movement of the Earth's axis and not a displacement of the stars. He described the motions of the Moon and movements of the planets and calculated their positions.

Copernicus believed the spherical shape of the heavens to be self-evident because the sphere is the perfect geometrical figure, having no boundaries and containing the largest volume for its size. It is the natural shape taken by such varied objects as the Sun, Moon, or even a drop of falling rain.

Then Copernicus compared the size of the celestial sphere to the Earth's orbit, which was merely a point at the center of the heavens. For this reason, the stars will not show any apparent shift in position caused by the revolution of the Earth. He refuted the notion of a stationary Earth and explained apparent diurnal motion as an effect of the Earth's rotation. By putting the Earth in motion, Copernicus gave it the same status as the planets (fig. 3.2).

## Configurations of the Planets

Copernicus placed the known planets in order of distance from the Sun. Mercury and Venus are called **inferior planets** because they are closer to the Sun than the Earth. The remaining planets known to Copernicus—Mars, Jupiter, and Saturn—are **superior planets** located farther from the Sun than the Earth.

As the planets revolve, they are seen in different configurations relative to the Earth and Sun (fig. 3.3). Venus is at **inferior conjunction** (position 1) in a line between the Earth and Sun. At **greatest western elongation** (position 2), the line of sight from the Earth is tangent to the planet's orbit. When Venus reaches **superior conjunction** (position 3), once again the planet, Sun, and Earth are in line. At **greatest eastern elongation,** (position 4), the planet is at its greatest angle east of the Sun.

Mars at **opposition** (position 5) reaches its closest approach to the Earth, followed by **western quadrature** (position 6) at a right angle to the Earth and Sun. The planet is at **conjunction** (position 7) when it is in the direction of the Sun and most distant from the Earth. At **eastern quadrature** (position 8), the planet is again observed at 90° elongation. If you were on Mars during quadrature, the Earth would appear to be an inferior planet at greatest elongation.

## The Sidereal Period

The time interval between two successive or similar configurations of a planet with respect to the Earth and Sun represents one **synodic period.** Copernicus explained the synodic period as an effect of the relative motion between the Earth and another planet as they revolve around the Sun. Knowing this, he was able to determine the **sidereal period,** the time required for a planet to complete one revolution with respect to the stars.

To find the sidereal period of Venus, we begin when the planet is at greatest eastern elongation at position $V_1$ and the Earth is at $E_1$ in figure 3.4. After 584 days, or one synodic period, Venus is at position $V_2$ and is again at greatest eastern elongation with the Earth, which is at position $E_2$. In that time, the Earth has

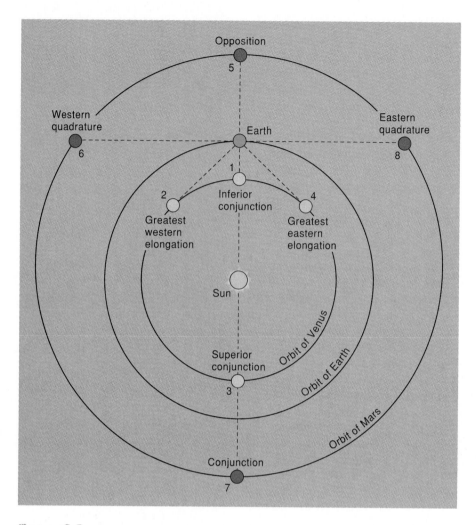

**figure 3.3**

Configurations of an inferior planet (Venus) and a superior planet (Mars).

revolved more than once (360° in 365 days) for a total of 576°, or one complete revolution of 360° plus an additional 216°. Since Venus revolves faster and occupies a smaller orbit, it must have gone twice around the Sun plus an additional 216° for a total of 936° in the same period of time.

How many days does it take Venus to complete one revolution of 360°, or one sidereal period, if it requires 584 days to revolve 936°?

Venus's sidereal period =

$$\frac{584 \text{ days} \times 360°}{936°} = 225 \text{ days}$$

## Relative Distances between the Sun and Planets

Consider the distance between the Earth and Sun as unity (*ES* = one unit as shown in figure 3.5). This distance varies dur-

ing the year due to the eccentricity of the Earth's orbit so our reference unit, known as the **astronomical unit (AU),** is the average or mean distance between the Earth and Sun.

Suppose we observe Venus at greatest western elongation along the line of sight *EV* in figure 3.5. Since line *EV* is tangent to the planet's orbit, angle *EVS* will be equal to 90°. The angle between Venus and the Sun measures 47°. The distance *VS* is determined by constructing a perpendicular from the Sun, *S*, to the line *EV*. By trigonometry we find the planet's distance to the Sun: it is the sine of 47°.

Venus's distance =
Earth's distance × sin 47°
$d = 1.00 \text{ AU} \times 0.73 = 0.73 \text{ AU}.$

Copernicus may have set the Earth in motion, but the heliocentric model failed to agree with the observed positions of

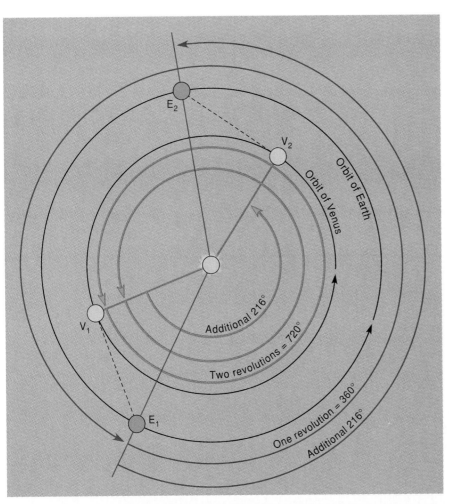

**figure 3.4**
Finding the sidereal period of Venus when
the synodic period is known.

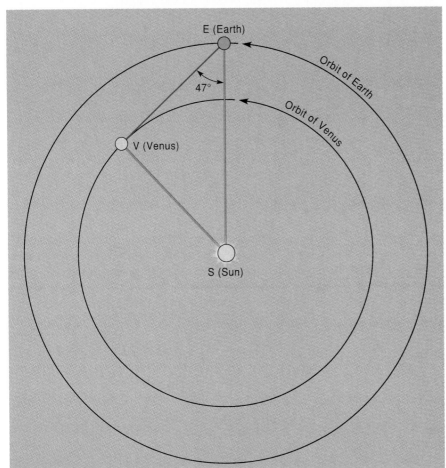

**figure 3.5**
Finding the distance of an inferior planet
(Venus) from the Sun in terms of Earth's
distance from the Sun (one astronomical
unit, or 1 AU).

the making of modern astronomy

45

## Distance between Mars and the Sun

Finding the distances to the superior planets requires another procedure. If the sidereal period is known, it is possible to compute the angular distance traveled by a superior planet from opposition to quadrature. In the case of Mars (fig. 3.6), about 106 days will elapse, amounting to an angular distance of 55°. In the same period of time, the Earth advances 104° for a difference of 49° of travel.

The distance from the Sun to Mars can be found by geometric construction. Let line $E_2S$ equal 1.00 AU. Construct a line from $E_2$ at right angles to line $E_2S$ in the direction that Mars will be at quadrature. At $S$, measure 49° from line $SE_2$ and draw line $SM_2$. The intersection of lines $SM_2$ and $E_2M_2$ locates Mars in its orbit and its distance from the Sun. By trigonometry,

$$\text{distance of Mars from Sun} = \frac{1.00 \text{ AU}}{\cos 49°} = 1.52 \text{ AU}.$$

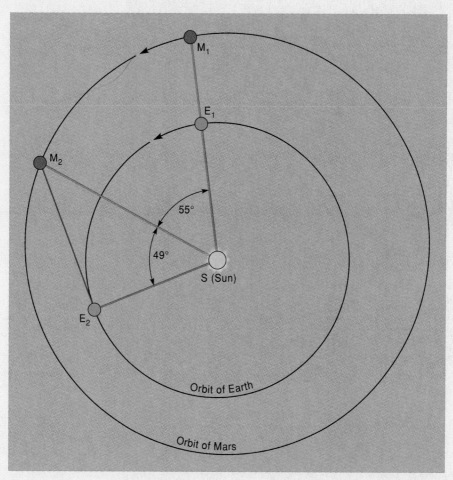

**figure 3.6**
Finding the distance of a superior planet (Mars) from the Sun in terms of Earth's distance (1 AU).

the planets. First of all, he placed the planets in circular orbits, which made it necessary to add epicycles to account for their varying speeds. In his scheme, the Sun merely replaced the Earth in the center, but it had no physical effect on the motions of the planets. The Copernican system provided an elegant geometric representation of the relative distances between the planets and the value of their sidereal periods. Retrograde motion was correctly explained as an effect of the difference in velocity between the Earth

and another planet. Copernicus's description of gravity as a property of the Sun, Moon, and planets led to the understanding of gravitation as a universal force.

## Tycho Brahe: Measurement of Position

After the publication of *De Revolutionibus* and before invention of the telescope, astronomy made moderate

progress by improvement in mathematics and the construction of more accurate observational instruments. Complex problems were solved by the use of Arabic numbers, the application of algebra to geometry, and later the invention of logarithms. Astronomical instruments such as cross staffs and quadrants were used to measure angles of less than one arc minute.

Tycho Brahe (1546–1601) (see fig. 3.7) is considered to have been the best visual observer before the telescope was

figure 3.7
Tycho Brahe.

QVADRANS MVRALIS
SIVE TICHONICVS.

figure 3.8
The mural quadrant at Uraniborg.

planets, in particular the planet Mars. His mural quadrant contained a graduated circle capable of measuring angles to less than one arc minute (fig. 3.8).

The comet of 1577 gave Tycho another opportunity to prove Aristotle wrong. He made meridian observations of the comet and found it to be celestial in origin; Aristotle had claimed that comets were atmospheric objects. Furthermore, the trajectory of the comet was a curved path that crossed the orbits of the planets as it moved toward and away from the Sun (fig. 3.9). Tycho's discoveries made the Greek geocentric model unacceptable. Instead, he designed his own semi-heliocentric world system.

## The Tychonic System

Tycho could not accept the Copernican system because he was unable to detect any shift in the positions of the stars caused by the Earth's revolution. This apparent displacement of a star's position was not detected until the nineteenth century.

Since he could not find evidence of the Earth's revolution, Tycho rejected the Copernican system and substituted a semi-heliocentric model. He placed the

invented. In 1572, Tycho observed a nova, and in other years several comets, which put to rest Aristotle's concept of geocentric crystal spheres. He devised a semi-heliocentric model that served as a transition between the Ptolemaic and Copernican systems.

A high point early in his career was the observation of a nova, an exploding star, in 1572. Tycho detected a "new star" in Cassiopeia that in time became brighter than the planet Venus. If a nova was a nearby object between the Earth and the Moon, as Aristotle claimed, the Earth's rotation would cause an apparent shift in its position. Finding none, Tycho looked for an easterly motion with respect to the stars that would have placed the nova in the solar system among the planets. Instead, the nova remained fixed among the stars, so Tycho identifed it as a stellar object.

In 1576, King Fredrick II of Denmark granted Tycho the North Sea island of Hveen to continue his astronomical work. He constructed two observatories, Uraniborg and Stjerneborg, where he prepared tables of positions of the Moon and

Sun and Moon in orbit around a central Earth, and the other planets in orbit around the Sun. The orbits of the inferior planets, Mercury and Venus, passed between the Earth and Sun to account for their observed configurations. Mars, Jupiter, and Saturn were placed in larger orbits in order to appear in opposition. The stars were attached to a sphere beyond Saturn (fig. 3.10).

In 1588, King Fredrick II died and his successor, Christian IV, did not provide Tycho with the financial support necessary to maintain the observatories at Hveen. Unsuccessful in his attempts to regain funds, Tycho left Denmark for Bohemia at the invitation of Emperor Rudolph II. At Prague, Tycho worked with assistants, in particular Johannes Kepler, to prepare the **Rudolphine Tables** of positions, which were finally completed by Kepler in 1627.

## Johannes Kepler: Determining the Orbits of the Planets

Johannes Kepler (1571–1630) (see fig. 3.11) was first introduced to the Copernican system while a student at the University of Tubingen. After completing his studies, he accepted a position as teacher of mathematics and astronomy in Graz, Austria. There Kepler introduced his idea of harmony in the motions and distances of the planets with the publication of the *Mysterium Cosmographicum,* or *Cosmographic Mystery* (1596). In this work, he accounted for the relative distances between the planets.

Kepler's publication attracted the attention of other scholars, including Tycho and Galileo, because the work represented the first argument in favor of the Copernican system since the publication of *De Revolutionibus.* The book made Kepler famous and led to his appointment as Tycho's assistant at Prague.

In 1600, Kepler joined Tycho and was assigned to investigate the orbit of Mars. This planet was of particular interest because no existing theory could adequately account for its observed positions. The Copernican and Tychonic systems resorted to circular orbits, which do not describe the true path of the planets

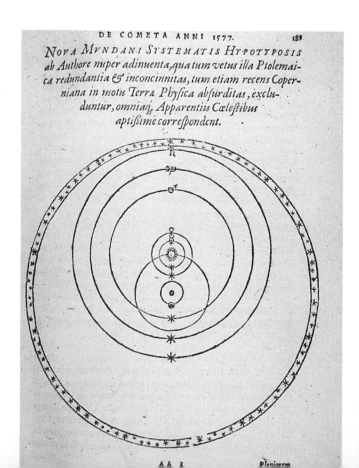

**figure 3.9**

A comet in an elliptical orbit of large eccentricity.

**figure 3.10**

An early engraving of Tycho's system.

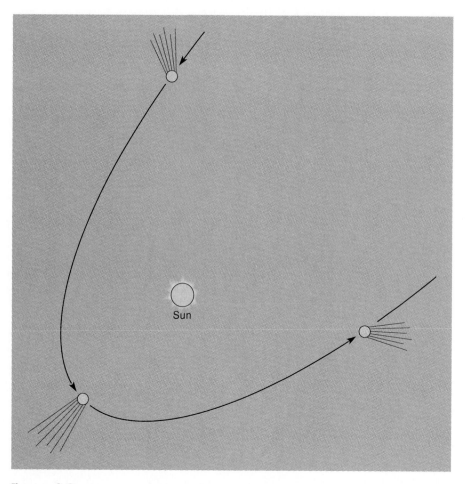

**figure 3.11**
Johannes Kepler.

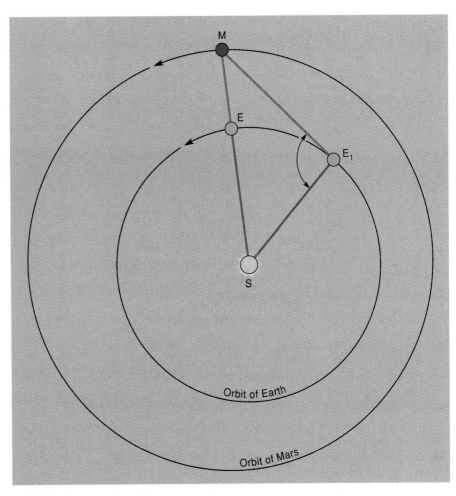

**figure 3.12**
The orbits of Earth and Mars. Kepler determined the orbit of Earth in terms of Mars' sidereal period.

around the Sun. As an added incentive to investigate Mars, Kepler was given access to Tycho's comprehensive tables of positions of the planet. Moreover, when Tycho died in 1601, Kepler was appointed his successor as imperial mathematician to complete the *Rudolphine Tables.* **Kepler's laws of planetary motion** were derived from Tycho's careful observations of the planet Mars.

## The Laws of Planetary Motion

Now Kepler proceeded to define the orbit of Mars. As we have seen, he differed with Tycho regarding the position of the Sun as the center of the system. According to Kepler, all measurements must be made relative to the Sun rather than the Earth because Mars' orbital plane passes through the Sun and not the Earth.

Before he could define the orbit of Mars, Kepler had to determine the orbit of the Earth. This he was able to do by plotting the position of Mars at successive intervals of its sidereal period based on data recorded by Tycho. The procedure keeps Mars in the same place in its orbit each time an observation is made. The position of the Earth is found by triangulation. As shown in figure 3.12, Mars is observed at opposition (position *M*) while the Earth is at position *E*. In

one sidereal period, Mars will return to *M*; the Earth will be at $E_1$. The intersection of lines $SE_1$ and $ME_1$ locates the Earth at one point in its orbit. By repeating the process using positions of Mars listed in Tycho's tables, Kepler was able to plot the Earth's orbit.

As shown in figure 3.13, Kepler discovered that a planet's orbital velocity increases (position *A* to *B*) as its distance from the Sun decreases. The velocity decreases (position *C* to *D*) as its distance increases. When he connected each point on the Earth's orbit to the Sun by a line, or *radius vector,* Kepler found that as the planet revolves, the radius vector sweeps out equal areas (*I, II, III*) in equal periods of time. This discovery was to become Kepler's *second law of planetary motion.*

Kepler proceeded to determine the orbit of Mars by reversing the method used to find the orbit of the Earth (fig. 3.12).

From Tycho's tables, Kepler selected oppositions of Mars and constructed the line *SEM* connecting the Sun, Earth, and Mars. In one sidereal period, Mars returns to position *M* while the Earth is at position $E_1$. Since the Earth's orbit is known, the intersection of lines $E_1M$ and *SEM* locates the position of Mars in its orbit. By repeating the procedure at oppositions that occur at other points, Kepler found the shape of Mars' orbit. (See four types of orbits in fig. 3.14.)

Then Kepler constructed radius vectors for Mars and applied the equal-area rule, which had worked well on the Earth's almost circular orbit. But there were discrepancies and, rather than believe that Tycho's tables contained errors, Kepler concluded that the orbit of Mars was not circular. After many trials using various oval shapes, he found that an elliptic orbit satisfied observation and provided the best fit. He was able to state what came to be called his *first law of planetary motion,* that planets travel about the sun in elliptic orbits with the sun located at one **focal point** (fig. 3.15). In 1609, Kepler published these results in the *Commentaries on the Movements of the Planet Mars;* they are expressed as his first and second laws of planetary motion:

1. Every planet revolves in an elliptic orbit with the Sun situated at one of the focal points.

2. The radius vector joining the Sun and a planet will sweep equal areas in the same interval of time (the law of equal areas).

In 1619, in **The Harmony of the Worlds** (*Harmonice Mundi*), Kepler tried to show a relationship between the harmony of the planetary movements (ratios of the distances to the periods of the planets) and the harmony found in the musical scale. When the mean distances to the Sun (*d*) and periods of revolution (*P*), were compared, he found that the period squared was proportional to the distance cubed. Kepler was mistaken about the harmony of music and astronomy, but the period-distance relationship is valid and is expressed as his *third law of planetary motion.*

3. The squares of the periods of any two planets are proportional to the cubes of their mean distances from the Sun.

This may be written as an equation:

$$\frac{P_1^2}{P_2^2} = \frac{d_1^3}{d_2^3} = \text{constant}.$$

When the periods (*P*) are given in years and the distances (*d*) in astronomical units (AU), the value of the constant is unity and the equation may be written
$$P^2 = d^3.$$

Find the period of Mars if its mean distance (*d*) =1.52 AU.

$$P^2 = (1.52)^3$$
Period of Mars = 1.88 years, or 687 days.

By 1627, Kepler's investigations of the positions of the planets made possible the publication of the *Rudolphine Tables* begun by Tycho over a quarter-century earlier. But Kepler's most

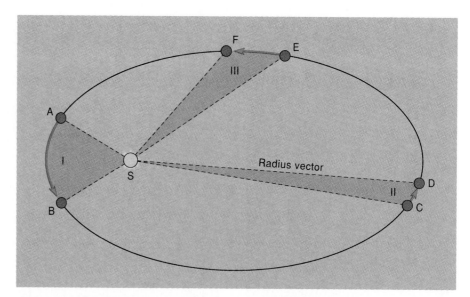

**figure 3.13**

Kepler's second law of planetary motion. The line connecting a planet to the Sun sweeps out equal areas (I, II, and III) in equal periods of time.

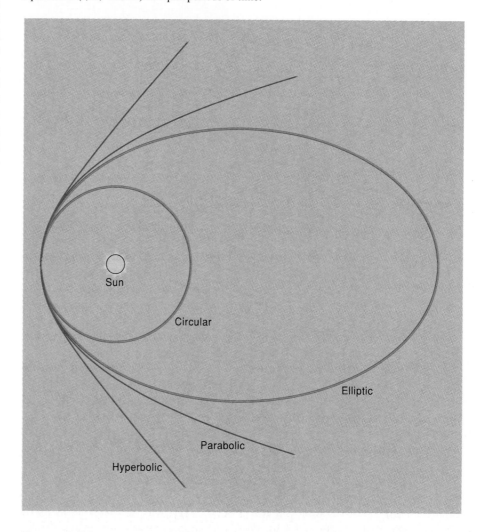

**figure 3.14**

Four types of orbits. Circular and elliptical orbits are closed curves around the Sun. A body in a parabolic or hyperbolic orbit will escape the gravitational attraction of the Sun.

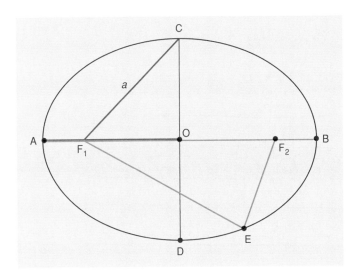

a.

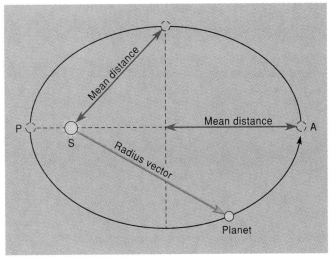

b.

▲ **figure 3.15**

*a.* An ellipse is an oval curve designated by a major axis (AB) and a minor axis (CD) intersecting at O. The semimajor axis is equal to one-half the major axis, AO or OB. From point C, a line *(a)* equal to the semimajor axis intersects AB at the focal points $F_1$ or $F_2$. The sum of the distances from any point (E) on the ellipse to the focal points ($EF_1 + EF_2$) is a constant equal to AB, the length of the major axis.

*b.* According to Kepler's first law, the Sun (S) is located at one focal point of a planet's orbit. The point (P) in the orbit is called the perihelion, meaning nearest to the Sun. The opposite point (A) is called the aphelion, or farthest from the Sun. The mean distance of a planet from the Sun is equal to the length of the semimajor axis of the planet's orbit. The ellipse in the diagram is greatly exaggerated; planetary orbits are very close to circular.

significant contributions to modern astronomy are his three laws of planetary motion, which served as a foundation for the science of celestial mechanics later developed by Isaac Newton.

## Galileo Galilei: The Foundation of Experimental Science

In his youth, Galileo (1564–1642) (see fig. 3.16) studied at the University of Pisa to prepare for a career in medicine. But his first interest was mathematics and physical science and, by 1589, he was serving as professor of mathematics at the University of Pisa. Here, and later at Padua, he challenged the dogmatic science of Aristotle by subjecting it to experimentation.

Galileo is known for his experiments in mechanics. He studied falling objects and the behavior of bodies in uniform motion, and he described inertia as a property by which a body resists a change in its state of motion. Aristotle had said

◀ **figure 3.16**
Galileo Galilei.

the making of modern astronomy

that a continuous force was necessary to *maintain* motion; Galileo argued that a force was needed to *change* it. Later, Newton incorporated these principles into his laws of motion.

Galileo made notable contributions to astronomy. He was the first to make systematic low-power telescopic observations. The publication of his discoveries in the **Sidereus Nuncius** gave additional support to the Copernican system.

### Sidereus Nuncius

In 1609, after receiving a report that the Dutch lensmaker Lippershey had invented a telescope, Galileo proceeded to study the principles of its optics and construction. His first telescope was capable of nine-power magnification.

When he turned his telescope to the Moon, Galileo found light-colored regions covered by pits and hollows. Dark circular areas were ringed by mountain ranges containing peaks and valleys similar to those found on the Earth. On the terminator, Galileo saw bright isolated peaks protruding out of the darkness while sunlight gradually flooded the valleys in between. He proved the Moon to be as irregular as the Earth and not a perfectly smooth sphere as Aristotle had claimed.

Galileo found that the stars were not magnified when viewed in the telescope but appeared as brighter points of light. He reported seeing 36 stars in the Pleiades cluster where six can be seen without a telescope. The glow of the Milky Way separated into a mass of countless stars surrounded by an unresolved haze of fainter stars.

Unlike the stars, the planets present round disks and are of globular shape. While observing Jupiter, Galileo discovered four of its moons arranged in a line along the planet's equator. He computed their periods of revolution and found that the satellites revolved around Jupiter in the same way as the planets around the Sun (fig. 3.17). His discovery was a strong argument in favor of the Copernican system.

Further evidence in favor of a heliocentric system was Galileo's observation of the phases of Venus. The apparent

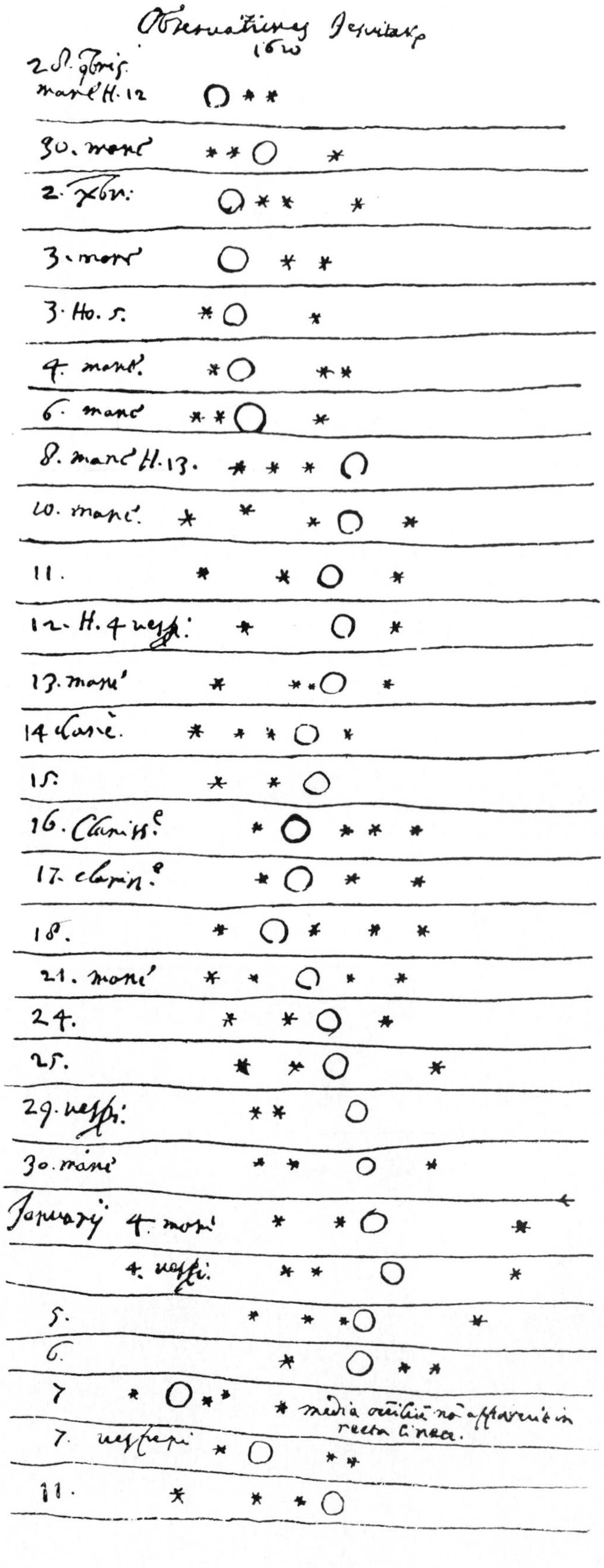

figure 3.17

Early sketch depicting Galileo's observations of the motions of Jupiter's satellites.

## observing Jupiter's satellites

The best time to observe Jupiter is between opposition and eastern quadrature when the planet can be seen in the southeast after evening twilight. In the telescope, Jupiter is resolved into a bright disk ringed by a system of satellites that change positions in the equatorial plane of the planet. A small telescope shows four bright satellites, the Galilean moons described by Galileo in 1610. In order of distance from Jupiter, the satellites are named Io, Europa, Ganymede, and Callisto. They have periods of revolution that range from 01d 18h for Io to 16d 18h for Callisto.

To study the motions of the satellites systematically, follow the procedure described by Galileo in the *Sidereus Nuncius.* For a period of several weeks, observe the planet and sketch the positions of the moons. Let the diameter of Jupiter be the unit distance and estimate the elongations of the satellites in terms of the diameter of the planet. Mark the date and time of observation and, if possible, make your observations at the same time each night.

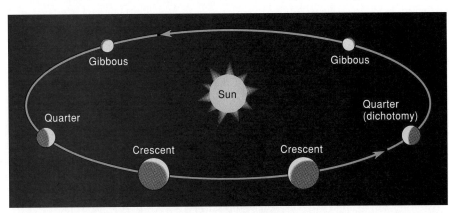

a.

b.

change in the size and shape of the planet could take place only if Venus revolved around the Sun rather than the Earth. Near superior conjunction, he saw the planet at its smallest size and at gibbous phase. As the planet advanced in its orbit, he observed that it increased in angular diameter and reached quarter phase at greatest elongation. As it approached the Earth, Venus showed a larger and brighter crescent before passing between the Earth and Sun at inferior conjunction (fig. 3.18). Galileo concluded that Mercury and Venus revolve around the Sun and not the Earth.

In 1632, Galileo published the ***Dialogue of the Two Principal Systems of the World.*** Using his telescopic observations as evidence, he defended the Copernican doctrine as true and ridiculed the Ptolemaic geocentric system and its proponents. For this he was accused of heresy and eventually confined to his home near Florence. However, he continued to write, and by 1638 his final work, the ***Dialogue Concerning the Two New Sciences,*** was completed. His treatise on uniform linear motion, the acceleration of falling bodies, and the parabolic trajectory of a projectile served as a foundation upon which Newton later based the laws of motion and universal gravitation.

## figure 3.18

*a.* Phases of Venus illustrated, and *b.* shown in photographs. From the Earth, the planet appears in crescent phase before and after inferior conjunction. Half the bright side is visible at greatest elongation east and west (quarter phase). Venus appears gibbous before and after superior conjunction. Note the changes in the planet's angular diameter as it approaches and recedes from the Earth.

the making of modern astronomy

## Galileo and the Science of Mechanics

In the *Dialogue Concerning the Two New Sciences,* Galileo introduces the meaning of change in position. He defines uniform linear motion of a particle as equal changes in distance in equal intervals of time. Galileo realized that distance traveled is proportional to the time interval if the speed of the particle is constant.

Moreover, his experiments with falling bodies made it clear that all objects fall with constant **acceleration** toward the Earth regardless of their size or density. Starting from rest, the distance traveled by a falling body is proportional to the square of the time interval needed to travel the distance. The acceleration, or rate of change of velocity, remains constant, meaning that the velocity increases uniformly with time.

Galileo experimented with objects in projectile motion (fig. 3.19). Any object thrown at an angle to the horizontal will have a uniform horizontal motion and a uniformly accelerated vertical motion. The resulting path is parabolic. He found that when a body is hurled horizontally while another is dropped vertically from the same height, they reach the ground at the same time.

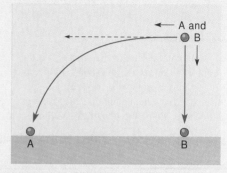

▲ **figure 3.19**
Galileo's projectile motion experiment. If body A is hurled horizontally and body B is dropped vertically from the same height, they will reach the ground at the same time.

## Isaac Newton: Principles of Natural Science

A visitor to Westminster Abbey in London will find an ornate monument and a stone slab in the floor carved with the name Newton. Here lies one of the greatest scientists of all time. At age 24 he described gravitation as a universal force; he made discoveries in the science of optics; and he invented the reflecting telescope. His accomplishments in mathematics include the development of calculus and the binomial theorem.

Isaac Newton (1642–1727) (see fig. 3.20) entered Trinity College at Cambridge University in 1661 and earned the degree of bachelor of arts in 1665. During the plague years, 1665 and 1666, death was widespread; to avoid infection, Newton was forced to live in the country. He occupied his time by formulating the **laws of motion** (the foundation for the science of mechanics) and the **law of universal gravitation.** By 1669, he was appointed professor at Trinity, where he gave lectures that were later incorporated into his major work, *Philosophiae Naturalis Principia Mathematica,* (*Mathematical Principles of Natural Philosophy*), known as the **Principia.**

**figure 3.20**
Isaac Newton.

## The Laws of Motion

In the *Principia* (1687), Newton formulated three new laws based upon Galileo's experiments on uniform motion, projectile motion, and the acceleration of falling bodies. As described earlier, Galileo had demonstrated that a stationary object will remain at rest, while one in uniform linear motion will continue in the same direction and speed unless its direction or speed is caused to change.

Newton showed that a *force* is required to cause a change in speed or direction of a body in motion. *Acceleration* is defined as the rate of change of velocity (either in speed or direction). The force required to cause acceleration is dependent upon the **mass,** or quantity of matter of the body in motion. Greater force must be applied to accelerate more massive objects in order to overcome the **inertia,** or resistance to change, which is directly proportional to the mass. Finally, a force exerted on an object (action), results in an equal and opposite force (reaction).

Newton's laws of motion are summarized as follows:

1. *Law of Inertia.* Every particle remains at rest or in uniform motion unless acted upon by an outside force.

2. *Law of Acceleration.* Acceleration is directly proportional to the force and in the direction of the straight line in which the force is applied.

3. *Law of Action and Reaction.* For every action, there is an equal and opposite reaction. The force (action) by a body on a second body is equal in magnitude but opposite in direction to the force (reaction) that the second body exerts on the first.

Newton used these principles to prove that Kepler's laws of planetary motion were due to the attractive force provided by the Sun. Next, he mathematically defined the attractive force as a property of all bodies.

## The Law of Gravitation

If a body revolving in an orbit constantly changes its speed and direction, a **centripetal force** that acts toward the cen-

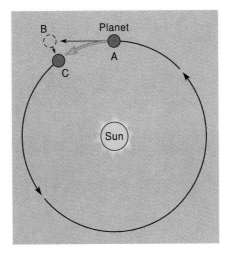

**figure 3.21**

The orbit of a planet around the Sun. Position A represents the initial position of the planet. In the absence of the Sun's attraction, the planet would move in a straight line to position B. In the presence of the Sun's attractive force, the planet will follow a curved path to position C; in essence, "falling" from B to C.

ter of the orbit must cause the acceleration (fig. 3.21). In the *Principia,* Newton describes **gravitation** as the attractive force exerted by all matter. The Sun and the planets, as well as the Earth and Moon, all interact by means of universal gravitational force.

Newton went on to describe the force between two bodies as directly proportional to the product of their masses, and inversely proportional to the square of the distance between them. Thus, the greater the mass of the bodies, the greater the force of attraction between them. If the distance separating them is reduced by one-half, the force of attraction increases to four times its previous value. Conversely, if the distance is doubled, the force is reduced to one-fourth of the original value.

Expressed mathematically, Newton's law of universal gravitation is

$$F = G \frac{m_1 m_2}{R^2}$$

where $G$ is the constant of gravitation, the constant of proportionality between two unit masses at a unit distance apart (its value in the metric or SI system is $G = 6.67 \times 10^{-11}$ Newton · meter$^2$ · kg$^{-2}$;

$m_1$ and $m_2$ are equal to the mass of the bodies; and $R$ is the distance between the bodies.

In accordance with this law, every body in the universe attracts every other body with a force that varies directly as the product of their masses and inversely as the square of their distance.

Newton's elegant theory of gravitation successfully accounted for other events in addition to the motions of planets and their satellites. Halley computed the orbit of the comet of 1682 and found it similar to the comets observed in 1531 and 1607. From this he predicted its return in the year 1758. When the comet reappeared on Christmas Day 1758, it was a triumph for Newtonian physics and Halley, for whom the comet is named.

In 1783, when Goodricke discovered the eclipsing binary star Algol, he provided evidence that Newton's law of gravitation extended beyond the Sun and planets. The Algol system consists of a large, faint component revolving about a smaller, brighter star in a period of about 69 hours.

In 1846, Newton's law of gravitation led to the discovery of a new planet by Leverrier and Adams. The location of the object was determined by irregularities in the orbit of Uranus caused by the attraction of the unknown planet, later named Neptune.

Before considering the modern interpretation of gravitational theory, we should understand the assumptions Newton made in arriving at his universal law. First of all, he did not prove there is a force of gravitation but merely supposed its existence by observing objects fall to the ground. If gravitation is a force of attraction possessed by all matter in the universe and is a function of mass and distance, then mass and space must be absolute quantities. In the universe pictured by Newton, events taking place would be the same for all observers regardless of their locations or their motions. Therefore, Newton stated as self-evident by definition the existence of absolute time, space, and motion.

Newton thought of time as flowing uniformly without change, independent of any external influence. To him, space remained the same while objects in

## Newton and Flights of the Space Shuttles

According to Newtonian mechanics, the acceleration of a body in orbit about the Earth varies inversely as the square of the distance from the center of the Earth. We can investigate this effect of gravitation by comparing the acceleration of a spacecraft in orbit with that of Newton's apple falling from the tree. On March 13, 1989, the space shuttle Discovery carried five astronauts into orbit 295 km above the Earth (fig. 3.22). At this altitude, the shuttle completed one revolution in a period of 90 minutes.

To determine the acceleration required to keep the astronauts in space, find the velocity of the shuttle by dividing the distance traveled (circumference of the orbit) by the period (time required to circle the Earth).

$$\text{Velocity } (V) = \frac{2 \times 3.1416 \times R}{P}$$

where

$R$ = radius of Earth + altitude of shuttle;

and

$P$ = period in seconds (90 minutes × 60).

$$V = \frac{2 \times 3.1416 \times (6378 \text{ km} + 295 \text{ km})}{5400 \text{ sec}}$$

$V = 7.76$ km/sec

According to Newton, the acceleration of the shuttle is equal to the square of its velocity ($V^2$) divided by the geocentric distance of the satellite ($R$).

$$a = \frac{V^2}{R} = \frac{60.22 \times 10^6 \text{ m}^2/\text{s}^2}{6.673 \times 10^6 \text{ m}} = 9.02 \text{ meters/sec}^2$$

At the Earth's surface (6378 km from the center of the Earth), an apple falls at an acceleration of 9.8 m/sec². The geocentric distance of the shuttle (6673 km) is about 1.04 times more distant from the Earth's center than the apple in the tree. Since the force of gravitation is inversely proportional to the square of the distance, the acceleration of the shuttle in orbit will be $(1/1.04)^2$ or 0.92 of the acceleration of the apple on the surface.

$$9.8 \text{ m/sec}^2 \times 0.92 = 9.02 \text{ m/sec}^2.$$

**figure 3.22**

The space shuttle Discovery launches from Kennedy Space Center. Shuttle missions make it possible to place payloads into orbit and launch space probes to other planets.

motion changed position from one absolute place to another. Moreover, Newton assumed the force of gravitation between bodies was transmitted instantaneously without the passage of time. To justify this notion, he proposed the existence of a universal ether through which gravitation was supposed to act.

## Albert Einstein: The Geometry of Space-time

The mechanics of absolute space, time, and motion, as well as the gravitational force, are not compatible with the physical laws governing electromagnetic and

nuclear phenomena. In 1864, James Clerk Maxwell discovered that electric and magnetic fields vary with time and should spread out in space at the speed of light. Also, he found that light is electromagnetic in nature.

Later in the nineteenth century, Albert Michelson and Edward Morley carried out a series of experiments to determine the absolute motion of the Earth through the ether. They reasoned that the revolution of the Earth should produce an ether drift that would cause the speed of two light beams approaching from different directions to be different as measured on the Earth. Experiments proved that an ether did not exist. More importantly, they confirmed that the velocity of light remains constant regardless of the state of motion of the energy source or the observer.

Other electromagnetic experiments showed that electrons are emitted when metals are subjected to a beam of radiation. Albert Einstein (1879–1955) described this photoelectric effect in a 1905 paper that interpreted electromagnetic radiation as discrete packets or quanta of energy called *photons*. These and other discoveries raised doubts about the validity of Newton's absolute space and time.

## The Special Theory of Relativity

In the same year he identified the photoelectric effect, Einstein published the *Principle of Relativity.* This **special theory of relativity** unified the concepts of space, time, matter, and energy, and extended the principles of mechanics to include all laws of physics. These laws are valid regardless of the state of uniform motion of the observer who makes the measurements. In the special theory, the velocity of light ($c$) is the only absolute; it is a constant of nature independent of the motion of the emitter or receiver of the radiation. Measurements of time, mass, and distance are relative, and their values depend upon the motion of the observer or the event taking place.

At speeds approaching that of light, ordinary concepts of space and time are no longer valid. There are no fixed or absolute dimensions. To a stationary observer, a meterstick moving lengthwise at high speed in space will appear shorter than a meterstick at rest on the Earth. A clock moving at high speed will keep time at a slower rate than a clock at rest. Three dimensions of space and one of time are needed to define any event taking place in the universe.

In the special theory, Newtonian mechanics is a special case and applies only at low velocities compared to the velocity of light. As the velocity of a body increases, its mass also increases and approaches an infinite value at the velocity of light. Another outcome of special relativity is the equivalency of mass and energy expressed in Einstein's famous equation, $E = mc^2$.

The **general theory of relativity** (1916) deals with gravitation as an effect of the curvature of space rather than an attractive force between masses. The universe and all physical phenomena are measured in a four-dimensional **spacetime,** three dimensions of space and one of time. The general theory will be treated in more detail in later chapters dealing with terminal stages of stars and galaxies, and the origin and structure of the universe.

## SUMMARY

Modern astronomy began when the concept of gravitation as a universal force was developed in the seventeenth century. From it came a new branch of astronomy called celestial mechanics, which deals with problems of mass and motion by the mathematical application of gravitational laws. Previously, the teachings of Aristotle were accepted without proof or verification.

The first significant challenge to the Aristotelian view came in 1543 when Copernicus introduced the heliocentric system. An Earth in orbit around the Sun made it possible to compute the relative distances and sidereal periods of the planets.

Kepler defined the orbits of the planets as ellipses rather than circles. He described the relationship between a planet's changing speed, distance from the Sun, and period of revolution in three laws of planetary motion.

Galileo was first to make telescopic observations and to use experimental methods that led to the laws of uniform motion.

Newton unified the work of his predecessors into three laws of motion and the law of universal gravitation. Expressed mathematically, Newton's law defines gravitation as a mutual attraction of every body in the universe by a force directly proportional to the quantity of matter, or mass, they contain, and inversely proportional to the square of the distance between them.

Newton's work remained unchallenged until the twentieth century, when Einstein described gravitation as an effect of the curvature of spacetime caused by the presence of matter. Accordingly, the planets orbit the Sun bound by the geometry of a four-dimensional universe of space and time.

## KEY TERMS

acceleration
astronomical unit (AU)
centripetal force
conjunction
*De Revolutionibus*
*Dialogue Concerning the Two New Sciences*
*Dialogue of the Two Principal Systems of the World*
eastern quadrature
$E = mc^2$
focal point
general theory of relativity
gravitation
greatest eastern elongation
greatest western elongation
*Harmony of the Worlds*
inertia
inferior conjunction

inferior planets
Kepler's laws of planetary motion
law of universal gravitation
laws of motion
mass
opposition
*Principia*
*Rudolphine Tables*
sidereal period
*Sidereus Nuncius*
spacetime
special theory of relativity
superior conjunction
superior planets
synodic period
western quadrature

# PROBLEMS

1. A planet is observed at an elongation of 40° east of the Sun. Later, the planet's elongation has increased to 60°. Is this an inferior planet? A superior planet? Explain your answer.

2. If a body in the solar system has a synodic period of 417 days, find its sidereal period and distance from the Sun.

3. Explain why the phases of Venus cannot be observed in a geocentric system.

4. In which configuration is Venus nearest to the Earth? Highest above the horizon?

5. Explain why the synodic periods of Mercury, Venus, and Mars are longer than their sidereal periods.

6. Why is your weight on the Moon about 1/6 of your weight on the Earth? Give your answer in terms of the acceleration of gravity.

7. If a spacecraft from the Earth to Mars travels in an orbit with a mean distance of 1.5 AU from the Sun, how long will it take to reach Mars?

8. Explain why the greatest elongation of an inferior planet cannot exceed 90°.

9. During one sidereal period, the distance between Mars and the Sun varies between 207 million km and 250 million km. When we observe Mars at its brightest magnitude, what is the configuration of the planet? At that time, where will Mars be in its orbit?

10. A transit describes the passage of a planet across the face of the Sun. List the planets that *do not* transit the Sun and give the reason for your answer.

# REFERENCES

Cohn, I. Bernard. 1960. *The Birth of a New Physics.* New York: W. W. Norton and Company.

Copernicus, Nicolaus. 1952. *On the Revolution of the Heavenly Spheres.* Trans. Charles Glenn Wallis. Great Books of the Western World. Chicago: Encyclopedia Britannica Press.

Einstein, Albert. 1931. *Relativity, the Special and General Theory.* Trans. Robert W. Lawson. Reprinted by permission of Henry Holt and Company. New York: Peter Smith.

Galilei, Galileo. 1952. *Dialogues Concerning the Two New Sciences.* Trans. Henry Crew and Alfonso de Salvio. Great Books of the Western World. Chicago: Encyclopedia Britannica Press.

Kepler, Johannes. 1952. *Epitome of Copernican Astronomy: IV and V.* Trans. Charles Glenn Wallis. Great Books of the Western World. Chicago: Enclyclopedia Britannica Press.

———. 1952. *Harmonies of the World: V.* Trans. Charles Glenn Wallis. Great Books of the Western World. Chicago: Encyclopedia Britannica Press.

Newton, Isaac. 1952. *Mathematical Principles of Natural Philosophy.* Trans. Andrew Motte, rev. by Florian Cajori. Great Books of the Western World. Chicago: Encyclopedia Britannica Press.

Sears, Francis W., Mark W. Zemansky, and Hugh D. Young. 1987. *University Physics.* 7th ed. Reading, PA: Addison-Wesley Publishing Company.

Vorontsov-Vel'yaminov, B. A. 1969. *Astronomical Problems.* Trans. P. M. Rabbitt. Oxford: Pergamon Press.

chapter

4

a  universe  of  matter,  force,  and  radiation

Star clouds in the constellation Sagittarius.

astronomy: through space and time    chapter 4

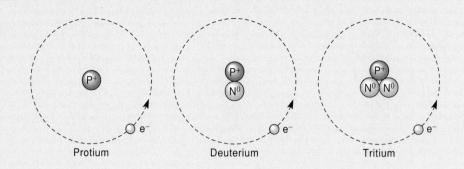

Protium          Deuterium          Tritium

**figure 4.1**

Isotopes of hydrogen. The most abundant type, protium, contains one proton and one electron.

Wen we turn our telescopes to the stars, we are confronted with large aggregations of material bodies in huge numbers at vast distances in space. Why did the universe form this way? What forces hold it together? How does energy in the form of **electromagnetic radiation** reach the Earth? The answers to these thought-provoking questions are found not only in the macrocosm, or large-scale universe, but also in the structure of the microcosm of atoms and the fundamental particles they contain. To this celestial hierarchy we add the forces of nature that interact with and bind together all the substance of the universe. Two forces, **gravitation** and **electromagnetism,** are familiar phenomena perceived by our senses. Two additional forces, the **weak** and **strong nuclear forces,** are known by their effect upon particles within the nucleus of the atom.

An investigation of matter and the forces of nature leads to our understanding of the dual nature of electromagnetic radiation. Light and other forms of electromagnetic radiation have wave characteristics—they can be reflected, refracted, and brought to a focus. But when radiation and atoms interact, energy behaves as though it were composed of pulsating streams of particles.

## Fundamental Particles

The atomic theory of matter as composed of elementary particles was established by English chemist John Dalton in 1804. According to his view, the atoms of a particular chemical element have identical properties. An *element* is defined as a substance composed entirely of particles that cannot be chemically divided into smaller units.

A few years later, English physician and chemist William Prout proposed that the mass of a given element is a multiple of the mass of hydrogen, the lightest element. Accordingly, atoms serve as building blocks for all material substances.

When **isotopes** were discovered, the notion that an atom consists of numerous hydrogen masses was found to be incorrect. An isotope is an atom of the same chemical element that has a different atomic mass. The experiments of J. J. Thompson in 1897 and Ernest Rutherford in 1910 confirmed the existence of electrified particles within the atom. Moreover, they found differences in the charge-mass ratio for positive ions and concluded that more than one kind of atom can make up a chemical element.

Since gravitational mass and inertial mass are equivalent, the mass of a charged particle can be measured by its acceleration in a magnetic field. Moreover, the electric charge of a particle is determined by the way it deflects in a magnetic field. Thus Thompson was able to identify the **electron** by its negative charge. Rutherford and his students, Hans Geiger and Ernest Marsden, discovered that the nucleus of the atom contains most of the mass and consists of positively charged particles that were named **protons.** These experiments led to the *planetary model,* which describes the atom as a miniature solar system containing a nucleus of positively charged protons surrounded by negatively charged electrons. The electrons are kept in orbit by the electrostatic force between the particles.

In 1920, Rutherford explained isotopes by proposing an additional particle in the nucleus that increases the atomic mass but does not alter the chemical properties of the atom. The particle was confirmed in 1932, when the **neu-** tron was discovered. The neutron has a mass slightly more than a proton and is electrically neutral.

Think of an atom as being composed of a nucleus of protons and neutrons surrounded by electrons in spherical shells. The simplest atom is hydrogen, which contains a single proton in the nucleus and one electron in orbit about the proton. The **atomic number** is determined by the positive charge; the number of protons in the nucleus. Thus the atomic number of hydrogen is 1, and all other elements have higher atomic numbers based upon the number of protons they contain.

Suppose a neutron is bound to the proton in the hydrogen nucleus. The atomic mass has approximately doubled, but the atomic number remains the same. Consequently, the chemical properties are unchanged, and the more massive particle becomes an isotope of hydrogen called a deuteron, or a particle of deuterium. Another isotope of hydrogen called tritium contains one proton and two neutrons (fig. 4.1).

Heavier atoms consist of increasingly more protons, neutrons, and electrons. The atomic number of helium, the second lightest element, is 2. It contains two protons and two neutrons in the nucleus and two electrons in orbit. Other familiar elements include carbon, with six protons and six neutrons, and oxygen consisting of eight protons and eight neutrons (fig. 4.2). Isotopes of these elements differ in atom mass but carry the same atomic number.

So far we have discussed electrically neutral atoms in which the number of

## The Ratio of the Electric Force to the Gravitational Force

The electric force acting on a body must be greater than the gravitational force provided by its mass or else all matter would break up into individual atoms. Consider the ratio of the electric force to the gravitational force between two electrons. The electrons carry like charges and therefore will repel each other. To determine the ratio of the two forces, we select two electrons at a unit distance from each other, and compute the electric force expressed by

$$F = \frac{(k \times Q_1 \times Q_2)}{R^2}$$

where $k$ = the electrical constant ($9.0 \times 10^9$ N $\cdot$ m²/C²); $Q_1$ and $Q_2$ = equal electric charges of the electrons (charge of electron = $-1.6 \times 10^{-19}$ coulombs [C]); and $R^2$ = the square of the distance between them.

Note the similarity between the equation for the electric force and the gravitational force between the particles, which is

$$F = \frac{(G \times M_1 \times M_2)}{R^2}$$

where $G$ = the constant of gravitation ($6.7 \times 10^{-11}$ N $\cdot$ m²/kg²); $M_1$ and $M_2$ = equal masses of the electrons (mass of electron = $9.1 \times 10^{-31}$ kg); and $R^2$ = the square of the distance between them.

The ratio between the two forces becomes

$$\text{ratio} = \frac{\text{electric force}}{\text{gravitational force}}$$

$$\text{ratio} = \frac{(k \times Q^2)}{(G \times M^2)}$$

$$= \frac{(9.0 \times 10^9 \text{ N} \cdot \text{m}^2/\text{C}^2)\,(-1.6 \times 10^{-19}\text{C})^2}{(6.7 \times 10^{-11} \text{ N} \cdot \text{m}^2/\text{kg}^2)\,(9.1 \times 10^{-31} \text{ kg})^2}$$

$$= \frac{2.3 \times 10^{-28}}{5.5 \times 10^{-71}}$$

$$= 4.2 \times 10^{42}.$$

The gravitational force is much weaker than the electric force and is effective only where large masses are involved.

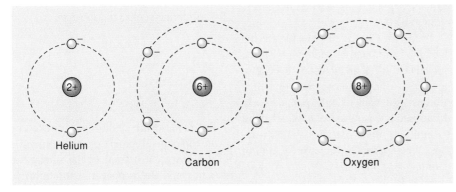

### figure 4.2

Atoms of helium, carbon, and oxygen. The atomic number of an element is the number of protons in its nucleus.

protons is balanced by an equal number of electrons. As the atomic number of an atom increases, the electrons occupy larger shells surrounding the nucleus. The first shell is limited to only two electrons, while the outer shells can hold eight or more electrons. Atoms are *ionized* when they are no longer electrically neutral but take on a negative or positive charge. An atom stripped of one or more of its electrons has an excess of protons and becomes a positively charged ion. When a neutral atom gains an electron, it becomes a negatively charged ion.

In summary, every atom is composed of a nucleus containing protons and neutrons surrounded by electrons in discrete shells. Protons carry a positive electric charge while electrons have an equal but negative electric charge. Neutrons have no charge and thus are electrically neutral. The negatively charged electrons are attracted by and spin around the positively charged nucleus. In the nucleus, the positive electric charges repel each other but are kept from flying apart by the strong nuclear force.

## Gravitation

As discussed in chapter 2, gravitation is the attractive force between all substance in the universe. From a huge galaxy to the tiniest atomic particle, all matter influences other matter through the mediation of this force. Gravitation is the weakest force, yet the cumulative mass of innumerable particles is sufficient to hold a galaxy of stars together.

Surrounding every material body is a gravitational field of unlimited range through which the effect of gravitation is detected. A gravitational event, such as the explosion of a massive star, is believed to send out, at the speed of light, a gravitational wave that creates ripples in the gravitational field.

## Electromagnetism

The electromagnetic force is the interaction between the electric and the magnetic forces that hold atoms and molecules together. This force keeps negatively charged electrons attracted to positively charged protons in all substances from the smallest atom to the largest star.

a universe of matter, force, and radiation

A particle may have either a positive or negative electric charge. Like charges repel; unlike charges attract each other. Just as a gravitational field defines the force acting upon a mass at a given distance, an electric field defines the force acting upon a charge at a given distance. However, the electric force can attract or repel while the gravitational force can only attract.

Electric charges are carried by a number of particles. We are interested in three particles that are among the basic units of the atom. *Protons* have a positive charge and, along with the electrically neutral *neutron*, they form the nucleus of an atom. A cloud of negatively charged *electrons* surround the nucleus. When the positive and negative charges are equal (same number of protons and electrons), the atom is electrically neutral.

A magnetic field is produced by a moving electric charge. When an electric current flows through a wire, a magnetic field is produced around the wire. In experiments in the mid-nineteenth century, Michael Faraday induced an electric current in a wire when he passed the wire through a magnetic field. In 1864, James Clerk Maxwell discovered the existence of electromagnetic waves produced by accelerating electric and magnetic fields. His description of electromagnetism is equal to Newton's achievement in gravitation and a key to our understanding of the propagation of radiation in space.

## Strong and Weak Nuclear Forces

In the atom, there are two forces affecting the properties of the nucleus. The *strong force* operates over a short range between protons and neutrons. This binding force is capable of overcoming the repulsion of the positively charged protons. Within the tiny region of the nucleus, no larger than a hundred-thousandth of an entire atom, the strong force holds the protons and neutrons together. Thus chemical elements are built from simple hydrogen to massive radioactive uranium. The strong force is millions of times greater than the electromagnetic force that holds the electrons in place about the nucleus.

Although the nucleus of an atom is too small to be seen, it can be visualized with the help of a model. Consider the nucleus as a cloudy ball of protons and neutrons spinning in shells that represent discrete energy levels. In turn, the protons and neutrons are divided into even smaller units called *quarks*. Introduced in 1963 by the physicists Murray Gell-Mann and George Zweig, quarks have exotic flavors (up, down, strange, charm, bottom) and properties (color) and behave as dimensionless points. Each type of quark carries a fraction of an electric charge (either + or -). Thus a combination of quarks can form a positively charged proton or a neutron with no electric charge at all.

When nucleons (protons and neutrons) are brought close enough together, the strong force attracts the particles to form heavier elements. This *fusion* process occurs at high temperature and pressure deep within the Sun and other stars. In the process, a fraction of mass is converted to an enormous amount of energy that is released as electromagnetic radiation.

The *weak force* is responsible for the decay of radioactive elements. If the nucleus of an element has an excess of neutrons—that is, more neutrons than protons—the nucleus will spontaneously decay into a less massive stable element by emitting alpha particles (helium nuclei), beta particles (electrons), and/or gamma rays (photons).

Radioactive decay is measured by the half-life of an element—the time required for one-half of its mass to decay. Suppose the half-life of a given element is 100 years; in that time, one-half of its mass will be reduced to some other element. In another 100 years, one-half of the remainder will decay, leaving one-fourth of the original mass; and so on (fig. 4.3).

The radioactive elements found in the Earth today originated in the explosion of one or more supernovae that contributed to the formation of the Sun and planets. Later, the radioactive elements heated the Earth to a molten state, causing heavier metals such as iron to sink to the core while lighter rocks formed the upper layers and surface.

When the half-life of a radioactive element is known, the age of the sample

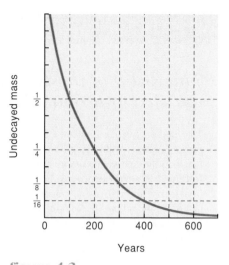

**figure 4.3**
Decay of a radioactive element. The number of undecayed nuclei decreases by one-half in each time period, which is called the half-life of the element.

can be determined by its rate of decay. The uranium isotope, $^{238}U$, decays into a series of elements terminating in the stable isotope of lead, $^{206}Pb$. Its half-life of 4.5 billion years is used for dating the Earth, lunar rocks, and meteorites.

## The Nature of Electromagnetic Radiation

The seventeenth century was marked by the rapid development of many branches of science; in particular, the science of optics and the propagation of light. In addition to his monumental work in gravitational theory, Isaac Newton wrote a discourse called *Opticks* on the properties of light, wherein he described the laws of **reflection** and **refraction,** as well as the **dispersion** of white light into a **spectrum** or rainbow of colors.

Newton was first to understand the nature of the colors found in white light. When he passed sunlight through a small opening in a screen and then into a triangular prism, the light emerged from the prism as a spectrum of colors in the following order: red, orange, yellow, green, blue, indigo, and violet (fig. 4.4).

Next Newton placed a second, inverted prism in the optical path behind the spectrum. The spectrum recombined in the prism and emerged as white light, thus proving that white light is a mixture of seven color regions. Then Newton al-

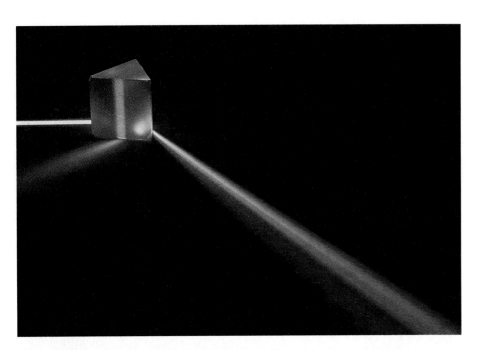

◀ **figure 4.4**

The visible spectrum. White light is a mixture of many wavelengths that make up seven "color" regions that are dispersed through a glass prism. Upon reaching the eye, the various wavelengths are interpreted as different colors.

**figure 4.5** ▼

Wave motion. *a.* In a transverse wave, such as a wave in water, the pulse moves perpendicular to the direction of travel. *b.* In a longitudinal wave, such as a sound wave traveling through air, the pulse moves in the direction of travel.

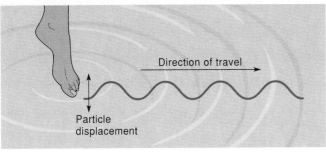

a.

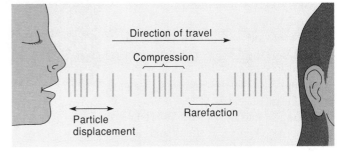

b.

lowed only one color in the band to pass through the second prism. This time, the entering light and the emerging light remained unchanged, thus proving that white light is made of a mixture of pure, indivisible colors in a continuous band from red to violet.

Newton and other physicists of his time accepted the *corpuscular theory* of light propagation. Light was believed to consist of small particles traveling in straight lines from a luminous source. But in 1665, the discovery of the phenomenon called *diffraction* (the bending of light when passing a sharp edge) showed that light traveled as an expanding wave.

The alternative to the corpuscular theory, the *wave theory* of light, was developed by a contemporary of Newton. In his *Treatise on Light,* Christiaan Huygens explained light as a succession of spherical waves in an all-pervading "luminiferous aether." Huygens conceived the aether to be composed of tiny spherical bodies capable of passing

through air, water, glass, or any other transparent substance. Accordingly, light was propagated from a luminous source by the undulations of the particles of the aether.

Let us investigate how periodic motion is produced by two kinds of waves. In a *transverse* wave (fig. 4.5a), the particles in the wave move perpendicular to the direction of wave propagation. The waves on a lake or the snapping of a rope are examples of transverse waves.

In a *longitudinal wave,* the pulse moves by alternating regions of compression and rarefaction of the particles in the direction of travel (fig. 4.5b). A sound wave is an example of a longitudinal wave.

In Huygens' model, light was transmitted by a longitudinal wave; tiny bodies in the aether compressed and rarified in expanding concentric spheres. At the time the two opposing views were presented, Newton's theory seemed to provide a better explanation for the observed properties of light. Huygens' ideas were

rejected and the corpuscular theory prevailed until the beginning of the nineteenth century, when light was described as a transverse wave.

The wave theory of light dominated scientific thinking for the remainder of the century. Yet, in *Opticks,* Newton almost anticipated twentieth-century relativity, quantum physics, and the dual nature of radiation. As an argument for the corpuscular theory, he states that the transmutation of matter into energy (light) is "conformable to the course of nature."

## The Wave Properties of Light

In the following discussion we describe the properties of light as a transverse wave. The waves are considered to be a series of pulses forming concentric spheres of increasing size called *wave fronts.* According to our model, light is propagated so that a point on the wave will travel radially from the source

63

perpendicular to the wave front (fig. 4.6). At an infinite distance from the source, the wave fronts are a series of parallel planes; rays are imaginary lines representing the direction of propagation (fig. 4.7).

## Reflection

Reflection occurs when a wave motion is turned back at the interface between two dissimilar media. In figure 4.8, the appproaching (incident) rays strike the reflecting surface and rebound as reflected rays.

Light is reflected in two ways: by *diffuse reflection* from an irregular surface and *specular reflection* from a mirror. When incident rays strike a rough surface they reflect at different angles. We see most objects by diffuse reflection. Because a mirror has a smooth surface, the reflected rays are turned back in a parallel direction. Plane or flat mirrors are used to change the direction of the incoming light in telescopes and other optical instruments (fig. 4.9a).

An image can be formed by a concave mirror (fig. 4.9b). In accordance with the law of reflection, light from a distant object that is reflected from the surface of a type of curved mirror known as a parabolic mirror will converge at a focal point. Parabolic mirrors are used in reflecting telescopes.

## Refraction and Dispersion

Radiant energy travels at $3 \times 10^5$ km/sec in a vacuum, but at a slower rate in air, water, crystal, or any other transparent substance. Refraction, or bending, of the radiation takes place at the interface where two transparent substances of different densities are in contact. If a wave front leaves air and enters glass perpendicular to the interface, only its speed will diminish. But when the light enters at an angle, as in a prism, part of the wave front will cross the interface and slow down in the glass while the remainder is still moving through air. When the entire wave front has passed the interface, the light proceeds through the prism at a different angle (fig. 4.10).

We have seen how the dispersion of light into colors was demonstrated by Newton, who used a triangular prism to

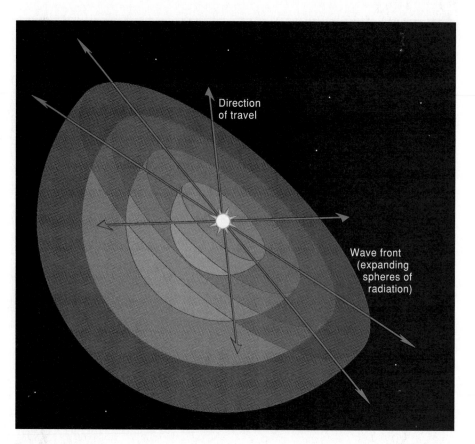

**figure 4.6**

In the wave theory, light is described as a series of concentric pulses moving radially from a source.

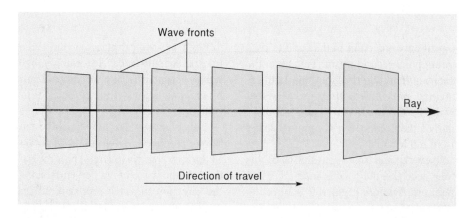

**figure 4.7**

Light from a distant source is described as a series of parallel wave fronts. Rays are depicted as imaginary lines representing the direction of travel.

produce the visible spectrum. But the nature of dispersion was not understood until the French physicist Fresnel measured the different wavelengths of light in 1821. Although all wavelengths of light travel at $c$ in the vacuum of space, in a transparent substance such as a glass prism, shorter-wavelength violet is transmitted at a slower rate than longer-wavelength red. The angle of refraction increases as the speed of the wave de-

creases, and violet will be refracted more than red. Other wavelengths produce colors in between.

Ultraviolet and infrared radiation are also dispersed through a glass prism. Around 1800, William Herschel discovered infrared while measuring temperatures of the colors in the visible spectrum. His thermometer recorded increasingly higher temperatures from violet to red and found the highest tem-

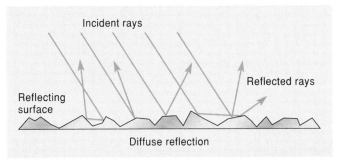

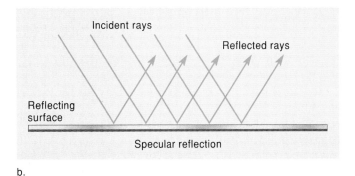

a.

b.

**figure 4.8**

*a.* Diffuse reflection. Light reflected from a rough surface is scattered and shows the surface. *b.* Specular reflection. Light reflected from a smooth surface such as a mirror is coherent and shows the original image.

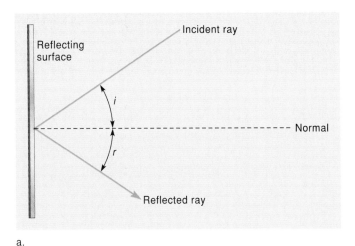

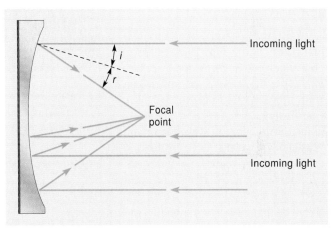

a.

b.

**figure 4.9**

*a.* Light reflected from a flat mirror. According to the law of reflection, the incident angle *i* and reflected angle *r* are equal. *b.* Light reflected from a parabolic mirror. The light rays converge at a single focal point. The angles *i* and *r* are equal.

perature reading outside the red portion of the spectrum where the invisible infrared is dispersed.

Ultraviolet was discovered in 1801 when silver chloride was applied to a projection of the spectrum. Starting with the color red, the chemical gradually darkened and turned black in the region beyond violet. This reaction indicated the presence of an invisible radiation of shorter wavelength than violet light (fig. 4.10).

## Interference and Polarization

Investigators in the early nineteenth century conducted skillful optical experiments demonstrating that light was wavelike in nature. We all have seen how drops of rain on a quiet pool make concentric waves that spread and interfere with each other (fig. 4.11). This can be shown with controlled experiments in a

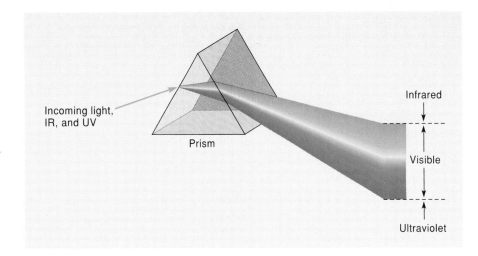

**figure 4.10**

Visible light and infrared (IR) and ultraviolet (UV) radiation are refracted and dispersed by a glass prism.

a universe of matter, force, and radiation

65

ripple tank. A similar **interference** phenomenon occurs with light. Instruments based on the principle of light interference are used in radio astronomy (see chapter 5).

The transverse wave motion of light also explains the property of light called **polarization.** An offshore water wave is polarized in the vertical plane since the wave action is limited to an up and down motion. A wave traveling from side to side is polarized in the horizontal plane.

## The Electromagnetic Wave

Electromagnetic energy is represented as a transverse wave where the vibration is perpendicular to the direction of propagation (fig. 4.12). All forms of radiant energy travel at the speed of light (*c*). What distinguishes one from the other are their differences in **wavelength** and **frequency.** Wavelength ($\lambda$) is the distance through which the energy is transferred between pulses or two adjacent crests (or any corresponding points) of a wave. The frequency (*f*) of vibration expresses the number of waves that pass a point in one second (cycles per second) measured in hertz (Hz). One Hz = one cycle per second. The **amplitude** of a wave represents the maximum value of the vibration.

The product of the wavelength ($\lambda$) and the frequency (*f*) for all forms of radiation will equal the velocity of light (*c*), or

$$c = \lambda \times f.$$

For example, a radio wave in the FM band with a 3-meter wavelength has a frequency of $1.0 \times 10^8$ Hz.

$$c = 3 \text{ m} \times (1.0 \times 10^8 \text{ Hz})$$
$$= 3.0 \times 10^8 \text{ m/sec.}$$

If a gamma ray has a wavelength of $1.0 \times 10^{-14}$ m, its frequency is

$$f = \frac{c}{\lambda}$$

$$= \frac{(3.0 \times 10^8 \text{ m/sec})}{(1.0 \times 10^{-14} \text{ m})}$$

$$= 3.0 \times 10^{22} \text{ Hz.}$$

Note that as the wavelength decreases, frequency increases. Indeed, radio waves

**figure 4.11**

Interference patterns of water waves from different sources. When the ripples travel through the same area at the same time, the waves are reinforced.

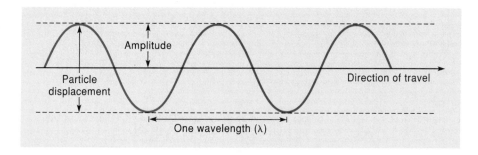

**figure 4.12**

The parts of a transverse wave. The wavelength ($\lambda$) is the distance from one point of a wave to the corresponding point on the next wave. Its amplitude is the maximum value of the vibration.

many meters in length have frequencies of only a few hertz. By contrast, gamma rays are so small that over 500 billion are needed to cover one centimeter while they vibrate 600 billion billion times every second (fig. 4.13).

Between the long radio waves and the short gamma rays are the light waves of the *visible spectrum.* These intermediate wavelengths range from $4.0 \times 10^{-7}$m for violet to $7.0 \times 10^{-7}$ m for red light. The differences in frequency are interpreted by our eyes as color. The wavelengths of light are also expressed in a number of convenient units of distance—the micrometer ($\mu$), the nanometer (nm), and the angstrom (A). Table 4.1 lists these wavelengths.

All radiation from radio waves to gamma rays form the **electromagnetic spectrum.** Each form is identified by its particular wavelength and frequency.

Let us leave these general discussions and turn to a more specific description of the properties of electromagnetic radiation. By 1864, Maxwell had established the existence of radio-frequency radiation caused by the oscillations of electric and magnetic fields. Moreover, he found the speed of wave propagation to equal *c,* the velocity of light, and that light is also a form of electromagnetic radiation.

This fundamental discovery can be represented by a three-dimensional rectangular coordinate system (fig. 4.14).

## wavelengths in the visible spectrum

| | Wavelength | | | |
|---|---|---|---|---|
| Color | meter (m) (× 10⁻⁷ m) | micrometer (μ) (1μ = 10⁻⁶ m) | nanometer (nm) (1 nm = 10⁻⁹ m) | angstrom (A) (1 A = 10⁻¹⁰ m) |
| red | 6.5–7.0 | 0.65–0.70 | 650–700 | 6500–7000 |
| orange | 6.0–6.5 | 0.60–0.65 | 600–650 | 6000–6500 |
| yellow | 5.5–6.0 | 0.55–0.60 | 550–600 | 5500–6000 |
| green | 5.0–5.5 | 0.50–0.55 | 500–550 | 5000–5500 |
| blue | 4.5–5.0 | 0.45–0.50 | 450–500 | 4500–5000 |
| violet | 4.0–4.5 | 0.40–0.45 | 400–450 | 4000–4500 |

The intersection of three perpendicular planes forms the $X$, $Y$, and $Z$ reference axes. A point on the wave is determined by its distance from each axis.

Imagine an electromagnetic wave from a source approaching in a train of wave fronts. Through any wave front construct a plane containing the $Y$ and $Z$ reference axes of the coordinate system so that the direction of wave propagation is along the $X$-axis. The origin $O$ of the wave is the intersection of the $X$-$Y$-$Z$ axes. The vector $E$ along the $Y$-axis and the vector $B$ along the $Z$-axis represent the amplitude and direction of the electric and magnetic fields. Each component is a transverse wave moving along the $X$-axis. Maximum amplitude is shown at $F_1$ and $F_2$.

Advancing along the $X$-axis, the oscillating electric and magnetic fields are generated perpendicular to each other. The magnetic field brings about a changing electric field which in turn reinforces the magnetic field. Detached from the source and moving at velocity $c$, the two fields recreate each other as electromagnetic waves of radiant energy.

## The Dual Nature of Electromagnetic Radiation

Having discussed how the wave theory successfully accounts for refraction, dispersion, interference, and polarization of light, we shall now consider why radiation acts like a stream of particles when it reacts with matter. For now, let us analyze this affinity between matter and en-

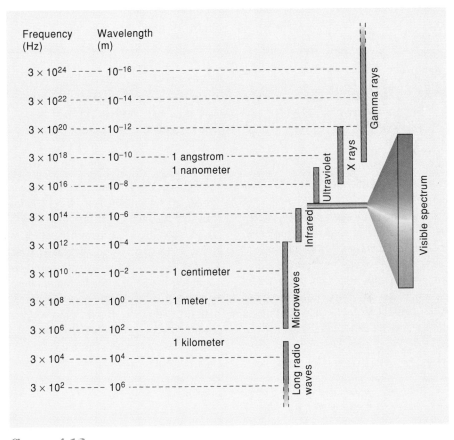

### figure 4.13

The electromagnetic spectrum is composed of radiation from short-wavelength, high-frequency gamma rays to long-wavelength, low-frequency radio waves.

ergy qualitatively. We have already seen how matter is composed of oscillating atoms and molecules. These vibrating molecules are in random motion and continuously change direction as they collide. The *heat* of a body is defined as the total molecular motion or kinetic energy possessed by a substance. If the kinetic energy of a body is changed, either by adding or subtracting heat, an increase

or decrease in molecular motion will occur.

**Temperature** represents the measure of the average random motion of the molecules in a body. Thus a change in kinetic energy causes a corresponding change in temperature. When heat is exchanged between two bodies of different temperatures, the kinetic energy of the molecules of higher temperature is

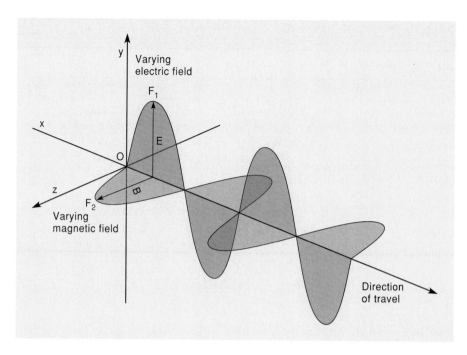

**figure 4.14**

An electromagnetic wave model is composed of an electric field and a magnetic field. The field vibrations are perpendicular to each other and to the direction in which the wave is traveling. A diagram that shows the strength and direction of the fields is called a vector diagram.

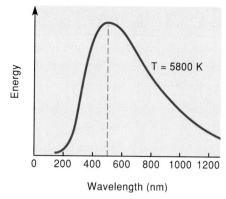

**figure 4.15**

Planck's curve for the sun. The intensity of radiation increases to a maximum of 500 nanometers wavelength.

transferred to the molecules of lower temperature.

There are three ways in which energy may be exchanged: by *conduction, convection* and *radiation*. In solids such as metals, heat is exchanged by conduction. If one end of an iron rod is heated and increases in temperature, the collision of vibrating molecules transfers or conducts the heat to every part of the rod. If the process continues until the temperature is the same throughout, the system has reached *thermal equilibrium.*

Liquids and gases can transfer energy by convection because the molecules in fluids are not bound together as firmly as the molecules in solids. As the heated molecules of a fluid collide and the distance between them increases, the warmer and less dense fluid rises and is displaced. This circulation transports the heat from a warmer to a cooler region.

**Radiation** is the process by which electromagnetic energy is transmitted across space without an intervening medium (recall Huygens' aether). In this case, the vibration of electrons, and not molecules, causes heated objects to emit energy as electromagnetic waves.

We can demonstrate how the wavelength of radiant energy is dependent upon the temperature of the source by a simple thought experiment. Heat an iron rod and watch its color change. At first, the rod feels warm—heat is re-emitted as infrared radiation. As the temperature increases, the iron rod becomes luminous and glows red, then orange, yellow, and finally white. We also note that the total radiant energy emitted is greater for a body at a higher temperature. Now let us direct our thought experiment to the Sun and stars.

## Blackbody Radiation

The above relationship between radiation and temperature applies to the Sun and stars with the following qualification. Stars are a close approximation to a **blackbody,** an object in thermal equilibrium that absorbs and radiates away all energy without reflection. Early this century, physicist Max Planck experimented with blackbody radiation and developed the fundamental law of radiation called **Planck's law.**

To describe the behavior of blackbody radiation, Planck introduced an abstract idea without any verification. In his model, electromagnetic radiation can be emitted or absorbed only in certain energy values that are multiples of a discrete unit called a **quantum.** Moreover, radiation can be thought of as a stream of elementary particles or **photons.** For any given frequency, the energy possessed by a photon is directly proportional to its frequency. Thus a quantum of high-frequency gamma rays possesses high energy, while a quantum of low-frequency radio waves has low energy.

The mathematical solution of Planck's law of radiation can be explained by another thought experiment. This time we shall measure the intensity of radiation at all wavelengths emitted by a blackbody at a given temperature. We select the Sun, which has an absolute surface temperature of about 5800 K, although it is not strictly a blackbody.

At shorter wavelengths, in the ultraviolet range, the intensity of radiation emitted by the Sun is low. As measurements are taken at increasingly longer wavelengths, the radiation from the Sun sharply increases to maximum at a wavelength of about 500 nanometers. From this peak, the intensity gradually diminishes as wavelength increases (fig. 4.15).

To explain the discrete energy states of electromagnetic radiation, Planck presumed that heated bodies contain oscillating electrified particles vibrating in the same frequencies as the emitted energy. Later, Planck identified the particles as

## Radiation Laws

Planck's fundamental law of radiation is expressed mathematically as

$$E = nhf$$

where

$h$ = Planck's constant ($6.62 \times 10^{-27}$ ergs/sec);

$f$ = frequency in Hz;

and

$n$ = an integer 1, 2, 3 . . . and so on.

Planck's complicated law incorporated two other radiation laws developed at the end of the nineteenth century. The first treats the relationship between the wavelength and the maximum intensity of blackbody radiation. **Wien's displacement law** states that the wavelength at which radiation from a light source is most intense is inversely proportional to the absolute temperature of the source, or

$$\lambda_m = \frac{k}{T}$$

where

$\lambda_m$ = wavelength in nm at maximum intensity;

$k$ = Wien's constant ($2.9 \times 10^6$ nm · K);

and

$T$ = absolute temperature (K).

At a higher temperature, the maximum intensity is displaced to the blue portion of the spectrum. Figure 4.16 shows the spectral distribution of radiation for stars of different temperatures. In accordance with Wien's displacement law, the peak wavelength is shifted to shorter wavelengths for stars of higher temperature.

What is the peak wavelength of the Sun if its absolute temperature is equal to 5800 K?

$$\lambda_m = \frac{2.9 \times 10^6 \,\text{nm} \cdot \text{K}}{5.8 \times 10^3 \,\text{K}}$$

$$= 5.0 \times 10^2$$

$$= 500 \,\text{nm}.$$

The second law, the **Stefan-Boltzmann law,** states that the total radiation emitted by a blackbody per cm$^2$/ sec is directly proportional to the fourth power of its absolute temperature. As an equation, the law is

$$E = \sigma T^4$$

where $E$ = energy in ergs/sec/cm$^2$; $\sigma$ = Stefan-Boltzmann constant ($5.67 \times 10^{-5}$ ergs/sec/cm$^2$/K$^4$; and $T$ = absolute temperature (K).

Using this equation, find the absolute temperature of the Sun if its energy emission is $6.29 \times 10^{10}$ ergs/sec/cm$^2$.

$$T^4 = \frac{6.29 \times 10^{10} \,\text{ergs/sec/cm}^2}{5.67 \times 10^{-5} \,\text{ergs/sec/cm}^2/\text{K}^4}$$

$$T = \sqrt[4]{1.11 \times 10^{15} \text{K}^4}$$

$$= 5.77 \times 10^3$$

$$\cong 5800 \,\text{K}.$$

**figure 4.16**

Spectral distribution of radiation for stars of different temperatures. In accordance with Wien's displacement law, the peak wavelength is shorter for a star of higher temperature.

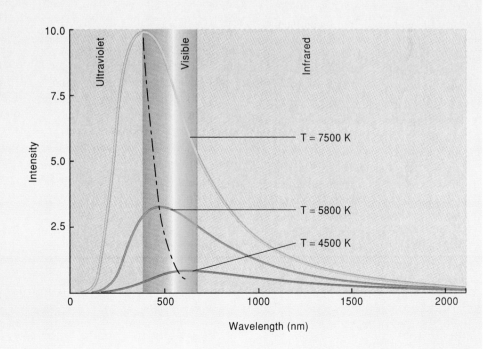

During the year, it is possible to observe the effects of Wien's displacement law in the colors of the stars. These colors range from red to blue-white, indicating a difference in the peak wavelength of radiation of each star. As Planck's curve shows, the stars radiate energy in all wavelengths, which can be observed as spikes of different colors as the stars twinkle. However, the peak wavelength will be more pronounced and gives a star its distinctive color. Thus a star whose maximum light intensity is situated in the red portion of the spectrum will appear red. A sunlike star with maximum light intensity in the middle of the spectrum will be yellow. The hottest stars will be blue-white. Keep in mind that a bright star near the horizon will appear to change colors, partially due to atmospheric refraction. For this reason, observe the stars when they are well above the horizon.

The following bright stars seen at various times during the year can be identified by their colors. To find the stars, refer to the seasonal star maps found in chapter 2.

| Star | Color |
| --- | --- |
| Sirius | white |
| Arcturus | orange |
| Vega | white |
| Capella | yellow |
| Rigel | blue-white |
| Procyon | yellow-white |
| Betelgeuse | red |
| Altair | white |
| Aldebaran | orange |
| Spica | white |
| Antares | red |
| Pollux | yellow |
| Castor | white |
| Deneb | white |

the electrons that had been discovered earlier by J. J. Thompson.

## The Photoelectric Effect

Support for the quantum theory and the dual nature of radiation was provided in 1905 when Albert Einstein used Planck's model to explain the *photoelectric effect*. By the end of the nineteenth century, it was known that electrons may be ejected when light strikes a metal surface. This phenomenon is caused by the transfer of energy from the incoming light to the electrons in the metal.

When Einstein increased the light intensity, the energy of the electrons remained unchanged but the number of electrons ejected increased. A discrete amount of energy is exchanged when light of a given frequency and the electrons interact. Moreover, when Einstein increased the frequency of radiation, the emitted electrons showed a corresponding increase in energy in accordance with Planck's theory.

## The Spectrum of Hydrogen

The investigation of spectra, in particular the spectrum of atomic hydrogen, is an important step in the understanding of light and Planck's quantum theory. This is achieved by means of a **spectroscope,** an apparatus capable of analyzing light in different wavelengths (fig. 4.17). Light enters the spectroscope through a narrow slit. Beyond the slit is a collimator lens to form a parallel beam of light sent to a triangular prism that separates the light into its primary colors.

The spectra of several substances are examined in the spectroscope. As a source of illumination, consider a glowing solid such as the filament of a tungsten lamp. The radiation from the lamp passes through the spectroscope and is dispersed into a **continuous spectrum** where the colors blend into each another without interruption (figs. 4.17a and 4.18a). A glowing liquid or gas under high pressure will also produce a continuous spectrum.

Now the experiment is modified by replacing the luminous solid with glowing gas at low pressure (fig. 4.17b). When viewed through the spectroscope, the light from the gas forms a series of bright lines of various colors rather than a continuous spectrum. Each line is an image of the slit in the spectroscope; the color represents the discrete wavelength of radiation emitted by the gas. Indeed, the lines of this bright-line or **emission spectrum** are separated by an amount corresponding to their frequencies and wavelengths (fig. 4.18b). Every substance, whether it be in the Sun and stars or in the laboratory, can be identified by its own emission spectrum. Hydrogen, the element we are primarily interested in studying, has a series of prominent lines in different color regions of the visible spectrum (fig. 4.20).

In 1814 and 1815, German physicist Joseph Fraunhofer investigated dark lines and bands that appear in the continuous spectrum of the Sun and stars. They are called **Fraunhofer lines,** and their nature was discovered by Kirchhoff and Bunsen in 1859 while studying the emission spectrum of luminous gases superimposed on the solar spectrum (fig. 4.19). They found that the dark D-lines of sodium (Na) in the solar spectrum changed to bright emission lines when a sodium flame was placed between the sunlight and the slit of the spectroscope. When the intensity of the solar spectrum was increased by exposing the apparatus to full sunlight, dark lines reappeared again.

Indeed, the dark lines are produced when light passes through a gas of lower temperature than the light source. In the experiment, the sodium flame absorbs the same wavelengths of sunlight as those it emits. When the sodium re-emits the absorbed wavelengths, they radiate in every direction so that only a fraction of

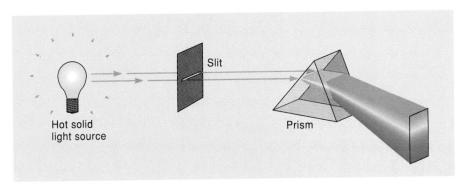

a. Continuous spectrum

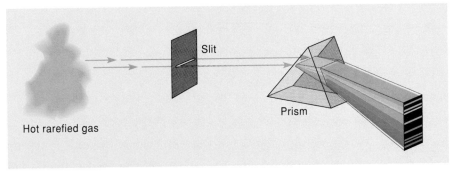

b. Emission-line spectrum

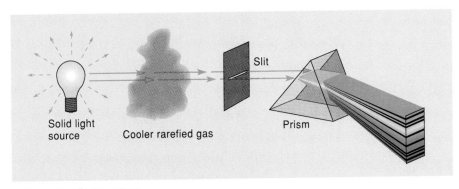

c. Absorption-line spectrum

**figure 4.17**

Continuous, emission-line, and absorption-line spectra. *a.* Radiation from a glowing solid such as a lamp filament produces a continuous spectrum. *b.* The bright-line spectrum of a glowing low-pressure gas identifies the wavelengths emitted by the gas. *c.* An absorption spectrum is produced when light passes through a rarefied gas that is at a lower temperature than the light source.

a. Continuous spectrum

b. Emission spectrum

c. Absorption spectrum

**figure 4.18**

*a.* A continuous spectrum. *b.* An emission spectrum showing bright lines. *c.* An absorption spectrum showing Fraunhofer lines.

a universe of matter, force, and radiation

71

▲ **figure 4.19**

Solar spectrum. The visible, or white light, portion of the spectrum of our Sun has been split into all its colors in this spectrogram. The dark absorption lines and bands indicate ionized atoms of elements in the Sun.

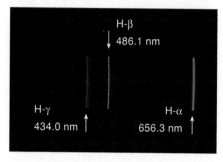

▲ **figure 4.20**

An emission spectrum of hydrogen showing three bright lines in the Balmer series.

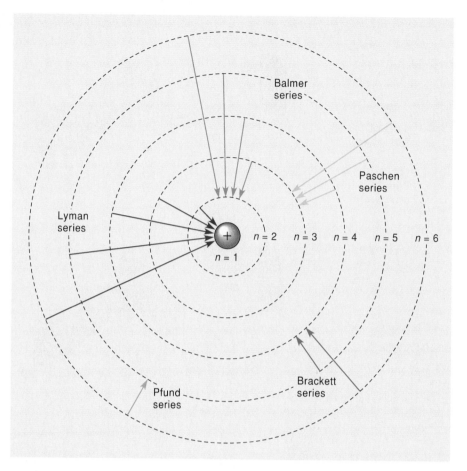

▲ **figure 4.21**

Model of electron orbits of the Bohr atom. A photon is emitted when an electron falls from a higher to a lower energy state.

these wavelengths reach the apparatus. Only the unaffected wavelengths reach the spectroscope and produce an **absorption spectrum** interlaced by dark lines and bands (figs. 4.17c, 4.18c, and 4.19).

In the Sun and stars, the energy from the high-temperature core produces a continuous spectrum. Over a period of time, this energy works its way by radiation and convection to the cooler and tenuous outer layers of the Sun. Here discrete wavelengths are absorbed and re-emitted, thereby producing the absorption spectrum identified by Fraunhofer (fig. 4.19).

## The Balmer Series of Atomic Hydrogen

When light from electrically excited hydrogen gas is dispersed by a diffraction grating in a spectroscope, the light is separated into bright lines of red, blue-green, violet, and deep violet light (fig. 4.20). The intervals between the lines differ, becoming increasingly closer to-

gether toward a limit in the high-frequency range.

In 1885, Johann Jacob Balmer expressed the positions of the lines by the so-called **Balmer series.** Starting with the longest-wavelength red line, he identified the lines by the letters of the Greek alphabet: Hα, 656.3 nm; Hβ, 486.1 nm; Hγ, 434.0 nm; Hδ, 410.2 nm; and so on.

## The Bohr Atom and the Quantum Theory

According to classical mechanics, an electron held in orbit by the centripetal attraction of the proton's electric charge will lose energy and eventually spiral into the nucleus of the atom. Obviously, this does not happen, and the simple planetary model had to be replaced by another compatible with Planck's theory.

In 1913, Bohr proposed an alternative model for the hydrogen atom, the

**Bohr atom.** He speculated that the electron is permitted to revolve in certain stable orbits (fig. 4.21). As long as the electron remains in one of these stationary orbits, it cannot lose energy and fall into the nucleus. But if the electron absorbs energy, it can do so only in discrete quanta and jumps into a higher permitted orbit. When the electron loses energy, it does so in discrete quanta and quickly returns to a lower permitted orbit. When an electron absorbs or emits energy while making a transition from one orbit to another, the energy absorbed or emitted will be a photon equal to the difference in the initial and final energy of the electron. When a transition takes place, the electron absorbs or emits energy at a wavelength corresponding to one of the spectral lines of hydrogen.

The normal state, or **ground state,** of the atom is the least energy state where the electron revolves in its smallest or-

## Energy Levels of Atomic Hydrogen

The Balmer series is stated more specifically as

$$\frac{1}{\lambda} = R\left(\frac{1}{m^2} - \frac{1}{n^2}\right)$$

where

$\lambda$ = wavelength in nm

$R$ = Rydberg constant ($1.097 \times 10^{-2}$/nm);

and

$m$ and $n$ are integers 1, 2, 3 . . . and so on.

Identify the hydrogen line in the Balmer series when $m = 2$ and $n = 3$.

$$\frac{1}{\lambda} = 1.097 \times 10^{-2} \left(\frac{1}{2^2} - \frac{1}{3^2}\right)$$

$$= 656.3 \text{ nm (the H}\alpha \text{ line).}$$

In the Bohr atom, the constants $n$ and $m$ in the Rydberg equation identify the initial ($n_i$) and final ($n_f$) energy states of the electron. Consider an electron in the excited state, where $n_i = $ .

The term $1/n_i^2$ becomes an infinitesimally small number approaching zero, and the Rydberg equation is reduced to

$$\frac{1}{\lambda} = R\left(\frac{1}{n_f^2}\right).$$

If the electron cascades to the ground state ($n_f = 1$) in one jump without intermediate stops, the wavelength emitted will be about 91.2 nm, which represents the limiting wavelength of ultraviolet radiation. If an electron at $n_i = 2$ returns to ground state, the wavelength of the emitted ultraviolet photon is

$$\frac{1}{\lambda} = R\left(\frac{1}{1^2} - \frac{1}{2^2}\right), \text{ and}$$

$$\lambda = 121.5 \text{ nm.}$$

As shown in figure 4.21, an atom returning to ground state from any excited state is represented by the *Lyman series* in the UV range. If an electron at energy level $n_i = 3$ or more returns to a final energy level $n_f = 2$, a photon in the visible *Balmer series* is emitted. A transition from $n_i = 3$ to $n_f = 2$ produces the first or H$\alpha$ line in the Balmer series. The H$\beta$, H$\gamma$, and H$\delta$ wavelengths occur when an electron falls from $n_i = 4$, 5, and 6 to energy level $n_f = 2$.

There are three series representing wavelengths from the near to the far infrared. These include the Paschen, Brackett, and Pfund series at a final energy level $n_f = 3, 4,$ and 5.

bit. The equilibrium is changed to an *excited state* when energy is absorbed and the electron jumps to a higher orbit. If the electron drops to a lower orbit or down to ground state, a pulse of radiant energy is emitted. Multiplied countless times, these absorptions and emissions provide the electromagnetic radiation that we interpret as images of the material universe.

In 1924, de Broglie proposed that all particles in the atom behave as waves. Instead of a point mass, consider an electron as a standing wave undulating at various energy levels. Indeed, as evidence of their wave nature, when electrons are diffracted, they form an electron interference pattern similar to the light interference pattern made by photons. Thus, Newton's seventeenth-century query on the interchangeability of matter and light was answered in the twentieth century by the discovery of the dual nature of atomic particles and electromagnetic radiation.

## SUMMARY

Electromagnetic radiation is an interaction of matter and energy. All chemical elements consist of atoms, which are the building blocks of material substances. The atom, as represented by the planetary model, contains a nucleus of positively charged protons and neutrons possessing no charge, surrounded by negatively charged electrons.

There are four forces of nature that interact with matter. Gravitation is the mutual attractive force of unlimited range exerted by a body on every other body in the universe. The electromagnetic force keeps the negatively charged electrons attracted to the positively charged protons. In the nucleus of the atom, the strong force binds protons and neutrons that form the chemical elements. The nuclear weak force is responsible for the decay of radioactive substances.

The wave theory successfully accounts for many of the properties of light and other forms of electromagnetic radiation. Reflection occurs when a wave motion is turned back at an interface between two dissimilar media. Refraction or bending of a wave takes place at an interface where two transparent substances of different optical densities are in contact. Dispersion spreads white light to form the colors of the visible spectrum. Interference occurs when light passes through small openings and emerges as bright and dark bands, which form when waves reinforce and cancel each other.

Electromagnetic energy is represented as a transverse wave moving at the speed of light. The wavelength is the distance that energy is transferred between any two corresponding points of the wave. The frequency of vibration expresses the number of waves that pass a point in one second. The amplitude of the wave represents the maximum value of the vibration.

The electromagnetic spectrum includes all wavelengths from the longest radio waves to the shortest gamma rays. The intermediate light waves of the visible spectrum range from the longer wavelength

a universe of matter, force, and radiation

73

red to the shorter violet. Differences in frequency are interpreted as the various colors of the visible spectrum.

The spectra of glowing solids or liquids and gases under high pressure are continuous bands of colors. The spectra of glowing gases under low pressure are bright-line spectra of separate bands that are characteristic for the various elements. If light from a source passes through a gas at lower temperature than the original source, the spectrum is an absorption spectrum with dark lines corresponding to the emission lines of the cooler gas.

Radiation behaves as a stream of particles or photons when it reacts with matter. Planck described electromagnetic radiation in terms of a discrete unit called a quantum, where the energy of the photon is proportional to its frequency of vibration.

In the Bohr model of the hydrogen atom, the electrons absorb or emit energy at wavelengths corresponding to the spectral lines of hydrogen. When a photon is absorbed, an electron jumps to a higher energy level. A photon is emitted when the electron drops to a lower energy level.

# KEY TERMS

| | |
|---|---|
| absorption spectrum | isotope |
| amplitude | neutron |
| atomic number | photon |
| Balmer series | Planck's law |
| blackbody | polarization |
| Bohr atom | proton |
| continuous spectrum | quantum |
| dispersion | radiation |
| electromagnetic radiation | reflection |
| electromagnetic spectrum | refraction |
| electromagnetism | spectroscope |
| electron | spectrum |
| emission spectrum | Stefan-Boltzmann law |
| Fraunhofer lines | strong nuclear force |
| frequency | temperature |
| gravitation | wavelength |
| ground state | weak nuclear force |
| interference | Wien's displacement law |

# PROBLEMS

1. Why is the Bohr model a better description of the hydrogen atom than the earlier planetary model?

2. List the various regions of the electromagnetic spectrum and explain the differences between them.

3. What takes place inside an atom to produce the bright lines of an emission spectrum?

4. Why are some heavy elements stable while others are radioactive?

5. How do we know that the binding nuclear force is stronger than the electromagnetic force?

6. Find the wavelength of the Hα, Hβ, Hγ and Hδ lines in the Balmer series using the Rydberg equation.

7. What is the frequency of a photon of 21-cm wavelength?

8. If the average temperature of the Earth is about 288 K, at which wavelength does it radiate?

9. In which region of the spectrum would you expect to find the wavelength computed in problem 8?

10. Explain why the various frequencies of light are dispersed at different angles by a prism.

11. What is an ideal blackbody? Describe its properties.

# REFERENCES

Arya, Atam P. 1974. *Elementary Modern Physics*. Reading, Pa.: Addison-Wesley Publishing Company.

Darrow, Karl K. 1952. The Quantum Theory. *Scientific American,* March.

Hänsch, Theodor W., Arthur L. Schawlow, and George W. Series. 1979. The Spectrum of Atomic Hydrogen. *Scientific American,* March.

Huygens, Christiaan. 1952. *Treatise on Light.* Trans. Silvanus P. Thompson, Great Books of the Western World. Chicago: Encyclopedia Britannica Press.

Newton, Isaac. 1952. *Opticks*. Great Books of the Western World. Chicago: Encyclopedia Britannica Press.

Pedrotti, Frank L., and Leno S. Pedrotti. 1987. *Introduction to Optics*. Englewood Cliffs, N.J.: Prentice-Hall, Inc.

Rae, Alastair. 1986. *Quantum Physics, Illusion or Reality?* Cambridge: Cambridge University Press.

Schrödinger, Erwin. 1953. What is Matter? *Scientific American,* September.

Sears, Francis W., Mark W. Zamansky, and Hugh D. Young. 1987. *University Physics*. 7th ed. Reading, PA: Addison-Wesley Publishing Company.

Weisskopf, Victor F., and E. P. Rosenbaum. 1955. A Model of the Nucleus. *Scientific American,* December.

chapter

# 5

o p t i c a l ,   r a d i o ,   a n d   h i g h – e n e r g y   a s t r o n o m y

The Very Large Array radio telescope complex west of Socorro,
New Mexico.

For over 300 years after Galileo first observed the sky through his telescope, visible light and some ultraviolet and infrared were the only frequencies known to astronomers. The discovery of other wavelengths in the nineteenth century and the development of quantum mechanics at the beginning of the twentieth century gave reason to believe that all forms of electromagnetic radiation exist in space. The problem was to devise suitable instruments and equipment to detect them.

Most electromagnetic radiation from cosmic sources is stopped by the atmosphere of the Earth. The frequencies that get through include the light we see, part of the radio spectrum, and a fraction of the ultraviolet and infrared bands. *Atmospheric windows* at these wavelengths allow astronomers to study this radiation with ground-based instruments. The remaining regions of the spectrum are blocked by the lower atmosphere and can be investigated only with balloons, rockets, and orbiting observatories.

In order to collect and analyze radiation, astronomers need **detectors** that measure and record data. A simple case is a visual observation in which a telescope collects the light and the eye serves as a detector. Generally, astronomers do not look through telescopes but instead substitute instruments that measure quantities in terms of standard units. For example, if a camera is used as a detector, the recorded image is a function of the exposure time and the chemical composition of the light-sensitive film. Similarly, other portions of the spectrum are studied with detectors that respond to those wavelengths.

For our purposes, the various regions of the spectrum will be grouped into three categories: the *optical spectrum* arising from transitions between energy levels of electrons, from the long IR Brackett series to the short UV Lyman series; the *radio region* containing all microwaves and radio waves; and the *high-energy region* that includes X-rays and gamma rays.

## Atmospheric Effects

Atmospheric refraction takes place when light enters the atmosphere and continually decreases in velocity as it passes through denser layers on the way to the surface. The portion of the wave in the denser air will be refracted more, causing the rays to curve downward. For an observer on the ground, refraction causes a star to appear slightly higher than its true direction (fig. 5.1). Low-frequency radio waves are refracted downward through the thin atmosphere above 100 km, where the air is electrically charged by the action of solar X-rays and ultraviolet radiation.

A rainbow is the most spectacular example of refraction, dispersion, and reflection of sunlight by drops of water in the air. During or after a rain shower, a rainbow may be seen as an arc of color opposite the sun. Sometimes there are two concentric rainbows: a primary bow with red on the inside edge, and a larger but fainter secondary bow with the colors reversed (fig. 5.2). Figure 5.3 shows how a primary and secondary rainbow are produced.

The blue color of the sky seen on a clear day is due to sunlight diffused in the atmosphere. This *scattering* is an interaction between the vibrating electric field associated with the Sun's radiation and the molecules making up the air. When light falls on a molecule, the electrons in the molecule vibrate in resonance with the frequencies of the incident beam. The natural frequency of the molecule is in the ultraviolet range. Therefore, more intense vibration takes

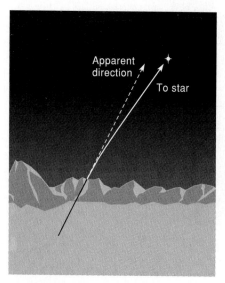

▲ **figure 5.1**
Atmospheric refraction causes a star to appear slightly higher than its true direction (angle is exaggerated).

**figure 5.2** ▶
A primary and secondary rainbow.

place in the shorter-wavelength blue part of the spectrum than in the longer-wavelength red portion.

When the Sun is near the horizon, its light passes through a greater thickness of atmosphere, water vapor, and dust particles. These factors create additional scattering to remove the blue altogether and leave orange and red to color the twilight sky.

## Optical Astronomy

The modern era of observational astronomy began at the beginning of the seventeenth century when telescopes were used for the first time. Dutch spectacle-maker Hans Lippershey is credited with the invention of the telescope in 1608, but Galileo was among the first to realize its astronomical value.

As we have learned, Galileo designed several telescopes using two lenses supported by a tube. His first telescope magnified three times, but eventually Galileo was able to increase the power to greater diameters. He saw the mountains and craters of the Moon, the phases of Venus, the satellites of Jupiter, and the stars of the Milky Way. Within a few years, other observers with similar instruments found the Great Nebula in Orion and the Andromeda galaxy.

## Image Brightness and Resolving Power

The brightness, or intensity, of light at the focus depends on the size of the **objective lens** or **primary mirror.** The objective lens is the large lens that forms the image in a refracting telescope. The primary mirror forms the image in a reflecting telescope. It follows that a mirror or lens with a larger surface area will gather more light and produce a brighter image than another with a smaller surface. The **light-gathering power** of a telescope is a measurement of this ability.

Light-gathering power increases in proportion to the square of the **aperture**—the clear diameter—of the mirror or lens. When the aperture is doubled, the area of the objective and the light-gathering power are increased by a factor of four. Accordingly, a star will appear four times brighter in a 20-cm telescope than in another with a 10-cm aperture. Of course the real advantage of the larger telescope with greater light-gathering power is its ability to form images of fainter objects. Stars that are four times fainter can be seen in the 20-cm telescope.

**Resolving power,** or the ability of a telescope to separate close binary stars or bring out fine details on the Moon and planets, depends upon the wavelength of the radiation and the diameter of the telescope. A larger telescope with greater resolving power can separate close binary stars, while in the smaller telescope the images of the stars overlap.

The above considerations are theoretical and do not show the limitations imposed by atmospheric **seeing.** Seeing is defined by the condition of the atmosphere. Atmospheric turbulence, haze, impurities, and other effects cause troublesome undulations and diffusion of the image. Good seeing indicates a calm, transparent atmosphere that permits a well-defined telescopic image. The major reason for building the Hubble Space Telescope was to improve the seeing—to obtain optimum resolution at visual wavelengths above the atmosphere.

## Types of Optical Telescopes

Astronomical telescopes are classified according to their optical systems. A **refracting telescope** uses an objective lens composed of several elements. A **reflecting telescope** has a primary mirror. A **catadioptric telescope** consists of a combination of a correcting lens and a primary mirror.

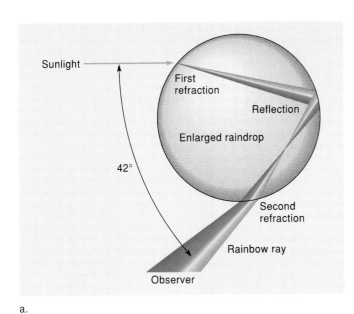

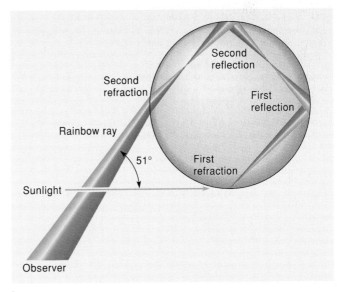

### figure 5.3

*a.* A primary rainbow is produced when sunlight enters the upper surface of a raindrop. *b.* A secondary rainbow is formed when sunlight enters the lower surface of a raindrop.

# methods and understandings 5.1

## Image Formation

*Diffraction,* the bending of light when passing an edge of an opaque object, occurs when a train of waves pass near an obstacle or through a small hole. The round opening of the largest telescope is merely a tiny aperture as compared to an incoming wave front from a distant star. Accordingly, light passes into the telescope tube and is diffracted, spreading into concentric rings and bending around any structural support. Instead of a star appearing as a point of light, diffraction and interference combine to produce a bright disk surrounded by fainter rings. The "star" you see is a diffraction pattern, sometimes called an Airy disk, named after George Airy, the nineteenth-century English astronomer who described the phenomenon.

A telescope lens is superior to the lens of your eye because its greater size allows more light to reach a focus. Thus faint stars that are invisible to the eye appear bright through the telescope. The *convex lens* of the eye or telescope objective brings the light to a focus by means of refraction. Think of the curved surface of a convex lens as an infinite number of small, flat areas at different angles to the parallel entrance rays. The ray passing through the lens along the central *optical axis* will not be refracted. From the center to the edge of the lens,

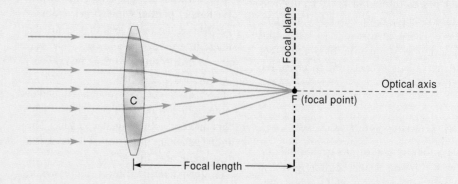

### figure 5.4

The focal point or focus of a thin double convex lens. Light from a distant source that is parallel to the optical axis converges at the focal point F. The focal length extends from the center of the lens, C, to F.

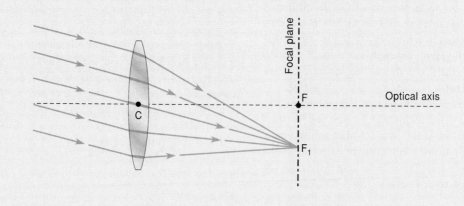

### figure 5.5

Off-axis light rays converge at point $F_1$ in the focal plane of the lens.

there is an increase in the angle between the light ray and the lens. This causes a corresponding increase in the angle of refraction. The curvature of the lens brings the emerging rays together at the **focal point.** The distance along the optical axis from the center of the lens to the focal point is called the **focal length** (fig. 5.4).

If the rays of light from a star arrive parallel to the optical axis, all light will focus the image at the center of the field. Off-axis rays from other stars enter and pass through the optical center of the lens at an angle to the optical axis. The light from these stars will also converge at the focal distance but at different focal points (fig. 5.5). All of the images lie in the **focal plane** of the lens, which is at the focal length perpendicular to the optical axis.

Light from different parts of the Sun, Moon, planets, or any other extended object reaches the lens as many point sources in

the same manner as a field of stars. If the Moon is centered in the telescope, the light from a point in the middle of the lunar disk will fill the lens and focus at the focal plane along the optical axis. Light rays from every other point will also fill the lens and focus elsewhere in the focal plane. The combined light of all points in the focal plane produces a real and inverted image.

A curved mirror can also bring light to a focus. Starlight reflected by a concave spherical mirror will converge along the optical axis (fig. 5.6). The rays near the optical axis are brought to a focal point *F* midway between the center of curvature *C* and the surface of the mirror, so that *F = C/2.* The rays at the edges converge on the axis between the focal point and the mirror.

Because lenses and spherical mirrors do not bring all rays to the same focus, the images off the optical axis are not as sharp as those formed on the axis. These defects, or *aberrations,* affect the

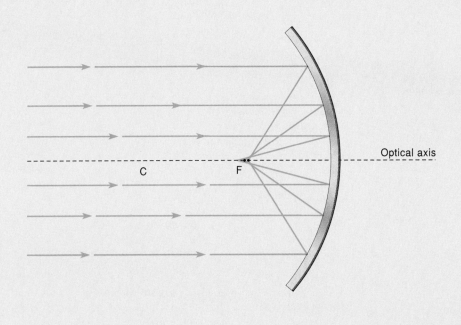

◄ **figure 5.6**

A concave spherical mirror. The central rays of light converge at the focus (F), while the edge rays are focused at points closer to the mirror along the optical axis. This phenomenon is known as spherical aberration.

Optical axis

C    F

▼ **figure 5.7**

*a.* Different wavelengths of light do not converge at the same focus, producing chromatic aberration. *b.* Chromatic aberration can be partially corrected by an achromatic objective that combines lenses of different composition.

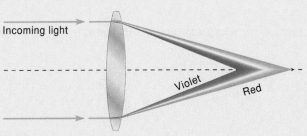

Incoming light

Violet

Red

a. Chromatic aberration

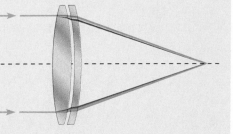

Incoming light

b. Achromatic lens

position as well as the appearance of an image. Telescopes and other optical devices using mirrors and lenses must be corrected for aberration.

When white light is dispersed by a lens, violet is refracted more than red, resulting in different focal lengths for each color of the spectrum (fig. 5.7). The spread in focal lengths produces a blurred image fringed in color. This **chromatic aberration** was a serious problem in the first telescopes, in which a simple convex lens was used to form the image. In an attempt to reduce the defect and bring the colors to the same focus, some seventeenth-century telescopes were made 50 meters long.

Chromatic aberration continued to limit the performance of telescopes until theoretical investigations of the **achromatic lens** began in 1733. Chromatic aberration is effectively reduced when lenses of different composition are combined (fig. 5.7). The dispersion of one lens is cancelled by the other, to bring most of the light to one focus. Later, in 1759, John Dolland constructed the first achromatic lenses.

When light passes through a lens or is reflected from a spherical mirror, the central rays are focused at a greater distance from the focal plane than the edge rays (fig. 5.6). This difference in focal length creates **spherical aberration,** which increases as the diameter of the lens or mirror is enlarged.

In a mirror, spherical aberration is corrected by changing the shape of the surface from a spheroid to a paraboloid. A paraboloidal surface focuses all the rays in the focal plane where the image is produced, as with a parabolic mirror (fig. 4.9b).

Lenses can be corrected for spherical aberration by changing the surface of curvature. But, unlike mirrors, grinding and polishing a new lens surface is difficult and does not correct the defect entirely. In practice, spherical aberration is minimized by the proper combination of components in the achromatic lens.

optical, radio, and high-energy astronomy

What is the size of the smallest lunar crater visible through a telescope? How much can an image be magnified? These are two questions to consider before selecting a telescope and planning a night of observation.

Resolution is measured in arc seconds (arcsec), and a small telescope with a clear aperture of 2.5 cm will separate a binary star with components that are 4.6 arc seconds apart. A telescope with an aperture ten times larger (25 cm) can resolve double stars separated by 0.46 arc seconds.

These values for resolving power are found by the expression

$$\text{resolving power} = \frac{206265 \text{ arcsec} \times \text{wavelength of light}}{\text{aperture of the telescope}}, \text{ or}$$

$$a = \frac{2.1 \times 10^5 \times \lambda}{d} \text{ arcsec}$$

where $a$ represents the resolution in arcsec; $\lambda$ the wavelength of light in cm; and $d$ the aperture in cm.

If the wavelength of light selected = $5.5 \times 10^{-5}$ cm, and $d = 25$ cm, then

$$a = \frac{2.1 \times 10^5 \text{ arcsec} \times 5.5 \times 10^{-5} \text{ cm}}{25 \text{ cm}}$$

$$a = 0.46 \text{ arcsec}.$$

Use this equation to find the resolving power of your telescope and test its performance by separating the double stars introduced in chapter 2.

The **magnifying power** of a telescope is the ratio between the focal length of the objective and the focal length of the **eyepiece.** The focal length of the objective is fixed, but eyepieces can be interchanged. Thus magnification can be increased or decreased by substituting eyepieces of different focal lengths.

To find magnification, divide the focal length of the objective by the focal length of the eyepiece.

$$\text{magnification (M)} = \frac{\text{focal length of the objective (F)}}{\text{focal length of the eyepiece (f)}}$$

As an example, suppose you observe the Moon in a refracting telescope with a 150-cm focal length. If the telescope is fitted with a 30-mm eyepiece, the image will be magnified 50 diameters. Insert a 10-mm eyepiece and the power will be increased to 150 diameters.

**figure 5.8**

The 1-m telescope at Yerkes Observatory, Williams Bay, Wisconsin, is the world's largest refractor.

The achromatic objective of a refracting telescope is usually a combination of two or more lenses, which are mounted in machined cells threaded into the top of the telescope tube. The length of the telescope is determined by the focal distance of the objective, generally about 15 times the aperture. The *f-ratio* or *f-number* of the telescope refers to the ratio between the focal length and the aperture.

$$\text{f-ratio} = \frac{\text{focal length of the objective lens}}{\text{diameter of the objective lens}}$$

Light converges to the eyepiece lenses, which are mounted in a cell with an outside diameter equal to the inside diameter of the telescope tube. Magnification is changed by replacing the entire eyepiece assembly with another of different focal length.

The largest refractor in the world, the 40-inch (1-m) f/19 Yerkes Observatory telescope has a focal length of 63 feet (19 m) (fig. 5.8). The 36-inch (91-cm) Lick Observatory refractor is second in size. For fieldwork, small portable refractors ranging in aperture from 6 cm to 10 cm are mounted on tripods.

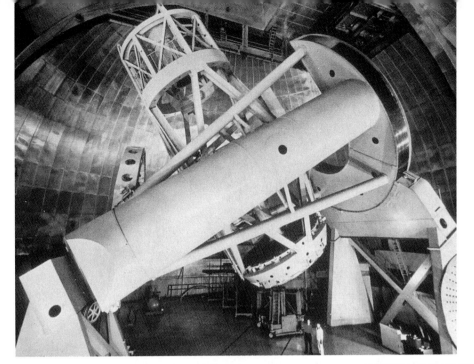

▼ figure 5.10
*a.* Newtonian focus. The light cone is diverted outside the telescope tube by a flat diagonal mirror. *b.* Cassegrain focus. The light cone is reflected through a hole in the primary mirror by a convex secondary mirror.

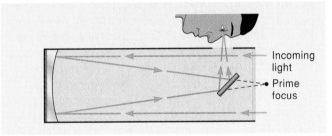

a. Newtonian focus

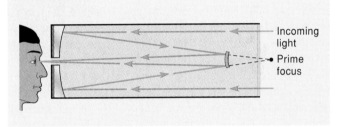

b. Cassegrain focus

A reflecting telescope collects incoming light in a parabolic mirror located at the lower end of the telescope tube. From here, light is reflected back up the tube to the *prime focus* where film holders and other instruments are mounted. The 200-inch (5-m) Hale Telescope on Mount Palomar is large enough to carry an astronomer in an observing cage at the prime focus (fig. 5.9). However, astronomers rarely look through large telescopes, but instead track objects under investigation through a smaller *guide telescope* mounted on the main instrument. The largest optical telescope utilizing a single mirror is the 240-inch (6-m) reflector on Mt. Pastukhov in the Caucasus Mountains of Russia.

In smaller reflecting telescopes, the prime focus cannot be used for visual work because the observer will obstruct the incoming light. To overcome this problem, various ways have been devised to divert the focus to an eyepiece outside the tube.

In a **Newtonian focus,** the light cone is diverted by a flat, diagonal **secondary mirror** mounted in the tube below the prime focus at 45° to the optical axis (fig. 5.10a). Only a negligible amount of incoming light is obstructed by the diagonal mirror, which is held in place by a thin metal support called "the spider." Generally, reflectors of this type range from f/8 to f/5 and decrease in focal ratio as the aperture increases.

If a convex mirror is substituted as the secondary, the light cone can be reflected through a hole in the center of the primary mirror to a **Cassegrain focus** outside the lower end of the tube (fig. 5.10b). Such telescopes have focal ratios beginning at f/10, since the focal distance is increased by folding the light cone in the tube.

The catadioptric telescope consists of a spherical mirror corrected for spherical aberration by use of an aspheric lens located at the center of curvature. One such system, a **Schmidt telescope,** is ca-

pable of photographing a large field of view almost free of aberration. The 48-inch (1.2-m correcting lens) f/2.5 Schmidt telescope at Mt. Palomar was used to photograph the National Geographic Society-Palomar Observatory Sky Atlas (fig. 5.11). Altogether, 879 fields, each about 7° square, were recorded down to a magnitude of +21 for stars and +19.5 for galaxies.

Catadioptric telescopes are not limited to major observatories. Today, small and medium-sized portable instruments that combine the features of the Schmidt and Cassegrain systems are available to the amateur observer. In these telescopes, light enters the tube and is brought to a focus at the top of the tube. A convex secondary mirror placed below an aspheric corrector reflects the light cone back down the tube and through the hole in the primary mirror to the eyepiece at the Cassegrain focus.

The optical telescopes described thus far can be used for solar observation if

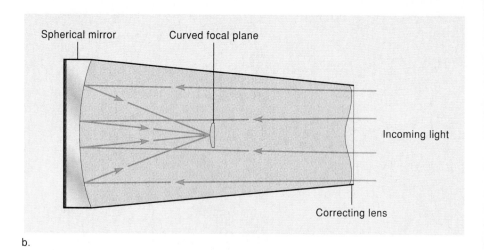

a.                                                    b.

**figure 5.11**

*a.* The 48-inch (1.2-m correcting lens) Schmidt telescope at Mt. Palomar Observatory. *b.* A cutaway view to show the optical system of a Schmidt telescope.

necessary precautions are taken to protect the eyes. For direct viewing, the aperture must be reduced and fitted with neutral density filters. Additional filters are placed at the eyepiece. But even filters allow infrared radiation to enter and perhaps cause damage to the eye. Lenses can crack from the concentrated heat of sunlight.

The best way to view the Sun is on a screen mounted behind the eyepiece. Not only is the method safe, but several people can look at the Sun at the same time.

Astronomers at large observatories use telescopes specially designed for solar work. In the United States, there are solar telescopes at Sacramento Peak Observatory, New Mexico, and Kitt Peak National Observatory, Arizona.

Kitt Peak's McMath Solar Telescope, the world's largest, has a focal length of 92 m. At the top of a 30-m tower, a 2-m heliostat reflects the sunlight down a 153-m water-cooled shaft, most of which is underground. At the bottom of this optical tunnel, a 1.5-m mirror reflects the light back up the shaft to a 1.2-m mirror located above ground level. Then the light is directed down to the observatory room where a 76-cm image of the Sun is produced. Here astronomers use instruments to investigate the solar spectrum, magnetic field, sunspots, and other phenomena related to the Sun.

There are different ways in which a ___ s supported. An **altazimuth** ___ ows the telescope to move ver-

tically and horizontally on two axes in altitude and azimuth. When large telescopes employ altazimuth mountings, computers are used to convert the horizontal and vertical motions to an east-west track along a diurnal circle parallel to the Earth's rotation.

An **equatorial mount** consists of a polar axis, and a declination axis that supports the instrument perpendicular to the polar axis. The telescope turns clockwise on the polar axis at the same speed as the diurnal motion of an object in the sky.

## Observational Techniques

A remarkable amount of information has been deciphered from photographs taken with a *spectrograph,* which is basically a spectroscope fitted with a camera. As described in chapter 4, the dark Fraunhofer lines in solar and stellar spectra are caused by absorption at discrete wavelengths by low-pressure gases in the upper layers of the Sun and stars. The chemical elements present are identified by comparing these dark lines with a bright-line comparison spectrum, which is produced on the photographic plate in the spectrograph before exposing the plate to the sky.

Spectrum analysis has revealed differences in the appearances of spectral lines when elements are ionized at high temperatures and combine to form compounds at lower temperatures. In 1896,

Dutch physicist Pieter Zeeman found that spectral lines split when light is in a magnetic field. This so-called **Zeeman effect** shows the Sun and stars to be magnetic.

Usually, stellar absorption lines are not found in the same position as the bright lines of the comparison spectrum. This displacement, or **Doppler effect** (discovered by Christian Doppler), is due to the change in the frequency of light from a moving source. If a star approaches, the number of waves received per second (frequency) increases and the spectral lines are shifted to the blue end of the spectrum. If a star recedes, the number of waves received decreases and the spectral lines are shifted toward the red. The velocity of a star toward or away from the Earth can be measured by the amount of shift of its spectral lines. The greater the displacement of the lines, the greater the velocity of the star (fig. 5.12).

Photographic and photoelectric techniques are applied to *photometry,* the measurement of the brightness of stars and extended objects. In photometry, radiation enters a detector with a light-sensitive surface that reacts to the incoming photons and records the intensity of the radiant energy.

Brightness measurements may be made by means of photographic photometry, in which images produced on photographic plates are compared with standard stars of known brightness. By using filters and special emulsions, the

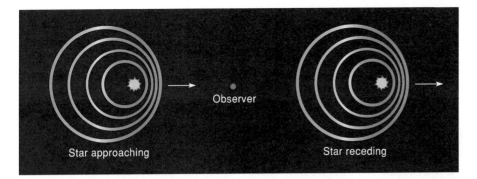

**figure 5.12**

The Doppler effect. When a light source approaches an observer, the frequency of wavelengths received by the observer increases, causing the spectral lines to shift toward the blue portion of the spectrum. When a light source recedes, the frequency of wavelengths decreases, causing the spectral lines to shift toward the red portion of the spectrum.

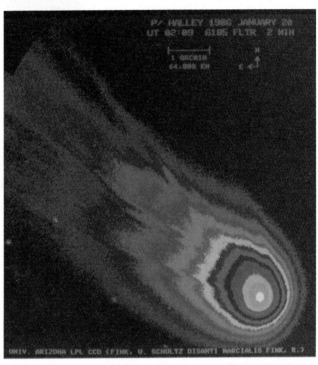

**figure 5.13**

CCD photographs of Halley's comet. The false-color display shows differences in brightness of various parts of the comet.

brightness is recorded in different colors allowing the temperatures of stars to be determined.

Photoelectric photometry is the measurement of light intensity by means of an electronic detector such as a photomultiplier or electron multiplier tube. A negatively charged plate or photocathode liberates photoelectrons when exposed to the impact of incoming photons. An electric current is created as the photoelectrons cascade to less negatively charged plates called dynodes where more electrons are liberated. All the electrons are collected at an anode, and amplified and recorded by a photon-counting device or meter.

A photodiode photometer employs a semiconductor and an electrometer am-

plifier in place of a photomultiplier tube. The incoming radiation is brought to the light-sensitive photodiode located at the focus of the telescope. From the photodiode, the signal is brought to the electrometer amplifier and sent to a voltage-to-frequency converter for processing.

There are other advantages to using a photodiode as a light-sensitive target. A **charge-coupled device** (**CCD**) is a detector capable of producing images on a monitor screen that are superior to photographs. Indeed, a 28-cm-aperture telescope equipped with a CCD camera has greater light-gathering power than a large observatory telescope. The imaging area of a CCD is an array of many rows of silicon photodiodes or *pixels*. The number of pixels per millimeter de-

termines the resolution of the image. When incoming photons strike a target, electrons are released and passed along the row to an amplifier where they are changed to digital signals and stored on videotape.

Various operations are made possible by image-processing techniques. The sensitivity and high efficiency of CCDs has permitted observers to detect faint nebulosities, planetary nebulae, and globular clusters surrounding distant galaxies. Fine details can be resolved and false-color schemes are used to enhance different brightness levels (fig. 5.13). These detectors are the most important photoelectric instruments introduced in recent years.

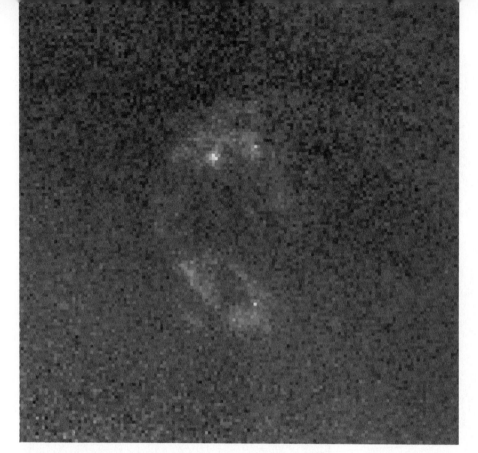

**figure 5.14**

Vela supernova remnant as seen by the Extreme Ultraviolet Explorer satellite during the all-sky survey made in 1992.

## Observing the Ultraviolet and Infrared Sky

Invisible ultraviolet and infrared rays may be brought to a focus in an optical telescope, but each spectral region requires detectors that are sensitive to its particular spectral band. Most lethal solar ultraviolet radiation is blocked by the ozone layers between 40 km and 160 km above the Earth's surface. Indeed, very little was known about UV from stellar and galactic sources until telescopes were sent aloft in balloons, and rockets.

Two gases in the lower atmosphere, carbon dioxide and water vapor, trap practically all infrared from the Sun and other sources. Only narrow bands in the ʳR spectrum pass through and reach the ⁿᵉ. Moreover, visible sunlight ab- the Earth is re-radiated into as infrared. Therefore, ⁿd telescopes are in- ʰle above sea ᵉs, the best site at the summit of and of Hawaii. Air-

craft, balloons, and rockets are used to reach higher altitudes.

When satellites were designed to carry telescopes into orbit around the Earth, the entire UV and IR spectrum was made available, unimpeded by atmospheric absorption. In 1968, the Orbiting Astronomical Observatory (OAO-2) was launched to study objects in the ultraviolet at wavelengths between 121.5 nm and 91.2 nm. By 1978, the International Ultraviolet Explorer (IUE) was positioned into an almost synchronous orbit above the equator about 40,000 km over the Atlantic Ocean. The Infrared Astronomical Satellite (IRAS) was placed into a polar orbit in 1983. The project was a joint effort by the United States, the Netherlands, and the United Kingdom.

Tens of thousands of IUE photographs have been returned to Earth. The satellite consists of a 46-cm Cassegrain telescope equipped with two spectrographs and diffraction gratings. The spectra are recorded on videotape and transmitted back to Earth where the image is reconstituted by computer.

IUE provided an opportunity to determine the effective temperature of very hot stars. You will recall from Wien's law that the wavelength at which radiation is most intense is inversely proportional to its absolute temperature. IUE observations were made of stars and gases having temperatures ranging between 10,000 K and 100,000 K. These observations revealed the presence of strong winds of ionized particles that are apparently accelerated by radiation from hot stars.

Other important observations include the confirmation of high-temperature gas in the region surrounding the center of our Galaxy, and the study of supernovae. According to theory, supernova explosions enrich the dust and gas clouds in interstellar space with heavy elements. In the early 1990s, the Extreme Ultraviolet Explorer Satellite (EUVE) made it possible to test the theory by studying the chemical abundances of various elements within supernovae remnants (see fig. 5.14).

The Infrared Astronomical Satellite (IRAS) made observations of objects that radiate at wavelengths ranging from about 7460 nm to a limit of 820 nm at temperatures between 10 K and 1000 K (fig. 5.15). Many of the sources were unknown or only partially understood simply because their infrared signals never reached Earth-based telescopes. From its orbit IRAS made a comprehensive survey of extended sources such as dust and gas clouds associated with stellar birth. In addition, studies were made of point sources related to solar system objects, as well as accretion disks surrounding distant stars. A discovery that received much attention was the detection of accretion disks composed of rock particles around the stars Alpha Lyrae and Beta Pictoris (fig. 5.16).

IRAS contained a reflecting telescope fitted with a 57-cm primary mirror. Radiation was reflected from the primary to the secondary mirror and folded back through a hole in the center of the primary mirror. The energy continued to a detector containing silicon and germanium semiconductors sensitive to IR radiation. Then the signals were transmitted to computers at stations in the

**figure 5.15**
The Infrared Astronomical Satellite (IRAS) observed objects at temperatures between 10 K and 1,000 K.

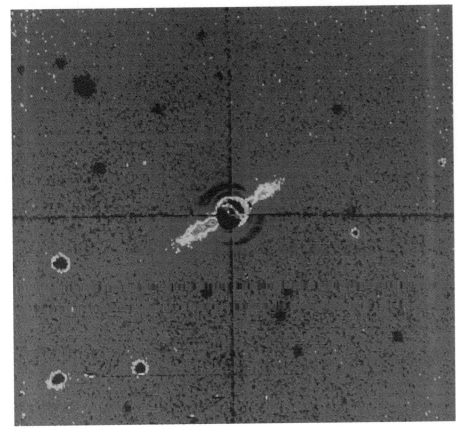

**figure 5.16**
IRAS image of the star Beta Pictoris. An accretion disk of rock particles surrounds the star.

United States, the United Kingdom, and the Netherlands.

IRAS had the advantage of "seeing" nonluminous objects such as rock and dust. Comets were discovered to have invisible dust tails extending millions of kilometers behind the nucleus. A swarm of debris left in the wake of a comet was identified as the source of the Geminid meteor shower observed about December 13 every year. The discovery of Comet IRAS-Araki-Alcock provided a basis for assuming that comets contain primitive constituents of the interstellar cloud that gave birth to the solar system.

When IRAS was pointed toward dust and gas clouds in the Milky Way, regions that appear as dark rifts in the visible spectrum were found to be strong IR sources. Deep inside these clouds new, unseen stars heat up surrounding layers of dust. Light from the stars is absorbed by intervening dust and gas, but their presence is confirmed by the longer IR wavelengths that travel unimpeded through the nebulae.

## Radio Astronomy

Radio astronomy began in the early 1930s when Karl Jansky, an engineer with Bell Telephone Laboratories, discovered radio-frequency radiation from space. While using an antenna and radio receiver designed to study radio-telephone interference, he noted a faint hiss that he correctly identified as radiation from the center of the Galaxy. A few years later, amateur astronomer Grote Reber built the first radio telescope, consisting of a paraboloidal reflector much like the large installations in use today (see fig. 5.17). After World War II, the study of cosmic radio emissions ushered in a new field of research, radio astronomy.

## Sources of Radio-Frequency Radiation

Radio emissions occur in a number of ways. Blackbody radiation is produced by thermal motion of electrons. An emission of 21-cm wavelength occurs when an electron in the ground state flips over and emits a photon (chapter 17). Radio

**figure 5.17**
The 100-m radio telescope at Effelsburg, Germany.

wavelengths are studied, the surface can be a wire grid.

In place of an eyepiece or optical detector, radio waves are brought to a focus at a metal antenna. Electrons in the antenna vibrate back and forth, duplicating the oscillation of the incoming radio wave. The electric signals in the antenna are amplified, brought to a radio-frequency detector, and recorded on videotape for analysis.

Because of the enormous difference in wavelength between light and radio waves, a radio telescope must be built much larger to approach the resolving power of its optical counterpart. You will recall from our earlier description of optical telescopes how the ability to resolve small objects depends upon the wavelength of the radiation and the diameter of the primary mirror. If we compare light at a wavelength of $5.5 \times 10^{-5}$ cm with a radio wave at 21 cm, then

$$\text{ratio} = \frac{21 \text{ cm}}{5.5 \times 10^{-5} \text{ cm}} = 382,000.$$

The 21-cm radio wave is 382,000 times longer than the wavelength of yellow light. Consequently, to achieve the intrinsic resolution of a 40-cm optical telescope, the radio reflector must be over 160 km in diameter. (Only intrinsic optical resolution is considered; atmospheric seeing is ignored.) To match the resolution of the 200-inch (5-m) Hale Telescope, a single radio telescope would require a diameter equal to the distance across the continental United States. The world's largest radio dish is the 300-m fixed reflector at Arecibo, Puerto Rico (fig. 5.18).

The problem of higher resolution demanded new approaches to overcome the limitations imposed on the size of radio telescopes by the wavelength of radiation. Certainly the construction of a filled-aperture telescope many kilometers in diameter is not the practical solution. Instead, English astronomer Martin Ryle reached the desired sensitivity by using two or more telescopes as a **radio interferometer.** Like their optical counterparts, radio waves of the same frequency combine and reinforce each other. Both telescopes are focused upon the same object and radiation from the source enters one antenna a fraction of a second

emission takes place when electrons are accelerated in magnetic fields (chapter 16). Several thousand point sources of intense radiation—*radio stars*—have been identified as the remains of supernovae (Crab Nebula; Cassiopeia A), interacting galaxies (Cygnus A), and normal galaxies (Andromeda galaxy). In addition, there is a general continuous radiation concentrated in the plane of our Galaxy with greatest intensity in the direction of the galactic core. Radiation also stems from the entire region about the center of the Galaxy.

## Radio Telescope Design

The most familiar type of radio telescope is the large parabolic reflector or dish that reflects radio waves in the same way a parabolic mirror reflects light (fig. 5.17). These are *filled-aperture telescopes,* in which the reflector consists of a continuous surface of sheet-metal or wire-mesh construction. The type of surface used in a parabolic reflector is determined by the wavelength under investigation. Shorter microwaves require a smooth metal surface. When longer

◄ **figure 5.18**
The 300-m radio telescope at Arecibo, Puerto Rico. The spherical surface of fine mesh is built into a bowl-shaped valley. The antenna is suspended by cables from three towers and can be moved more than 15° from the vertical.

▼ **figure 5.19**
The Very Large Array (VLA) radio-telescope complex in New Mexico. **a.** The Y-formation of 27 antennas with 25-m reflectors. **b.** For greatest resolution, the antennas are extended for a distance of 21 km.

a.

b.

before the other. The time lag depends upon the baseline between the telescopes and the angle between the source and the baseline.

The telescopes use the *aperture synthesis* technique, in which many observations are made by moving the telescopes to different positions within a radius of about 800 m. The time-varying voltages from the antennas are then processed by computer and displayed as a radio map that shows contours of equal intensity surrounding the source.

The theory behind aperture synthesis can be visualized in the following way. Instead of one large filled-aperture telescope, imagine the same area made up of many smaller antennas. If all the antennas are combined, their sum will approach the area of the large single telescope.

The same effect can be achieved if two or more components are joined together electrically as an interferometer.

In 1962, Ryle used steerable parabolic reflectors situated on a track in an east-west alignment. By moving one of the telescopes along the track, it was possible to change the baseline between them by a maximum distance of one mile. The rotation of the Earth changed the position of the source with respect to the telescope array so that the baseline covered all possible directions in 12 hours. By repeating the operation daily

using a different baseline, only a few antennas were necessary to fill in the gaps and achieve the resolution of a large instrument. In 1974, Ryle shared the Nobel Prize in physics for his development of aperture synthesis.

By 1972, the National Science Foundation and Congress had approved the construction of the *Very Large Array* (*VLA*) on the Plains of San Augustin near Socorro, New Mexico (fig. 5.19). The VLA consists of 27 antennas, each of 25-m diameter, arranged in a Y-formation. Each arm of the configuration extends almost 21 km along a railroad track. The antennas can be positioned the entire length of the arms for greatest resolution. For low resolution, the antenna baseline is reduced to less than 1 km.

In the VLA control room, the signals from each antenna are amplified, converted to digits, and cross-correlated with the signals from the other antennas. The system gives the VLA an equivalent aperture of about 32 km. Indeed, the large collecting area of the VLA has provided detailed images of nearby objects in the solar system as well as distant supernovae, quasars, and active galaxies (fig. 5.20).

We noted that antennas need baselines of thousands of kilometers to resolve the fine details of radio sources. Such distances are not possible in the VLA and similar systems because the antennas are connected by cable. An important step to extend the baseline was taken in 1967 by a team at the Royal Radar Establishment, Malvern, England. An interferometer with a 127-km baseline was formed by a 25-m telescope in Malvern and the MK-1 or MK-2 telescope at Jodrell Bank connected by a radio link. At a wavelength of 6 cm and the ability to measure angular diameters of 0.025 arc second, the system had greater resolution than an optical telescope.

optical, radio, and high-energy astronomy

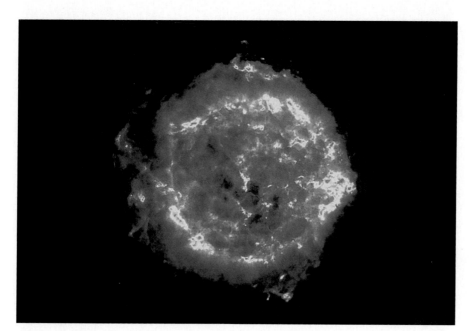

**figure 5.20**

A VLA false-color radio image of Cassiopeia A in the constellation Cassiopeia that has been identified as a supernova remnant.

A major breakthrough in improved resolution occured with the development of the *Very Long Baseline Interferometer* (*VLBI*). Two or more antennas separated by thousands of kilometers are controlled by synchronized atomic clocks and tape recorders situated at each site. The tapes from each antenna contain the signals and the precise time they were received. The signals are digitized and the tapes are correlated in a computer.

The VLBI technique makes it possible to extend the baseline across continents to distances exceeding 10,000 km. A new complex of radio telescopes called the Very Long Baseline Array (VLBA) is scheduled for the 1990s. The installation includes 10 antennas spaced over the distance from Hawaii to Puerto Rico.

Moreover, there are plans to obtain baselines greater than the diameter of the Earth by placing antennas in orbit. American and European investigators have proposed the Quasat satellite to collect data in different orientations during each revolution.

## High-Energy Astronomy

Like their optical counterparts, X-rays are produced when electrons in various shells about the nucleus of an atom absorb and emit energy. X-rays are associated with electrons occupying the filled inner shells of the heavier elements. These electrons are tightly bound so that a large amount of energy is required to displace them into a higher shell.

When an electron in a filled shell close to the nucleus is excited from the ground state, it jumps to a higher unfilled outer shell. An X-ray photon is emitted when a second electron in an outer shell cascades to ground state to fill the vacancy left in the inner shell.

The tenuous upper atmosphere is opaque to X-rays; it acts as a shield and screens all X-ray wavelengths before they reach the surface. Soft X-rays (wavelengths of $10^{-6}$ cm) are stopped by only a few centimeters of air. Indeed, all X-rays from the Sun and other sources are absorbed above 40 km. For this reason, the study of X-rays coming from space was impossible until the use of high-altitude rocket probes and, later, orbiting satellites.

Some of the discoveries made with ground-based radio telescopes were precursors of later investigations of X-rays by orbiting observatories. Radio sources such as supernova remnants, neutron stars, radio galaxies, and quasars possess high temperatures and must also emit photons in the high-energy range. You will recall how Planck's law expresses the energy possessed by a photon for any given frequency. For X-rays with a frequency of $10^{17}$ Hz, the energy will be about 400 electron volts (eV), while the temperature of the source will approach $5 \times 10^6$ K. Hard X-rays are emitted from sources at frequencies of $10^{20}$ Hz and temperatures of $10^9$ K.

High-energy astronomy began in the late 1940s when World War II rockets were adapted for scientific investigation of the upper atmosphere. At altitudes above 90 km, strong X-ray signals were detected coming from the Sun. By the 1950s, the association between X-ray emission and sunspots was confirmed. The ionization of neutral gases in the Earth's upper atmosphere was of particular interest because high-energy solar radiation (X-ray and UV) is responsible for the formation of conducting layers of charged particles that affect radio communication (fig. 5.21).

In the 1960s, X-ray astronomy was further advanced with the Orbiting Solar Observatory (OSO) and the Orbiting Astronomical Observatory (OAO). The OSO contained X-ray photon counters and, later, instruments to study the solar X-ray spectrum and locate strong sources of radiation. The last OAO, named Copernicus, contained instruments designed to investigate interstellar UV and X-ray sources.

As X-ray astronomy advanced, more sophisticated spacecraft were launched to study galactic as well as extragalactic objects. In December 1970, the X-ray satellite Uhuru was sent aloft from Kenya into an equatorial orbit. The X-ray sources identified by Uhuru proved to be rather unique. One in particular, Cygnus X-1, consists of a blue giant star in a close orbit about an unseen companion. The invisible companion has a mass exceeding 10 solar masses and an accretion disk made of matter pulled from the outer layers of the blue giant. The best

**figure 5.21**

The Sun's corona from solar Maximum Mission Satellite. The colors in this false-color image represent regions of increasing density from dark blue to yellow.

explanation for the phenomenon is that the blue star is the secondary component of a binary system with a black hole as the primary. Matter leaves the blue giant, spirals into an accretion disk surrounding the black hole, and emits X-rays before plunging into the cosmic maelstrom.

An X-ray telescope such as the High Energy Astronomical Observatory (HEAO) has a series of highly polished concentric paraboloid and hyperboloid surfaces that reflect radiation to a focus. At the focal point, the signal is brought to various instruments such as spectrometers and imaging detectors.

HEAO-2, named Einstein, was launched in 1978 and remained operational until 1981. It contained four paraboloid and hyperboloid collecting surfaces, giving the telescope an angular resolution of a few arc seconds. Image-

forming detectors were used and the amplified signals were encoded and transmitted to mission control at Goddard Space Flight Center, Maryland.

Gamma rays, the most energetic form of electromagnetic radiation, extend from the hard X-ray region to increasingly greater frequencies beyond $10^{24}$ Hz. There are several ways in which gamma rays are generated. Gamma ray photons are emitted during energy transitions within the nuclei of atoms when a nucleon in an excited energy state returns to ground state. These energetic waves also arise during non-nuclear actions. If a negatively charged electron smashes into its antiparticle, a positively charged positron, both particles are annihilated into photons of gamma radiation. In another process, gamma rays are emitted when an electron spirals rapidly in a strong, uniform magnetic field.

In each instance, the radiation is generated by active, high-temperature sources such as emission nebulae, the energetic center of the Galaxy, supernovae remnants, and interacting binary stars. Extragalactic sources include entire galaxies and quasars.

Cosmic gamma rays were discovered over 30 years ago by means of instruments carried aloft in rockets and balloons. In 1989, Australian astronomers measured electron-positron collisions in the direction of the center of the Galaxy.

Satellites and orbiting observatories equipped with gamma ray detectors have discovered discrete sources as well as diffuse emission throughout the Galaxy (fig. 5.22). In 1979, HEAO-3 carried a gamma ray telescope designed to collect data and map a large region of the sky.

As gamma ray photons enter the telescope, they are guided to a shielded

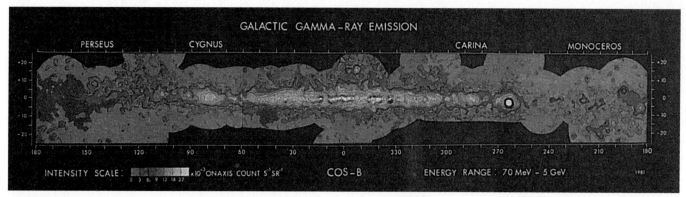

**figure 5.22**

Regions of gamma-ray intensity in the Milky Way galaxy as measured by the European COS B satellite. Regions of highest intensity are yellow; regions of lowest intensity are blue.

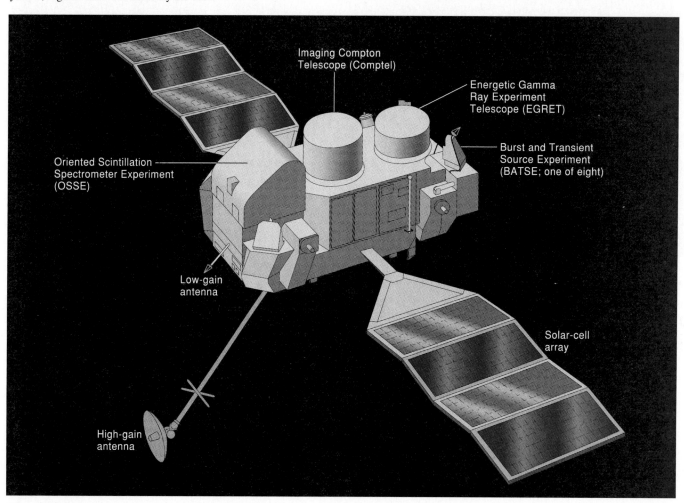

**figure 5.23**

The Gamma Ray Observatory (GRO) is designed to survey the entire sky at gamma ray wavelengths.

detector where scattering takes place. Electrons collide and create an electric current which is a measure of the energy carried by the incoming gamma ray photon.

The Gamma-Ray Observatory (GRO) was launched by the space shuttle Atlantis in April 1991 (fig. 5.23). GRO (renamed the Compton Observatory after the physicist Arthur Holly Compton) has four instruments to investigate gamma rays from solar flares, white dwarf stars, supernovae, neutron stars, black holes, emission nebulae, and the centers of active galaxies and quasars (see chapters 16 and 19). Its mission is to map the sky in gamma rays, search-ing for sources in a frequency range of $10^{20}$ Hz to $10^{22}$ Hz.

Another orbiting observatory, the Cosmic Background Explorer (COBE), was launched in 1989. The satellite contains instruments designed to detect the 2.74 K microwave radiation believed to be remnant emission from the early universe (chapter 20).

a.

b.

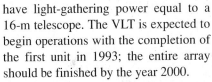

c.

**figure 5.24**
*a.* The Keck Telescope uses 36 segmented mirrors incorporated into a single reflector.
*b.* The telescope is in operation at Mauna Kea, Hawaii.
*c.* A test image taken prior to final installation of the mirror-alignment system shows the galaxy NGC 1232.

## Innovations in Ground-Based and Space Astronomy

Advances in astronomy, as in other sciences, are made by the continuous improvement in instrument design and observing techniques. One way to increase the light-gathering power of optical telescopes to use several mirrors working in concert as one large collecting surface.

This design incorporates many mirrors into a single segmented reflector. The Keck Telescope is in operation on the 4200-m summit of Mauna Kea in Hawaii. The completed mirror consists of 36 hexagonal segments forming a single concave array (fig. 5.24). To insure that all mirrors are aligned to a common focus, there are 168 sensors located between the segments. Data from the sensors are fed into a processing computer that corrects the position of each mirror by means of actuators located behind each segment. The Keck Telescope is 10 m across and has four times the light-gathering power of the Hale Telescope.

The European Very Large Telescope (VLT) consists of an array of four 8-m telescopes with a 150-m baseline. When the telescopes are combined, they will have light-gathering power equal to a 16-m telescope. The VLT is expected to begin operations with the completion of the first unit in 1993; the entire array should be finished by the year 2000.

Perhaps the most ambitious recent venture in new telescopes was the launching of the Hubble Space Telescope (HST) into orbit in 1989. Free of the effects of the Earth's atmosphere, the 2.4-m primary mirror was expected to achieve separations of 0.06 arcsec and produce sharper images than any present ground-based telescope.

The HST uses a Cassegrain optical system. The incoming radiation is reflected from the primary to a 0.31-m secondary mirror mounted about 5 m from the primary. Then the light is folded back through the central opening in the primary mirror to a focus in the scientific instrument bay.

The telescope is a closed cylindrical tube 4 m in diameter and 13 m long. A door-sunshade at the front and baffles inside the tube protect against stray light from the Sun and Moon entering the tube and damaging the instruments. The

optical, radio, and high-energy astronomy

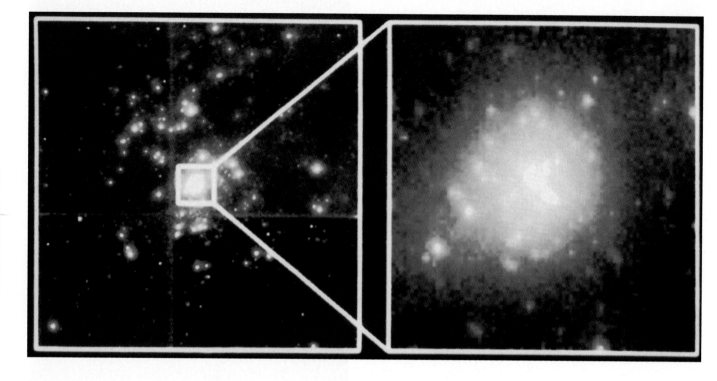

**figure 5.25**

Hubble Space Telescope images of stellar formation in the Large Magellanic Cloud, one of two galaxies only about 100,000 light-years from our Milky Way system.

remainder of the telescope consists of an optical assembly and focal plane assembly shroud protecting the scientific instruments.

The incoming radiation is focused on the image plane located in the scientific instrument bay. At the focal plane, radiation ranging from infrared to ultraviolet is reflected to cameras, photometers, and spectrographs. Data is collected and transmitted to receiving stations on the Earth by way of communications satellites.

Despite spherical aberration and mechanical problems, the Hubble Space Telescope has produced high-resolution images of the planets Mars, Jupiter, and Saturn, emission nebulae, globular clusters, and the supernova SN 1987A (see fig. 5.25). The telescope is scheduled for repair in 1994.

## SUMMARY

Astronomers detect and measure radiation by means of telescopes and other instruments that are sensitive to different portions of the electromagnetic spectrum. Most radiation from space is blocked by the atmosphere and is investigated by high-altitude balloons, rockets, and orbiting observatories. Ground-based telescopes are used to study light, some ultraviolet and infrared radiation, and most of the radio spectrum.

Optical telescopes are classified according to the way in which light is examined. Refracting telescopes use achromatic objective lenses; reflecting telescopes have primary mirrors.

Various instruments attached to the focus of a telescope serve as detectors to collect, measure, and process data. These accessories include cameras, spectrographs, photometers, and CCD cameras.

When Earth-orbiting satellites were designed to carry telescopes, astronomers were able to investigate the UV and IR regions of the spectrum above the atmosphere. The International Ultraviolet Explorer (IUE) observed hot stars, ionized gases, and supernovae remnants. The Infrared Astronomical Satellite (IRAS) made a comprehensive survey of interstellar dust and gas, point sources within the solar system, and accretion disks surrounding distant stars.

Orbiting observatories also study high-energy radiation, X-rays, and gamma rays. The High Energy Astronomical Observatory (HEAO-2), named Einstein, contained four nested mirror arrays that gave the telescope an angular resolution of a few arc seconds.

Unlike X-rays, gamma rays penetrate into detectors where electron scattering takes place. The resulting electric current is a measure of the intensity of the incident gamma radiation.

The Cosmic Background Explorer (COBE) contains instruments designed to study energy emitted during an early period in the history of the universe.

The most familiar type of radio telescope is the large parabolic reflector, which is a filled-aperture telescope consisting of a continuous surface of sheet metal or wire-mesh construction.

A radio interferometer consists of two or more radio telescopes that are focused upon the same object. This unfilled-aperture system is used to overcome the limitations imposed by the size of single radio telescope. Examples include the Very Large Array (VLA) and the Very Long Baseline Interferometer (VLBI).

There are several ways to increase the light-gathering power of optical telescopes. Multiple-mirror telescopes combine a number of smaller mirrors that work in unison to provide the light-gathering power of one large reflector. The Keck Telescope is a segmented mirror of 36 hexagonal mirrors forming a single concave array 10 m in diameter.

The Hubble Space Telescope is an orbiting 2.4-m reflector capable of producing sharper images than present-day ground-based telescopes. Data from cameras, spectrographs, and photometers are collected and transmitted to Earth by way of communications satellites.

# KEY TERMS

| | |
|---|---|
| achromatic lens | light-gathering power |
| altazimuth mount | magnifying power |
| aperture | Newtonian focus |
| Cassegrain focus | objective lens |
| catadioptric telescope | primary mirror |
| charge-coupled device (CCD) | radio interferometer |
| chromatic aberration | reflecting telescope |
| detector | refracting telescope |
| Doppler effect | resolving power |
| equatorial mount | Schmidt telescope |
| eyepiece | secondary mirror |
| focal length | seeing |
| focal plane | spherical aberration |
| focal point | Zeeman effect |

# PROBLEMS

1. On a clear night, the stars near the horizon appear fainter than the stars overhead. Explain.

2. Describe the optical systems of refracting and reflecting telescopes and how each functions.

3. Name the different regions of the electromagnetic spectrum and explain how each region is investigated.

4. Give the reasons why the largest optical telescopes are reflectors rather than refractors.

5. What are some of the advantages in constructing arrays rather than single radio telescopes?

6. How do high-energy telescopes differ from ground-based optical telescopes?

7. How can the resolving power of a radio array be increased without changing the baseline?

8. Why is the sky blue during the day and orange-red at twilight?

9. In what way does diffraction determine the kind of image formed by starlight entering an optical telescope?

10. List the various aberrations of lenses and mirrors and explain how they are corrected.

11. What property of an optical telescope determines the brightness or intensity of light at the focal point?

12. How is the magnifying power of an optical telescope increased or decreased?

13. Which is brighter, the Moon at low or high magnification? Why?

14. What is the purpose of the aspheric lens of a catadioptric telescope?

15. Find the angular resolution of a VLBI that has a 10,000-km baseline operating on a wavelength of 6 cm.

16. Theoretically, what is the diameter of the smallest lunar crater that can be resolved by the Hubble Space Telescope? Let the angular diameter of the moon equal 1860 arc seconds.

17. If two stars have an angular separation of 1.0 arc second, what size telescope will you need to resolve the stars? Let the wavelength of light equal 550 nm.

# REFERENCES

Allen, David A. 1975. *Infrared, the New Astronomy.* New York: John Wiley and Sons, Inc.

Beatty, J. Kelly. 1985. HST: Astronomy's Greatest Gambit. *Sky and Telescope* 69, no. 5 (May).

Böhm-Vitense, Erica. 1980. Outlook for Ultraviolet Astronomy. In *The Universe at Ultraviolet Wavelengths.* NASA Conference Publication 2171. Greenbelt, Md.: NASA Goddard Space-flight Center.

Bok, Bart J. 1983. The Promise of the Space Telescope. *Mercury* (Astronomical Society of the Pacific) 12, no. 3 (May/June).

Bradt, H., and R. Giacconi, eds. 1973. *X-Ray and Gamma-Ray Astronomy.* Lancaster, Eng.: D. Reidel Publishing Company.

Carter, William E., and Douglas S. Robertson. 1986. Studying the Earth by Very-Long-Baseline Interferometry. *Scientific American* 255, no. 5 (November).

Chaisson, Eric J. 1992. Early Results from the Hubble Space Telescope. *Scientific American* 266, no. 6 (June).

Christiansen, W. N., and J. A. Hogbom. 1985. *Radio Telescopes.* 2d ed. Cambridge: Cambridge University Press.

Culhane, J. Leonard, and Peter W. Sanford. 1981. *X-ray Astronomy.* New York: Charles Scribner's Sons.

Field, George B. 1984. The Future of Space Astronomy. *Mercury* 13, no. 4 (July/August).

Giacconi, Riccardo. 1980. The Einstein X-Ray Observatory. *Scientific American* 242, no. 2 (February).

Gold, Michael. 1984. The Cosmos through Infrared Eyes. *Science 84* (American Association for the Advancement of Science), 5, no. 2 (March).

Gordon, Mark A. 1985. VLBA—A Continent-Sized Radio Telescope. *Sky and Telescope* 69, no. 6 (June).

Gustafson, John R. 1988. The Keck Observatory. *Mercury* 17, no. 2 (March/April).

Harris, Clifford. 1986. Silicon Eye: A CCD Imaging System. *Sky and Telescope* 71, no. 4 (April).

Henden, Arne A., and Ronald H. Kaitchuck. 1982. *Astronomical Photometry.* New York: Van Nostrand Reinhold Company.

Hey, J. S. 1973. *The Evolution of Radio Astronomy.* New York: Science History Publications.

Kniffen, Donald A. 1991. The Gamma Ray Observatory. *Sky and Telescope* 81, no. 5 (May).

Leventhal, Marvin, and Crawford J. MacCallum. 1980. Gamma-Ray-Line Astronomy. *Scientific American* 243, no. 1 (July).

Norris, Ray. 1988. The Australia Telescope. *Sky and Telescope* 76, no. 6 (Dec.).

Pedrotti, Frank L., and Leno S. Pedrotti. 1987. *Introduction to Optics*. Englewood Cliffs, N.J.: Prentice-Hall, Inc.

Tucker, Wallace, and Ricardo Giacconi. 1985. *The X-Ray Universe*. Cambridge, Mass.: Harvard University Press.

Tucker, Wallace, and Karen Tucker. 1986. The Mushrooms of San Augustin. Part One: Building the Very Large Array. *Mercury* 15, no. 5 (Sept./Oct.).

———. 1986. The Mushrooms of San Augustin. Part Two: Using the Very Large Array. *Mercury* 15, no. 6 (Nov./Dec.).

Verschuur, Gerrit L., and Kenneth I. Kellerman, eds. 1974. *Galactic and Extra-Galactic Radio Astronomy*. New York: Springer-Verlag.

chapter

6

an  overview  of  the  solar  system

Apollo 17 astronaut Harrison Schmitt exploring
the surface of the Moon.

A lthough small on the cosmic scale, our solar system is huge in terms of terrestrial standards. The overwhelming distances between the planets became more apparent during the Apollo mission to the Moon. The astronauts required four days to reach our nearest neighbor in space. From the Moon, we viewed the Earth as a planet: a small, living world surrounded by the distant stars. Our home in space seemed far away, yet a voyage to the Moon is merely a small step when compared to the distances of the planets in the solar system.

Our horizons were pushed farther back when unmanned probes were successfully launched to the planets and beyond. Voyages to these other worlds required months and years to complete. To us, planetary distances remain great, but we are reminded that the solar system is no more than a tiny speck in an endless void of stars and galaxies.

## Members of the Solar System

We begin our journey through the solar system with the Sun, a typical star that appears brighter than any other star simply because of its proximity to the Earth and other planets. As the dominant member of the family, the Sun contains over 99% of the total mass of the solar system. It has a diameter of 1,392,000 km, and a volume large enough to contain 1.3 million Earths. To appreciate the size of the Sun, imagine the entire mass of the solar system divided into 1000 parts. Take 998 parts for the Sun and another part to form the planet Jupiter. The remainder represents the mass of all the other members (fig. 6.1).

The planets revolve in elliptical orbits at varying distances from the Sun. Keep in mind that an orbit is simply an abstraction; a curve traced by a planet in space; the apparent path of a body relative to a fixed frame of reference. As Kepler's first law tells us, the apparent orbit of a planet is an ellipse with the

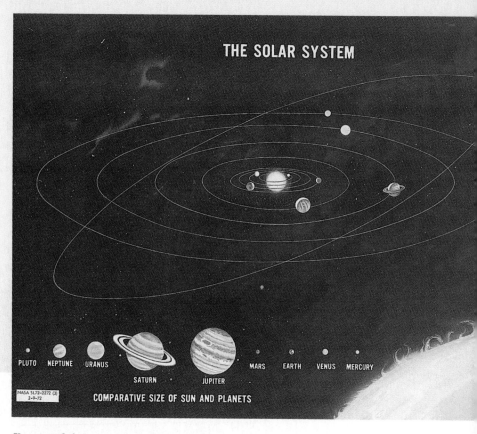

**figure 6.1**
Our solar system, a family of planets revolving around the Sun.

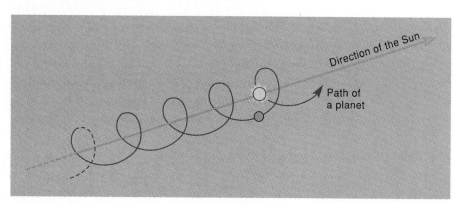

**figure 6.2**
Movement of the Sun and planets through space.

Sun situated at one focal point (see fig. 3.15).

Meanwhile, the Sun is traveling among the stars at the rate of about 19 km/sec in the direction of the constellation Hercules. If the Galaxy is our reference frame rather than the Sun, the apparent orbits of the planets are not closed curves but helices centered on the path traced by the moving Sun (fig. 6.2).

The bodies in the solar system are categorized according to their physical properties and locations. The first group contains the nine **major planets.** In order of average distance from the Sun, they are Mercury, Venus, Earth, Mars, Jupiter, Saturn, Uranus, Neptune, and Pluto. Because of its highly elliptical orbit, Pluto is closer to the Sun than Neptune until the year 1999.

The second class of planets are the **minor planets,** also called **asteroids** (little stars). The asteroids number in the thousands and, in general, are found in orbits between Mars and Jupiter. The largest and first to be discovered, Ceres, has a diameter of only about 1000 km. Most of the asteroids are small, irregular blocks of rock.

Planets may be identified by their positions with respect to the Earth. Mercury and Venus are called **inferior planets** because they are nearer to the Sun than the Earth. The **superior planets** are farther from the Sun than the Earth.

Although there are differences among the major planets in regard to size, density, composition, rotation, revolution, number of satellites, and distance from the Sun, they are conveniently divided into two distinct groups: **terrestrial** and **Jovian planets.** Mercury, Venus, Earth, and Mars are the terrestrial, or Earth-like, planets. They are relatively small bodies of high mean densities, solid surfaces, slow axial rotation, and few if any satellites. The Jovian, or Jupiter-like planets, include Jupiter, Saturn, Uranus, and Neptune. They are enormous spheres of large mass, low densities, extensive atmospheres, rapid rotation, and numerous satellites. Pluto and Mercury are *lesser planets* that can be classified with the Moon and large satellites of the Jovian planets.

Another category of bodies in the solar system are the **satellites,** or moons that revolve about the planets. Most of the solar system's satellites accompany the Jovian planets. The terrestrial planets Mercury and Venus do not have satellites. The Earth has one, the Moon; Mars has two. Altogether there are over 50 known satellites associated with the Jovian planets.

**Meteoroids** are metallic and rocky bodies that permeate the solar system. They range in size from 100-kg blocks to tiny microscopic grains. When they enter and pass through the Earth's atmosphere they become incandescent and appear as bright streaks of light called **meteors.** Larger bodies that do not vaporize reach the surface as **meteorites.**

**Comets** are icy bodies in elongated orbits, many reaching far beyond the orbit of Pluto. They become visible when they approach the Sun and their outer layers vaporize into gaseous and dusty tails.

## Relative Sizes and Distances of the Planets

The planetary system can be better visualized if we scale down the Sun and planets to more familiar dimensions. Picture the radius of the Earth's orbit, 1 AU, or $1.5 \times 10^8$ km, reduced to 1 km. On this scale, the Sun would be a sphere 9.3 m in diameter separated from an 8.5-cm Earth by a distance of 1 km. Note that about 109 Earths placed side by side equal the distance across the Sun. The Moon would be a 2.3-cm sphere 2.7 m from the Earth. Mercury, about one-third of the Earth in size, would be only 3.2 cm in diameter and 400 m from the Sun. Venus would be 8.1 cm in diameter, almost as large as the Earth, and located 723 m from the center of the solar system. Mars would be a little more than half the diameter of Earth, or 4.5 cm across, with an orbital radius of 1.5 km.

In summary, the terrestrial planets are relatively small bodies located near the Sun. The Earth is the largest member of the group, followed by Venus. They are flanked by the planets Mercury, nearest to the Sun, and Mars, which is more distant than the Earth.

Next, there is a wide gap representing the region occupied by the minor planets. Think of the asteroid belt as a thin disk, several kilometers wide, separating the terrestrial and Jovian planets. Imagine this expanse filled with thousands of particles varying in size from 7 mm down to microscopic grains.

Beyond the asteroids, the distances between the planets increase dramatically. In our scaled-down solar system, the first giant planet, Jupiter, would be almost 1 m across, or about 11 times the diameter of Earth, placed 5.2 km from the Sun. Saturn, almost as large as Jupiter, would be 80 cm across, over nine times the size of Earth. Add Saturn's rings and the system would extend to 1.8 m, or almost double the diameter of Jupiter. Saturn would be 9.5 km from the Sun, nearly twice as far away as Jupiter.

Uranus, about 34 cm across or four times larger than Earth, would be located at 19.2 km or twice the distance of

Saturn. Neptune, Uranus's twin, would have a diameter of 32.4 cm and an orbital radius of 30 km, half again as far away. Finally there is little Pluto, which would be only 1.5 cm across, making it the smallest planet and less than half the size of Mercury. Most of the time, Pluto would be farthest from the Sun in an orbit at a mean distance of 39.5 km. Its companion satellite, Charon, would be only 8 mm in diameter and about 13 cm from Pluto.

From the giant planets to distances far beyond the orbit of Pluto, there are billions of icy comets that occasionally swing close to the Sun. To portray these members in our model, think of a tenuous halo of innumerable tiny specks of ice and rock more than 60,000 km from the Sun.

As our model attempts to show, there are vast distances and very little substance within the region of space influenced by the Sun. Yet the solar system seems almost congested with matter when compared with the sizes and distances of the stars. If the Sun were a 9.3-m ball situated 1 km from the Earth, the next star would be another glowing sphere almost 300,000 km away.

## Physical and Photometric Properties of the Planets

Once the size, form, and orientation in space of a planet's orbit are known, it is possible to compute the planet's mass, linear diameter, density, brightness, and reflectivity. These and other data are obtained by means of various detectors introduced in chapter 5.

### Mass

Consider mass as the material content of a planet. The mass of one planet may be found by the gravitational effect of another body. The task is simplified if the planet possesses a satellite. Then the mass of the planet can be computed from the period and mean distance of its companion.

## Finding the Mass of a Planet

The mass of a body can be found by a more definitive interpretation of Kepler's third law. In chapter 3, the law was stated simply as a relationship between a planet's sidereal period ($P$) in years, and the mean distance from the Sun ($a$) in astronomical units:

$$P^2 = a^3.$$

The squares of the periods of any two planets are proportional to the cubes of their mean distances from the Sun, or

$$\frac{P_1^2}{P_2^2} = \frac{a_1^3}{a_2^3}.$$

By rearranging the terms in the equation,

$$\frac{a_1^3}{P_1^2} = \frac{a_2^3}{P_2^2} = \text{a constant (unity)}.$$

When Newton developed the law of universal gravitation, he found the constant in Kepler's third law to be the sum of the mass of the primary body ($M$) and the secondary body ($m$). Newton's derivation of Kepler's law can be written as

$$(M + m) = \frac{a^3}{P^2}$$

where

$(M + m)$ = the combined masses of the Sun and Earth;

$a$ = the astronomical unit ($AU$), the mean distance between the Sun and the Earth; and

$P$ = the sidereal year, the Earth's period of revolution.

The law provides a reliable method of determining the total mass of two revolving bodies such as a planet and its satellite. The motion of the Moon around the Earth is compared with the motion of a satellite around a planet. If the mass of the satellite is ignored, the mass of the planet is found in terms of the Earth-Moon system as unity (see Methods and Understandings 9.1, The Mass of Jupiter).

## Size and Density

The linear diameter (distance measured in km) of a planet may be found by measuring its angular diameter (apparent displacement in arc) with a micrometer mounted on the ocular end of a telescope. The micrometer consists of a fixed and a movable wire attached to a graduated screw. By framing the planet between the wires in the reticle, its apparent diameter in arc seconds can be accurately measured. Knowing the distance between the planet and the Earth, its linear diameter can be computed. Once the diameter and mass of a planet have been found, its volume and mean density are determined.

## Magnitude and Albedo

In the solar system, only the Sun is self-luminous. All other objects shine by reflected sunlight. Whether incandescent or reflective, the measure of brightness of a body is called its *magnitude*. How bright an object appears to be for an observer on the Earth depends upon several factors: its size, distance from the Sun and Earth, and reflectivity.

Bodies that revolve around the Sun are continually changing their distances from the Earth and appear fainter or brighter at different configurations. At opposition, its closest approach to the Earth, a superior planet will reach maximum magnitude. An inferior planet will be brightest between greatest elongation and inferior conjunction. Most comets move in highly elongated orbits and some become bright enough to be seen when they are in the vicinity of the Sun.

The measure of a body's reflectivity, its **albedo,** is defined as the ratio between the amount of light reflected and the amount received from the Sun. Rocky planets and satellites with little or no atmosphere will absorb more and reflect less solar radiation than a planet shrouded in a thick, cloudy layer of opaque gases. A planet with an irregular surface of dark rocks will have a low albedo, while another with a dense atmosphere will have a higher albedo. The albedos of the planets range from a low 0.106 for Mercury to a high 0.650 for Venus. The Earth's albedo of 0.367 lies between these extremes.

## The Inferior Planets Mercury and Venus

Mercury and Venus are as different from one another as the Moon and the Earth.

The nearest planet to the Sun is no more than 4879 km in diameter; larger than Pluto and half again larger than the Moon, but smaller than the largest satellites of Jupiter and Saturn. The albedo of Mercury (0.106) and the Moon (0.12) are about the same, which indicates that they have similar surface structures (fig. 6.3).

The orbit of Mercury has greater **eccentricity** than the other terrestrial planets. Thus its distance from the Sun varies from 46 million km at **perihelion** (closest approach to the Sun) to almost 70 million km at **aphelion** (greatest distance from the Sun). At greatest elongation, the angular separation between Mercury and the Sun varies from a minimum of 18° to a maximum of 28°.

Venus is sometimes referred to as our planet's twin since its diameter of 12,104 km is almost equal to the Earth's 12,756 km. The planet is about 81% as massive as the Earth.

Venus revolves in a nearly circular orbit in a period of 225 days. Its rotational period of 243 days makes a day on Venus longer than its year. Moreover, an axial tilt of 177° to its orbit gives Venus a clockwise rotation.

Mercury

Moon

**figure 6.3**

In some respects, the surface structure of the planet Mercury and the Moon are similar.

## Transits of Mercury and Venus

Transits describe the passage of Mercury or Venus as dark spots across the disk of the Sun. These events can only occur when Mercury or Venus have reached inferior conjunction at or near a *node,* the intersection between a planet's orbit and the ecliptic plane.

At most inferior conjunctions, the planets pass above or below the Sun. In figure 6.4, the Earth is on the *line of nodes* of Mercury's orbit—i.e., the intersection of the planet's orbital plane and the ecliptic plane—at position $E_1$ in May and position $E_3$ in November. Consequently, transits of Mercury can occur only during these months (fig. 6.5). During the rest of this century, transits of Mercury are scheduled for November 6, 1993, and November 15, 1999.

Transits of Venus are extremely rare and happen at eight-year intervals separated by more than a century. As shown in figure 6.4, the Earth passes the line of nodes at position $E_2$ in June and position $E_4$ in December, allowing transits of Venus in these months. The next transits of the planet will be observed on June 8, 2004, and June 6, 2012.

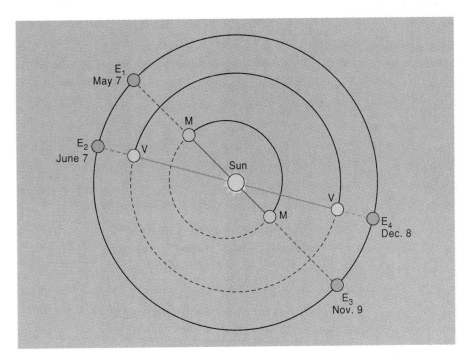

**figure 6.4**

Transits of Mercury and Venus. The Earth passes the line of nodes of Mercury's orbit in May ($E_1$) and November ($E_3$), and the line of nodes of Venus's orbit in June ($E_2$) and December and ($E_4$). If Mercury and Venus are in favorable positions at or near those times, a transit will occur.

99

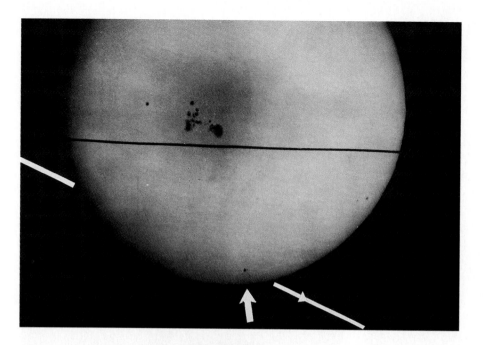

**figure 6.5**

At one time, the transits of Mercury and Venus were used to compute the length of the astronomical unit. The arrow shows the path of Mercury across the solar disk.

# SKY WATCHERS 6.1

## Mercury as the morning and evening star

Due to its proximity to the Sun, Mercury is elusive and difficult to see. The best time to observe the planet is at greatest elongation in the early evening in spring and early morning in autumn, when Mercury is at a high altitude above the horizon.

Figure 6.6a shows the Sun at twilight below the western horizon during spring in the Northern Hemisphere. When Mercury is at greatest elongation east at this time of the year, the ecliptic is north of the celestial equator. A line drawn from the planet to the setting Sun will be almost perpendicular to the observer's horizon, so that the altitude

of Mercury will be about the same as its angular distance from the Sun. A favorable elongation occurs in the beginning of April.

At morning twilight before sunrise in autumn (fig. 6.6b), Mercury will appear at greatest elongation west. Once again, the line between Mercury and the rising Sun is almost vertical.

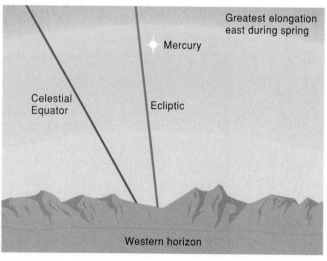

a.                    b.

**figure 6.6**

In the Northern Hemisphere, the best times to view Mercury are *a.* at dusk when it is at greatest eastern elongation, and *b.* at dawn when it is at greatest western elongation.

**figure 6.7**

The crescent Earth as seen from orbit around the Moon.

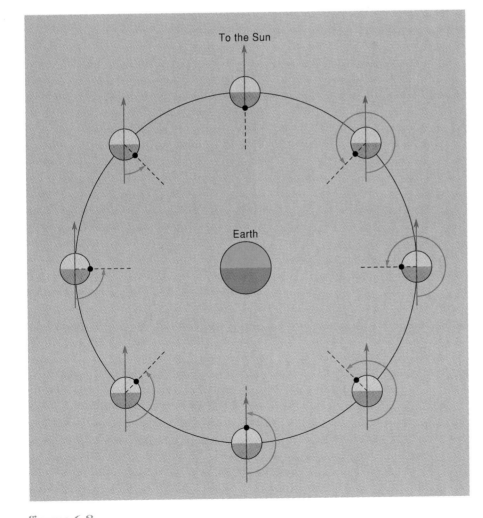

**figure 6.8**

The Moon's synchronous rotation. The Moon completes one rotation for each revolution and thus always keeps the same side facing toward the Earth. A surface feature on the face of the Moon remains in the same position throughout the orbital period.

# The Earth and Moon

Our Earth and the Moon form a unique planet-satellite system (fig. 6.7). Generally, planets are much larger and more massive than their accompanying satellites. The Earth is one of the smaller planets, yet only four satellites of Jupiter and Saturn exceed the Moon in size.

But there are vast differences between these companions in space. The Earth is large enough to retain an atmosphere and has a higher albedo than the airless Moon; therefore, the Earth is brighter than the Moon. If we could view them from a distance of one AU, the Earth would appear as a blue starlike object at −3.86 magnitude. The Moon at +0.21 magnitude would be a yellow point of light alternating positions with the Earth as both revolve around the Sun.

The Moon and most of the satellites of the other planets have periods of rotation that are equal to their sidereal periods of revolution. This *synchronous rotation* causes the Moon to keep the same hemisphere facing the Earth as it rotates and revolves in a period of 27.322 days (fig. 6.8).

## Size and Shape of the Earth

Ancient Greek astronomers knew the Earth was spherical, and Eratosthenes estimated its circumference. But observational proof of its dimensions and form was not obtained until the seventeenth century. By that time, astronomers were accurately measuring the linear distances between cities, and determining the zenith angle of the stars at each location. Moreover, these measurements and the determination of the period of a pendulum at different latitudes proved the Earth to be an oblate spheroid (fig. 6.9).

Earlier, Newton had explained why the Earth is not a perfect sphere. He proposed that axial rotation caused a flattening of the poles thereby reducing the Earth's polar diameter. The modern value for the Earth's polar diameter, 12,713 km, is 43 km less than its equatorial diameter (fig. 6.10).

In 1774, Nevil Maskelyne, Astronomer Royal at Greenwich, England, first determined the mass and density of the Earth by the gravitational attraction of a

chapter 6

astronomy: through space and time

figure 6.9 ▶
An exaggerated figure of the Earth. The difference in angular measurement between the astronomical zenith and the geocentric zenith proved the Earth to be an oblate spheroid. If the Earth was precisely spherical, the astronomical and geocentric zeniths would coincide at all points on the Earth's surface.

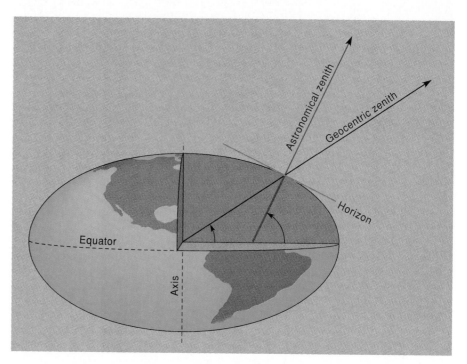

▲ figure 6.10
The Earth from space.

mountain in Perthshire, Scotland. Plumb lines were placed north and south of the mountain, and the angular deviation of the plumb line from the vertical measured the attraction of the mountain. The amount of deflection depends on the distance and mass of the mountain. Its mass was estimated from measurements of its volume and density. Maskelyne compared the attraction of the mountain with the attraction of the Earth and obtained values for the mass and density of the planet.

Later, English scientist Henry Cavendish obtained a more precise value for the Earth's density by means of a torsion pendulum. He attached two small lead spheres to a horizontal arm suspended by a wire. When large spheres were placed close to the smaller spheres, their gravitational attraction caused a slight movement in the arm. The ratio of attraction of the spheres to each other and the attraction of the Earth to their masses gave a value of 5.48 g/cm³ for the mean density of the Earth. The present value is 5.515 g/cm³.

## Distance, Size, and Apparent Orbit of the Moon

We can find the distance to the Moon by using the radius of the Earth as a baseline (fig. 6.11). The angle α (3422″) repre-

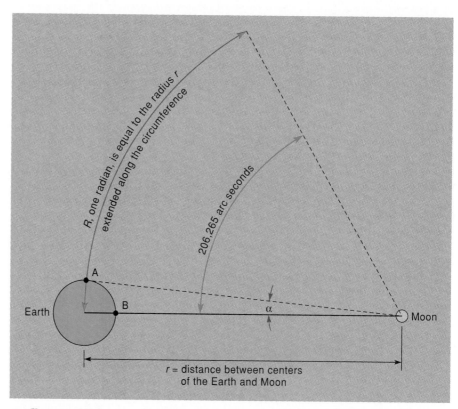

▲ figure 6.11
Measuring the distance to the Moon using the radius of the Earth as the baseline.

sents the displacement or parallax of the Moon against the background stars as seen from points A and B on the surface of the Earth. The distance between the Earth and Moon may be computed in the following way. Construct an arc with

a radius equal to r. Extend the arc for a distance R along the circumference equal in length to the radius, r. Distance R is known as a *radian*. The angle formed by a radian is equal to about 57.29° or 206, 265 arc seconds. Since r = R, the

102

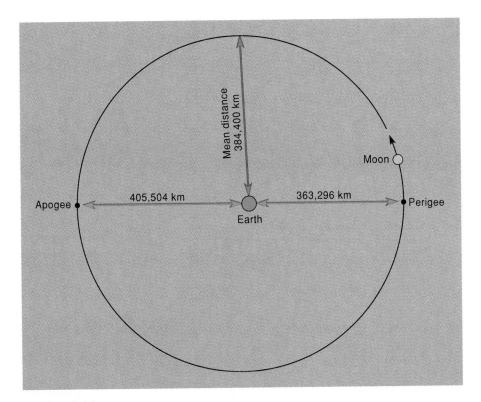

**figure 6.12**

The apparent orbit of the Moon.

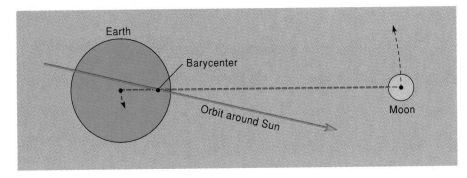

**figure 6.13**

The centers of the Earth and Moon revolve around the barycenter in one sidereal month.

ratio between the distance to the Moon and the radius of the Earth will be equal to the ratio between the angle formed by a radian and the parallax of the Moon.

$$\frac{\text{distance to the Moon}}{\text{radius of the Earth}} = \frac{\text{angle formed by a radian}}{\text{parallax of the Moon}}$$

The distance $r$ between the centers of the Earth and Moon is expressed by

$$r = \frac{206,265 \text{ arcsec} \times 6378 \text{ km}}{3422 \text{ arcsec}}$$
$$r = 384,441 \text{ km}.$$

The Moon revolves in an apparent elliptical orbit with the Earth at one focal point at a mean distance of 384,400 km (fig. 6.12). At **perigee,** nearest to the Earth, 363,296 km separate the two bodies. At **apogee,** farthest from the Earth, they are 405,504 km apart. The Moon's orbital period of 27.322 days is called the **sidereal month.**

The Moon's apparent orbit is not entirely a closed curve. The Earth and Moon revolve around a common center of mass which is located about 1678 km below the Earth's surface (fig. 6.13). It is the center of mass, called the **barycenter,** that follows a smooth orbit around the Sun. The Earth and Moon exchange positions about the barycenter as they trace concave paths around the Sun.

The mass of the Moon may be found from the ratio of the distances of the Earth and Moon from the barycenter to the ratio of their masses. Let the distance from the center of the Earth to the barycenter equal 4700 km, and the distance from the barycenter to the center of the Moon equal 382,000 km. If the mass of the Earth is $5.97 \times 10^{24}$ kg,

$$\frac{\text{mass of the Moon}}{\text{mass of the Earth}} = \frac{\text{distance of the Earth}}{\text{distance of the Moon}}$$

$$\text{mass of the Moon} = \frac{(4700 \text{ km})(5.97 \times 10^{24} \text{ kg})}{382,000 \text{ km}}$$

$$= 7.35 \times 10^{22} \text{ kg}.$$

## The Red Planet Mars

The last terrestrial planet, Mars, lies beyond the Earth at a mean distance of 1.523 AU, or about $227.9 \times 10^6$ km from the Sun. Mars has an equatorial diameter of 6794 km, slightly more than half that of Earth, and at mean opposition an apparent diameter of almost 18 arc seconds. When oppositions occur, it is distinguished as a brilliant orange-red object among the stars of the zodiac. At its closest approach to the Earth, Mars brightens to -2.8 magnitude (see fig. 6.14).

Although Mars has an atmosphere, its albedo is only 0.150, which is comparable to the reflectivity of Mercury (0.106) and not the Earth (0.367) or Venus (0.650). The atmosphere of Mars is thin, so that a greater percentage of radiation is reflected by its surface rather than its atmosphere.

Mars is half the size of the Earth but its mass is only 0.11 (Earth's mass = 1), and its mean density only 3.94 gm/cm³. Thus in some respects Mars is like the Moon as well as a terrestrial planet.

However, Mars does resemble our planet in other ways. Its rotational period of 24h 37m is almost equal to a day on the Earth. When the planet is observed through a telescope, the same surface features are seen at about the same hour on successive nights. But the difference of 37m in rotation between the

**figure 6.14**
Mars as seen from the Viking orbiter, showing prominent volcanoes and the canyon Valles Marineris in the lower center.

Earth and Mars causes a gradual change of the hemisphere facing the observer. In addition, Mars is inclined on its axis by about the same number of degrees as the Earth. The planet's equator is tilted 25.2° to its orbital plane compared to the Earth's 23.5°.

## Oppositions of Mars

Mars does not reach maximum brilliance at every opposition. The reason lies in the eccentricity of its orbit of 0.093, which is greater than the other planets except Mercury and Pluto. Because the orbit of the Earth is almost circular, the distance between Mars and the Earth at opposition will vary from a minimum of $54.5 \times 10^6$ km to a maximum of $102.6 \times 10^6$ km.

Favorable oppositions occur during the months of August and September

**figure 6.15**

A Hubble Space Telescope composite image of Mars taken in December 1990, shortly after opposition. The dark feature near the center is Syrtis Major planitia, which is believed to be composed of coarse sand deposits.

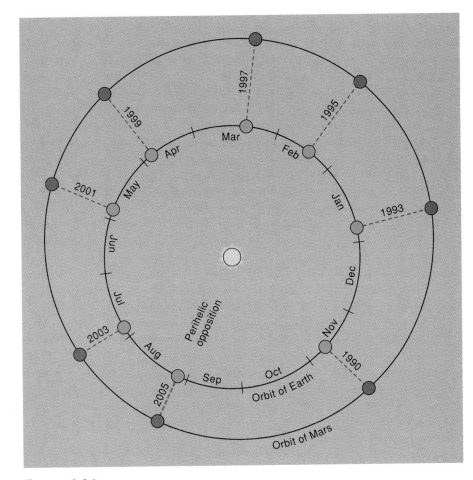

**figure 6.16**

Mars comes to perihelic opposition in 2005.

when Mars is near perihelion (fig. 6.15). Because the synodic period of the planet is equal to 779.91 days, or about 49 days longer than two years, oppositions advance and return again to a favorable position every 15 to 17 years. As a contributing factor, the Earth reaches aphelion a short time before a perihelic opposition with Mars, making it the most favorable opposition (fig. 6.16).

## The Giant Planets Jupiter and Saturn

Jupiter (see fig. 6.17) is distinguished as the second brightest planet. At mean opposition, the visual magnitude of Jupiter reaches −2.70, indicating a high albedo of 0.50. The planet's mean distance from the sun is $777.8 \times 10^6$ km. The inclination of Jupiter's axis to its orbital plane is only 3.0°, less than all the planets except Mercury. Jupiter reaches opposition every 399 days.

The planet is impressive in its dimensions as well as its visual appearance. An equatorial diameter of 142,984 km gives Jupiter a volume greater than 1300 times the Earth. Yet its mean density is only 1.33 g/cm$^3$. These values indicate that Jupiter does not possess the rocky surface of a terrestrial planet but is a vast sphere of hydrogen and helium layers extending down to a small, compressed core.

Another feature of Jupiter is the oval shape of its disk. The oblate form is the result of its rapid rotation in 9h 56m. A point on Jupiter's equator will revolve at 754 km/m, or about 27 times as fast as a point on the Earth's equator.

Jupiter has 16 satellites; the four brightest, Io, Europa, Ganymede and Callisto, are the Galilean moons, so called because they were discovered by Galileo in 1610. Of the remaining satellites, three were found during the flybys of Voyagers 1 and 2 in 1979.

Saturn, second to Jupiter in size, is 120,536 km across at its equator (see fig. 6.17). The planet spins rapidly on its axis in a period of 10h 30m, causing a pronounced equatorial bulge. Saturn has a low mean density, only 0.70 g/cm$^3$, which is less than the density of water. Like Jupiter, Saturn is composed of lighter elements that form an extensive atmosphere around a dense core.

◄ Jupiter ▲ Saturn

**figure 6.17**

Close-up views of Jupiter and Saturn, photographed by the Voyager spacecraft.

**figure 6.18**

The rings of Saturn as seen from Earth when the planet is at different locations in its orbit.

Saturn has a visual magnitude of +0.67 and an albedo of 0.47. From the Earth, it appears straw yellow, similar in color to the bright star Pollux in Gemini.

But the most impressive feature of Saturn is its ring system. The other Jovian planets also have particle rings revolving in the equatorial plane, but they are most tenuous and cannot be viewed directly through a telescope.

From Earth, the rings do not always appear the same because Saturn's equator and rings are inclined 26.7° to the plane of the orbit (fig. 6.18). As the planet revolves around the Sun, the planet's axis and rings maintain the same orientation in space. Consequently, in a sidereal period of 29.46 years, the Sun will alternately shine on the north or upper side and the south or lower side of the rings. At other times the rings appear edge-on.

In addition to its ring system, Saturn has nine satellites that are visible from the Earth. Nine more were discovered during the Voyager flybys in 1980 and 1981.

## Uranus, Neptune, and Pluto

From antiquity, Saturn was believed to be the most distant planet from the Sun. Then, in 1781, William Herschel found a hazy disk that he first identified as the nucleus of a comet. Further observations of its motion confirmed the object to be a new planet which was designated Uranus to conform with the mythological names of the other planets.

Uranus

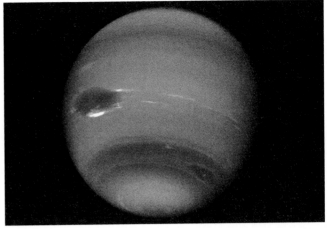

Neptune

▲ **figure 6.19**
Voyager 2 images of Uranus and Neptune.

Uranus reaches a visual magnitude of +5.52, which is bright enough to be seen with the unaided eye. Before its discovery, the planet had been mistakenly recorded as a star by several observers. These earlier sightings helped determine the orbit of the planet.

After its discovery, Uranus showed a difference in its computed and observed orbital positions. By the 1840s, astronomers were investigating the possibility that the irregularities were caused by the gravitational influence of an unknown planet.

The French astronomer Urbain Jean Joseph Leverrier applied Newton's gravitational theory to determine the mass and probable distance of a planet beyond Uranus. His computations placed the unknown planet in the constellation Capricornus and estimated its angular diameter at three arc seconds. In 1846, at Berlin Observatory, Johann Gottfried Galle found the planet within a degree of its predicted position. Earlier, the English astronomer John Couch Adams had independently arrived at the same results as Leverrier, and both share in the discovery of Neptune.

Owing to the distances of Uranus and Neptune, their physical properties remained virtually unknown until the successful flyby mission of Voyager 2 (fig. 6.19). In the telescope, their images appear as small green disks. Uranus and Neptune have about the same diameters and possess atmospheres of hydrogen and methane.

The discovery of Neptune was a triumph for the application of Newton's

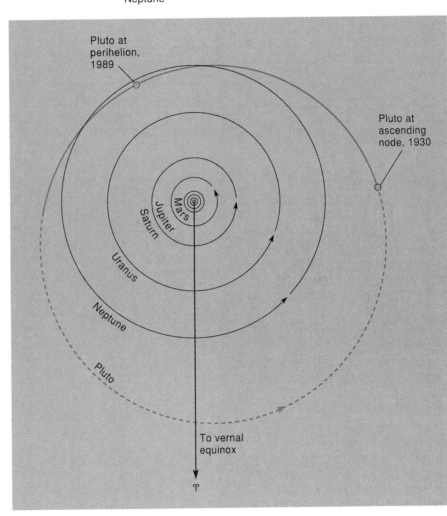

**figure 6.20**
Orbits of the major planets. Pluto has a highly eccentric orbit.

laws to the motions of the planets. Since some of Uranus's perturbations could not be explained, a search for a trans-Neptunian planet continued through the nineteenth and into the twentieth century. Finally in 1930, after a painstaking search along the ecliptic, Clyde Tombaugh discovered Pluto in the di-

rection of the stars in Gemini. Later, astronomers found that Pluto does not have sufficient mass to cause the perturbations of the orbit of Uranus that led to Tombaugh's discovery.

When the discovery was confirmed and its orbit determined, Pluto revealed unexpected properties (fig. 6.20). At a

107

mean distance of 39.4 AU and an orbital eccentricity of 0.246, Pluto at perihelion is nearer to the Sun than Neptune. The planet requires 248 years to complete one revolution. Pluto's satellite, Charon, was detected in 1978.

## Asteroids and Comets

Most of the asteroids, or minor planets, occupy orbits in the wide gap separating the terrestrial and Jovian planets. Thousands of asteroids are known, which suggests that they are fragments of larger bodies that once occupied the region between Mars and Jupiter called the *asteroid belt.*

Not all asteroids are restricted to the asteroid belt. There are others that travel to within 30 million km of the Sun. Some of these interlopers are Earth-grazers and approach within 1 million km of our planet. Can an asteroid collide with the Earth? The surfaces of the Earth, Moon, and other planets and satellites give ample evidence of earlier collisions with asteroid-type bodies. Large blocks of rock and metal continue to strike the Earth, but recent falls have not attained the size needed to inflict catastrophic damage. The metallic and stony bodies of different sizes that do reach the surface of the Earth are called meteorites. The largest known meteorite weighs about 64 tons.

Astronomers believe that a cloud of a trillion or more comets extends tens of thousands of astronomical units into interstellar space. At these distances, comets exist as chunks of ice mixed with light particles of carbon, hydrogen, oxygen, and nitrogen as well as dust grains composed of silicates and iron.

From time to time, a comet falls inward toward the Sun. These are *long-period comets* that require hundreds of years to complete one revolution around the Sun. The gravitational attraction of a massive Jovian planet might change a comet's orbit into one of small eccentricity. Such *short-period comets* remain in the solar system in orbits similar to those occupied by Earth-crossing asteroids. Comet Halley is the most famous short-period comet.

When a comet approaches the Sun, its outer layers vaporize and form a dust and gas envelope, or *coma,* around the solid nucleus. Radiation pressure of the Sun forces the material in the coma away from the direction of the Sun into dust and gas tails. Billions of particles are left in the comet's wake as interplanetary dust. The Earth encounters cometary debris, which enters the atmosphere at high speed. The particles are heated to incandescence and form bright streaks called meteors.

## The Evolution of the Solar System

Although the origin of the solar system is not entirely understood, we can determine its age and probable formation through the observation of young stars, the analysis of chemical abundances, and evidence from theoretical studies. The age of the Earth and meteorites can be found by the isotopic analysis of rubidium and uranium-bearing minerals. In 4.5 billion years, half of a quantity of uranium, $^{238}_{92}U$, will disintegrate to lead, $^{206}_{82}Pb$, and helium, $^4_2He$. The present abundance of these isotopes indicates that the solar system had its beginning about 4.6 billion years ago. The Sun and stars were formed out of the clouds of dust and gas found in the spiral arms of the Galaxy. The nature of the clouds and how they become stars is treated in chapter 15. Here our concern will be the role they played in the birth of our planetary system.

A model describing the evolution of the Sun and planets must account for the regularities found within the system. With the exception of Mercury, Mars, and Pluto, the planets revolve in almost circular orbits inclined to each other by only a few degrees. There seems to be a regularity in the distances between planets. All the planets and most of the satellites revolve in the same direction.

Recent models of the origin of the planets as well as those proposed centuries ago fall into two distinct groups, the *catastrophic theory* and the *nebular theory.* The first was suggested by G. L. Buffon in 1749. He believed that the

planets were fragments ejected from the Sun by the impact of a large comet. The second was described by Immanuel Kant in 1755 and further developed by Pierre-Simon Laplace in 1796. According to the nebular theory, the primitive Sun consisted of a nucleus of gas surrounded by a slowly spinning cloud. As the nebula contracted, its rotation caused a series of rings to form in the equatorial plane of the primitive Sun. The material in each ring eventually became planets and their satellites (fig. 6.21).

The elegant nebular scheme of Laplace does not conform with fundamental physical laws, in particular, the principle of *conservation of angular momentum.* The angular momentum of a point on a spinning body is defined as the product of its mass and velocity, and its distance from the center of revolution. In an ideal revolving system, the total angular momentum will remain constant. To conserve its angular momentum, a point on a contracting nebula will increase in velocity as the radius of the nebula decreases in length (fig. 6.22).

Accordingly, the cloud should evolve into a rapidly spinning star possessing most of the angular momentum. But the Sun spins slowly in a period of about 25 days and contributes less than 1% of the total angular momentum of the solar system. The remaining 99% is distributed among the planets.

A version of the catastrophic theory involving the collision or near collision of the Sun and a passing star was proposed to account for the transfer of angular momentum from the Sun to the planets. In the *tidal theory,* the gravitational attraction of the star caused a bulge of solar material to break away and form into the members of the solar system.

But it is unlikely that a stream of solar gas would condense into regularly spaced planets. Instead, the material would have been dispersed by the radiation pressure of the Sun.

### A Modern Nebular Theory

Today, an updated version of Laplace's theory provides a logically consistent model for the origin of the Sun as well

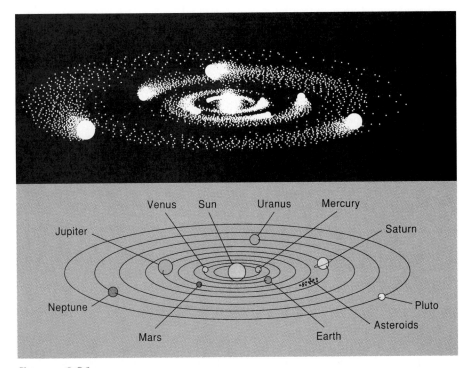

**figure 6.21**

The nebular hypothesis of Pierre-Simon Laplace.

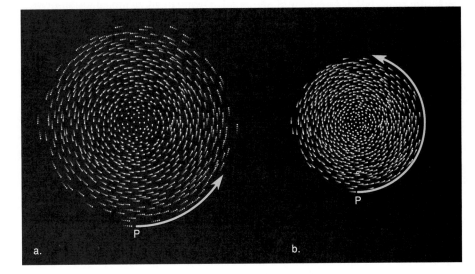

**figure 6.22**

*a.* A particle, P, on the periphery of a collapsing solar nebula. *b.* As the nebula contracts, the particle will increase in velocity, thus conserving its angular momentum.

as the formation of the planets. Our present understanding indicates that there must have been a time when a flat disk of small solid bodies, or **planetesimals,** and gas surrounded the young evolving Sun. The formation of such a protoplanetary disk is not an unusual event in the history of a star.

In 1984, an analysis of IRAS data revealed an excess of far-infrared radiation from the bright star α Lyrae (Vega). The low temperature of the radiation is interpreted as evidence of a disk of protoplanetary material. Later, other stars, ε Eridani and β Pictoris, were discovered to have similar IR excess. At present, a dozen or more stars are known to have disks representing an early phase of planetary formation.

Further evidence for the source of protoplanetary material can be found in the abundances of certain chemical elements in the interstellar nebulae, the Sun, and the planets. The ratio of deuterium to hydrogen in the atmosphere of Jupiter is about the same as in the interstellar clouds. But in the Sun, the ratio of the same substances is found to be less by a factor of 100. Since the Sun formed out of a cosmic cloud, there must have been a time when more deuterium was present. The depletion occurred when deuterium took part in thermonuclear fusion at an early period in the Sun's formation. Evidently, the protoplanetary material detached from the contracting nebula and retained its chemical abundances prior to thermonuclear ignition in the evolving Sun (see fig. 6.23).

Another scenario points to a link between the evolution of the solar system and the destruction of a nearby massive star. In a supernova explosion, a shock wave is transmitted through the interstellar medium. On reaching a denser fragment of nebulosity, the shock wave compresses the cloud and triggers its collapse. Finally, the solar cloud is seeded with heavy elements from the core of the supernova.

**figure 6.23**

The Omega nebula consists of hydrogen gas and dust where stars are formed.

## Formation of the Sun and Planets

About five billion years ago, a huge nebula of dust and gas in one of the spiral arms of the Galaxy fragmented into a large number of spherical clouds. One of these globules was to become the Sun and planets. At this point, the cloud was about 100,000 AU in diameter and possessed a slow axial spin. A density wave within the spiral arm and perhaps a nearby supernova explosion caused the cloud to collapse into a **solar nebula.** As contraction continued and rotational speed increased, the solar nebula flattened at the poles and extended its equatorial diameter into a lens-shaped disk. At the same time, there was an increase in temperature and density towards the center of the collapsing mass.

In the gaseous disk, interstellar dust acted as nuclei, providing surfaces for molecules to condense into small particles. In the outer region of the disk where the Jovian planets were to form, the temperature was low (100 K-400 K) and molecules condensed into crystals of water ice. Near the contracting **protosun,** where the terrestrial planets were to form, the temperature was high enough (500 K-1600 K) to allow only the heavier elements and compounds such as metals and silicates to condense.

At some time, the revolving disk separated into concentric rings at distances presently occupied by the planets. In the rings, condensates moved about erratically, collided, and joined together to form grains. Eventually, the grains collected into larger bodies, planetesimals, which ranged up to kilometers in diameter. Then the planetesimals grouped into larger **protoplanets** that cleared the detritus in the rings as they gained more mass through gravitational accretion.

In the inner orbits, contraction of the protoplanets' cores raised temperatures

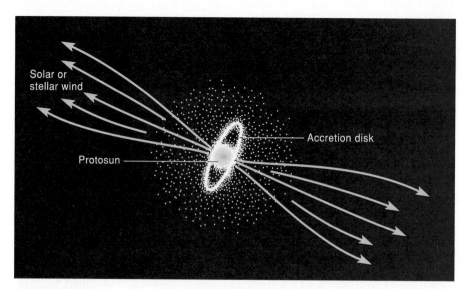

**figure 6.24**
The Sun as a young T Tauri star. Matter is swept into bipolar jets by the solar wind.

above 1000 K. Radioactive elements further increased temperatures to above the melting point of rock and metals. The heavier metallic elements iron and nickel settled to the cores; the less-dense silicates differentiated into layers between the cores and surfaces of the new planets.

In contrast to the region where the terrestrial planets formed, in the outer rings the planetesimals were composed of ice. As protoplanets accreted, the ice was heated and vaporized while the hydrogen and helium in the rings shrouded the evolving planets with thick atmospheres. The rapidly spinning protoplanets formed equatorial disks that evolved into rings and satellites of the giant planets.

The region between Mars and Jupiter was a transitional zone where hundreds of thousands of asteroid-size planetesimals evolved. The chemical composition of the protoplanets was determined by distances from the Sun. The original asteroids on the inner boundary of the zone contained the heavier elements

found in the terrestrial planets. The more distant members in the outer regions were rich in silicates similar to the grains of the accretion disk.

Owing to gravitational instability, the original asteroids did not accumulate into a planet. It is believed that the perturbations of Jupiter and disintegration through collisions created the multitude of fragments found in the present asteroid system.

At this stage, the protosun was an active T Tauri star, a young protostar with an energetic stellar wind (fig. 6.24). The star was surrounded by an accretion disk, while a sizable portion of its mass was ejected as bipolar jets. Like the Sun, T Tauri stars possess slow rotational speeds. The loss of energy of rotation may be the result of mass ejection in the stellar wind. Also, the sporadic flareups known to occur in T Tauri stars, and perhaps in the protosun, may have stripped away much of the uncombined gas and fine grains that remained in the emerging planetary system.

## SUMMARY

The planets and other members of the solar system form a group of bodies separated by vast distances from the nearest stars. The Sun, the central body of the system, is a typical star and appears brighter than any other star because of its proximity to the Earth.

The principal members of the solar system are the planets, which revolve in elliptical orbits at different distances from the Sun. These planets are divided into various classes according to their physical properties and locations.

There are nine major planets; in order of distance from the Sun they are Mercury, Venus, Earth, Mars, Jupiter, Saturn, Uranus, Neptune, and Pluto. The terrestrial planets are Mercury, Venus, Earth, and Mars. They are small planets of high mean densities, with solid surfaces, slow axial rotation, and few if any satellites.

The Jovian planets include Jupiter, Saturn, Uranus, and Neptune. They are enormous spheres of large mass, low densities, extensive atmospheres, rapid rotation, and numerous satellites.

Minor planets are also referred to as asteroids. The asteroids number in the thousands and, in general, occupy orbits between Mars and Jupiter.

Another category of solar-system objects is the satellites that revolve around the planets. Altogether there are over 50 satellites, most of which are associated with the Jovian planets. Among the terrestrial planets, the Earth has one—the Moon—while Mars has two. Pluto has one satellite.

The smaller members of the solar system include meteoroids, which are metallic and rocky particles that permeate interplanetary space. Meteors are bright streaks made by meteoroids as they vaporize in the Earth's atmosphere. Larger bodies that reach the Earth's surface are called meteorites. Comets move in elongated orbits that extend from beyond the orbits of the planets to the vicinity of the Sun.

The solar system began about five billion years ago, when a huge interstellar cloud of dust and gas fragmented and contracted into a solar nebula. As contraction continued and rotational speed increased, the solar nebula flattened at the poles and extended its equatorial diameter into a gaseous disk. In the outer region of the disk, molecules condensed into water ice. In the inner region, the temperature was high enough to condense only metals and silicates.

The revolving disk separated into rings at distances now occupied by the planets. In the rings, particles collected into larger planetesimals and, by accretion, into protoplanets.

The terrestrial planets formed in the inner orbits where protoplanets contained the heavy elements. Protoplanets in the outer orbits were composed of ice, hydrogen, and helium that accreted into the Jovian planets. Equatorial disks formed the particle rings and satellites of the giant planets.

# KEY TERMS

| | |
|---|---|
| albedo | meteoroid |
| aphelion | minor planet |
| apogee | perigee |
| asteroid | perihelion |
| barycenter | planetesimal |
| comet | protoplanet |
| eccentricity | protosun |
| inferior planet | satellite |
| Jovian planet | sidereal month |
| major planet | solar nebula |
| meteor | superior planet |
| meteorite | terrestrial planet |

# PROBLEMS

1. List the physical characteristics of the planets and describe the differences between the Jovian and terrestrial planets.

2. If a rotating interstellar cloud contracts into a protostar, will its period of rotation increase, decrease, or remain the same? Give the reason for your answer.

3. If a planet is observed at an elongation of 85°, is it an inferior or superior planet? Why?

4. Describe the changes in the appearance of Saturn's rings during one revolution of the planet.

5. How does a modern version of the nebular theory account for the physical, chemical, and dynamic properties of the solar system?

6. At opposition, Mars does not always reach maximum brilliance. Why?

7. Describe the currently accepted theory of the origin of the solar system.

8. Explain why transits of Mercury and Venus do not occur each time the planets are at inferior conjunction.

9. When is the best time of the year to observe Mercury as an evening star? Why?

10. If an asteroid has a sidereal period of two years, how often will it reach opposition?

11. Ceres has a mean distance of 2.77 AU. Find its sidereal period.

12. Compute the volume of Jupiter expressed in terms of the Earth's volume. (Let the Earth's radius = 1.)

13. Suppose an inferior planet in a circular orbit has a greatest elongation equal to 30°. How far is the planet from the Sun?

14. Find the sidereal period of the planet in problem 13.

15. You are on Planet X in orbit around a star, Alpha, which is identical to the Sun. Planet X is four times as far from Alpha as the Earth is from the Sun. What is the sidereal period of Planet X?

# REFERENCES

Aumann, H. H. 1985. IRAS Observations of Matter Around Nearby Stars. *Publications of the Astronomical Society of the Pacific* 97, no. 596 (October). San Francisco: Astronomical Society of the Pacific.

Boss, Alan P. 1989. Low-Mass Star and Planet Formation. *Publications of the Astronomical Society of the Pacific* 101, no. 643 (September).

Dermott, S. F., ed. 1976. *The Origin of the Solar System.* New York: John Wiley and Sons, Inc.

Moore, Patrick. 1989. The Discovery of Neptune. *Mercury* (Astronomical Society of the Pacific) 18, no. 4 (July/August).

Nieto, Michael Martin. 1972. *The Titius-Bode Law of Planetary Distances.* Oxford: Pergamon Press.

Reynolds, John H. 1960. The Age of the Elements in the Solar System. *Scientific American* 203, no. 5 (November).

Schramm, David N., Robert M. Clayton. 1978. Did a Supernova Trigger the Formation of the Solar System? *Scientific American* 239, no. 4 (October).

Smart, W. M. 1979. *Textbook on Spherical Astronomy.* 6th ed. Revised by R. M. Green, Cambridge: Cambridge University Press.

Stahler, Steven W. 1988. Understanding Young Stars: A History. *Publications of the Astronomical Society of the Pacific* 100, no. 634 (December).

Tombaugh, Clyde W. 1986. The Discovery of Pluto. *Mercury* 15, no. 3 (May/June).

U.S. Naval Observatory. Nautical Almanac Office. 1989. *The Astronomical Almanac.* Washington, D.C.: U.S. Government Printing Office.

# chapter

# 7

## the earth and moon system

The Earth and Moon from the Galileo
spacecraft on its way to Jupiter.

A bout five billion years ago, the Earth ac-creted into a sphere greater in size than its present diameter. As mass accumulated, the planet compressed and formed a dense core. The contraction, accompanied by the fission of radioactive elements, increased the temperature to the melting point of metals and rock.

The gravitational accretion and radio-active heating triggered a new stage in the development of the Earth. The mixture of metals and rock in the partially molten planet separated into zones by a process called *differentiation.* The heavy metals, iron and nickel, settled into the **core,** while a **mantle** of dense silicates formed above the core. Lighter silicates floated to the surface, cooled, and became the Earth's **crust.** Finally, fountains and geysers of molten rock squeezed out of the mantle, adding to the developing crust (fig. 7.1). Cracks and fissures vented gases that rose above the surface and formed a primitive atmosphere.

High in the cooler upper atmosphere, water vapor condensed into thick clouds that shielded the surface from the rays of the Sun. Rain fell but evaporated before reaching the hot lava plains. Eventually the temperature dropped sufficiently for the waters to remain on the surface and collect in shallow basins. All this time, volcanic activity continued to build up the surface and supply atmospheric gases.

It rained continuously for thousands of years. Water poured from the highlands in streams and rivers that carried dissolved salts and other minerals from the crust into newly formed seas. At last, the intense volcanic activity subsided, the incessant rains stopped, the skies cleared, and the Sun's rays bathed the primeval oceans and landforms of the emergent planet.

**figure 7.1**
Eruption of volcanic material expelled from a vent.

## The Interior Structure and Composition of the Earth

Our understanding of the Earth's interior is based largely upon observations of seismic waves produced by earthquakes and underground nuclear testing. Such waves travel through the Earth and are refracted and reflected by layers of different density and elasticity. There are two types of seismic waves: primary *P-waves* and secondary *S-waves.* P-waves travel at about 10 km/sec. As longitudinal waves, they alternately compress and stretch the Earth in the direction of propagation. S-waves advance at approximately 5 km/sec. As tranverse waves, they cause the Earth to shake at right angles to the direction of travel. S-waves are absorbed upon entering molten regions within the Earth.

A boundary or **discontinuity** exists at several depths marking the interface between zones of different density and composition (fig. 7.2, top). The nearest to the surface is the *Mohorovičić Discontinuity,* or *Moho,* which separates the crust and the mantle. Its depth varies with the thickness of the crust from 10 km below the ocean floor to 30 km below the continents. Additional discontinuities exist at the boundary of the upper and lower mantle.

There are regions on the surface called shadow zones where P- and S-waves reflected from the interior are not detected on the surface. The locations of the

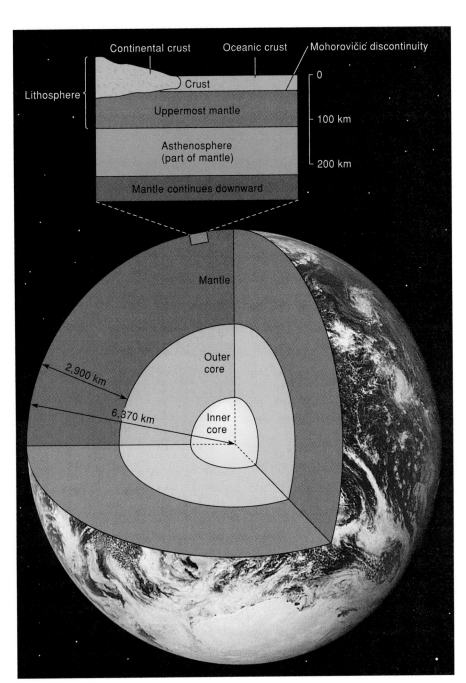

**figure 7.2**

Cross-section through the Earth. *(Top)* The relationship of the upper layers. The crust ranges in thickness from 5 km to 50 km. *(Bottom)* The relationship of the mantle and core. The equatorial radius of the Earth is 6378 km; the polar radius is 6356 km.

shadow zones indicate a discontinuity between the mantle and the core at a depth of 2900 km (fig. 7.2, bottom). Above this discontinuity, S-waves travel unrestricted, proving the mantle to be made of rock. Below the boundary where the S-waves are absorbed, the core is in a molten state. When P-waves enter the core, they are refracted and increase in velocity. The changes show the presence of a solid inner core of the same composition as the liquid outer core.

## The Inner and Outer Cores

Since the late 1950s, a global network of seismographic stations has monitored earthquakes and underground nuclear explosions. Results from these observations have provided an understanding of the structure and composition of the Earth's center.

The inner core has a radius of about 1220 km, a little less than the radius of the Moon. The density of the core is estimated to be about 17 gm/cm³, which agrees with the value that iron and nickel would have at the calculated pressures found at the center.

The solid inner core is enclosed by a transitional zone about 500 km thick. Above the transitional zone is the 1700-km-thick outer liquid core, making the entire core almost twice the size of the Moon. Because the fluid outer core is capable of conducting an electric current, it is the likely source of an induced magnetic field. Electric currents are maintained by the dynamo action of the spinning core.

## The Mantle

The most extensive layer, the mantle, represents nearly 70% of the Earth's mass. As described previously, the Mohorovičić discontinuity marks the boundary of the mantle and the crust (fig. 7.2). From the Moho, the mantle continues down to the narrow boundary above the liquid outer core. A density ranging from 3.3 gm/cm$^3$ below the crust to 5.6 gm/cm$^3$ above the core is evidence that the mantle is made of silicates rather than metals.

Evidence for the composition of the upper mantle has come from extraterrestrial and terrestrial sources. Stony meteorites contain various silicates and oxides in the same proportions as in certain igneous rocks on the Earth. Assuming a similar composition for the Earth, the mantle should consist of silicates containing oxides of magnesium, iron, aluminum, and calcium. Moreover, the Earth's crust contains intrusions of igneous rock from the upper mantle that give further evidence of the Earth's interior composition.

## The Crust

The crust is defined as the solid portion of the Earth above the Moho. The crust is a very thin layer or veneer of rock that makes up the continents and the ocean floors. Continental crust varies in thickness from region to region but averages about 35 km in depth. It consists of a variety of granitic rock that is rich in aluminum silicates of lower density (2.7 gm/cm$^3$). Sedimentary rock, formed by the accumulation of sediment, extends over large areas of continental crust. Oceanic crust varies between 5 to 12 km in thickness and is made of basaltic rock containing iron and magnesium of higher density (3.0 gm/cm$^3$). Table 7.1 compares oceanic and continental crust.

Intrusions of igneous rock indicate a relationship between the crust and the upper mantle. Indeed, the outer part of the Earth, called the **lithosphere,** includes the crust and a thin layer of the upper mantle.

## Table 7.1

### characteristics of oceanic crust and continental crust

| | Oceanic Crust | Continental Crust |
|---|---|---|
| Thickness | 7 km | 30 to 50 km (thickest under mountains) |
| Seismic P-wave velocity | 7 km/second | 6 km/second (higher in lower crust) |
| Density | 3.0 gm/cm$^3$ | 2.7 gm/cm$^3$ |
| Probable composition | Basalt (gabbro in lower crust) | Granite, other plutonic rocks, schist, gneiss (with sedimentary rock cover) |

From Charles C. Plummer and David McGeary, *Physical Geology*, 4th ed. Copyright © 1988 Wm. C. Brown Communications, Inc., Dubuque, Iowa. All Rights Reserved. Reprinted by permission.

Continental lithosphere varies in thickness from 100 km to 150 km while oceanic lithosphere ranges from 10 to less than 100 km thick.

## Continental Drift and Plate Tectonics

The similar shapes of several continents, the east coast of South America and west coast of Africa in particular, led German meteorologist Alfred Wegener in 1912 to propose the hypothesis of continental drift. About 200 million years ago, all the land masses were joined together in one large supercontinent, Pangaea. About 50 million years later, Pangaea divided into two large continents, Laurasia and Gondwanaland. Laurasia fragmented into North America, Europe, and Asia, while most of Gondwanaland became South America, Africa, Antarctica, and Australia (fig. 7.3). The hypothesis explained why the east coast of South America and the west coast of Africa appear to fit together like two pieces of a puzzle. In the 1960s, exploration of the seafloor provided data that confirmed continental drift and led to the concept of **plate tectonics**.

The theory of plate tectonics describes the processes that produce changes in the Earth's crust and upper mantle. The rigid lithosphere is divided into a pattern of slabs or plates floating on a hot plastic layer called the *asthenosphere* (fig. 7.4). The plates are moving with respect

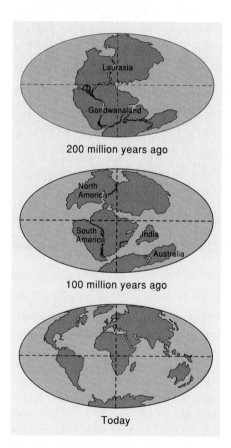

**figure 7.3**

The breakup of Pangaea and subsequent continental drift.

to each other, separating continents and forming new oceans.

Where the plates come together, or where they separate, there are regions of earthquakes and volcanic activity. Stresses crack the surface rock and produce rift valleys that widen and eventu-

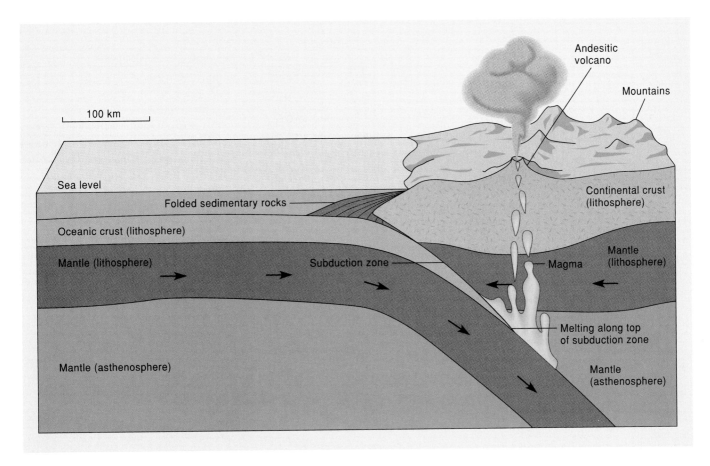

**figure 7.4**
Magma forming at a converging plate boundary.

ally become part of the sea. On the ocean floor, the upwelling of magma from the asthenosphere causes seafloor spreading along the length of mid-oceanic ridges (fig. 7.5). Evidence for seafloor spreading was obtained by means of drill cores removed from the ocean floor. Cores nearest to the ridges contain young crust with the least sedimentation, while the more distant samples are older and have deeper layers of sediments.

Moreover, successive reversals of the Earth's magnetic field were recorded as bands of alternating magnetic polarity duplicated on both sides of the ridge. These investigations confirmed that the basalt rock of the ocean floor is of the same age and magnetic polarity at equal distances on either side of a mid-oceanic ridge. Seafloor spreading carries the new lithosphere away from the ridge as additional magma rises to the ocean floor. Equilibrium is maintained as equal amounts of lithosphere are returned to

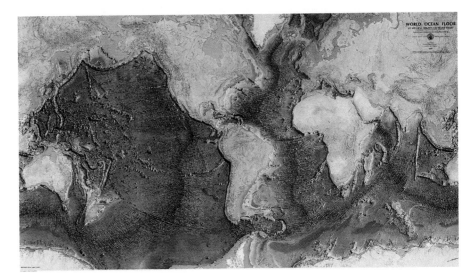

**figure 7.5**
The ocean floors of the Earth. Seafloor spreading occurs as magma from the upper mantle intrudes rift valleys along mid-oceanic ridges.
"World Ocean Floor," by Bruce C. Heezen and Marie Tharp, 1977. Copyright by Marie Tharp, 1977.

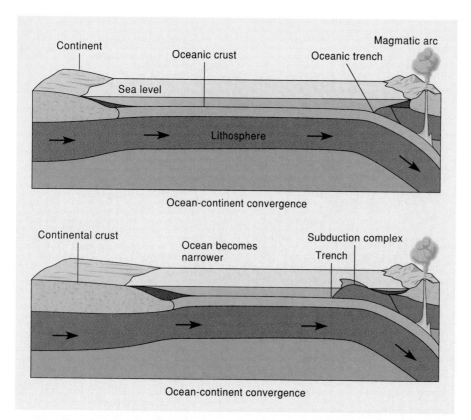

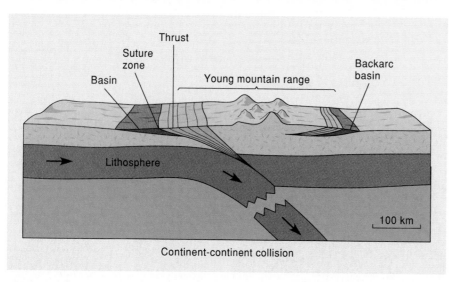

**figure 7.6**

Plate motion toward a converging boundary.

the asthenosphere where tectonic plates converge (fig. 7.4).

Most tectonic plates are capped with both continental and oceanic crust. Where two plates meet along continental margins, the denser oceanic plate slides below the lighter continental plate and sinks back into the partially molten asthenosphere. This **subduction** produces an ocean trench where the plates

meet (fig. 7.6). The continental plate buckles, and volcanic offshore island arc systems are formed by magma derived from partial melting of mantle rock above the subducting plate. As subduction continues, continental rock is deformed into coastal mountain ranges.

When two continental plates converge, their crusts wrinkle and form a mountain chain in the interior of the new

larger continent (fig. 7.6). An example is the Ural Mountains between Europe and Asia. Another continent-continent convergence created the Himalayas when the Indian peninsula collided with Asia. As the two land masses approached each other, the oceanic crust and lithosphere on the leading edge of the Indo-Australian plate subducted beneath the Eurasian plate. The continental crust and lithosphere collided while the oceanic lithosphere broke off; it continues to sink into the asthenosphere. The stresses and faulting of the colliding land masses formed the Himalayan Range. Ocean-ocean convergence takes place where two plates are capped with seafloor crust. One plate subducts beneath the other to form an ocean trench and an island arc of andesitic volcanoes.

## The Earth's Land, Sea, and Air

The Earth is set apart from the other planets by the interaction of its vast expanse of ocean and atmosphere. It is the only planet known to have any significant amount of liquid water (71% of its surface). Together, the sea and air shape the land and influence the entire planetary environment.

### Heat Transport in the Ocean and Atmosphere

Probably the most important functions of the ocean and the atmosphere are to maintain thermal equilibrium and moderate global climate. Radiant energy from the Sun falls on the Earth as direct rays in the equatorial region and as slanted rays at the poles. Consequently, more energy per unit area strikes the Earth in the equatorial region than elsewhere on the globe.

About 51% of solar radiation reaches the surface directly or is scattered downward by the atmosphere. The remaining radiation is absorbed in the atmosphere (13%) or scattered and reflected upward into space (36%).

On land, solar radiation is absorbed at the surface; in the ocean, radiation penetrates to a depth of many meters. To maintain a radiation balance, the light

118

energy absorbed by the Earth must be radiated to the atmosphere as infrared or heat energy. Some of the thermal energy is absorbed by water vapor and carbon dioxide molecules in the atmosphere. The absorption of infrared energy by the atmosphere causes additional heating called the **greenhouse effect.** This property allows sunlight to enter the atmosphere easily while IR radiation is released with greater difficulty. The Earth's surface is warmer than it would be without the additional source of energy provided by the greenhouse effect.

Of great significance is the heat carried into the atmosphere in the *hydrologic cycle* of evaporation, condensation, and precipitation. When photons of radiation strike the molecules in any body of water, they transfer energy to the water molecules, change state, and enter the atmosphere as water vapor. Convection currents cause the air to rise and cool, which condenses the water vapor into clouds.

## The Vertical Structure of the Atmosphere

The Earth's atmosphere consists almost entirely of nitrogen and oxygen, with traces of other gases, as shown in table 7.2.

The first layer of atmosphere above the surface, called the **troposphere,** extends from sea level to an average height of 12 km (fig. 7.7). The temperature in the troposphere gradually decreases from an average of 290 K at the surface to 220 K at the next layer, the **stratosphere.** Here the temperature gradually rises to 270 K at 50 km altitude. Most shortwave radiation is absorbed at this level, a process that is vital to life on Earth. The Sun emits a sufficient amount of ultraviolet energy to destroy plants and animals if such radiation were to reach the surface. Fortunately, X-rays and most ultraviolet rays are absorbed by the uppermost layers of the atmosphere. Longer

**figure 7.7** ▶

Structure of the Earth's atmosphere. The ozone layer extends from the stratosphere to an altitude of about 50 km.

# Table 7.2

## composition, by volume, of the atmosphere

| Constituent | Percent | Parts per Million |
|---|---|---|
| Nitrogen | 78.084 ± 0.004 | |
| Oxygen | 20.946 ± 0.002 | |
| Carbon dioxide | 0.033 ± 0.001 | |
| Argon | 0.934 ± 0.001 | |
| Neon | | 18.18 ± 0.04 |
| Helium | | 5.24 ± 0.004 |
| Krypton | | 1.14 ± 0.01 |
| Xenon | | 0.087 ± 0.001 |
| Hydrogen | | 0.5 |
| Methane ($CH_4$) | | 1.5 |
| Nitrous oxide ($N_2O$) | | 0.5 |

### Important Variable Gases

| | | |
|---|---|---|
| Water vapor | 0–2 percent | |
| Ozone | { 0–0.07 p.p.m. (ground level) | |
| | 1–3 p.pm. (20–30 km) | |

From Horace R. Byers, "The Atmosphere Up to 30 Kilometers" in *The Earth As a Planet,* Gerard P. Kuiper (ed.). Copyright © 1954 University of Chicago Press, Chicago, IL. Reprinted by permission.

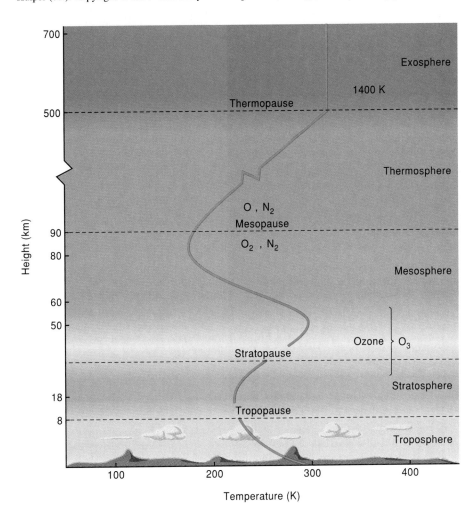

119

## Ozone Depletion by Chlorofluorocarbons

Interdisciplinary studies by scientists have shown that a relationship exists among the biological, chemical, and physical processes that influence the composition of the atmosphere. In 1985, meteorologists discovered a loss of ozone in the stratosphere above the Antarctic continent during spring in the Southern Hemisphere. Depletion of stratospheric ozone allows an increase in the amount of ultraviolet radiation that reaches the surface of the Earth. If the ozone levels continue to drop, the increased exposure to UV radiation is expected to have disastrous effects upon plant and animal life.

In 1989, about 70% of the ozone over Antarctica, representing 10% of the total amount over the entire hemisphere, disappeared during September and early October. Theories were proposed to explain the erosion of the ozone; for example, that it was caused by the production of nitrogen oxides by the action of sunlight.

However, as early as 1974, investigators had shown that the chemical element chlorine reacts with and breaks down ozone into atomic oxygen.

Atmospheric scientists believe that ozone losses in the middle latitudes of the Northern Hemisphere are due to the release of manufactured chlorofluorocarbon chemicals (CFCs). The CFCs are distributed globally by circulation of the atmosphere. During winter in the Arctic region, ozone is destroyed by the reaction of CFCs and icy cloud particles carried aloft by spiraling atmospheric winds.

High-altitude aircraft were used to investigate the CFC region contained over the Antarctic continent by circumpolar winds. There is a causal relationship between the concentration of chlorine compounds and the depletion of the ozone shield. The process begins with the rapid global distribution of CFCs in the troposphere. The compounds are carried into the stratosphere and are dissociated by the action of ultraviolet radiation. Chlorine is released, which breaks down the ozone layer.

ultraviolet rays are absorbed by diffuse bands of ozone located in the stratosphere between 15 and 50 km altitude.

Ozone (O₃) is a molecule consisting of three oxygen atoms. Ozone molecules are produced in the atmosphere by ultraviolet radiation in the following way. Most oxygen molecules in the atmosphere are composed of two atoms (O₂). UV radiation splits a fraction of oxygen molecules into oxygen atoms (O). Occasionally an oxygen molecule and an oxygen atom combine into a molecule of ozone. These ozone molecules form layers that are opaque to UV and therefore prevent most of the deadly rays from reaching the surface.

The *mesosphere* begins at the top of the stratosphere and extends to an altitude of 80 km. In the absence of energy absorption, the temperature in the mesosphere gradually decreases to 205 K. The *thermosphere* begins at 90 km and continues to an altitude of 700 km. Once again the temperature increases as atoms and molecules absorb the shortest and most energetic UV radiation. The temperature approaches 1500 K at the top of the thermosphere. The *exosphere* is the uppermost layer extending beyond 5000 km above the surface. The thermosphere and exosphere contain an ionized region called the **ionosphere.**

**figure 7.8**

Earth from space. Compare the climatic regions—tropical, desert, temperate, and polar—with the wind and pressure systems in figure 7.9.

## Oceanic and Atmospheric Circulation

The interaction of atmospheric and oceanic systems is demonstrated by the circulation of global winds and ocean currents (figs. 7.8, 7.9, and 7.10). The greater intensity of solar radiation in the lower latitudes causes an energy imbalance between the equatorial and polar regions.

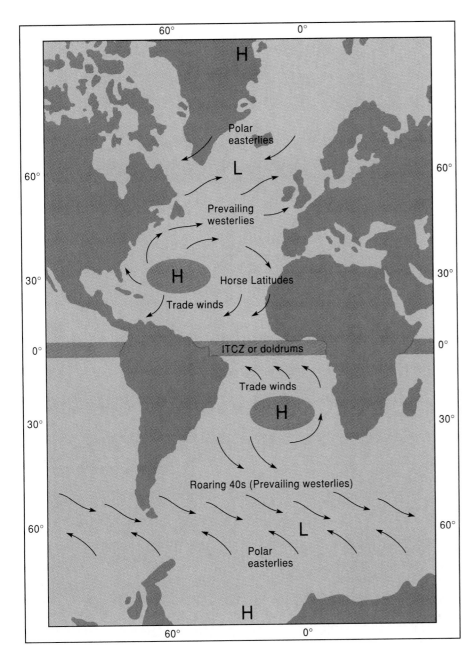

**figure 7.9**
Wind and pressure systems. The intertropical convergence zone (ITCZ) and high pressure systems in the northern and southern Atlantic Ocean are regions of calms.

Thermal energy is absorbed and transported in the atmosphere from the warm equatorial region to the temperate and polar regions. The process moderates the temperature of the Earth's surface.

During the year, the Sun provides the Earth with radiation at an almost constant rate. The Earth remains in thermal equilibrium because the incoming solar energy is balanced by the amount radiated into space. The Earth would slowly become warmer if it were to retain more energy than it loses. Conversely, the Earth would cool if it were to radiate more energy than it receives.

Not all parts of the Earth receive energy at the same rate. In addition to the imbalance between the tropics and the poles, there is a seasonal difference due to the Earth's revolution and the inclination of its axis. Each hemisphere receives more radiation in summer and less during winter. These conditions give rise to the seasons.

# The Magnetosphere

In our discussion of the vertical structure of the atmosphere, the ionosphere was identified as a region of ionized particles. The ionization is the result of the dissociation of oxygen and nitrogen by absorption of solar radiation. The ionosphere extends from the upper mesosphere and thermosphere into the exosphere (fig. 7.7).

At various levels, increases in the density of the ionized gases, or *plasma,* form different layers located at altitudes ranging from about 110 to 300 km. Above these layers the density of the plasma gradually decreases to a minimum at the *plasmapause* which marks the lower boundary of the **magnetosphere** at about 20,000 km altitude. Within the magnetosphere, the behavior of plasma is governed by interaction of the solar wind and the Earth's magnetic field.

The Earth's magnetic field has a shape similar to that produced by a bar magnet in its core, although the Earth's field is produced by electric currents. The magnetic field lines enter the Northern Hemisphere and emerge from the Southern Hemisphere at various angles of dip or inclination and extend into space around the Earth. The north and south magnetic poles are located on the surface at a distance from the geographic poles.

In the magnetosphere there are two stable regions of high-energy particles trapped by the magnetic field (fig. 7.11). Discovered by physicist James Van Allen, one was found from data collected by the first American satellite, Explorer 1, in January 1958. The second was detected in December 1958 by instruments aboard Pioneer 3. The **Van Allen radiation belts** are concentric rings of particles located in the plane of the magnetic equator. The inner belt spans an altitude from 1000 km to 5000 km and consists of high-energy protons at a maximum intensity at 3000 km. The less-energetic outer belt containing electrons is situated between 15,000 to 20,000 km altitude.

We have evidence that high-energy protons and electrons from the solar wind are captured by the Earth's magnetic field and spiral around magnetic field lines toward the poles. The field lines

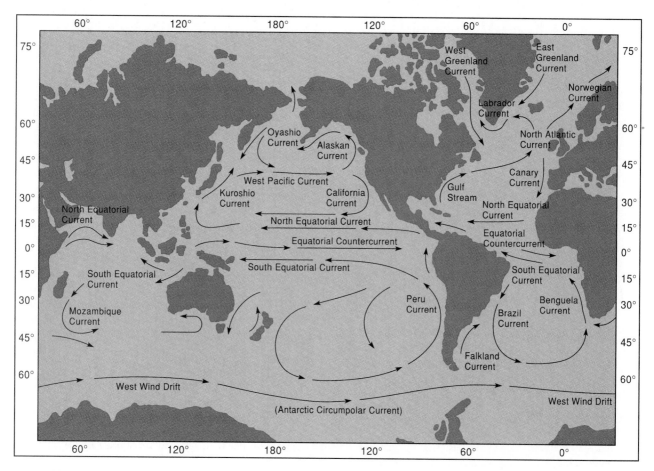

▲ **figure 7.10**
The major currents in the oceans of the world.

**figure 7.11** ▶
The Earth's magnetosphere.

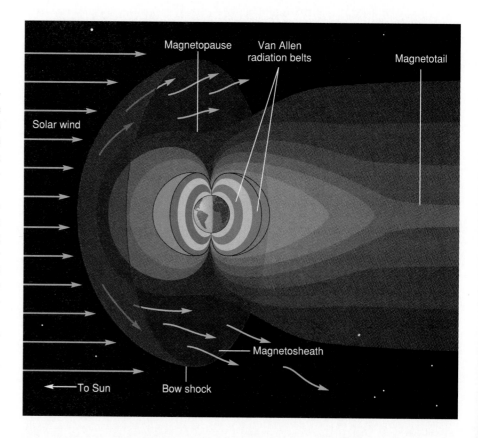

converge at the poles causing the spiraling particles to reverse and move in the opposite direction. The trapped particles travel in a continuous loop, forming the Van Allen belts. Particles are added when powerful eruptions occur on the Sun during maximum solar activity.

Beyond the Van Allen belts the magnetosphere reaches about 95,000 km in the direction of the Sun. The incoming solar wind encounters the Earth's magnetic field and forms a bow shock that deflects the solar particles. Once inside the bow shock, the particles enter a turbulent region called the *magnetosheath*.

The *magnetopause* designates the boundary between the Earth and interplanetary space. It is divided into two lobes: one in the direction of the Sun to a distance of about 60,000 km, and the *magnetotail* extending 6 million km in

**figure 7.12**
The aurora australis over Antarctica, photographed from the space shuttle Discovery in 1991. High-energy particles collide with the ionosphere to produce luminous arcs, rays, and curtains of ionized oxygen and nitrogen.

the opposite direction. High-energy particles from the magnetotail enter the lower magnetosphere to become part of the Van Allen belts.

Moreover, particles from the magnetotail and the Van Allen belts collide with the ionosphere to produce *auroras* at altitudes of about 100 km. Auroras appear as luminous arcs, rays, and streamers of ionized oxygen and nitrogen atoms. The ionized particles are in two plasma rings situated about 1000 km from the magnetic poles. They are called the **aurora borealis** in the Northern Hemisphere and the **aurora australis** in the Southern Hemisphere. Auroras have been photographed during several flights of the space shuttles (fig. 7.12).

## The Moon: Satellite of the Earth

Up to the present, we have described the Moon's changing appearance and considered some of its physical and orbital properties. Now we will take a closer look at our satellite and its relationship with the Earth and the Sun.

## The Sidereal and Synodic Months

The month is approximately the period of time required by the Moon to complete one revolution. The length of the month depends upon how the time interval is measured. The *calendar month* is a division of the year between 28 and 31 days in length that reconciles the cycles of the Moon's phases to the length of the solar year. A more rigorous definition of the month is required to determine our satellite's position, its phases, occultations of planets and stars, eclipses, and other phenomena relating to the Moon.

The moon advances eastward in its orbit at a rate of about 13° per day and returns to a given starting point in a period of 27.322 days. This time interval is called the **sidereal month.** It represents the Moon's period of revolution in its apparent elliptical orbit. An **anomalistic month** of 27.555 days defines the Moon's period in two successive passages of perigee. A **nodical month** of 27.212 days is defined as the period between two successive passages of the Moon with respect to the ascending node of its orbit.

The **synodic month** is the time required by the moon to complete all its phases. In figure 7.13a, the Moon is in conjunction at new-moon phase and below the horizon at sunset. After new moon, a small part of the illuminated hemisphere is visible from the Earth as a crescent. Seven days after new phase, the Moon is at first-quarter phase. In ten days the Moon is waxing gibbous. Full phase occurs 14 days after the new moon.

When full, the Moon sets in the west at dawn as the Sun rises in the east (fig. 7.13b). After full phase, the Moon advances in its orbit and returns to new phase again. The waning gibbous moon is seen 20 days after the start of lunation; last-quarter phase in 22 days; and a waning crescent before new-moon phase.

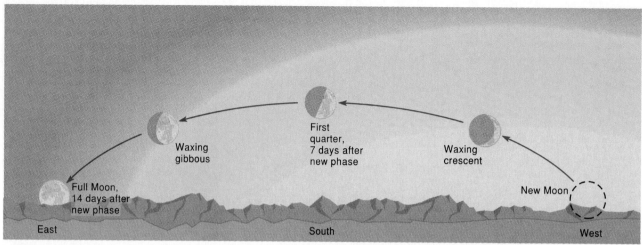

a. Sky at sunset

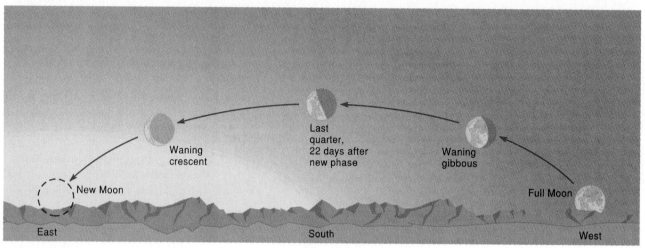

b. Sky at dawn

▲ figure 7.13

The phases of the Moon during one synodic month. *a.* The waxing Moon from new to full phase is shown at sunset. *b.* The waning Moon full to new phase is shown at sunrise. The time required by the Moon to complete its phases, one lunation, is 29.531 days.

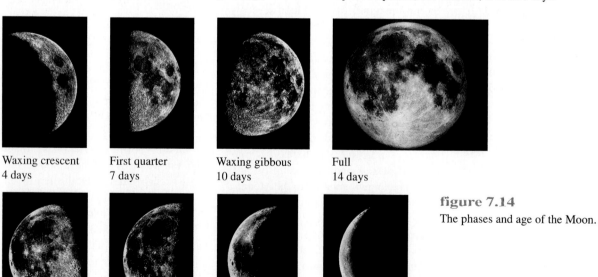

Waxing crescent
4 days

First quarter
7 days

Waxing gibbous
10 days

Full
14 days

figure 7.14
The phases and age of the Moon.

Waning gibbous
20 days

Last quarter
22 days

Waning crescent
24 days

Waning crescent
26 days

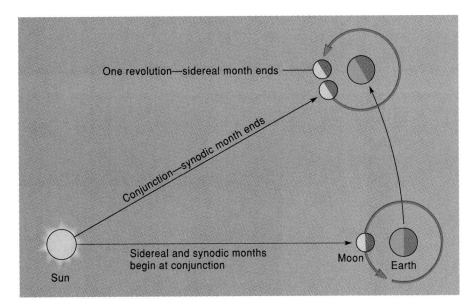

figure 7.15

Sidereal and synodic months. The Moon completes one revolution in 27.322 days but requires 29.531 days to pass through its phases.

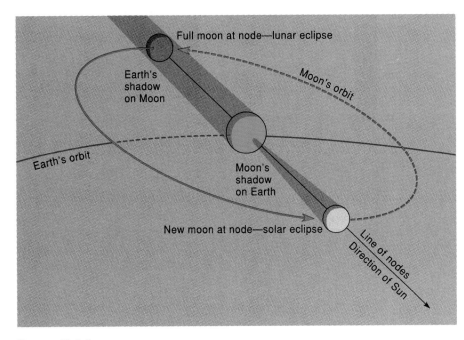

**figure 7.16**

An eclipse of the Sun or Moon takes place when the Moon is in conjunction or opposition at or near a node. Such an alignment occurs about every six months at opposite points on the Earth's orbit.

The age of the Moon is expressed as the number of days elapsed since new-moon phase (fig. 7.14).

The length of the synodic month is 29.531 days, which is longer than the sidereal month by 2.21 days. The difference in length is caused by the revolution of the Earth and Moon around the Sun (fig. 7.15).

## Eclipses

**Solar eclipses** happen during conjunction when the Moon passes between the Earth and the Sun (fig. 7.16). The eclipse is central when the centers of the Sun and Moon coincide. If the Moon is at or near perigee, its angular size is greater than the Sun's and the eclipse will be *total* for all places where the dark *umbra* of the Moon's shadow cone crosses the surface of the Earth. The duration of totality varies from a fraction of a second to a maximum of about 7 1/2 minutes.

The most exciting astronomical event to witness is a total solar eclipse. The apex of the Moon's conical dark shadow, or umbra, forms a small dark oval that sweeps across the Earth in a narrow band called the **path of totality.** As the eclipse progresses, the dark Moon gradually covers the bright solar disk; the temperature drops and a strange, foreboding stillness shrouds the land. Suddenly you are immersed in shadow as the diffused light of the Sun's corona, or outer atmosphere, surrounds the dark Moon. Bright coronal streamers extend several million kilometers from the Sun while planets and familiar bright stars appear in the darkened sky (see fig. 7.17). Totality ends as unexpectedly as it began; the stars and planets fade as an emerging Sun brightens the landscape. The Moon continues its constant journey and in a day or two can be seen as a thin crescent east of the setting Sun.

When the Moon is at or near apogee, its apparent diameter is less than the Sun's and the eclipse is *annular*. At such a time, the Sun appears as a bright ring, or annulus, centered on the dark Moon. A *partial eclipse* will be observed at all places within the *penumbra* or lighter shadow of the Moon.

A **lunar eclipse** takes place during full-moon phase when the Moon is immersed in the shadow of the Earth. If the entire Moon is in the umbra, the eclipse will be total. It will be partial when only a portion of the Moon passes into the dark shadow.

At the Moon's distance, the average diameter of the Earth's shadow is almost three times the size of the Moon. When the center of the Moon crosses the axis of the Earth's shadow, the eclipse can last for almost 1 1/2 hours.

During totality, the disk of the Moon shines with the orange and red light of twilight. Sunlight is refracted into the

a.

b.

**figure 7.17**

*a.* The Moon leaving the umbra of the Earth's shadow. Note the curvature of the shadow on the lunar surface. *b.* The inner corona of the Sun was visible during the total solar eclipse of July 11, 1991.

shadow by the Earth's atmosphere and bathes the Moon in a coppery glow. A lunar eclipse can be observed from the entire night side of the Earth where the Moon is above the horizon.

Before an eclipse can occur, there are a number of conditions that must be fulfilled. The Sun may be anywhere on the ecliptic when conjunctions and oppositions take place every synodic month. But for an eclipse to happen, the Sun must be at or near one of the *nodes* in the Moon's orbit during conjunction or opposition. A node is the point of intersection between an orbit and the ecliptic. The Moon's orbit is inclined about 5.0° and intersects the ecliptic at two opposite points. The Sun passes the two nodes twice or sometimes three times in one year, so eclipses occur in opposite months; January and July, March and September, June and December (see table 7.3).

Two or three solar eclipses will take place worldwide in any year. Solar and lunar eclipses may happen two weeks apart, and a combination of seven solar and lunar eclipses represents the maximum number that may occur in one year.

The ancient Chaldeans and Babylonians were aware that eclipses repeat at regular intervals over a period of 18 years and 11 days (6585.5 days). The cycle is called a **saros.** A saros contains 223 synodic months, 239 anomalistic months, and 242 nodical months. Thus in one saros, the Moon will reach the same phase, at a node, in the same part of its orbit. After each saros, eclipses of the Sun and Moon will occur again in the same order. Examples of the saros cycle are found in table 7.3. On July 11, 1991, a total eclipse was observed in Hawaii and Mexico. The next eclipse in this cycle will take place July 22, 2009—18 years and 11 days later.

## The Tides

The *tides,* or the alternate rising and falling of the oceans, are a familiar sight along the continental margins. The waters rise during **flood tide** and move inland to a maximum height called high tide. Then the waters recede at **ebb tide** to a minimum, or low tide.

By the first century A.D., people were aware of a relationship between the time of high tide and the position of the Moon. But the reason for the phenomenon was not understood until the seventeenth century, when Newton explained the tides as an action of the gravitational attraction of the Moon and Sun.

The mass of the Moon is negligible compared to the mass of the more distant Sun. From this we might conclude that the Sun provides a greater tide-raising force. But the nearness of the Moon more than compensates for the Sun's greater bulk, making the Moon's attraction about 2.2 times more effective.

### Theory of the tides

Imagine that the Earth is a perfectly smooth sphere covered by an ocean of uniform depth. Our hypothetical planet neither rotates nor revolves and is isolated from all outside gravitational influences. Under these conditions, the oceans would remain unchanged without any periodic rise and fall. If a large body such as the Moon were placed nearby, its gravity would create a tidal force which will vary inversely with respect to the distance from different points on the Earth and the center of the attracting body.

The portions of the oceans nearest to the body are attracted more than the center of the Earth so that a bulge or high tide forms in the direction of the attracting body. The center of the Earth is closer to the body than the ocean in the opposite hemisphere. Thus the waters on the far side are least attracted and are left

## total and annular eclipses, 1991—2010

| Date | Type | Maximum Duration | Locale |
|------|------|------------------|--------|
| 15 January 1991 | Annular | 7 m 55 s | Tasmania, New Zealand |
| 11 July 1991 | Total | 6 m 54 s | Hawaii, Mexico, Central and South America |
| 4 January 1992 | Annular | 11 m 43 s | partial: Hawaii; end: California |
| 30 June 1992 | Total | 5 m 21 s | Uruguay, Atlantic Ocean |
| 10 May 1994 | Annular | 6 m 14 s | Mexico, U.S. |
| 3 November 1994 | Total | 4 m 23 s | S. America |
| 29 April 1995 | Annular | 6 m 38 s | S. America |
| 24 October 1995 | Total | 2 m 10 s | S. Asia |
| 9 March 1997 | Total | 2 m 50 s | Mongolia, U.S.S.R., Arctic |
| 26 February 1998 | Total | 4 m 09 s | Panama, Colombia, Venezuela |
| 22 August 1998 | Annular | 3 m 14 s | Indonesia, Malaysia, Oceania |
| 16 February 1999 | Annular | 1 m 18 s | Australia |
| 11 August 1999 | Total | 2 m 23 s | Europe, S. Asia |
| 21 June 2001 | Total | 4 m 57 s | Angola, Zambia, Mozambique |
| 14 December 2001 | Annular | 3 m 54 s | Pacific Ocean, Central America |
| 10 June 2002 | Annular | 1 m 13 s | Pacific; ends off Baja California |
| 4 December 2002 | Total | 2 m 04 s | Southern Africa, W. Australia |
| 31 May 2003 | Annular | 3 m 41 s | Arctic |
| 23 November 2003 | Total | 1 m 57 s | Antarctica |
| 8 April 2005 | Ann/Total | 0 m 42 s | Panama, Colombia, Venezuela |
| 3 October 2005 | Annular | 4 m 31 s | Portugal, Spain, N. and E. Africa |
| 29 March 2006 | Total | 4 m 07 s | Africa, Turkey, U.S.S.R. |
| 22 September 2006 | Annular | 7 m 09 s | N.E. South America, Atlantic |
| 7 February 2008 | Annular | 2 m 14 s | Antarctica |
| 1 August 2008 | Total | 2 m 27 s | N. Canada, N. Greenland, Asia |
| 26 January 2009 | Annular | 7 m 56 s | Indonesia |
| 22 July 2009 | Total | 6 m 40 s | India, Bangladesh, China, S. Japan Is. |
| 15 January 2010 | Annular | 11 m 11 s | Africa, India, Myanmar, China |
| 11 July 2010 | Total | 5 m 20 s | S. Chile, S. Argentina |

Source: Data from F. Espenak, *Fifty Year Canon of Solar Eclipses, 1986–2035*, NASA Reference Publication 1178 (revised), NASA, Greenbelt, MD.

behind to form a second bulge opposite the high tide on the hemisphere closest to the attracting body. A depletion of water, or low tide, will occur at points on the Earth's surface perpendicular to the line connecting the centers of the Earth and the attracting body, because the water has shifted laterally on the surface toward the regions of high tide.

Of course the actual tides are far more complex than those in our theoretical model. There are motions of the Earth-Moon system to consider, and the diurnal, monthly, and annual behavior of the tides due to the changes in the declinations of the Sun and Moon. Moreover, the position and shape of continents, the slope of their margins, and the shape, size, and depth of ocean basins all contribute to the range between low and high tides throughout the world. There are a number of coastal areas where tidal ranges are more pronounced, such as those in the Bay of Fundy (16 m) in eastern Canada, and the Bay of St. Malo (10 m) in France.

### Effect of the Earth's rotation

Imagine yourself at the Earth's equator with the Moon at the zenith at high tide. As the Earth rotates, you will experience two high tides and two low tides (fig. 7.18). Meanwhile, the Moon advances about 13° in its orbit so that 24 h 50 m will be required to bring the Moon to the meridian to complete a *tidal day* or *lunar day*.

There are variations in the height of the tide produced by the changing configurations of the Sun and Moon as well as their distances from the Earth. A **spring tide** occurs during new phase and full phase when the Sun and Moon are in conjunction and opposition (fig. 7.18a). On such occasions, the Sun and Moon act together to produce a tide of maximum height. A **neap tide** is an unusually low high tide that occurs at first-quarter and last-quarter phase when the Moon is in quadrature (fig. 7.18b). The tide is modified as the attractive forces

the earth and moon system

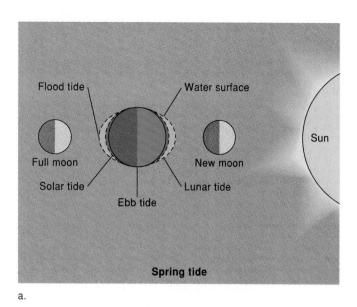

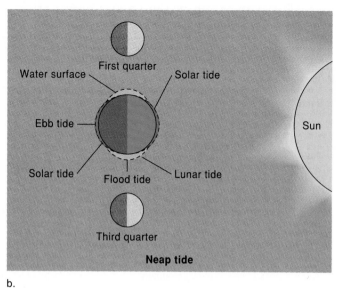

a.

b.

**figure 7.18**

Tides are caused by the gravitational attraction of the Moon and Sun. There are two high tides (flood tides) and two low tides (ebb tides) alternating each day. *a.* At new and full phases, the effect is additive, resulting in a higher spring tide. *b.* At first and last quarter phases, the tide is at its lowest range, or neap tide.

of the Sun and Moon act at right angles to each other.

## The Face of the Moon

Whether viewed by the unaided eye or more dramatically through a telescope, the Moon is a beautiful object to behold (fig. 7.19). Its illuminated surface appears as a silvery disk of blended hues. Even a small telescope can resolve its features into bright highlands scarred by impact **craters.** The term **mare,** or sea, is used to describe dark, flat lava plains that cover about one-third of the lunar surface visible from the Earth. These lowland areas have been flooded by molten rock from the Moon's interior.

A most compelling sight are the majestic mountain ranges bordering the curved maria. During first and last quarter, when sunlight strikes the mountains at low elevation, long shadows are cast onto the surrounding moonscape. Isolated peaks along the *terminator,* the line separating night and day, catch the Sun's light and sparkle as bright jewels above the darkened surface. Lunar mountains are named after prominent mountain ranges on the Earth, such as the Alps, Caucasus, and Apennines. They are frequently crossed by deep chasms and valleys.

### Lunar highlands and craters

The lighter-colored, densely cratered highlands represent the oldest region of the lunar crust. As in the case of other bodies in the solar system, the moon's primitive surface was scarred during the accretion stage by bodies ranging in size from tiny particles to huge planetesimals. The resulting craters represent the most common feature on the Moon. They are named after famous philosophers, scientists, and explorers.

The smaller craters, up to a few kilometers across, are cup-shaped indentations surrounded by the fragments blown out at impact. The largest craters, or **walled plains,** have diameters up to 200 km. They are of an entirely different structure than small craters, with a flat floor and quite often a mountainous peak at the center. The inner wall is steeply terraced while the outer wall gently slopes to the surrounding lunar surface.

Bright **rays** streak out from some of the more recently formed craters such as Tycho and Copernicus. The rays are seen best during full-moon phase, extending as far as 2000 km across highlands and flat plains. They are pulverized deposits ejected during the formation of the crater (fig. 7.19).

The largest planetesimals to strike the Moon must have been many kilometers across. There are depressions called **basins** that exceed 300 km and show a concentric ringlike structure (fig. 7.20).

## Voyages to the Moon

More was learned about the Moon in one decade of satellite exploration than in the centuries since Galileo first viewed the lunar surface through his telescope. The period of successful investigation began in 1959 when the Soviet space probe Lunik 3 returned pictures of the far side of the Moon (see table 7.4). The hidden hemisphere is a heavily cratered highland region containing large basins that lack the conspicuous maria found on the familiar near side.

### Unmanned satellite investigations

From 1964 through 1965, American Ranger satellites televised close-up pictures before crashing onto the lunar surface. Thousands of images from heights starting at 2000 km down to about 400 m above the surface were transmitted back to Earth. The final pictures before impact showed craters less than a meter in diameter.

### observing the Mare Imbrium basin

As the second brightest object in the sky, the Moon claims the attention of all Sky Watchers. Only a small telescope is necessary to remove the mystery of its dark and light surface shadings and reveal a variety of craters, mountain ranges, and flat plains. Before you begin observing, refer to a map of the Moon and select an interesting region containing prominent features.

We have decided to observe Mare Imbrium during gibbous phase before and after full moon. Mare Imbrium is found in the Northern Hemisphere enclosed by a series of mountain ranges: the Jura, Alps, Caucasus, Apennines, and Carpathians. Starting west at the Heraclides Promontory, we follow the Jura Mountains northeast to the Laplace Promontory. These prominences mark the boundary of the circular plain called Sinus Iridum, which lies in the 483-km arc formed by the Jura range. The mountains rise 3.87 km above the floor of the Sinus Iridum.

Continuing east into the Alps, we encounter Plato, a walled plain jutting into the Imbrium basin. Plato is about 105 km in diameter and 2.4 km deep. Its smooth, dark floor was flooded when lava oozed from the interior of the Moon. To the east of Plato is the Alpine Valley, which cuts through the range from Mare Imbrium north into Mare Frigoris. The Alps continue in an arc east and southeast for 560 km to the Agassiz Promontory northwest of the crater Cassini.

In Mare Imbrium there are a number of prominent features worthy of our attention. The solitary mountain peak, Pico, casts its shadow on the floor of the basin directly south of the crater Plato. Between Laplace Promontory and Plato there is the Straight Range, a 90-km mountain chain that may have been part of a crater inundated when the mare was formed.

The Caucasus Mountains make up the eastern boundary of Mare Imbrium. Continuing in an arc towards the south and west are the Apennines and finally the Carpathians to complete the circular Imbrium basin.

There are several nearby craters to identify. West of the Caucasus and north of the Apennines is a group of three craters, Aristilles, Autolycus, and Archimedes. The largest, Archimedes, is 82 km across and has a flat floor similar to Plato's but lighter in color. The 60-km crater Eratosthenes stands at the south end of the Apennines, guiding the observer to the conspicuous crater Copernicus south of the Carpathian range. Copernicus is 97 km in diameter and about 3.8 km deep. It is a comparatively young, terraced crater formed by impact after Mare Imbrium solidified. Bright rays that extend from Copernicus are best observed during full-moon phase.

**figure 7.19**

A composite image of the Moon made up of photographs of the first and third quarters joined at the terminator to provide maximum contrast between surface features. The flat basins are darker than the cratered highlands. Mountain ranges rise along the edge of Mare Imbrium. Bright rays of debris streak out from more recently formed craters.

**figure 7.20**

Mare Orientale has a concentric, ringlike structure caused by the impact of a large meteoric body.

## Table 7.4

### unmanned lunar missions[*]

| Series Name, Number | Dates | Objectives |
|---|---|---|
| *Soviet* | | |
| Luna 1–3, 9–14, 16, 17, 19, 20–24 | 1959–1976 | Impact Moon; photograph lunar terrain from orbit; soft landing with photography; land and deploy Lunokhod; obtain samples and return to Earth |
| Zond 3–8 | 1965–1970 | Lunar flyby with photography; circumlunar flight with return to Earth; some carried biological payloads |
| *American* | | |
| Pioneer 1, 4 | 1958–1959 | Fields and particles studies; neither impacted Moon |
| Ranger 7–9 | 1964–1965 | Hard-landing with TV of impact sites |
| Surveyor 1, 3, 5–7 | 1966–1968 | Soft-landing; TV, soil mechanics, chemical composition, magnetic properties, Earth and astronomical TV |
| Lunar Orbiter 1–5 | 1966–1967 | Orbital photography of *Apollo* landing sites and other areas; micrometeorite flux; radiation measurements |
| Explorer 35 | 1967 | Fields and particles measurements in lunar orbit |
| Explorer 49 | 1973 | *Radio Astronomy Explorer*; very-low-frequency radio astronomy from lunar orbit |

[*]Totally unsuccessful missions not included

From Paul D. Lowman, Jr., "Moon, Space Missions" in *The Astronomy and Astrophysics Encyclopedia*. Copyright © 1992 Van Nostrand Reinhold Company, New York, NY. Reprinted by permission.

In preparation for the manned Apollo program, five lunar orbiting missions were launched by NASA in 1966 and 1967. With future Apollo landing sites in mind, Lunar Orbiters 1, 2, and 3 were placed in orbits to provide coverage within five degrees of the Moon's equator. Orbiters 4 and 5 were injected into near-polar orbits and photographed most of the lunar surface. The film was scanned by an onboard photomultiplier tube, and an electric signal proportional to the intensity of the transmitted light was generated and transmitted to the receiving station back on Earth. The greatest achievements of the Lunar Orbiters were the close-up details of the surface.

The Lunar Orbiter missions were instrumental in the discovery of anomalies in the gravitational field of the Moon. The Orbiters increased in speed as they approached large maria basins. The accelerations indicate a greater concentration of mass under the maria than elsewhere on the surface. These so-called *mascons* (from *Mass Con*centrations) may be the result of seepage of denser rock from the interior to the floor of the basin. Apollo descent trajectories were modified to compensate for the excess of gravity in the maria.

In February 1966, the Soviet spacecraft Luna 9 made the first soft landing near the crater Cavalerius in the western region of Oceanus Procellarum. One important objective of this and later Soviet and American missions was to prove the lunar surface capable of supporting manned vehicles.

In June 1966, the American Surveyor 1 landed about 700 km southeast of Luna 9. The Surveyor camera system transmitted pictures of a gently rolling surface studded with craters ranging in size from several meters down to small craterlets. Large blocks and smaller rock fragments lay partially buried in the fine dusty *regolith,* or surface layer.

In 1967 and 1968, four more lunar landers—Surveyors 3, 5, 6, and 7—touched down at different sites in preparation for the Apollo flights. The chemical nature of Mare Tranquillitatis was studied by means of an alpha-scattering instrument carried by Surveyor 5. The abundance of oxygen, silicon, and aluminum in the surface confirmed that the regolith is similar in composition to basalt. Surveyor 6 touched down on a flat area in Sinus Medii in November 1967. The pictures returned to Earth confirmed the area as a prime site for a later Apollo landing. The final mission, Surveyor 7, landed in the southern highlands about 30 km from the crater Tycho in January 1968.

### The Apollo missions

In December 1968, Apollo 8, carrying three astronauts, made the first circumnavigation of the Moon. In May 1969, the Apollo 10 Command and Service Modules were placed into lunar orbit. The Lunar Excursion Module (LEM) containing two astronauts dropped to within 17 km of the surface (see table 7.5).

Apollo 11 astronauts left the first footprints on the Moon in the soil of Mare Tranquillitatis in July 1969. Rock samples returned to Earth were dated as 3.2 to 3.9 billion years old. Six more Apollo missions were launched between 1969 and 1972 to map the Moon from orbit and obtain samples of surface material from widely separated areas.

Apollo 12 touched down on the flat terrain of Sinus Medii near the sites of Surveyor 3 and 6 (fig. 7.21). A service module explosion aboard Apollo 13 prevented the spacecraft from making a

## manned lunar missions

| Number | Date | Landing Site | Accomplishments |
|---|---|---|---|
| Apollo 8 | Dec. 1968 | Circumlunar | First manned mission to Moon; photography; visual observations |
| Apollo 10 | May 1969 | Circumlunar | Manned mission with lunar module separation; 50,000-ft perilune without landing; photography |
| Apollo 11 | July 1969 | Mare Tranquillitatis | First manned landing on Moon; sample collection; EASEP emplacement; photography (surface and orbital) |
| Apollo 12 | Nov. 1969 | Oceanus Procellarum | Second manned landing; sample collection; ALSEP emplacement; photography (surface and orbital) |
| Apollo 13 | April 1970 | Lunar flyby | Service module explosion forced landing abort; emergency return to Earth; far side photography accomplished |
| Apollo 14 | Jan. 1971 | Near Fra Mauro crater | Investigated Imbrium ejecta blanket; ALSEP emplacement; photography (surface and orbital); active seismic investigations |
| Apollo 15 | July 1971 | At base of Apennines | First use of lunar rover; sample collection; ALSEP emplacement; orbital remote sensing; subsatellite launch |
| Apollo 16 | April 1972 | Near Descartes, Central Highlands | First landing in true highland terrain; sample collection; ALSEP emplacement; orbital remote sensing; subsatellite launch |
| Apollo 17 | Dec. 1972 | Taurus-Littrow Valley | Last *Apollo* landing; sample collection; ALSEP emplacement; orbital remote sensing; first geologist on Moon |

From Paul D. Lowman, Jr., "Moon, Space Missions" in *The Astronomy and Astrophysics Encyclopedia.* Copyright © 1992 Van Nostrand Reinhold Company, New York, NY. Reprinted by permission.

### figure 7.21

In 1969, Apollo 12 astronauts retrieved the camera and other parts from the unmanned Surveyor 3 spacecraft that had landed on the Moon more than two years earlier.

the earth and moon system

a.

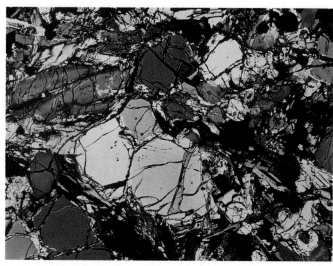

b.

**figure 7.22**

*a.* A sample of lunar rock, called the "Goodwill Rock," returned by Apollo 17 astronauts. *b.* A photomicrograph of a thin section of Apollo 12 lunar sample identifies the composition as a fine- to medium-grained basalt.

lunar landing. Apollo 14 landed in the Fra Mauro region, which is flooded by lava and surrounded by severely eroded ridges believed to be ejecta from the formation of Mare Imbrium. Apollo 15 touched down on the edge of Mare Imbrium near Hadley Rille, a conspicuous formation in the Apennine region. A *rille* is a sinuous channel found in valleys, craters, and maria. The rocks discovered included *anorthositic breccia,* which are among the oldest found on the Moon. Apollo 16 landed in a highland region near the crater Descartes between Mare Nectaris and Mare Nubium. The highland samples included breccia rich in aluminum and calcium. Other rocks contained radioactive elements such as uranium and thorium (see fig. 7.22). The final mission, Apollo 17 (1972), landed in the Taurus range in a rugged region of mountain peaks, craters, and gaping clefts. About 110 kg of specimens were collected, including an orange-colored soil containing titanium oxide.

## Origin and Evolution of the Moon

In the last hundred years or so, theorists have proposed three classical models to explain the origin of the Moon. The first, the *fission hypothesis,* was suggested by George H. Darwin in 1879. Darwin be-

lieved that at an early stage in solar system evolution, enough mass broke away from the Earth to form the Moon. If the Earth and Moon were together, the rotational period of the single body would equal about four hours. Such a rapid spin would cause particles and larger fragments to move into a ring structure in the Earth's equatorial plane. In time, the particles in the ring would accrete and form the Moon.

The model fails to explain differences between theory and observation. It does not account for the inclination of the Moon's orbit to the Earth's equatorial plane, and why the Earth and Moon, as a single body, evolved with a high rotational rate while other terrestrial planets rotate slowly.

In another scenario, called the *coaccretion hypothesis,* the Moon coalesced from material already in orbit around the evolving protoearth. The Moon and the Earth formed as separate bodies through the accumulation of particles in the solar nebula. But the coaccretion model fails to account for a number of differences between the Earth and Moon. For example, the mean density of the Moon (3.34 gm/cm³) is about the same as the density of the Earth's mantle below the crust. The Earth has an iron core that represents about one-third of its total mass. Samples of lunar rock returned by the Apollo missions show

very little metallic iron. Moreover, at present, the Moon lacks a magnetic field like the Earth's, although remnant magnetism was discovered in the oldest crustal rock. The model cannot explain such differences in a two-body system that evolved in the same region of the solar nebula.

The hypothesis known as *intact capture* says that the Moon coalesced and acquired its unique chemical properties in an orbit far from the Earth. At some later time, the Moon passed close to and was captured by our planet.

There are several problems left unanswered by the intact-capture model. Some mechanism must be present to slow the Moon's orbital velocity before capture can take place. The Moon may have lost energy through collisions with a number of smaller bodies already in orbit around the Earth. If the Moon had an orbital velocity similar to that of the Earth, then the Moon and Earth must have formed at the same distance from the Sun and would have similar chemical composition.

### Results of the Apollo missions

None of the three classical models are compatible with the observational data provided by lunar exploration during the 1960s and 1970s. The analysis of lunar rock samples, measurements made by Apollo astronauts on the Moon, and investigations from orbit provided scientists with the data needed to establish a modern theory of lunar evolution (see fig. 7.23).

In six Apollo missions, about 400 kg of rock and soil samples were returned for analysis. These samples provided an understanding of the chemical composition of the lunar surface and the Moon's history. The light-colored highland anorthosite was cemented into breccia sometime between the formation of the lunar crust and about 3.8 billion years ago. The rocks collected from the maria are composed of dark-colored basalt rich in ferromagnesian minerals. They are younger than specimens found in the highlands, ranging in age from 3.2 to 3.8 billion years.

Each Apollo mission was equipped with an instrument package containing various scientific instruments to be placed on the lunar surface. The purpose was to measure the effects of micrometeoric impacts and the solar wind, detect the presence of a lunar magnetic field, take temperature readings below the surface, and determine the internal structure of the Moon with seismographs. A laser signal from the McDonald Observatory in Texas was reflected from a mirror placed on the lunar surface. The time required for the signal to reach the Moon and return to Earth continues to provide an accurate measurement of the Earth-Moon distance.

No significant magnetic field was detected. However, the residual magnetism found in a number of rock samples suggests the presence of a field at an earlier time in lunar history. Because a measureable magnetic field is not present, the structure and composition of the Moon's center is not known.

Seismic experiments revealed a discontinuity separating the anorthositic crust from the top of the mantle. The lunar crust was found to vary in thickness from about 50 km on the side facing the Earth to about 150 km on the far side. Moreover, the selenographical center of the Moon is displaced from the center of mass by about 2 km. These conditions may have caused upwelling of magma and maria formation in the nearside basins. The maria basalt varies from a few km to as much as 20 km in thickness.

**figure 7.23**

Apollo 17 landed in the Taurus mountain range near the crater Littrow, in a rugged region of mountain peaks, boulders, craters, and clefts.

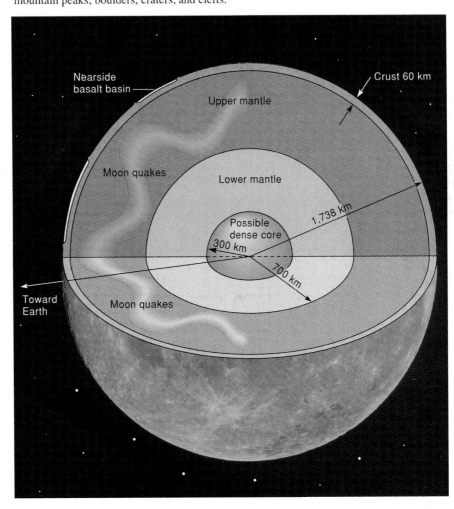

**figure 7.24**

Interior of the Moon. Upwelling of magma from the mantle formed the nearside basins. Seismic experiments revealed discontinuities separating the crust and mantle, and the upper and lower mantle. The upper mantle is solid; the lower mantle may be semi-liquid rock. It is not known if an iron core exists.

A second discontinuity is found at a depth of about 1000 km, a region where there is a physical change in the structure of the mantle. The upper mantle is solid and, if a core does not exist, the lower mantle may be a relatively hot, semiliquid rock down to the center (fig. 7.24).

From surface experiments and estimates of the ages of the rocks, we can infer how the face of the Moon was formed. About 4.4 billion years ago, the Moon had cooled enough for anorthositic rocks with high melting points to form a crust. From 4.4 to 3.8 billion years ago, the Moon was subjected to an intense bombardment by meteorites and large planetesimals. Craters and basins were formed while rock fragments were cemented into breccia.

Some scientists believe that about 3.8 to 3.2 billion years ago the moon was heated by radioactive decay. Molten rock from the interior seeped to the surface through the thinner crust facing the Earth. Wave after wave of lava covered the basins until the maria were formed. Meteoric bombardment abated and fewer large craters scarred the newly formed basalt plains. Continuous impact by smaller meteorites formed the granulated regolith covering the surface.

### Giant impact hypothesis

A *giant impact* model was proposed independently by two groups of investigators: Alastair G. W. Cameron and William R. Ward; and William K. Hartmann and Donald R. Davis. In the giant impact hypothesis, the Moon was formed when the Earth was struck by a protoplanet of a mass equal to that of Mars (fig. 7.25). The impact occurred after the young Earth had differentiated and heavy

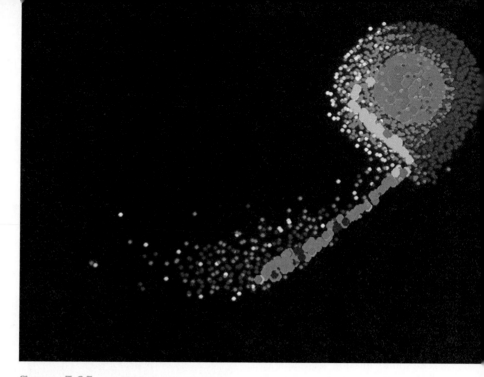

**figure 7.25**

A computer simulation of the formation of the Moon according to a giant impact model.

metals had settled into the core. A mantle of denser rock was in place below the crust.

The protoplanet collided with the Earth at a velocity of about 12 km/sec and vaporized a portion of the Earth's crust and mantle into an extensive jet. The ejecta consisted of a mixture of material from the projectile as well as the upper layers of the planet. Very little if any material from the Earth's core was vaporized. The plume condensed into particles that formed a ring of detritus around the Earth. Subsequently, the particles clumped together to form the Moon.

Although the giant impact hypothesis has not been verified, it is supported by many astronomers. For the present, the model represents the best explanation based upon the analysis of lunar rock and other data provided by the Apollo missions.

## SUMMARY

At an early stage in its development, the partially molten Earth differentiated into zones of varying density. Iron and nickel settled into the core, dense rocks formed the mantle, and lighter rocks floated to the surface and became the crust. Gases from the interior, including water vapor, formed an atmosphere. Finally the Earth cooled and the water vapor condensed into water that filled the ocean basins.

Our understanding of the Earth's interior is based upon observations of seismic waves. The waves identify discontinuities existing at depths marked by zones of different density and composition.

The solid inner core of iron and nickel is nearly as large as the Moon. The outer core of fluid iron is the source of the Earth's magnetic field.

Most of the Earth's mass is found in the dense, rocky mantle. The mantle consists of silicates containing magnesium, iron, aluminum, and calcium.

The lithosphere includes the crust and a thin layer of the upper mantle. Continental crust is made of granitic rock, while oceanic crust is basalt.

The theory of plate tectonics describes the changes in the Earth's crust and the processes that produce them. The spreading and convergence of continental and oceanic crust builds mountains, forms volcanic offshore islands, and produces new ocean floor.

The Earth is distinguished by the interaction of its vast expanse of ocean and its atmosphere. Solar energy is absorbed in the atmosphere through the evaporation of water from the surface. Energy is transported from the low latitudes toward the poles by global winds. The winds create oceanic circulation that further moderates the climate.

A month is the time required by the Moon to complete one revolution. A sidereal month of 27.322 days is the Moon's period of revolution in its orbit. A synodic month of 29.531 days is the time required by the Moon to complete its phases.

Eclipses of the Sun take place at new-moon phase when the Sun is at or near one of the nodes of the Moon's orbit. Lunar eclipse occur at full-moon phase when the center of the Earth's shadow is at or near a node.

Ocean tides are produced by the gravitational attraction of the Moon and Sun. Usually, there are two high tides each day and two low tides in between. At new and full moon, the tides are more pronounced. At quarter moon, the attraction of the Sun and Moon act in different directions to reduce the range of the tides.

The surface of the Moon is covered by cratered highlands and dark, flat lava plains called maria. Satellite investigations of these features began in 1959 when the hidden side was televised by a Soviet space probe. Later investigations included closeup images of the near side made by American Ranger satellites. Lunar Orbiter missions identified future Apollo landing sites and made close-up images of the lunar surface.

Surveyor satellites were landed on the surface to prepare for the Apollo program. Studies were made at various sites in the lunar highlands and maria regions. Soil samples revealed the composition of the surface and proved its capability to support manned vehicles.

Six Apollo landings were made between 1969 and 1972 to map the moon and obtain samples of surface material. The rocks and soil returned to Earth were found to be breccia, anorthosite, and basalt. The study of lunar rocks provided an understanding of the history of the lunar surface.

# KEY TERMS

| | |
|---|---|
| anomalistic month | mare |
| aurora australis | neap tide |
| aurora borealis | nodical month |
| basins | path of totality |
| core | plate tectonics |
| craters | rays |
| crust | saros |
| discontinuity | sidereal month |
| ebb tide | solar eclipse |
| flood tide | spring tide |
| greenhouse effect | stratosphere |
| ionosphere | subduction |
| lithosphere | synodic month |
| lunar eclipse | troposphere |
| magnetosphere | Van Allen radiation belts |
| mantle | walled plains |

# PROBLEMS

1. Explain how the present atmosphere of the Earth may have been produced.

2. How does the subduction process contribute to maintaining the equilibrium of the Earth's crust?

3. Discuss the important scientific achievements of the Apollo missions.

4. Describe the various surface features observed on the Moon.

5. Describe the major zones of the Earth from the surface to the center.

6. Why does it take the Moon a longer period of time to pass through its phases than to complete one revolution in its orbit?

7. Imagine yourself an astronaut on the Moon observing an eclipse of the Sun by the Earth.
   a. What kind of eclipse will be seen by people on the Earth?
   b. How many days are required for two successive conjunctions of the Earth and Sun?

8. What evidence do we have for the composition of the Earth's mantle?

9. How does plate tectonic theory explain the formation of continental ranges such as the Ural Mountains?

10. Explain how the location of shadow zones indicates the structure of the Earth's mantle and core.

11. Discuss the differences between the Earth and Moon in terms of their internal structure.

12. Explain why some maria contain a large number of craters while others are covered by few craters.

13. What experiments by the Apollo astronauts were designed to study the interior structure of the Moon?

14. Explain how the Earth's atmosphere and oceans moderate the global temperature.

15. What type of rock is found in continental crust? In oceanic crust? How are they different?

16. How has fossil magnetism provided evidence for seafloor spreading?

17. What experimental evidence do we have for the composition of the Earth's core?

18. What region of the Moon has the greatest number of craters? Explain why and give reasons for your answer.

19. Describe the Apollo landing sites and explain why different regions of the Moon were selected.

20. Why are auroras observed at higher latitudes rather than near the equator?

# REFERENCES

Anderson, J. G., D. W. Toohey, and W. H. Brune. 1991. Free Radicals Within the Antarctic Vortex: The Role of CFCs in Antarctic Ozone Loss. *Science* (American Association for the Advancement of Science) 251, no. 4989 (January 4).

Bloxham, Jeremy, and David Gubbins. 1989. The Evolution of the Earth's Magnetic Field. *Scientific American* 261, no. 6 (December).

Briggs, Geoffrey, and Frederic Taylor. 1982. *The Cambridge Photographic Atlas of the Planets*. Cambridge: Cambridge University Press.

Bolt, Bruce A. 1973. The Fine Structure of the Earth's Interior. *Scientific American* 228, no. 3 (March).

Bonatti, Enrico. 1987. The Rifting of Continents. *Scientific American* 256, no. 3 (March).

Cadogan, Peter. 1983. The Moon's Origin. *Mercury* (Astronomical Society of the Pacific) 12, no. 2 (March/April).

Carrigan, Charles R., and David Gubbins. 1979. The Source of the Earth's Magnetic Field. *Scientific American* 240, no. 2 (February).

Cortright, Edgar M., ed. 1970. *Exploring Space with a Camera*. Washington, D.C.: NASA.

Duxbury, Alyn C., and Alison B. Duxbury. 1989. *An Introduction to the World's Oceans*. Dubuque, Iowa: Wm. C. Brown Publishers.

Gedzelman, Stanley David. 1980. *The Science and Wonders of the Atmosphere*. New York: John Wiley and Sons, Inc.

Heirtzler, J. R. 1968. Sea-Floor Spreading. *Scientific American* 219, no. 6 (December).

Heirtzler, J. R., and W. B. Bryan. 1975. The Floor of the Mid-Atlantic Rift. *Scientific American* 223, no. 2 (August).

Hess, Wilmot, Robert Kovach, Paul W. Gast, and Gene Simmons. 1969. The Exploration of the Moon. *Scientific American* 221, no. 4 (October).

Hones, Edward W. 1986. The Earth's Magnetotail. *Scientific American* 254, no. 3 (March).

Knittle, Elise, and Raymond Jeanloz. 1991. Earth's Core-Mantle Boundary and Results of Experiments at High Pressures and Temperatures. *Science* 251, no. 5000 (March 22).

Kosofsky, L. J., and Farouk El-Baz. 1970. *The Moon as Viewed by Lunar Orbiter.* Washington, D.C.: NASA.

Landsberg, Helmut E. 1953. The Origin of the Atmosphere. *Scientific American* 189, no. 2 (August).

Lanzerotti, Louis J. 1988. Earth's Magnetic Environment. *Sky and Telescope* 76, no. 3 (October).

Melosh, H. Jay. 1992. "Moon, Origin and Evolution." In *The Astronomy and Astrophysics Encyclopedia,* edited by Stephen P. Maran. New York: Van Nostrand Reinhold.

Menard, H. W. 1969. The Deep-Ocean Floor. *Scientific American* 221, no. 3 (September).

Molnar, Peter, and Paul Tapponnier. 1977. The Collision Between India and Eurasia. *Scientific American* 236, no. 4 (April).

Montgomery, Carla W. 1990. *Physical Geology.* Dubuque, Iowa: Wm. C. Brown Publishers.

Morrison, David, and Tobias Owen. 1988. Our Ancient Neighbor, the Moon. *Mercury* 17, no. 3 (May/June).

———. 1988. Our Ancient Neighbor, the Moon. Part 2: History and Origin. *Mercury* 17, no. 4 (July/August).

Mutter, John C. 1986. Seismic Images of Plate Boundaries. *Scientific American* 254, no. 2 (February).

Nance, R. Damian, Thomas R. Worsley, and Judith B. Moody. 1988. The Supercontinent Cycle. *Scientific American* 259, no. 1 (July).

O'Nions, R. K., P. J. Hamilton, and Norman M. Evenson. 1980. The Chemical Evolution of the Earth's Mantle. *Scientific American* 242, no. 5 (May).

Oort, Abraham H. 1970. The Energy Cycle of the Earth. *Scientific American* 223, no. 3 (September).

Schoeberl, Mark R., and Dennis L. Hartmann. 1991. The Dynamics of the Stratospheric Polar Vortex and Its Relation to Springtime Ozone Depletion. *Science* 251, no. 4989 (January 4).

Siever, Raymond. 1974. The Steady State of the Earth's Crust, Atmosphere, and Oceans. *Scientific American* 230, no. 6 (June).

Stewart, R. W. 1969. The Atmosphere and the Ocean. *Scientific American* 221, no. 3 (September).

Tazieff, Haroun. 1970. The Afar Triangle. *Scientific American* 222, no. 2 (February).

Thurman, Harold V. 1985. *Introductory Oceanography.* 4th ed. Columbus, Ohio: Charles E. Merrill Publishing Company.

Toksoz, M. Nafi. 1975. The Subduction of the Lithosphere. *Scientific American* 233, no. 5 (November).

Wyllie, Peter J. 1975. The Earth's Mantle. *Scientific American* 232, no. 3 (March).

chapter

8

the terrestrial planets:
Mercury, Venus, and Mars

A global view of Venus without its cloud cover,
produced from data supplied by the Magellan
spacecraft.

Our exploration of the solar system continues with the terrestrial planets, Mercury, Venus, and Mars. Like the Earth, they are comparatively small bodies characterized by high mean density, solid surfaces, and few if any satellites. Each planet will be described as seen through a telescope. Then, using data obtained by spacecraft, we will examine some tantalizing close-ups of each planet and learn about their atmospheres, magnetic fields, and interior structures.

## The Scorched Planet Mercury

Telescopic study of Mercury is complicated by its proximity to the Sun. When viewed at twilight, the planet is near the horizon where atmospheric turbulence blurs the telescopic image. Mercury is seen best at greatest elongation east in the afternoon before sunset, and at greatest elongation west in the morning after sunrise. Because Mercury is so difficult to observe, its surface remained a mystery until the use of radar in 1965.

In 1800, Johann Schröter became the first astronomer to report surface features on Mercury. During the planet's crescent phase, he claimed to have seen the southern horn blunted by the shadow of a mountain peak. Other astronomers, notably William Herschel, failed to confirm Schröter's observations. At the end of the nineteenth century, Schiaparelli made a systematic study of the planet and concluded that Mercury has a synchronous rotation of 88 days. Then, in 1965, the 305-m (1000-ft) radio telescope at Arecibo, Puerto Rico, was used to analyze signals reflected from the planet's surface. These studies confirmed a 59-day spin for Mercury, which is nearly two-thirds of its orbital period. Mercury has a 3:2 spin/orbit ratio and completes three rotations in every two revolutions.

Crater Kuiper

a.

### figure 8.1

Mariner 10 images of Mercury on March 29, 1974, as **a.** the spacecraft approached and **b.** moved away from the planet during its initial flyby. The prominent crater Kuiper is seen above center in the incoming view. Caloris Basin is the multi-ringed formation on the terminator in the outgoing view of the planet.

Caloris
Basin

b.

## The Surface of Mercury from Mariner 10

Scientists got their first glimpse of Mercury's surface as Mariner 10 flew by on March 29, 1974. Its cameras revealed a Moonlike surface covered by a confusion of craters, large basins, sinuous plains, and escarpments stretching unimpeded across a tortuous landscape. Heavily **cratered regions** show evidence of meteoric impact. Like their lunar counterparts, some craters possess rays that cover the surface with ejecta for many kilometers. The incoming hemisphere is distinguished by many craters, in particular a bright-rayed crater named Kuiper (fig. 8.1). It is about 40 km in diameter and is surrounded by small secondary craters formed by the ejecta from primary impacts. Debris from older formations appears darkened by the incessant rain of micrometeorites, solar radiation, and high-energy particles of the solar wind.

Separating the cratered terrain are **intercrater plains** that constitute about one-third of the planet's surface. These areas are also dotted with smaller secondary craters.

The high-resolution cameras aboard Mariner 10 revealed a unique region called the chaotic or **peculiar terrain** on the incoming hemisphere (fig. 8.2). It is a hilly, irregular tract of smooth-floored craters and valleys ranging up to 100 km in length. This lineated terrain appears to have wrinkled during some past cataclysmic event. The craters have flat floors like the lava-filled craters on the Moon, but in the peculiar terrain the craters have been deformed by the same destructive process that folded the adjacent hills.

The mystery of the hilly and lineated region was solved when Mariner 10 passed behind Mercury and photographed the receding hemisphere. Diametrically opposite the peculiar terrain is a huge impact basin comparable to the Mare Orientale on the Moon (figs. 8.3 and 7.20). The large, multiringed formation was named the **Caloris Basin** because of its location at one of the hot subsolar points of Mercury at perihelion. The basin consists of a series of concentric ringed mountains 1300 km in diameter. Some of the peaks reach two km above the surrounding surface. The plains inside the basin are filled with secondary craters, ridges, and fractures. Apparently, Caloris Basin was formed when the planet was struck by a large meteoric object. The impact produced seismic waves that penetrated the planet and focused on the opposite side, where the disturbance produced the peculiar terrain seen in figure 8.2.

Beyond Caloris Basin are found **smooth plains** up to 800 km diameter, suggestive of the flat maria found on the Moon. There are ancient buried craters with only their rims above the plain, while many young craters can be identified by the light-colored ejecta strewn

◄ **figure 8.2**

A hilly, irregular tract of peculiar terrain on Mercury. The region contains smooth-floored craters and Arecibo Valles, a 100-km-long valley piercing the deformed surface, seen at the lower right side of this photograph.

**figure 8.3** ►

The multi-ringed Caloris Basin, 1300 km in diameter, seen at the left side of this photograph.

## methods and understandings 8.1

### A Solar "Day" on Mercury

The 3:2 ratio of Mercury's rotation and revolution creates an unusual solar "day." In one rotational period, lasting 59 Earth days, the apparent motion of the Sun from east to west is 6.1° per day. At the same time, the planet's 88-day revolution causes the Sun to advance eastward at a rate of 4.1° per day. The difference between the two motions, about 2.0° per day, represents the average rate at which the Sun would appear to cross the sky for an observer on the surface. Thus one solar "day"—from "sunrise" to "sunrise"—on the planet is about the same length as two Mercurian "years." The observer on the planet's scorched surface could look forward to 88 Earth days of sunshine from dawn to dusk (fig. 8.4).

Mercury reaches perihelion during the 88-day period that the Sun remains above the horizon. At perihelion, the acceleration of the planet causes the Sun to appear to advance eastward at a greater rate than its westward move-ment. A visitor to Mercury would see the Sun reverse its direction in the sky, travel east, stop, and resume its west-ward trek after perihelion passage. If the event were seen at dawn, the Sun would rise, dip below the eastern hori-zon, and rise again. The Sun would cross the observer's meridian twice from east to west when perihelion pas-sage occurs at noon. At dusk, the Sun would set, rise above the western horizon, set again, and remain below the horizon for 88 days of darkness until Mercury completes another circuit in its orbit.

The 3:2 resonance was significant during the Mariner 10 mis-sions in 1974 and 1975. The spacecraft was launched into a solar orbit with a period of revolution equal to 176 days (two sidereal

**figure 8.4**

The 3:2 ratio of Mercury's counterclockwise rotation and revolution. The planet makes three rotations for every two revolutions. At perihelion, position 1, the arrow pointing toward the Sun marks the subsolar point (the point on the equator at which the sun is directly overhead). At position 2, Mercury has completed one-half rotation, and the arrow points in the opposite direction. By position 3, the planet has completed one full rotation. When Mercury returns to perihelion, position 4, the planet has rotated one and one-half times, and the original subsolar point is in the opposite direction of position 1. Thus at perihelion, when Mercury is nearest the Sun, there are only two subsolar points, on opposite sides of the planet.

periods of Mercury). The first encounter between the planet and the spacecraft occurred during a flyby on March 29, 1974. Two more encounters took place on September 21, 1974, and March 16, 1975, when the spacecraft completed one sidereal period of revolution. Meanwhile, Mercury made two revolutions in its or-bit and three rotations on its axis. Thus, during each flyby, the same hemisphere of Mercury was televised back to Earth.

**figure 8.5**
A scarp bisecting a crater on Mercury.

radially about their centers. Evidently, craters filled the region before molten rock seeped from the interior. A large number of smaller secondary craters formed after the surface solidified.

A distinctive feature of the cratered terrain are long, curved cliffs, or **lobate scarps,** that rise about two km above and extend several hundred km across the surface (fig. 8.5). They are found in large numbers and give evidence of an earlier period of crustal movement. Scarps are generally aligned in a northwest to southeast direction and many cut across and offset craters by several kilometers. Other scarps terminate in cratered regions. Evidently, they were formed during the final stages of meteroric bombardment.

Why are scarps missing on other cratered worlds found in the solar system? Mercury is unique because early in its history internal contraction caused global shrinking that led to the formation of scarps. The heights of the scarps indicate a reduction in the planet's radius by about two km.

## Physical Properties

The purpose of the Mariner 10 mission went beyond taking pictures of the tiny, elusive planet. In addition to cameras, the Mariner 10 spacecraft was equipped with an infrared radiometer to determine the surface temperature; ultraviolet spectrometers to search for an atmosphere; a plasma analyzer to measure charged particles of the solar wind; and a magnetometer to detect the presence of a magnetic field. Radio signals furnished data on the mass and size of the planet.

Although Mercury is saturated by radiant energy from the Sun, radiometer data indicate a wide range in temperature between the day and night hemispheres. At perihelion, in the heat of the overhead Sun, temperatures soar to 700 K, which is hot enough to melt lead. On the dark hemisphere the temperatures plunge to about 100 K, which is colder than the night side of the Moon.

Size, temperature, and low surface gravity rule out the possibility of Mercury retaining an extensive atmosphere.

This was confirmed as the spacecraft passed out of sight behind Mercury and radio signals were sharply interrupted by the limb of the planet. The signal would have been scattered and refracted if Mercury had an atmosphere. However, the ultraviolet spectrometers aboard the spacecraft detected a thin layer of hydrogen and helium that may have originated in the solar wind. The elements sodium and potassium in this tenuous atmosphere may be a by-product of radioactivity in the crustal rocks.

The mass and volume (and from these the density) of Mercury were determined by radio signals from the spacecraft. Mercury has an unexpectedly high density for a small planet—(5.43 g/cm$^3$). In this respect, it is more like Earth and Venus than Mars and the Moon. Magnetometer data from Mariner 10 support the theory that Mercury has a large iron core.

## The Magnetosphere

Investigators were caught off-guard when the spacecraft indicated the presence of

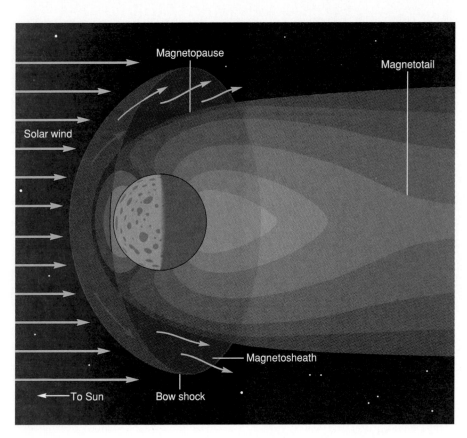

**figure 8.6**
The magnetosphere of Mercury.

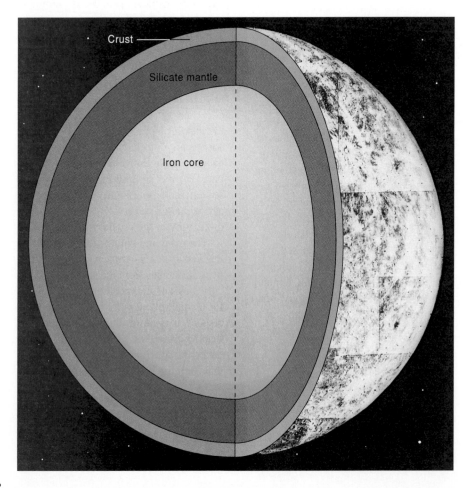

a dipolar magnetic field. Interplanetary space has a weak magnetic field that was monitored during the incoming flight. When Mariner 10 reached Mercury, the strength of the field increased sufficiently to produce a cavity in the solar wind about the planet. Just like the Earth, Mercury is enclosed by a magnetosphere consisting of a bow shock in front, a magnetosheath, and a magnetopause (fig. 8.6). The solar wind pushes the magnetic field downstream into an extended magnetotail.

Two possible explanations for Mercury's magnetic field have been proposed: the planet produces the field by a self-induced dynamo effect, or the planet is permanently magnetized. In order for a slowly rotating planet to induce a magnetic field by the dynamo effect, an iron core must represent a large percentage of its total volume (fig. 8.7). Mercury fills this requirement with its high density and an iron core as large as the Moon.

An alternate explanation suggests that at one time, Mercury had a rapid rotation, which generated an induced magnetic field by the dynamo action of its iron core. Eventually, the rotational period of the planet slowed down into its stable spin/orbit ratio while its magnetism was retained in a permanent intrinsic field.

## The Veiled Planet Venus

Years ago, astronomers discovered the thick cloud cover of Venus during transits of the planet and the Sun. When Venus is partially immersed in the solar disk, its outer limb is brightened by a ring of light representing its illuminated atmosphere. A similar effect is seen near inferior conjunction when sunlight is refracted beyond the cusps and forms a ring of light around the darkened limb.

In the early 1960s, powerful radar instruments probed beneath the atmosphere of Venus and measured its rotational pe-

◄ **figure 8.7**
The iron core of Mercury is as large as the Earth's moon. If the planet has an induced magnetic field, like the Earth does, then its outer core will be fluid.

## successful missions to Venus and Mercury

| Mission | Launch | Mission Type |
| --- | --- | --- |
| Mariner 2 | Aug. 27, 1962 | Venus flyby |
| Venera 4 | June 12, 1967 | Venus atmospheric probe |
| Mariner 5 | June 14, 1967 | Venus flyby |
| Venera 5 | Jan. 5, 1969 | Venus atmospheric probe |
| Venera 6 | Jan. 10, 1969 | Venus atmospheric probe |
| Venera 7 | Aug. 17, 1970 | Venus atmospheric/surface probe |
| Venera 8 | Mar. 27, 1972 | Venus atmospheric/surface probe |
| Mariner 10 | Nov. 3, 1973 | Venus flyby |
| | | Mercury flyby |
| | | Mercury flyby |
| | | Mercury flyby |
| Venera 9 | June 8, 1975 | Venus orbiter/lander |
| Venera 10 | June 14, 1975 | Venus orbiter/lander |
| Pioneer Venus 1 | May 20, 1978 | Venus orbiter |
| Pioneer Venus 2 | Aug. 8, 1978 | Venus atmospheric probes (4) |
| Venera 11 | Sept. 9, 1978 | Venus flyby/lander |
| Venera 12 | Sept. 14, 1978 | Venus flyby/lander |
| Venera 13 | Oct. 30, 1981 | Venus flyby/lander |
| Venera 14 | Nov. 4, 1981 | Venus flyby/lander |
| Venera 15 | June 2, 1983 | Venus orbiter |
| Venera 16 | June 7, 1983 | Venus orbiter |
| Vega 1 | Dec. 15, 1984 | Venus lander, balloon |
| Vega 2 | Dec. 21, 1984 | Venus lander, balloon |
| Magellan | May 4, 1989 | Venus orbiter |

From Stephen Cole, "Mercury and Venus, Space Missions" in *The Astronomy and Astrophysics Encyclopedia.* Copyright © 1992 Van Nostrand Reinhold Company, New York, NY. Reprinted by permission.

riod. The returning radar echo showed a difference in frequency, or Doppler shift, when reflected from the east and west limbs of the rotating body. The difference in frequency between the echo from the approaching and receding limbs of a planet causes a broadening of the spectral lines of the returning signal. The width of the lines indicated that Venus spins clockwise (retrograde) in a period of 243 days. Moreover, the reflected radar signals established the equatorial radius of Venus at 6052 km.

By the late 1960s, the 305-m radio telescope at Arecibo was operational and provided high-resolution images of surface details down to 10 km. The observations were made a few weeks before and after inferior conjunction when Venus is at its closest approach to the Earth. The region mapped by radar contains plateaus, circular depressions, and large craters.

But only a restricted area of Venus's surface can be mapped this way. The combination of the retrograde rotation and prograde revolution keeps the same hemisphere of the planet facing the Earth at inferior conjunction. Venus rotates clockwise 1.48° per day and revolves counterclockwise 1.60° per day. Thus the Sun advances from west to east at a rate of about 3.08° per day, and a solar day on Venus is the equivalent of about 117 Earth days. Since there are nearly five Venusian solar days in every synodic period, the same hemisphere always points towards the Earth at inferior conjunction.

## Exploring Venus by Spacecraft

Since 1961, Venus has been under constant surveillance by spacecraft from the United States and the former Soviet Union. The flights have varied from simple flyby missions to complex orbiters, surface landers, and atmospheric balloon probes. Twenty-two successful spacecraft have been launched, from the Mariner 2 mission in 1962 to the Magellan orbiter in 1989 (table 8.1).

The upper clouds and atmospheric temperature were investigated as Mariner 2 came within 34,800 km of the planet. No evidence of any significant magnetic field was detected.

In October 1967, the Soviet Venera 4 passed into the inhospitable atmosphere of Venus for the first hard landing on the surface. The descent through the atmosphere confirmed the lack of a magnetic field as reported by Mariner 2. In addition, the atmosphere was found to be over 90% carbon dioxide; its temperature varied from about 300 K to 500 K; and pressure increased from less than 1 to 20 Earth atmospheres.

Earth-based radar experiments were underway when Mariner 5 made a close approach in October 1967. At a distance of about 3400 km, radio signals from the spacecraft provided temperature and pressure profiles of the upper atmosphere. These data were extrapolated to the surface by combining the measurements from the spacecraft with the distance to the surface previously determined by radar observations. The pressure at the surface was found to be over 90 bars (Earth atmospheres) and the temperature as high as 750 K.

Additional atmospheric data were transmitted by Venera 5 and 6 in May 1969. In the following year, the first soft landing was made by Venera 7. In July 1972, the soft lander Venera 8 analyzed the chemical composition of surface rock. Also, the spacecraft discovered that diffused sunlight penetrates the cloud cover and illuminates the Venusian landscape.

The first spacecraft images of Venus were obtained when Mariner 10 passed

the terrestrial planets: Mercury, Venus, and Mars

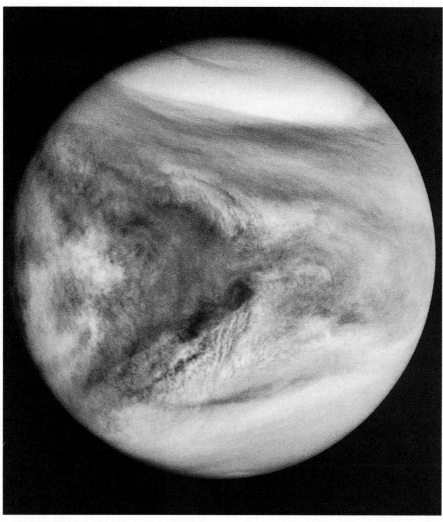

**figure 8.8**

Sulphuric acid clouds of Venus. This image from the Pioneer Venus Orbiter spacecraft reveals the circulation of the upper clouds from the middle latitudes to the poles.

▼ **figure 8.9**

A wide-angle view of surface rocks on Venus, photographed by one of the Venera landers.

within 5800 km of Venus on its way to Mercury in February 1974. The pictures of Venus in ultraviolet light revealed structural bands of clouds spiraling about the planet from the middle latitudes into a vortex at each pole. The upper clouds circulate across the planet in only four days, confirming earlier estimates of atmospheric motion detected in ground-based telescopes (fig. 8.8).

Venera orbiter/landers were the first spacecraft to return pictures of the Venusian surface (fig. 8.9). The vehicles were placed in orbit around the planet while capsules descended through the upper atmosphere by parachute. Studies of the surface composition and temperature were made and television images were acquired. Venera orbiters transmitted more information about the composition and temperature of the atmosphere, the magnetic field, and the effects of the solar wind. Venus was found to have a magnetic field induced by electric currents in its ionosphere.

Venera flyby/landers made soft landings and transmitted data on surface conditions. The spacecraft carried spectrometers that analyzed the soil at various locations and found it to be different types of basalt.

The Venus 1 orbiter (Pioneer 12) and Venus 2 atmospheric probes (Pioneer 13) reached Venus in December 1978. The orbiters were designed to map the surface by radar, and study the planet's magnetism and interaction with the solar wind. Four probes and a bus (mother ship) descended through the atmosphere to measure winds, temperature, pressure,

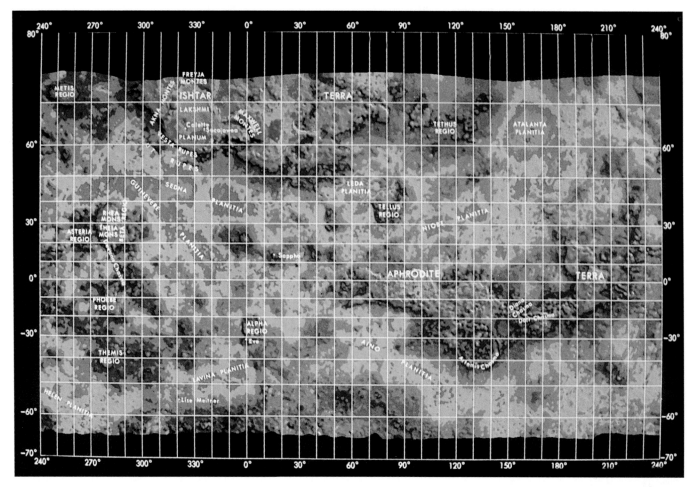

**figure 8.10**

Radar map of the surface of Venus based on measurements made by the Pioneer Venus 1 orbiter. The blue areas represent undulating upland plains. The yellow regions are large terrae, comparable to continents on Earth.

and density changes from high altitude down to the surface. Topographic maps were made of 93% of the surface between 74° north and 63° south latitudes (fig. 8.10). The radar altimeter aboard the Venus orbiter recorded elevations reaching 6000 m above the average radius ("sea level") of the planet.

Two Venera orbiters were placed in polar orbits in October 1983. On-board imaging systems resolved surface features as small as 2 km across. For eight months the Veneras mapped the northern hemisphere above 30° latitude, in the region not covered by the Pioneer orbiter.

The Venera missions were followed by the twin spacecraft Vega 1 and 2 in June 1985. The Vegas dropped probes into the atmosphere of Venus and continued in their orbits for a rendezvous with Comet Halley (see chapter 11). Two capsules released soft landers by para-

chute while two instrument packages were kept aloft by balloons.

The Magellan spacecraft entered Venus orbit on August 10, 1990, after a 15-month journey from Earth. The radar mapping mission was designed to produce high-resolution images covering 90% of the planet's surface. As the satellite travels in an elliptical polar orbit, the mapping radar scans a strip of surface area roughly 20 m wide and 15,000 km long.

The Magellan orbiter carries an onboard radar system, called a *synthetic aperture radar,* that "sees" through the extensive cloud cover to the surface. The signals echo from the surface to the spacecraft where they are recorded on tape. Later, the signals are telemetered to the Earth where image elements are digitally assembled into units called mosaics. Each mosaic represents a region

of the Venusian surface area about 530 km square.

## The Surface of Venus

Although very nearly the size and mass of the Earth, our "twin" in space turned out to be unique and different in many respects. In general, Venus is very smooth, but there are mountain ranges, plateaus, volcanoes, and rift valleys that rival similar features on Earth. There are two areas called **terrae** that are comparable to the continental land masses on Earth. About 65% of the planet's surface consists of undulating upland plains. Other areas called **planitiae** are extremely flat and represent lowlands. Isolated plateaus (**regiones**) contain volcanoes (**mons**). There are several mountain ranges (**montes**) and many deep channels (**chasmate**).

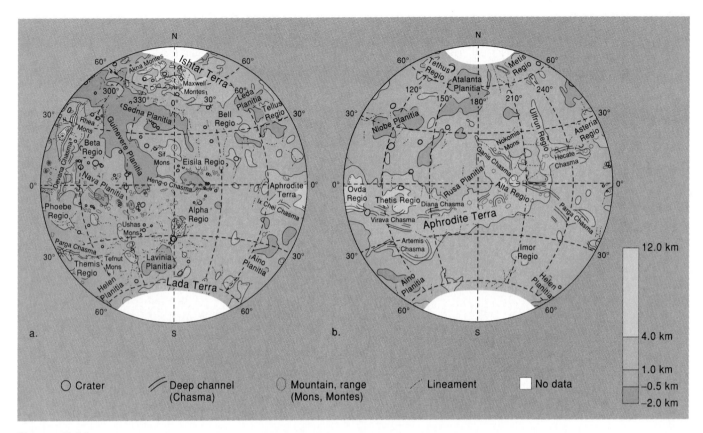

**figure 8.11**

Equal-area projections of the surface of Venus. *a.* Ishtar Hemisphere. *b.* Aphrodite Hemisphere.
Source: James Cook Archive of Space Exploration, Victoria, B. C., 1983.

Venera 8, 11, 13, and 14 made soft landings in the relatively smooth plain area and carried out various experiments at each site. The Venera 8 gamma-ray experiment determined the amount of uranium, thorium, and potassium in the surface and found it to be similar to terrestrial igneous rock. Venera 11 measured the temperature, air pressure, and wind velocity. Venera 13 and 14 transmitted pictures of the landscape and took samples of the soil. The images of the Venusian terrain showed flat rocks and interstices of rock dust.

The plains are marked by numerous craterlike depressions ranging up to 800 km in diameter. Planetary scientists believe the surface of Venus to be geologically young, and the craters are no more than 800 million years old.

Another feature of the Venusian landscape is the planitiae, which extend in discontinuous areas across the entire planet (fig. 8.11). They have smooth surfaces and lie about 1.5 km below the mean level. One, named Atalanta Planitia,

is a flat circular basin similar to the maria found on the Moon (fig. 8.11b). Planitiae have fewer craters than the upland plains and represent young basaltic crust formed by the upwelling of molten rock from the interior of the planet. Lavinia Planitia contains a number of craters such as Howe, shown in figure 8.12.

Higher than the upland plains are two large continental masses located in opposite hemispheres. Ishtar Terra (fig. 8.11a) is as large as the continental United States; Aphrodite Terra is about equal in size to Africa (fig. 8.11b).

Ishtar contains a plateau, Lakshmi Planum, which lies between 4 and 5 km above the mean level. The mountain ranges Maxwell Montes, Akna Montes, and Freyja Montes rise above the relatively flat tableland. The highest peaks extend to an altitude of 11 km. Lakshmi may have formed when layers of lava congealed over an uplifted section of ancient crust.

Mountain peaks are situated in the eastern and western regions of Aphrodite

Terra at elevations between 4 and 6 km above a rolling terrain scarred with many straight and sinuous channels. A number are bow-shaped, such as the prominent Artemis Chasma. In the center of the plateau another mountain group rises to a height of 3 km.

There are elevated regions containing large shield volcanoes and deep faults extending thousands of kilometers across the surrounding surface. One such area, Beta Regio, is found to the south and west of Guinevere Planitia (fig. 8.11a). Venera 9 landed here and returned pictures of a barren volcanic landscape covered by flat rocks. Venera 10 also landed in the Beta Regio region but at a greater distance from the volcanoes. The area surrounding the spacecraft experienced tectonic activity some time in the past.

Magellan returned detailed images of a sweeping panorama of sculptured plains, mountain ranges, impact craters, and plateaus (see photo at beginning of chapter). The vast plains of Venus are filled with meandering channels extend-

**figure 8.12**
Magellan image of the Lavinia Planitia region in the far south of Ishtar Hemisphere. The foreground crater, named Howe, has a diameter of 37 km.

ing for hundreds of kilometers (fig. 8.13). They are remarkably constant in width, ranging between 1 and 2 km. In the past, the plains were flooded by extensive lava flows from numerous shield volcanoes. There are large mountain ranges indicating that tectonic activity took place some time in the past, but no evidence exists for the large-scale plate movement found on the Earth.

The surface of Venus is believed to be geologically young. Scientists have compared the cratering rate on Venus to that on other terrestrial planets and the Moon, and they estimate the age of the crustal material on Venus to be between several hundred million and one billion years. The lava flows from Maat Mons, an 8-km high volcano in Aphrodite Terra, may be only a few million years old (figs. 8.11b and 8.14).

**figure 8.13**
Meandering channels southwest of Themis Region in the southern hemisphere of Venus.

## The Atmosphere of Venus

According to our present understanding of the evolution of the terrestrial planets, the original atmosphere of Venus was lost and replaced by gases vented from the interior of the planet. The secondary atmosphere of Venus contained carbon dioxide, nitrogen, sulphur compounds, and water vapor. The water vapor may have condensed and combined with the sulphur to form a highly concentrated solution of sulphuric acid. In contrast, on the Earth, where lower temperatures prevailed, the water vapor condensed to form oceans.

The American Pioneer spacecraft and various Soviet Veneras have confirmed the composition of the present Venusian atmosphere to be about 96.5% carbon dioxide and 3% nitrogen by volume. The remaining constituents include water vapor, oxygen, carbon monoxide, sulphur compounds, and the noble gases neon, argon, and krypton. In contrast to our own planet, the total water vapor content in the atmosphere of Venus is infinitesimal. Soviet estimates show that if all the water vapor on Venus condensed to liquid, a layer of water 1-cm thick would cover the surface.

Why does the Earth differ so much from its nearest planetary neighbor? The answer is found in the Earth's distance from the Sun. The lower temperature and large bodies of water on our home planet made it possible for the carbon dioxide to be chemically bound in carbonates dissolved in the oceans and contained in the crust instead of remaining in the atmosphere.

The atmosphere of Venus has a vertical structure (fig. 8.15). The first layer, called the troposphere, extends from the surface to a height of about 70 km. Near the surface, convection currents rise in a clear but red-colored sky. Between 10 and 50 km the atmosphere is stable and global winds circulate from the equator to the poles. At 30 km altitude the sky is marked by a thin, hazy layer of aerosols, possibly sulphuric acid and dust. In the troposphere the temperature decreases from 750 K at the surface to about 600 K at the lower haze level.

A cloud deck consisting of three distinct layers is found between 50 and 70

### figure 8.14

A ground-level image of Maat Mons was obtained by combining Magellan radar and altimetry data. (Vertical exaggeration is 10x.) The peak, which is 8 km high, is one of the largest volcanoes on Venus. The dark areas in the foreground are lava flows that may be only a few million years old.

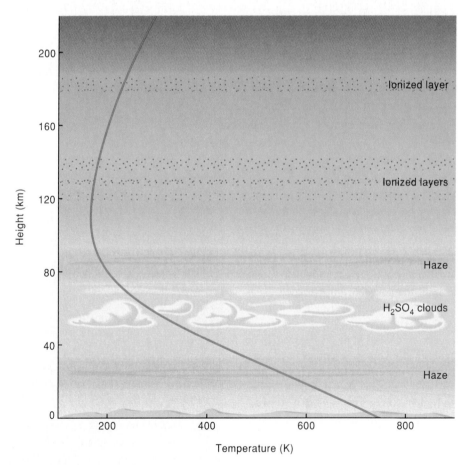

### figure 8.15

The structure and temperature curve of the atmosphere of Venus.

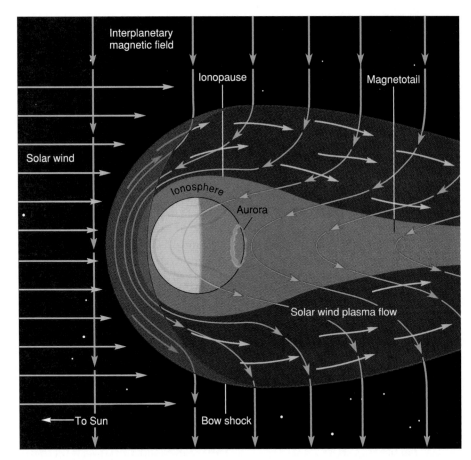

**figure 8.16**

The magnetosphere of Venus. Note the aurora-like glow that forms in the ionosphere at the equatorial region on Venus's night side.

km altitude. At the base of the lower clouds the temperature is about 356 K; it decreases to 225 K at the top of the upper clouds.

Radio and polarization data from Earth-based observations indicate that the upper clouds of Venus contain concentrated sulphuric acid. These findings were confirmed by experiments aboard the Veneras 9 and 10 as they plunged through the atmosphere to a soft landing on the surface. The Veneras identified differences in the sizes of the acid particles found in each cloud layer.

The clouds in the upper troposphere are in a region of greatest wind velocity. The Mariner 10 flyby showed a latitudinal cloud motion of 150 m/sec, or a rotational period of about four days. The period was detected by following a distinctive Y-shaped cloud feature (fig. 8.8). A slower north-south convective circulation was identified by the movement of clouds from the equator to the poles. Air heated at the equator rises to higher altitudes and migrates to the north and south. A surface flow returns to the equator as the upper air descends at the poles. The top of the upper cloud layer lies at the boundary of the troposphere and the upper atmosphere of Venus. At higher altitudes, there are additional layers of sulphuric-acid haze to 90 km altitude, where temperatures drop to 200 K.

The Pioneer Venus and Veneras 9 and 10 made plasma and magnetic field measurements where the solar wind interacts with the planet. Since Venus and the Earth have about the same diameter, mass, and density, we can expect that both have similar internal structure. However, there is a basic difference between the two planets. Because of its slow rotation, Venus lacks the intrinsic magnetic field generated by an electrically conducting core. The weak magnetic field measured by detectors aboard the spacecraft is caused by the interaction of the solar wind and electrified layers in the upper atmosphere (fig. 8.16). There is an ionosphere consisting of two weakly ionized layers at 120 km and 130 km altitude. The electron density reaches a maximum at the main ionization layer located at about 140 km. An additional weakly ionized layer is found at 180 km. The ionosphere of Venus acts as a barrier to the interplanetary magnetic field which spirals outward from the Sun (fig. 11.10). The incoming solar wind drapes the magnetic field into a bow shock ahead of the planet and a comet-like magnetotail in the direction opposite the Sun.

## The Greenhouse Effect

The Earth and Venus maintain a global energy balance by radiating into space the same amount of energy they receive from the Sun. Some of the solar energy is reflected into space as the planet's albedo, while the remaining energy is absorbed by the surface and radiated to the atmosphere as heat.

To get an idea of why the surface temperature of Venus is high, let us look at how its radiation balance is maintained. Recall how solar energy enters the Earth's atmosphere and is reflected, scattered, and finally absorbed at the surface (chapter 7). A portion of the incident solar radiation (36%) is reflected into space. About 13% is absorbed in the atmosphere, and the remaining 51% is absorbed by the oceans and continents. The sunlight that reaches the surface is reflected into space or radiated into the atmosphere as thermal energy. Water vapor and carbon dioxide in the Earth's atmosphere absorb thermal energy and cause additional heating, which produces a so-called **greenhouse effect.**

Because it is located nearer to the Sun, Venus receives about twice as much radiation at the top of its atmosphere as the Earth receives. But the upper atmosphere and dense cloud layers on Venus reflect and scatter most of the radiation (65%) back into space. The sky at the surface of Venus is completely overcast and dimly lighted. Only 3% of the incident solar radiation reaches the surface. This fraction of light energy penetrates the transparent carbon dioxide atmosphere and is absorbed by the surface.

Data provided by Veneras 11 and 12 confirm that the high surface temperature on Venus is the result of the greenhouse effect caused by the carbon dioxide atmosphere and the dense sulphuric-acid cloud cover. Carbon dioxide effectively absorbs most of the infrared energy radiated from the surface, but not enough to bring the surface temperature above 700 K. Since some infrared wavelengths pass through the carbon dioxide blanket and into space, an additional absorber of energy is necessary to maintain a high temperature. The Veneras and Pioneer found traces of water and sulphur dioxide, which are also capable of trapping radiation in the clouds. However, most of the absorption of infrared radiation is due to the abundance of carbon dioxide.

Models of the atmospheres of Venus and the Earth must account for the differences between the planets, especially the deficiency of water on our sister planet. Both the Earth and Venus have experienced volcanic activity. On the primitive Earth, volcanoes expelled large quantities of carbon dioxide and water vapor into the atmosphere. The Earth cooled and water vapor condensed to form vast oceans. The atmospheric carbon dioxide dissolved in the oceans and formed minerals that were converted into carbonate rocks. The temperature on Venus is too high for oceans to exist, so carbon dioxide could not be fixed in carbonate rocks but remains as the principal constituent of the atmosphere.

Why Venus's atmosphere is so dry remains a mystery. What happened to the atmospheric water vapor? Some scientists argue that early in its complex history, Venus may have been covered by shallow seas a few meters deep. The primordial seas evaporated and hydrogen and oxygen atoms dissociated in the upper atmosphere. One in about 6000 hydrogen atoms had a deuterium nucleus. Most of the lighter hydrogen atoms escaped into space while many heavier deuterons remained in the atmosphere. Oxygen diffused and returned to the lower atmosphere and reacted with surface rock. Supporting this view is the enrichment of the deuterium/hydrogen ratio present in the water vapor found in the Venusian atmosphere. Detected by instruments aboard the Pioneer Venus atmospheric probe, the deuterium enrichment on Venus is about 100 times that found on Earth.

The process contributed to the formation of an effective radiation blanket, which raised the surface temperature. Once started, the process continued as a chain reaction until most of the water was removed from the surface. The increase in water vapor and $CO_2$ liberated from the exposed crustal rocks triggered a *runaway* greenhouse effect that continued until the present heat balance was attained on the surface as well as in the atmosphere.

## The Red Planet Mars

Mars has intrigued the public more than any other planet. At favorable opposition its apparent diameter reaches 25″ of arc, making the planet a splendid object to observe with telescopes of moderate aperture. Unlike Venus, which is seen as a cloudy crescent, Mars reveals a fully illuminated disk covered by contrasting surface markings. The variegated surface of Mars has been recognized for centuries (fig. 6.15). At the time of their discovery and long after, many believed the dark grey and green regions were seas, the lighter orange areas were continents, and the conspicuous white polar caps were ice and snow.

Indeed, the similarity between Mars and the Earth led some people to wonder if the planet was capable of supporting intelligent life. Later, seasonal change in the color of the surface markings was attributed to the growth of primitive plants. These ideas were put to rest when the environment on Mars was found to be entirely too hostile to support any known form of life.

Because of its axial tilt of 25.2°, Mars has seasons like the Earth, except they are twice as long. The dark markings change color as seasonal dust storms sweep across the surface. The polar caps wax and wane as ice sheets alternately advance in winter and retreat in summer. Telescope investigations made prior to space missions to Mars indicated that the darker surface areas are composed of volcanic rock and the orange-colored regions contain an abundance of iron oxides.

The seasonal changes in the size of the polar caps requires a transfer of energy between the atmosphere and the surface. During winter, the ice caps reach their maximum size and extend as far as the middle latitudes. By summer, the caps shrink to a small area centered at the poles. These changes, along with the appearance of fog, haze, and clouds, indicate a change of state of atmospheric carbon dioxide. Further investigation confirmed $CO_2$ as the principal constituent in the atmosphere, followed by nitrogen and traces of water vapor and oxygen. The presence of $CO_2$ in such large quantities led early investigators to believe the polar caps to be frozen carbon dioxide.

### Missions to Mars

In the 1960s and 1970s spacecraft were launched to Mars by the United States and the former Soviet Union (table 8.2). The early images returned to Earth showed a region of the southern hemisphere filled with impact craters similar to those found on the Moon. The craters seen on the dismal landscape gave no indication of the many startling features soon to be discovered. A global view of Mars was achieved in 1971 when Mariner 9 was placed in orbit around the planet. The spacecraft traveled in an eccentric path at an inclination of about 64° to the planet's equator. Its distance above the surface ranged from 1650 to 17,100 km. The results of the Mariner 9 mission not only confirmed the findings of the first three Mariners but also showed close-up pictures of volcanoes, plains, channels, enormous canyons and mountainous terrain.

Further launch opportunities allowed the United States to dispatch Viking orbiters and landers to Mars in 1976. The vehicles were placed into orbits and transmitted about 5500 detailed images of the planet over a period of two years. These images permitted scientists to construct detailed physiographic maps of Mars (fig. 8.17). Two Viking landers were deployed to take samples on the

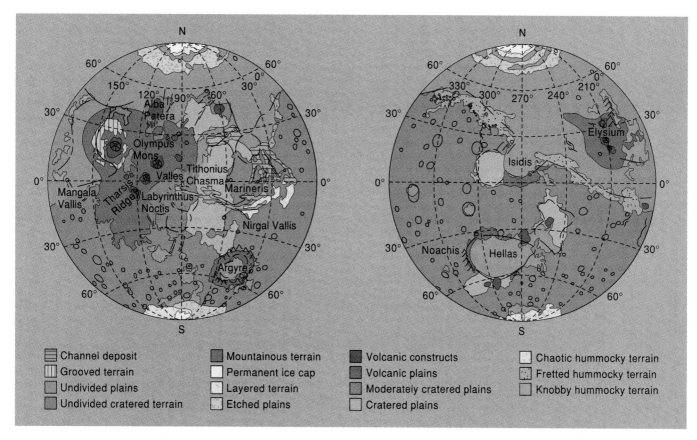

**figure 8.17**
Physiographic map of the geological features of Mars.
Source: U.S. Geological Survey.

The legend of the map reads:

Channel deposit
Grooved terrain
Undivided plains
Undivided cratered terrain
Mountainous terrain
Permanent ice cap
Layered terrain
Etched plains
Volcanic constructs
Volcanic plains
Moderately cratered plains
Cratered plains
Chaotic hummocky terrain
Fretted hummocky terrain
Knobby hummocky terrain

## Table 8.2

### successful missions to Mars

| Mission | Launch | Mission Type |
|---|---|---|
| Mariner 4 | November 1964 | Flyby |
| Mariner 6 | February 1969 | Flyby |
| Mariner 7 | March 1969 | Flyby |
| Mars 2 | May 1971 | Crash-landed |
| Mars 3 | May 1971 | Orbiter/lander |
| Mariner 9 | May 1971 | Orbiter |
| Mars 5 | July 1973 | Orbiter |
| Mars 6 | August 1973 | Orbiter/lander |
| Viking 1 | August 1975 | Orbiter/lander |
| Viking 2 | September 1975 | Orbiter/lander |
| Phobos 2 | July 1988 | Orbiter |
| Mars Observer | September 1992 | Orbiter |

Source: Data from NASA.

surface of Mars. Viking 1 touched down in Chryse Planitia, a hilly region in the northern hemisphere. Viking 2 made its landing in Utopia Planitia, which is part of a huge **undivided plains terrain** covering a large portion of the northern hemisphere.

## The Search for Life

One of the main objectives of the Viking missions was to search for organic matter and living organisms on Mars. Both Viking spacecraft were equipped with laboratories to carry out biological experiments. The Martian soil was tested to determine whether any organisms were present, and if they ingested nutrients and atmosphere and released organic compounds back into the environment. The soil was injected with a nutrient that contained organic compounds and radioactive carbon. If organisms were present, they might take in the nutrients and give off carbon dioxide. Chemical changes were noted during the experiments, but no organic material or living organisms were detected in the Martian soil.

## The Surface of Mars

Mariner spacecraft observed the **cratered terrain** in the southern hemisphere. The boundary of this type of terrain circles

**figure 8.18**
Old undivided cratered terrain in the southern hemisphere of Mars. The region is covered with flat-bottomed craters and sinuous channel systems.

**figure 8.19**
Argyre Planitia is an impact basin 740 km in diameter. Compare Argyre to Mare Orientale on the Moon and to Caloris Basin on Mars.

the planet and at one point extends to +40° latitude. It is an upland region representing an ancient surface covered by craters in various stages of decay. Like the surfaces of other terrestrial planets and the Moon, the cratered terrain shows the effect of bombardment by meteoric bodies early in the planet's history. Moreover, there is evidence of lava seepage that cooled and formed smooth intercrater plains (fig. 8.18).

The southern cratered terrain is raised in elevation about 2 km higher than the northern hemisphere. At the boundary of the ancient cratered uplands, slumping has produced a rippled surface called **fretted hummocky terrain** of isolated blocks, mesas, and cliffs.

In addition to craters, the ancient terrain contains large impact basins; the largest, Hellas Planitia, has a diameter of about 2000 km. Another, known as Argyre Planitia, is a multi-ringed mountain formation similar to Caloris Basin on Mercury and Mare Orientale on the Moon. The basins are depressed several kilometers below the surrounding terrain (fig. 8.19). There are sinuous valleys or channels that resemble dry river beds extending for hundreds of kilometers across cratered landscape. Where the channels terminate, there are fan-shaped piles of sediments that may have been carried down by primordial flood waters or ice flows that cut through the channels.

When Mariner 9 was placed into orbit above Mars, a global dust storm kept the planet obscured for several months. After the atmosphere cleared, the spacecraft cameras recorded astonishing features. Centered on the equator is the **Tharsis bulge,** a large, irregular volcanic dome reaching 10 km in elevation and extending thousands of kilometers

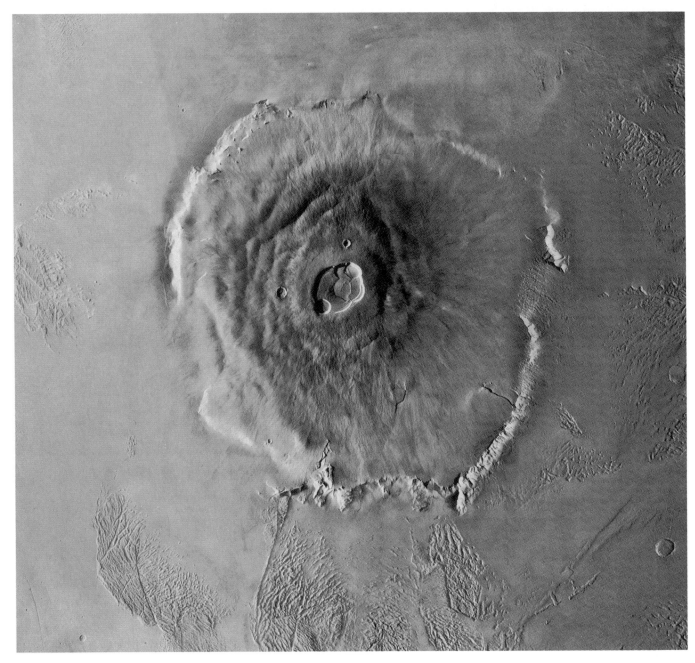

**figure 8.20**

Olympus Mons, a gigantic shield volcano. The volcanoes on Mars are dormant.

from north to south. A ridge through the center of the Tharsis bulge is dominated by shield volcanoes that dwarf similar structures on the Earth.

Three large volcanoes, each about 400 km in diameter, stretch across Tharsis ridge from the southwest to the northeast. The largest volcano in the solar system, **Olympus Mons,** lies to the northwest (fig. 8.20). Olympus Mons has a diameter of over 500 km and is 25 km high. If placed along the east coast of the United States, the volcano would extend from Boston, Mass. to Washington, D.C.

What internal processes were responsible for such a massive outpouring of molten rock? Compare the Tharsis shield volcanoes with those found on the Hawaiian Islands. A hot spot beneath the crust produces a lava flow through feeder tubes to the seafloor. The molten rock oozes out and deposits layers of basalt that eventually build up into a volcanic island. The volcanically active island of Hawaii boasts the Earth's largest shield volcano, Mauna Loa, which extends 10 km above the sea floor. Olympus Mons on Mars is over twice as high and five times larger in diameter than Mauna Loa.

Why should a small planet produce large shield volcanoes? Mars has a lower gravity than the Earth and its surface is not broken up into moving plates. Thus, on Mars, a basaltic shield will build up in one spot on the surface as long as the subsurface activity continues. On the Earth, where crustal plates are mobile, shield volcanoes grow above the magma

**figure 8.21**
The Candor Chasma region is part of an extensive canyon system on Mars known as Valles Marineris.

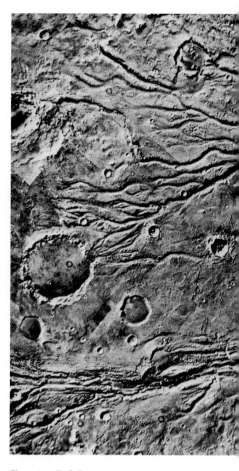

**figure 8.22**
The channels stretching across Chryse Planitia are believed to be the result of floodwaters or ice flows that cut through the cratered landscape early in the history of Mars.

source and then move on to form a chain of volcanic islands.

Starting east of Tharsis bulge, in a moderately cratered region known as Coprates, there is an enormous rift system extending 4000 km, more than the distance across the continental United States. This canyon, named **Valles Marineris,** averages 100 km across and 6 km in depth (fig. 8.17). Along the canyon complex there are many sinuous branches that appear to be dry river beds (fig. 8.21). Valles Marineris may have originated by east-west faulting of the crust. When subsurface layers were exposed, permafrost ice may have melted, causing upper layers to collapse. The released water cut channels and carried the materials down to lower elevations.

The Valles Marineris canyon system begins near the Tharsis bulge in a complex fractured region named Labyrinthus

Noctus. Continuing eastward, the canyon cuts through cratered plains to a **chaotic hummocky terrain,** a type of terrain laced with faults and fractures. Then the canyon turns north and branches out into many channels south of Chryse Planitia, the landing site of Viking 1.

From orbit, Chryse Planitia has the appearance of a relatively smooth plain containing craters, ridges, and a network of channels snaking across the surface (fig. 8.22). The view from the Viking 1 lander shows a flat, yellowish-brown landscape similar to the rocky deserts found on the Earth (fig. 8.23). The entire region is littered with irregular rocks up to several meters across; they are probably ejecta from nearby craters. Many of the rocks are pitted and resemble vesicular basalt.

A fine-grained sediment covers the field of boulders and in some places the

powdery material has been blown into drifts by the wind. Where the drifts have been eroded by a change in wind direction, the exposed surfaces are layered, showing that the deposits were made over a long period of time.

The Viking 2 lander touched down in the Utopia Planitia, part of the extensive northern plains region. In general, Utopia is similar to the Chryse region; there are boulders strewn about the surface that show the same vesicular texture. Apparently trapped gases formed holes before the rock solidified, giving them a pitted appearance (fig. 8.24).

The composition of the Martian surface is about the same at both landing sites. Presumably, global dust storms have mixed and distributed surface materials over vast areas. The soil samples examined by the landers were found to be composed of iron-rich clays, which

**figure 8.23**
A view of Chryse Planitia from the Viking 1 lander. The landscape is covered with rocks, some of which were ejected from nearby craters. The yellow color of the Martian sky is caused by dust particles suspended in the thin Martian atmosphere.

**figure 8.24**
An image from the Viking 2 lander on the Utopia Planitia in the northern plains region of Mars. During winter, a layer of frost covers the surface.

contribute to the yellow-brown color of the surface. Most of the soil composition by weight is silicon dioxide ($SiO_2$) and the iron oxide hematite ($Fe_2O_3$), followed by oxides of magnesium, calcium, and aluminum. The soil is magnetic due to the presence of iron oxides.

The north and south poles of Mars contain unique geological features. During each seasonal cycle of the planet, carbon dioxide in the atmosphere is deposited at the winter pole in a vast ice sheet extending into the middle latitudes. During seasonal change, there is a rapid retreat as the ice sublimates and returns to the atmosphere. A residual polar cap of water ice remains at the north pole and a solid carbon dioxide cap at the south pole.

The retreat of the northern ice cap exposes layers of dust deposits that measure several kilometers in thickness. They appear as red-colored valleys about 50 km apart that spiral from the pole in a counterclockwise direction (fig. 8.25). The accumulation of ice and dust is evidence of atmospheric circulation from the equatorial regions to the poles over a period of millions of years.

Surrounding the permanent north polar ice cap are dust dunes that resemble sand dunes found in the deserts of the Earth. Their similarity to terrestrial dunes

**figure 8.25**
The northern ice cap of Mars during summer.

suggest that Martian dunes were sculptured by the wind into parallel ridges over 1 km apart. A dune field discovered by Mariner 9 covers the entire floor of a crater 150 km in diameter.

## The Atmosphere and Magnetosphere of Mars

While the two Viking landers collected rock and soil samples, other instruments investigated the properties of the

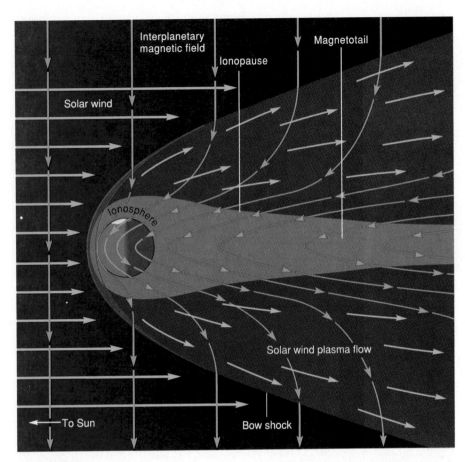

**figure 8.26**
The magnetosphere of Mars. Like Venus, Mars has a weak magnetic field.

pressure. There are spiral cloud formations of water ice that are similar to the clouds associated with cyclonic vortices in the middle latitudes of the Earth. As the Martian seasons change, clouds are seen to form and dissipate over different regions. During autumn, a haze of water ice and frozen carbon dioxide forms a blanket over the advancing polar cap. Low-lying clouds of water ice create a sinuous mist in the valleys and canyons. Topographic uplifting occurs when air in motion approaches a mountain or elevated terrain and ascends the windward slope. In the Tharsis region the air is forced to rise up the western flanks of the volcanoes where ice clouds extend as high as the rims of the calderas.

Both the Mariner 4 and Soviet Mars probes indirectly detected a weak magnetic field by measuring the ionization level of the upper atmosphere. Various explanations have been suggested as the source of the field: a small molten core is producing a weak dynamo effect; Mars has a solid core and the field is caused by residual magnetism; Mars, like Venus, has a magnetic field due to the ionization of its upper atmosphere by the action of the solar wind (fig. 8.26).

## The Satellites of Mars

The two tiny satellites of Mars, **Phobos** and **Deimos,** were discovered by Asaph Hall in 1877. The inner satellite, Phobos, is 9378 km from the center of Mars and revolves in a circular orbit above the planet's equator in a period of 7h 39m. Deimos also has a circular orbit and is 23,459 km from the planet's center. Its period of revolution is 30h 18m.

The flights of Mariner 9 and the Viking orbiters provided physical and photometric data unavailable to Earth-based telescopes. Mariner 9 transmitted 29 pictures of Phobos, the larger satellite, and nine of Deimos. Phobos was found to be ellipsoidal with diameters equal to 27 × 22 × 19 km. Deimos is smaller and has the same shape as Phobos (fig. 8.27). Its diameters are 15 × 12 × 11 km. Like our Moon, these satellites have synchronous rotation and thus keep the same side toward Mars.

Phobos and Deimos show evidence of meteoric bombardment. On Phobos,

atmosphere. One surprise was a yellow-pink sky rather than a familiar blue. Evidently dust particles are always suspended in the atmosphere, not just during dust storms as previously believed. The presence of atmospheric dust, and especially global dust storms, indicates that the lower atmosphere is subject to convective turbulence caused by differential heating of the planet. Moreover, seasonal advance and retreat of the polar ice caps confirms that a significant amount of carbon dioxide is exchanged between the atmosphere and the surface.

Years ago, the atmosphere of Mars was far different from the one observed today. When the great volcanoes of Mars were active, methane, ammonia, carbon dioxide, and water vapor poured into the atmosphere. The methane and ammonia molecules were dissociated by the Sun's ultraviolet radiation. The water vapor condensed to form permanent ice caps, and combined with elements in the crust.

Today, the Martian atmosphere consists of over 95% carbon dioxide, almost 3% nitrogen, 1.6% argon, 0.1% oxygen, and traces of water vapor—about the same composition as the atmosphere of Venus.

But unlike Venus, Mars has an extremely thin atmosphere. Measurements made by the Viking 1 lander show that the atmospheric pressure varies between 6.9 and 9.0 millibars (mb) as carbon dioxide is alternately deposited in and evaporated from the polar caps. On Earth, the air pressure is about 1000 mb (one bar) or 100 times greater than the pressure on Mars. The mean global temperature of Mars is a cold 250 K, although the southern hemisphere can reach a comfortable 295 K at noon in summer. The temperature of the cold, thin atmosphere is below the freezing point most of the time.

Mariner 9 cloud photographs show evidence of cyclonic circulation between air masses of different temperature and

Many investigations dealing with the motions of the planets require weeks of observations before sufficient data has been obtained. Plotting the retrograde loop of Mars during opposition is no exception. Therefore, plan your investigation to begin about six weeks before opposition takes place, and continue observing for six weeks after opposition (see figs. 1.8 and 6.16).

All you will need is a pencil, a flashlight with a red filter, and an equatorial sky map showing the ecliptic and the stars of the zodiac. You can find the position of Mars for your starting date by referring to a celestial calendar and current map of the sky provided by monthly publications such as *Astronomy* and *Sky and Telescope*.

Mark the date and initial position of Mars on your sky map six weeks before opposition. Continue to observe Mars two or more times each week. Record the dates of observation and positions of Mars until six weeks after opposition. Draw a line connecting the positions of Mars during the 12-week period. Your diagram will show two stationary points before and after opposition when the path of the planet makes a retrograde loop. Why does a superior planet change direction during opposition and not elsewhere in its orbit?

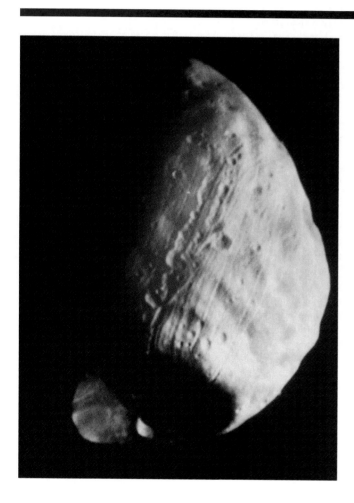

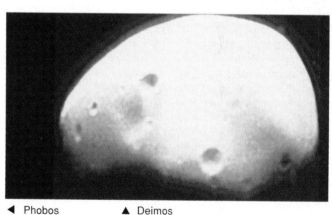

◀ Phobos        ▲ Deimos

**figure 8.27**
The satellites of Mars: Phobos and Deimos.

ies made of Phobos and Deimos by Mariner 9 and the Viking orbiters are no exception. Why are the satellites of Mars shaped like huge potatoes? How does a low-mass body retain a regolith surface? How did the satellites evolve?

The excessive number of impacts, large and small, probably molded Phobos and Deimos into their present ellipsoidal shape. The collisions produced seismic waves that passed through the satellites and shattered fragments from the opposite side. The parallel grooves on Phobos are probably fractures caused by the meteoric bombardment.

The regolith layer found on the surface of both satellites was laid down during meteoric impact. The escape velocity is low on these tiny bodies, and although most of the ejecta must have been lost to space, a sufficient amount was retained to form the dusty rubble on the surface. Indeed, Viking images

the largest crater, Stickney, has a diameter of about 10 km. In the southern region, the crater Hall extends from the pole to +50° latitude. Roche, the third largest crater, is in the northern hemisphere. The Viking orbiter detected rows of parallel grooves on Phobos extending from the north polar region to the middle latitudes.

The surface of Deimos is not as extensively cratered because a thick regolith has covered many small and shallow formations. There are a number of impacts, notably Voltaire, 2 km in diameter, and Swift, 1 km across.

As in all scientific investigations, new discoveries in astronomy raise more questions than are answered. The stud-

the terrestrial planets: Mercury, Venus, and Mars

showing secondary craters support this explanation.

The similarities in the orbital and photometric properties of the satellites suggest a common origin. But even though the Viking 2 orbiter came within 30 km of Deimos, the origin and evolution of the satellites has yet to be resolved.

Both objects are dark in color and may be blocks of basalt or an accretion of meteoric material called carbonaceous chondrite. If the satellites are composed of basalt, they could be the fragments of a larger body shattered by a passing asteroid. But if Phobos and Deimos have a composition similar to chondritic meteorites, they may have formed out of an accretion disk surrounding the evolving Mars. Some investigators have proposed that the satellites are captured asteroids (chapter 11), while others believe it unlikely that two passing asteroids could establish circular orbits in the equatorial plane of the planet.

In 1989, the Soviet spacecraft Phobos 2 attempted to unravel the mystery by landing a probe on Phobos to examine its surface. A communication failure doomed the landing project when contact with the spacecraft was lost. However, Phobos 2 remained in an elliptical orbit about Mars and continued to telemeter data back to Earth. The mission determined that the solar wind at Mars interacts with the ionosphere as the solar wind does at Venus. At the Earth, the solar wind is deflected by our planet's magnetic field.

# SUMMARY

Because Mercury is difficult to observe, many of its characteristics were unknown until the use of radio telescopes and the flyby mission of Mariner 10. Reflected radar signals confirmed a 59-day rotational period that is almost exactly two-thirds of its orbital period.

Mariner 10 on-board cameras revealed a surface covered by craters, basins, sinuous plains, and escarpments. The heavily cratered regions show evidence of meteoric impact. There is a chaotic region named the peculiar terrain. The formation of the large multi-ringed Caloris Basin caused seismic waves that passed through the planet and produced the peculiar terrain seen on the opposite side.

The long, curved cliffs, or lobate scarps, found in the cratered terrain indicate an earlier period of tectonic activity when internal contraction reduced the planet's radius.

Mercury has a magnetosphere consisting of a bow shock, magnetosheath, and magnetotail. The planet's magnetism may be a permanent intrinsic field or an induced field produced by its large iron core.

Radar signals transmitted to the surface of Venus indicated that the planet spins clockwise in a period of 243 days. Mariner 10 photographs of Venus revealed bands of clouds spiraling from the middle latitudes to the poles. Venera soft landers returned pictures of the planet's surface. The Magellan orbiter mapped most of the surface by radar.

Generally, Venus is smooth but there are mountain ranges, plateaus, volcanoes, and rift valleys. Areas called terrae are comparable to land masses on the Earth. Other regions, called planitiae, are flat lowlands. There are isolated plateaus containing volcanoes and deep channels. The surface temperature of Venus reaches 750 K.

The Pioneer and Venera spacecraft confirmed that the atmosphere of Venus consists of about 96% carbon dioxide and 3% nitrogen at a surface pressure 95 times greater than the Earth's. There is a cloud deck consisting of sulphuric acid layers between 50 and 70 km altitude. The clouds in the upper troposphere are in the region of greatest wind velocity.

There is an ionosphere where electron density reaches a maximum at 140 km altitude. An induced magnetic field produces a magnetosphere when incoming solar wind forms a bow shock and a plasma tail behind the planet.

Venera data confirm that the high surface temperature on Venus is the result of a runaway greenhouse effect. Once underway, the process continued until the present heat balance was reached. The greenhouse effect is caused by the carbon dioxide atmosphere and sulphuric acid clouds.

Mars has seasons like the Earth except they are twice as long. Dark markings on the surface change colors with the seasons while the ice caps alternately advance in winter and retreat in summer. The darker surface areas contain volcanic rock, and the orange-colored regions iron oxides.

Mariner 9 returned images of ancient cratered terrain in the southern hemisphere and close-up pictures of volcanoes, plains, channels, canyons, and mountainous terrain elsewhere on the planet. In the ancient terrain there are basins formed by the impact of large bodies early in the history of Mars. Sinuous channels extend for hundreds of kilometers; they appear to be dry river beds.

Large shield volcanoes dominate the Tharsis ridge. The largest volcano, Olympus Mons, lies northwest of Tharsis. East of Tharsis there is an enormous rift system named Valles Marineris. The canyon may have originated by east-west faulting of the crust.

The view from the Viking 1 lander shows a flat, yellow-brown landscape similar to rocky deserts on the Earth. The Viking 2 lander touched down at a site strewn with irregular rock ejected from nearby craters.

During each seasonal cycle, atmospheric carbon dioxide is deposited as ice at the winter pole. As the seasons change and the ice retreats, a residual cap of water ice remains at the north pole where huge layers of dust deposits are exposed. Surrounding the permanent northern ice cap are dunes that have been sculptured by the wind.

Clouds are seen in the thin, cold atmosphere of Mars. A haze of water ice and frozen carbon dioxide covers the advancing polar caps. Fog and mist form in the valleys and canyons. Clouds are uplifted to the tops of the volcanoes on Tharsis ridge.

Mars has two satellites, Phobos and Deimos. The larger satellite, Phobos, has larger impact craters and parallel fractures in its surface. Deimos has fewer, smaller craters than Phobos and a smoother surface. Impact by huge blocks probably molded Phobos and Deimos into their present ellipsoidal shape.

# KEY TERMS

Caloris Basin

chaotic hummocky terrain

chasmate

cratered regions

cratered terrain

Deimos

fretted hummocky terrain

greenhouse effect

intercrater plains

lobate scarps

mons

montes

Olympus Mons

peculiar terrain

Phobos

planitiae

regiones

smooth plains

terrae

Tharsis bulge

undivided plains terrain

Valles Marineris

# PROBLEMS

1. If Mercury is nearer to the Sun than Venus, why does the surface of Venus have a higher temperature?

2. List the distinctive properties of Venus known before and after space missions were made to the planet.

3. What evidence is there that water once existed on the surface of Mars?

4. Why do Mars and Venus lack the kind of mountain systems found on the Earth?

5. Mercury is very hot on the day hemisphere and very cold on the night hemisphere. Explain.

6. Mercury is the only terrestrial planet without an atmosphere. Why?

7. By what process is carbon dioxide transported and deposited at the poles of Mars?

8. Why is carbon dioxide abundant in the atmospheres of Venus and Mars but exists in only small quantities in the Earth's?

9. Compare the surfaces of Mercury and the Moon. How are they similar? How do they differ?

10. Explain how the greenhouse effect has been of major importance in the evolution of Venus.

11. Imagine yourself on Mars observing Phobos and Deimos. How long does it take for each satellite to rise and set? In which direction do they appear to travel?

12. Why is Mercury more difficult to observe than Mars?

13. Why does the same hemisphere of Venus face the Earth at every inferior conjunction?

14. Why are the shield volcanoes on Mars larger than those on the Earth?

15. There are scarps on the surface of Mercury but not on the other terrestrial planets and the Moon. Explain.

16. What important scientific information might be obtained by a landing on Phobos?

17. Discuss the topographic features of Mars and compare them with those found on Venus and the Earth.

18. Explain why manned expeditions are planned for Mars but not for Mercury and Venus.

19. Only a flyby mission, Mariner 10, was made to Mercury, while flybys, orbiters, and landers were sent to Venus and Mars. Discuss the purposes, advantages, and disadvantages of each mode of exploration.

20. If Mercury has a 3:2 spin/orbit ratio, what will be the length of a solar day on the planet?

# REFERENCES

Arvidson, Raymond E., Alan B. Binder, and Kenneth L. Jones. 1978. The Surface of Mars. *Scientific American,* 238, no. 3 (March).

Beish, Jeff D., and Donald C. Parker. 1988. 1988: A Great Year for Mars. *Astronomy,* 16, no. 3 (March).

———. 1988. Exploring Mars in 1988. *Sky and Telescope,* 75, no. 4 (April).

Blamont, Jacques. 1987. Exploring Venus by Balloon. *The Planetary Report,* (The Planetary Society) 7, no. 1 (January/February).

Briggs, G. A., and F. W. Taylor. 1982. *The Cambridge Photographic Atlas of the Planets.* Cambridge: Cambridge University Press.

Burgess, Eric. 1985. *Venus: An Errant Twin.* New York: Columbia University Press.

Carr, Michael H. 1983. The Surface of Mars: A Post-Viking View. *Mercury,* (Astronomical Society of the Pacific) 12, no. 1 (January/February).

Chapman, Clark R. 1983. The Vapors of Venus and other Gassy Envelopes. *Mercury* 12, no. 5 (September/October).

———. 1988. Mercury's Heart of Iron. *Astronomy* 16, no. 11 (November).

Cordell, Bruce M. 1984. Mercury: The World Closest to the Sun. *Mercury* 13, no. 5 (September/October).

Davies, Merton E., and Bruce C. Murray. 1971. *The View from Space.* New York: Columbia University Press.

Dick, Steven J. 1988. Discovering the Moons of Mars. *Sky and Telescope* 76, no. 3 (September).

Fimmel, Richard O., Lawrence Colin, and Eric Burgess. 1983. *Pioneer Venus.* Washington, D.C.: NASA.

Horowitz, Norman H. 1977. The Search for Life on Mars. *Scientific American* 237, no. 5 (November).

Montoya, Earl J., and Richard O. Fimmel. 1988. Pioneers in Space: The Story of the Pioneer Missions. *Mercury* 17, no. 2 (March/April).

Murray, Bruce. 1977. "Mars from Mariner 9." In *The New Astronomy and Space Reader,* edited by John C. Brandt and Stephen P. Moran. San Francisco: W. H. Freeman and Company.

————. 1975. "Mercury." In *The Solar System,* edited by Dennis Flanagan. San Francisco: W. H. Freeman and Company.

Murray, Bruce, and Eric Burgess. 1977. *Flight to Mercury.* New York: Columbia University Press.

Pettengill, Gordon H., Donald B. Campbell, and Harold Masursky. 1980. The Surface of Venus. *Scientific American* 243, no. 2 (August).

Pollack, James B. 1975. "Mars." In *The Solar System,* edited by Dennis Flanagan. San Francisco: W. H. Freeman and Company.

Veverka, Joseph. 1977. Phobos and Deimos. *Scientific American* 236, no. 2 (February).

Weaver, Kenneth F. 1973. Journey to Mars. *National Geographic,* February.

Young, Andrew, and Louise Young. 1975. "Venus." In *The Solar System,* edited by Dennis Flanagan. San Francisco: W. H. Freeman and Company.

the giant planets: Jupiter and Saturn

Views of Jupiter and Saturn from the Hubble
Space Telescope.

Beyond the outermost terrestrial planet, Mars, and the fragmented bodies in the asteroid belt, we encounter the Jovian planets Jupiter and Saturn. They are the largest of the four giant planets of our solar system, all composed of lighter elements that form a striking contrast to the rock and metal worlds found nearer to the Sun.

The disparity between the terrestrial and Jovian planets can be traced to the composition of the accretion disk around the protosun when the solar system evolved (see chapter 6). Near the Sun where temperatures were high, the intense solar wind blew the primordial hydrogen and helium to the outer regions of the solar system, leaving the heavier elements to form the terrestrial planets. At greater distances from the Sun, the lighter elements remained as the main constituents of the outer planets.

In the final stages of their evolution, the giant planets formed into huge hydrogen and helium spheres surrounded by atmospheres containing clouds of water and ammonia ice crystals. In turn, each body developed its own **ring system** and the many satellites characteristic of the Jovian planets.

## Jupiter

Of all the celestial spectacles, the view of Jupiter through a telescope ranks among the most impressive. The planet appears as a large, bright oblate spheroid representing an extensive and dense atmosphere. Across the disk there are a number of light and dark parallel bands of clouds. Like a miniature solar system, the four **Galilean satellites** repeat their revolutions about the planet.

Jupiter's rapid rotational period of only 9h 56m is responsible for the planet's pronounced equatorial bulge and the banded structure of its stratified clouds. In a small telescope only one or two prominent bands are seen, while a large instrument shows clouds over the entire equatorial and middle latitudes. Dark, rose-colored clouds are called

**figure 9.1**
Voyager 1 image of Jupiter from a distance of 33 million km.

**belts,** while light-colored clouds are identified as **zones** (fig. 9.1).

### Missions to Jupiter

In December 1974, the Pioneer 10 spacecraft made its closest approach to the giant planet and passed within 132,252 km of its banded clouds. One year later,

Pioneer 11 approached Jupiter from below the orbital plane and photographed both polar regions. In addition to photographs, the spacecraft performed a series of experiments designed to explore the Jovian environment. The objectives were to map the planet's magnetic field, measure energy levels in the magnetosphere, and study the characteristics of

**figure 9.2**
View of Jupiter taken from Voyager 1. Two of Jupiter's moons, Io (*left*) and Europa (*right*), orbit above the planet.

radio emissions from Jupiter and the planet's interaction with the solar wind. Radio occultations were used to determine the density of the atmosphere when the planet came between the spacecraft and the Earth.

After the Jupiter encounters, the Pioneer spacecraft went their separate ways. Pioneer 11 crossed the plane of the rings of Saturn in 1979, while Pioneer 10 continued its infinite journey out of the solar system and to the stars. After 26,000 years of travel, Pioneer 10 will reach the distance of Proxima Centauri, the next star beyond the Sun.

The Voyager 1 and 2 spacecraft made their epic rendezvous with the giant planet in 1979 and performed successfully during data-gathering and picture-taking missions. These flights confirmed the nature of the planet's turbulent, cloudy atmosphere, discovered a faint particle ring, and revealed the interaction between the planet's magnetic field and the Galilean satellite Io.

Voyager images showed Jupiter's atmosphere to be a complexity of tempestuous flows and eddies, dark elongated bodies, red spots, and white ovals (fig. 9.2). Close-ups of the Galilean moons showed active volcanoes on Io, a smooth icy surface on Europa, the **grooved terrain** of Ganymede, and the cratered landscape of Callisto. After the encounters, a gravitational assist by Jupiter placed the two Voyagers into new trajectories toward their next destination, the planet Saturn.

Galileo, the most recent spacecraft to explore Jupiter, was designed to reach its goal by gravity assists from the Earth and Venus. The spacecraft was launched in October 1989 from the space shuttle Atlantis into a complex trajectory that required one Venus flyby (February 1990) and two Earth flybys (December 1990 and December 1992) before proceeding to Jupiter. After the Venus flyby and the first encounter with Earth, Galileo was accelerated into a larger el-liptical orbit that carried the spacecraft to within 1600 km of Gaspra, a small member of the main asteroid belt (chapter 11). Galileo returned to the vicinity of the Earth for a second gravity assist and a new trajectory to its final goal—the investigation of Jupiter's environment. The spacecraft encountered another asteroid, Ida, in August 1993, and will arrive at Jupiter in December 1995.

While approaching Jupiter, the spacecraft will release an instrument package that will plunge below the Jovian cloud deck, deploy a parachute, and slowly drift into the lower atmosphere. The main Galileo spacecraft will be placed in orbit to relay data from the descending probe to the Earth. Instruments aboard the orbiter will analyze high-energy particles, electric and magnetic intensities, and the meteorology and composition of Jupiter's atmosphere.

## Interior Structure

The work of Wildt and, independently, Peek in the 1930s pointed to hydrogen as the principal constituent of the Jovian planets, and helium as the second most abundant element. Later their findings were confirmed when ultraviolet photometers aboard Pioneers 10 and 11 found Jupiter's upper atmosphere contains about 85% hydrogen and 15% helium by mass, and traces of other gases.

The internal distribution of Jupiter's mass may be inferred by comparing the planet's period of rotation and degree of polar flattening. The oblateness shows that the greatest mass is located deep in the interior and is compressed to a high density. It is generally agreed that the interior of Jupiter consists of three shells of increasing temperature and pressure (fig. 9.3). The outermost layer, the atmosphere, extends to a depth where the pressure has increased sufficiently to change gaseous hydrogen to the liquid state. The **liquid molecular hydrogen** shell extends to a depth of 59,000 km from the center, where the extreme pressure separates molecular hydrogen to atomic hydrogen stripped of its electrons. The result is a dense fluid of electrically charged particles called **liquid metallic hydrogen.** The liquid metallic layer rests on the core 13,400 km from the center. The outer portion of the core may be methane and ammonia liquid/ice above an iron-silicate inner core about 6700 km in radius.

This model representing the Jovian interior accounts for the transport of internal heat and the mechanism for generating a strong magnetic field. Analysis of Jupiter's infrared spectrum by radiometers aboard the Pioneer spacecraft showed that the total infrared radiation emitted by Jupiter is nearly twice the amount of energy received from the Sun. Indeed, 70% of its thermal radiation is produced within the planet and transported by conduction and convection to the atmosphere. Since its formation, the interior of Jupiter has been slowly losing its heat energy to space.

The electrically conducting metallic hydrogen is believed to be the source of Jupiter's magnetic field. Radio telescope observations in the 1950s, and Pioneer

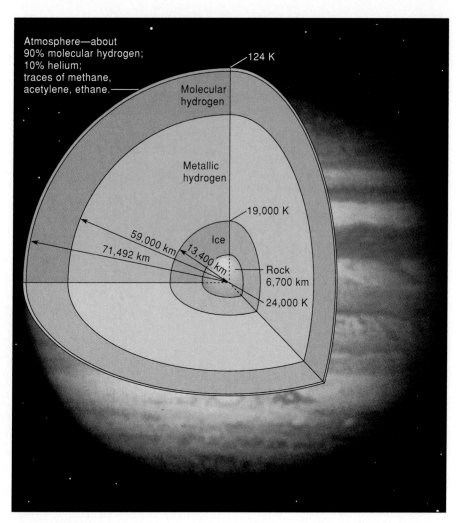

**figure 9.3**
The internal structure of Jupiter.

and Voyager studies in 1979–80, confirmed that Jupiter has a strong dipole magnetic field tilted about 11° to the rotational axis. The magnetic axis is offset and does not pass through the center of Jupiter. Moreover, the polarity is reversed; on Jupiter, a compass would point south. Radio measurements support the theory that the dynamo action of the liquid metallic hydrogen generates a magnetic field. The field rotates at a rate of 9h 55m 30s and is more than 10 times stronger at Jupiter's cloud tops than Earth's magnetic field at its surface.

## Atmosphere and Clouds

The dynamic atmosphere of Jupiter begins above the liquid hydrogen level

where the pressure is low enough for hydrogen to exist as a gas (fig. 9.4). There is no distinct boundary between the two layers but a slushy transition zone where hydrogen gradually changes from a liquid into a gaseous atmosphere. Occultation experiments aboard spacecraft and ground-based observations cannot probe more than about 60 km below the base of the lowest cloud level.

The atmosphere of hydrogen and helium represents only 1% of the total mass of the planet. In addition to these gases there are small quantities of ammonia, methane, hydrogen sulfide, and water vapor as well as traces of deuterium, acetylene, ethane, and phosphine.

The innermost layer, or troposphere, extends to about 60 km above the highest

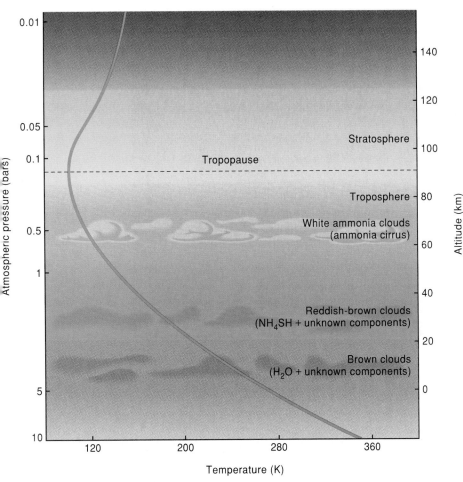

**figure 9.4**

Temperatures, pressures, and cloud levels in Jupiter's atmosphere were obtained by instruments aboard the Voyager spacecraft.

cloud base. In this region the pressure and temperature gradually drop to 100 mb and 90 K. The troposphere is a region where warmer gases are carried aloft by convective currents. The rising gases cool, condense, and form the distinctive clouds observed at various altitudes.

The vertical cloud structure in the troposphere above a pressure of 10 bars includes a thin base cloud composed of water ice ($H_2O$) at about two bars; a clear gas level; a dense ammonia cloud ($NH_3$) that may also contain ammonium hydrogen sulfide ($NH_4SH$) crystals; an ammonia haze layer; and a second clear layer.

There is a temperature inversion 35 km above the upper clouds marking the boundary between the troposphere and stratosphere. The increase in temperature is due to a layer of methane and dust that absorbs solar ultraviolet radiation. Above this aerosol layer is another clear gas region which extends to the tenuous ionosphere where molecules are ionized by ultraviolet radiation from the Sun.

The colorful clouds are the most impressive features of Jupiter photographed by the Pioneer and Voyager spacecraft. The conspicuous belts are filled with many contrasting elements. The North and South Equatorial Belts are separated by the Equatorial Zone (fig. 9.5). In a large-aperture telescope, the South Equatorial Belt is resolved into two separate bands. Beyond the equatorial region there are North and South Tropical Zones followed by North and South Temperate Belts. At higher latitudes, there are North and South Temperate Zones. Polar Regions form caps at each pole.

The close-up images by the Voyagers confirm that the light-colored zones are regions of bright clouds similar to the circulation cells found in the Earth's atmosphere. Apparently, the zones are rising high-pressure regions while the belts represent descending low-pressure regions. As it rises, the air mass cools and gaseous ammonia condenses into a band of bright, puffy clouds of ammonia crystals. The cool air mass and clouds spread and sink back to a lower level in the belt region. The convective circulation coupled with the planet's rapid rotation deflects the atmosphere into parallel high- and low-pressure zones and belts. Between the zones and belts the circulation produces high-speed east and west winds. In the equatorial region, jet streams measuring 150 m/sec are found between the Equatorial Zone and the North and South Equatorial Belts. Numerous hooks, eddies, and swirls make up the fine structure of the atmospheric streams.

A most remarkable feature called the **Great Red Spot** is found in the South Tropical Zone (fig. 9.6). The earliest sighting of the Great Red Spot is usually credited to Giovanni Cassini in the seventeenth century, although some historians believe the honor should go to Robert Hooke or Eustachio Divini. The spot at one time extended 40,000 km and was distinguished by its deep red color. Today, it has faded to a salmon or light pink color and is reduced in length to about 25,000 km, or twice the Earth's diameter.

Voyager pictures indicate that the Great Red Spot is a huge anticyclonic air mass extending several kilometers above the surrounding cloud level. Associated with the Red Spot are a number of white ovals that are high-pressure regions containing clouds of ammonia crystals. The Great Red Spot and the white ovals rotate in periods of a few days as they slowly drift westward between east-west zonal winds.

## Magnetosphere

The rotation of the strong magnetic field generated in Jupiter's interior creates a magnetosphere that extends into space hundreds of times the radius of the planet (fig. 9.7a). Evidence for the magnetic field came in 1955, when Bernard Burke

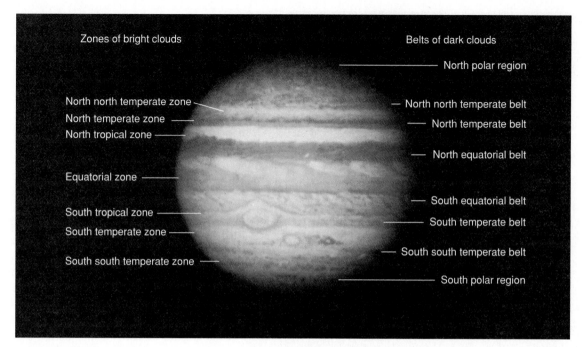

Zones of bright clouds

North north temperate zone
North temperate zone
North tropical zone

Equatorial zone

South tropical zone
South temperate zone

South south temperate zone

Belts of dark clouds

North polar region

North north temperate belt
North temperate belt

North equatorial belt

South equatorial belt
South temperate belt

South south temperate belt

South polar region

▲ **figure 9.5**
The zones and belts of Jupiter's cloud structure.

**figure 9.6** ▶
Voyager 1 image showing the Great Red Spot and numerous eddies and swirls in the atmospheric streams.

and Kenneth Franklin announced the discovery of radio-frequency emissions from Jupiter. The duration of the radio bursts implied that an ionized layer or ionosphere was present in the upper atmosphere of the planet. Like the Earth, Jupiter has a magnetic field and, with it, a magnetosphere in which electrified particles emit radio-frequency radiation. The magnetosphere of Jupiter is formed in the same manner as the Earth's—ionized particles from the Sun interact with the planet's magnetic field. The sunward lobe of the magnetosphere fluctuates in size from about 60 to 100 $R_J$ ($R_J$ = radius of Jupiter), while the night-side lobe is attenuated into a slender magnetotail reaching beyond the orbit of Saturn. When these planets are in opposition, Jupiter's magnetotail interacts with Saturn's magnetic field.

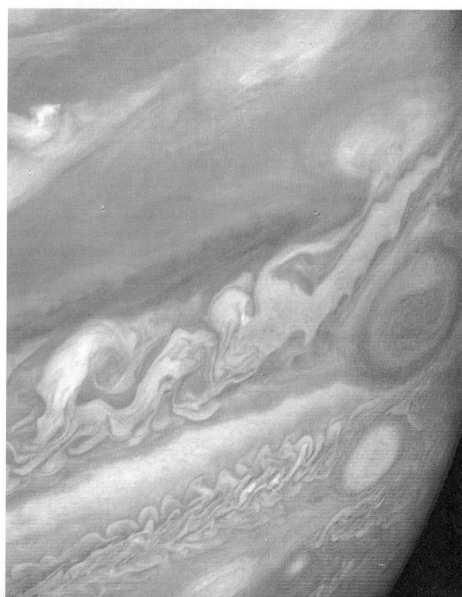

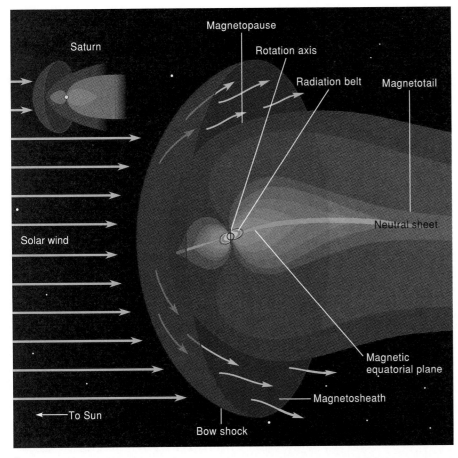

a.

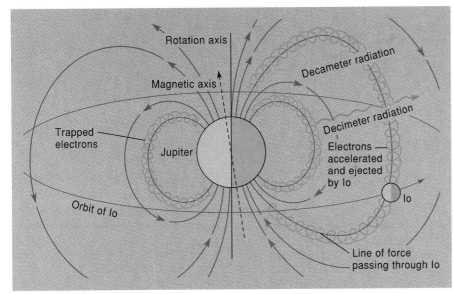

b.

**figure 9.7**

*a.* Jupiter's magnetosphere. The planet's rapid rotation concentrates charged particles into a current sheet in the magnetic equatorial plane. *b.* Jupiter's radio emissions.

Pioneer and Voyager experiments confirmed that the radio emissions in Jupiter's magnetic environment originate from three sources:

1. *Thermal radiation* is produced by molecular motion in the Jovian atmosphere and interior.

2. *Decimetric radiation* (wavelength of 0.1 m) is caused by electrons spiraling in the magnetic field close to the planet (fig. 9.7b). Electromagnetic radiation emitted by high-velocity electrons moving in magnetic fields is called *synchrotron radiation*.

3. *Decametric radiation* (wavelength of 10 m or more) is attributed in part to an effect caused by the revolution of Io, the Galilean moon nearest to Jupiter. The nature of Io's interaction with the magnetosphere was revealed during the Pioneer 10 and Voyager 1 and 2 missions.

The Jovian magnetosphere can be conveniently studied in three parts: the inner region from the planet out to 20 $R_J$; the middle region between 20 and 60 $R_J$; and the outer region where variations in magnitude and direction are caused by changes in the solar wind.

Pioneer 11 confirmed the existence of ionized particles trapped in magnetic field lines in the same way as the Van Allen radiation belts are trapped within the Earth's magnetosphere. Jupiter's belts reach greatest intensity at about 20 $R_J$ from the center of the planet. There are significant differences between the more intense Jovian radiation belts and their terrestrial counterparts. In particular, the rapid rotation of Jupiter has warped the magnetic field lines into a lenticular shape about the magnetic equator, with greatest intensity at about 20 $R_J$. Electrically charged particles confined in the field form a **current sheet** in the plane of the magnetic equator.

As we have seen, there is an interaction between Io, the innermost Galilean satellite, and Jupiter's magnetic field. Io tunnels through a doughnut-shaped cloud of ionized sulphur and oxygen as it revolves in its orbit around Jupiter. The electric currents generated by Io's revolution may be the source of the auroral displays observed in Jupiter's ionosphere.

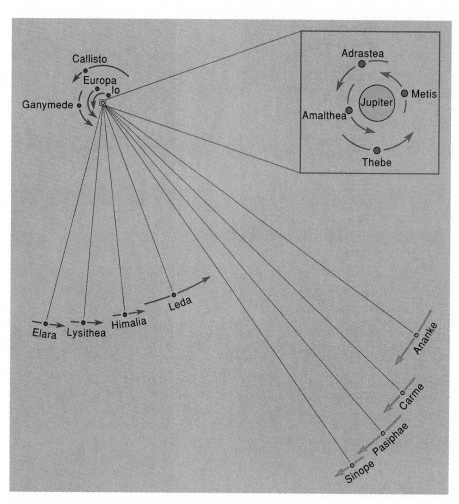

**figure 9.8**
The 16 satellites of Jupiter are grouped according to their distances from the planet. Those in the outermost group revolve retrograde, or contrary to the direction of the other satellites.

## Satellites, Rings, and Asteroids

The 16 known satellites of Jupiter may be classified into four categories according to their relative distances from the planet (fig. 9.8). In the first group are the four large and bright Galilean moons: Io, Europa, Ganymede, and Callisto, all discovered in 1610. Io, the innermost Galilean satellite, has a period of 1d 18.5h and revolves at a mean distance of 422,000 km. Callisto, the fourth moon, takes 16d 16.5h to complete its orbital period some 1,883,000 km from Jupiter.

Only the four Galilean satellites were known until Amalthea was discovered in 1892. At 181,000 km from the planet, it makes one revolution in about 12 hours. Amalthea and three satellites discovered by Voyager 2—Adrastea, Thebe, and Metis—form the second category,

an inner group 128,000 km (Metis) to 222,000 km (Thebe) from Jupiter.

Beyond the Galilean moons there are two more groups of four satellites each. One includes Leda, Himalia, Lysithea, and Elara, revolving between 11,094,000 km and 11,737,000 km from the center of the planet. The outermost group of satellites include Ananke, Carme, Pasiphae, and Sinope. These remote satellites are distinguished by their retrograde revolution in orbits between 21,200,000 km and 23,700,000 km from Jupiter.

The outer edge of the faint ring system of Jupiter lies inside the orbit of Adrastea. Discovered by Voyager 1, the rings consist of microscopic particles and larger blocks, possibly up to meter-sized. The brighter rim is located about 58,000 km from the cloud tops and is 6400 km

thick. A tenuous second ring may extend to Jupiter's atmosphere. Erosion of surface material from the satellites Adrastea and Metis may be the source of particles needed to sustain the rings (see fig. 9.9).

The **Trojan asteroids** represent two groups of minor planets that are controlled by the gravitational attraction of Jupiter and the Sun. They revolve in Jupiter's orbit and are located 60° ahead of and 60° behind the planet (fig. 9.10). The asteroids oscillate about the vertices of equilateral triangles called **Lagrangian points,** where they remain in equilibrium as the system revolves about the Sun.

The Galilean satellites are remarkably similar to the planetary system about the Sun (fig. 9.11). The inner terrestrial planets are smaller and denser, composed of rock-forming elements. The outer Jovian planets have a greater abundance of ice-forming materials which, together with hydrogen, produce water, ammonia, and methane.

The Galilean satellites are divided in the same way. The rocky inner satellites Io and Europa have densities and compositions similar to terrestrial planets. The outer two satellites Ganymede and Callisto have retained a higher ratio of volatile elements in the form of ice and are more like the giant planets.

The Voyager encounters provided a better understanding of the satellites' interior structures. Io has a radius of 1815 km and a density of 3.5 gm/cm³. The satellite may have a solid core overlain by a molten silicate mantle extending to a thin crust covered with sulphur and frozen sulphur dioxide. Europa is 1569 km in radius and has a density slightly less than Io at 3.0 gm/cm³. A solid core below a rocky mantle is believed to extend 1450 km from the center. Its water-and-ice crust is about 100 km thick.

A radius of 2631 km makes Ganymede the largest satellite in the solar system and larger than the planets Mercury and Pluto. Its relatively low density of 1.9 gm/cm³ indicates that Ganymede contains a large amount of ices in addition to rock. Its central region is believed to consist of a solid silicate core about 2000 km in radius, and a

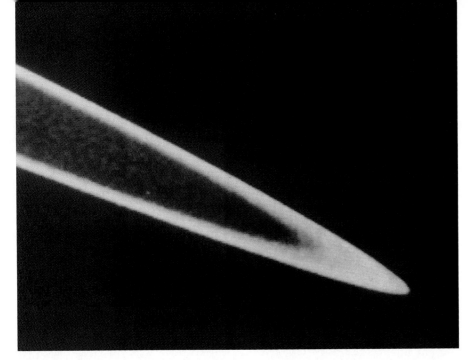

figure 9.9
Photomosaic of Jupiter's ring system from images returned by Voyager 2.

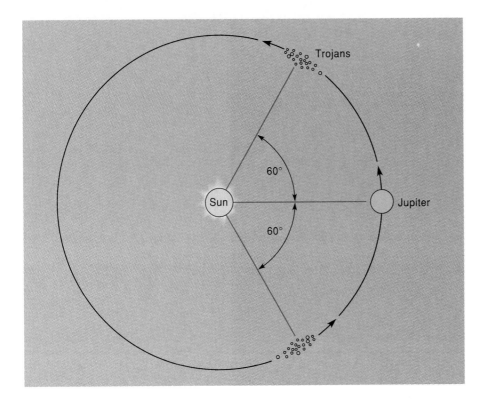

figure 9.10
Location of Trojan asteroids in Jupiter's orbit.

mantle of water or ice perhaps 600 km thick. The thin icy crust of Ganymede is about 75 km thick. Callisto, another large satellite, has a radius of 2400 km and a density of only 1.8 gm/cm³, the lowest

of all the Galilean satellites. It has a solid silicate core over a 1000-km mantle of soft ice or water, and a crust of ice and rock about 150 km thick.

## Io

The innermost Galilean satellite is the most puzzling object in orbit around Jupiter. Io resembles our Moon in size, density, and distance from its planet, but there are fundamental differences between the two satellites. Unlike the Moon, Io is dominated by volcanoes spewing geysers of sulphur dioxide; upwelling lava in multicolored streams pours from calderas and radiates hundreds of kilometers across the surface (fig. 9.12).

The strange activities on Io are directly related to its orbital motion about Jupiter. Io revolves in a slightly eccentric orbit because of Jupiter's gravitational influence, and to a lesser degree, that of Europa and Ganymede. The resulting variation of Io's distance from Jupiter causes a periodic oscillation of the tidal bulge raised on Io's surface. This so-called **tidal flexing** heats the interior of Io sufficiently to account for the volcanic activities on the surface.

The remarkable pictures from the Voyager spacecraft revealed eight erupting sulphurous volcanoes with umbrella-shaped plumes rising as much as 70 to 300 km altitude. There are many dark spots from which sinuous flows twist across the surface. Multicolored features are believed to be sulphur dioxide frost mixed with elemental sulphur or sulphur compounds.

## Europa

The smallest Galilean satellite has a diameter of 3138 km, or slightly smaller than the Moon. In contrast to the reddish hue of Io, Europa appears brighter and white in color and has an albedo of 0.64, the highest reflectance of all the Jovian satellites. The Voyager 1 pictures showed a smooth, icy surface covered with a network of linear markings giving Europa the appearance of a cracked porcelain shell. In addition to bright surface areas, there are mottled or spotted regions of darker hue which are crossed by intersecting linear streaks. When Voyager 2 came within 204,000 km of the satellite's surface, the prominent markings were resolved into fractures between 3 and 70 km in width and up to 3000 km in length. Most of the furrows are fairly straight;

**figure 9.11** ▶

Montage of the four Galilean satellites of
Jupiter. Views from the Voyager spacecraft.

Jupiter

Io

Europa

Callisto

Ganymede

▼ **figure 9.12**

A high-resolution image of a volcanic
eruption on Io. The plume from the volcano
Pele extends to an altitude of about 300 km
on the limb of the moon in this view. Debris
is scattered in concentric circles over 1000
km from the volcano. Some of the material
is ejected into space and forms a torus
centered on the satellite's orbit around
Jupiter.

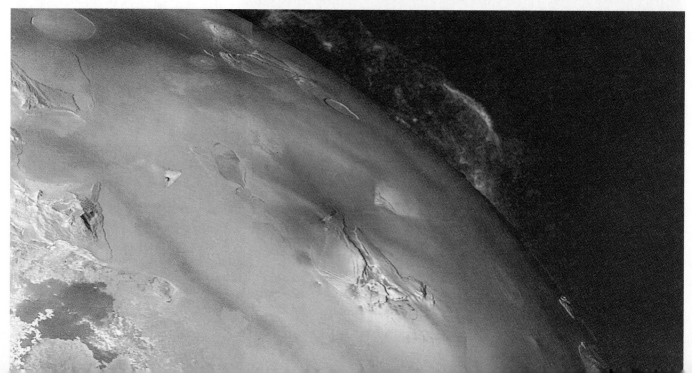

## eclipses  and  transits  of  the  Galilean  moons

Sky Watchers are encouraged to observe the Galilean moons pass in and out of Jupiter's shadow, as well as their transits across the luminous disk of the planet. The eclipse phenomena of the satellites are similar to those of the Moon but are unique in several ways.

Because Jupiter is huge and far from the Sun, its shadow cone extends more than 88 million km into space, almost as far as the distance between the Earth and Mercury at inferior conjunction. Moreover, with the exception of Callisto, the orbital inclination of the moons to Jupiter's equator is less than one-half degree. Consequently, the three inner satellites pass into the shadow of the planet in total eclipse at each revolution. Callisto sometimes passes above or below or grazes the shadow.

Prior to opposition when the Earth is at $E_1$ (fig. 9.13) and Jupiter is west of the Sun before dawn, its satellites are seen to enter the shadow at a distance from the limb of the planet. During ingress, the satellites gradually fade and disappear from view and remain hidden behind the planet after they leave the shadow. Then they pop out as bright

points of light from behind the opposite limb of the planet. At opposition, the Sun, Earth ($E_2$), Jupiter, and Jupiter's shadow are in line and only occultations take place. The satellites enter and leave the shadow behind the disk of the planet.

After opposition when the Earth is at $E_3$, Jupiter is east of the Sun and eclipses can be observed in the early evening. Jupiter's disk hides the ingress of the inner moons and only their egress can be seen. However, the third and fourth satellites are far enough from Jupiter to allow ingress and egress to be seen beyond the eastern limb of the planet.

During a transit, a satellite passes across Jupiter's disk. As a rule, the satellite is brighter than the planet's limb but becomes more difficult to see as it nears the center of the disk.

Of greater interest is the shadow a moon casts upon the upper atmosphere of Jupiter. Prior to opposition, the shadow precedes and falls on the disk before transit of the satellite. After opposition, the shadow crosses the disk behind the satellite.

Look for the schedule of geocentric phenomena of Jupiter's moons in various popular astronomical publications and *The Astronomical Almanac* (fig. 9.14).

**Jupiter's Satellites May, 1992**

The curving lines represent Jupiter's four bright (Galilean) satellites: **I**, Io; **II**, Europa; **III**, Ganymede; and **IV**, Callisto. Jupiter itself is indicated by the center pair of vertical lines. The horizontal lines mark $0^h$ Universal time on successive dates; 1 mm vertically is very nearly four hours. A curve is broken when the satellite is in the planet's shadow or when passing on its far side, perhaps being occulted. West is to the left and east to the right, to match the view seen by a Northern Hemisphere observer with an astronomical (inverting) telescope. The bottom section of the diagram shows where the satellites disappear (*d*) or reappear (*r*) during eclipses by Jupiter nearest midmonth. *Sky & Telescope* diagram.

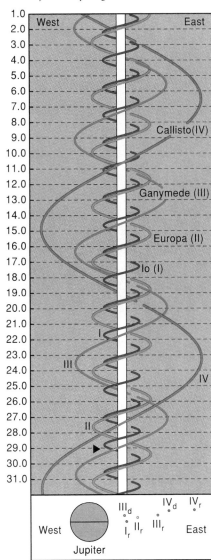

### figure 9.14

Geocentric phenomena of Jupiter's four Galilean satellites.

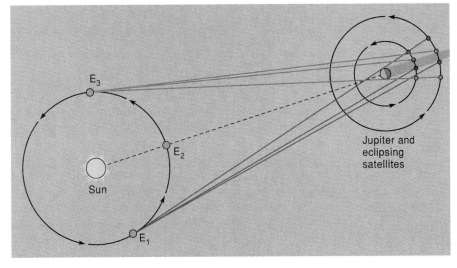

### figure 9.13

The curious eclipse phenomenon of Jupiter's satellites, seen before and after opposition.

the giant planets: Jupiter and Saturn

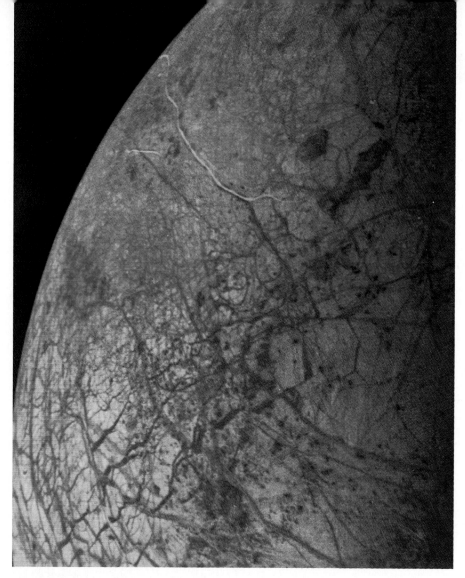

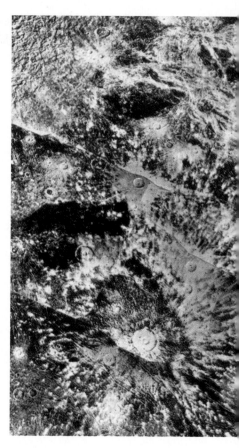

**figure 9.16**
Images of Ganymede revealed craters with rays of ice ejecta covering ancient, dark crust, and younger, light-colored, grooved terrain.

**figure 9.15**
Europa has a smooth icy surface covered with a network of linear streaks.

others are a snarl of scalloped and irregular streaks (fig. 9.15).

Europa's appearance suggests that water from the interior froze into a sheet of ice perhaps 25 km thick. A layer this deep would cover any irregular rocky surface formed during the early accretion period. The lack of impact craters is evidence that the icy surface is comparatively recent, perhaps no more than hundreds of millions of years old. Only three craters between 18 and 25 km in diameter are known, although smaller undetected craters may exist.

The early history of Europa may be inferred from the evolution of other small terrestrial bodies. During contraction, and later by the fission of radioactive elements, sufficient energy was released to cause the interior to separate into layers.

Volatile elements, in particular water, vented from the interior, cooled, and formed the icy crust.

The tidal effect on Europa of Jupiter and Ganymede has been suggested as an alternate explanation for internal heating. The fissures in the surface may be the result of tidal flexing. Darker slushy ice in the warmer interior may have been forced upward to fill the crevasses in the surface.

### Ganymede

The Voyager encounters with Ganymede identified a unique surface composed of ice combined with silicates. Voyager 1 pictures showed the hemisphere facing Jupiter to contain two distinct types of terrain: dark regions representing old, heavily cratered crust; and a younger,

lighter-colored region characterized by complex patterns of parallel grooves and ridges.

Craters in the dark primitive region vary in size and appearance. There are younger, bowl-shaped formations with their rims intact. Larger craters with central peaks and ray systems formed by ejecta are scattered about the surface. The ray systems are brighter where fresh ice from the interior has covered the dark, ancient crust. The oldest impacts appear as "ghost craters" that have almost completely merged into the surface (fig. 9.16).

The grooved terrain occupies most of the surface in broad belts between the darker ancient regions. Parallel bands ranging from 5 to 15 km apart stretch several hundred kilometers in a network of channels which evidently were created by deformation of the icy crust. There is evidence of tectonic processes

## The Mass of Jupiter

Newton's derivation of Kepler's third law of planetary motion may be used to determine the combined mass of Jupiter and one of its satellites. Newton's solution is

$$(M_J + m_S) = \frac{d^3}{P^2}$$

where $(M_J + m_S)$ represents the combined mass of Jupiter and one of its satellites. The distance $(d)$ between Jupiter and its satellite is given in units of the mean distance between the Earth and Moon. The period $(P)$ of the satellite's revolution around Jupiter is given in units of the Moon's revolution around the Earth.

If we let Io represent the satellite, then

$$(M_J + m_I) = \frac{d_{J/I}^3}{P_{J/I}^2}$$

where

$M_J$ = the mass of Jupiter

$m_I$ = the mass of Io

$P_{J/I}$ = the orbital period of Io (1.769 days)

and

$d_{J/I}$ = the mean distance of Io ($422 \times 10^3$ km).

Since the mass of Io is negligible compared to the enormous bulk of Jupiter, we can attribute all the mass of the system to the planet. If the mass of Jupiter is found in terms of the Earth-Moon system as unity, the equation becomes

$$M_J = \frac{(d_{J/I} / d_{E/M})^3}{(P_{J/I} / P_{E/M})^2}$$

where

$P_{E/M}$ = orbital period of the Moon (27.322 days);

and

$d_{E/M}$ = mean distance of the Moon ($384.4 \times 10^3$ km).

$$M_J = \frac{(422 \times 10^3 / 384.4 \times 10^3)^3}{(1.769 / 27.322)^2}$$

$M_J$ = 317 Earth masses.

where faults have laterally displaced the parallel grooves.

Voyager 2 took high-resolution pictures of the opposite hemisphere of Ganymede. The most prominent feature is a large, ancient, cratered area divided by an extensive band of light-colored terrain. A series of curved ridges extend in concentric arcs to form a large impact basin similar to those found on the inner terrestrial bodies. The craters and basins indicate that Ganymede's primitive crust had already hardened prior to the onset of heavy meteoric bombardment.

### Callisto

When Voyager 1 reached Callisto, it flew within 124,000 km of the hemisphere facing Jupiter and revealed a surface of ice mixed with silicates that is glutted with craters. Callisto lacks vertical relief and shows little change since the period of heavy meteoric bombardment that occurred early in the history of the solar system (fig. 9.17).

During the Voyager 1 encounter, several huge impact basins were

**figure 9.17**

Voyager 1 image of impact basins on Callisto. The largest is 600 km in diameter and resembles the ringed basins found on the Moon, Mercury, and Mars.

the giant planets: Jupiter and Saturn

173

photographed. The largest has a diameter of 600 km and is surrounded by a series of concentric rings extending 1500 km from the center. Although similar in appearance to other ringed basins of rocky materials found on terrestrial bodies, Callisto's impact basins and craters were formed in ice. Evidently, collision with a large meteoric body took place at a time when the icy crust was more flexible and could not support the high mountainous ring structures seen on the terrestrial bodies.

## The Ringed Planet Saturn

Like its Jovian neighbor, Saturn is a self-contained system of multiple rings and satellites (fig. 9.18). Indeed, there is a strong physical resemblance between Saturn and Jupiter. Both planets are characterized by their rapid spin, strong magnetic fields, and internal heat source. The equatorial radius of Saturn measures 60,268 km; its rotational period of 10h 30m causes a polar flattening of 6450 km, which is greater than the radius of Earth. Saturn has the lowest density of all the planets, only 0.7 gm/cm³, less than the density of water.

**figure 9.18**

This computer-processed image of Saturn enhances the banded cloud structure in the atmosphere and the principal components of the ring system.

### Missions to Saturn

In 1979, after a successful encounter with Jupiter, Pioneer 11 became the first spacecraft to reach Saturn. Approaching from below, Pioneer crossed the ring system and passed within 20,930 km of Saturn's cloudy atmosphere. On its outward passage, the spacecraft crossed the rings again and continued to Saturn's largest moon, Titan.

In addition to close-up images of Saturn and Titan, Pioneer 11 confirmed the presence of a magnetic field, an ionosphere, radiation belts, and a magnetosphere. Saturn was found to emit more energy than it receives from the Sun, which suggests an intrinsic heat source. Close-up images showed an absence of large spots in Saturn's atmosphere; gravitational and temperature studies confirmed its liquid and metallic hydrogen structure.

In 1980 Voyager 1, and in the following year Voyager 2, reached Saturn and came up with a bounty of data and close-up pictures of the giant planet. Its atmosphere has faint bands of clouds, stretched parallel to the equator, which are driven by currents of high-speed winds; rotating spots and irregularities are enmeshed in the circulation pattern produced by cloud motions.

But the splendor of Saturn is its impressive ring system that extends along the equatorial plane (fig. 9.19). Voyager television cameras transmitted detailed pictures of countless particles in alternating light and dark, narrow bands.

One objective of these missions was to determine the geological structure of the satellites of Saturn, in particular the large satellite Titan. Measurements indicated that Titan has an atmosphere composed of nitrogen, and the smaller satellites are made of ice and rocky materials.

After completing its scientific investigation of Saturn, Voyager 2 was placed into a trajectory for a rendezvous with Uranus.

### Interior Structure

Theoretical models for the composition, and the internal temperatures, pressures, and structure of Saturn are essentially the same as for Jupiter. Hydrogen is the principal constituent (nearly 80%), followed by helium (20%) as the second most abundant element. Small quantities of oxygen (1.0%), carbon (0.4%), iron (0.2%), neon (0.2%), nitrogen (0.1%), and silicon (0.1%) make up the remainder of Saturn's mass. These substances are found in different shells of increasing temperature and pressure at various levels within the planet (fig. 9.20).

The outermost layer, or atmosphere, extends from the uppermost clouds to a

figure 9.19

The rings of Saturn are composed of rocks, dust, and ice ranging in size from boulders to microscopic grains. The prominent gap in the ring system is called the Cassini division.

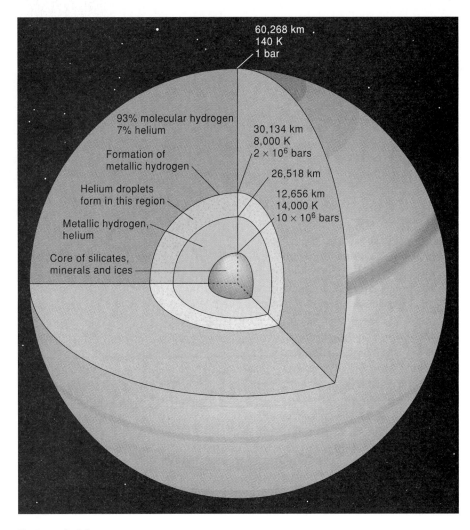

60,268 km
140 K
1 bar

93% molecular hydrogen
7% helium

Formation of
metallic hydrogen

30,134 km
8,000 K
$2 \times 10^6$ bars

26,518 km

Helium droplets
form in this region

12,656 km
14,000 K
$10 \times 10^6$ bars

Metallic hydrogen,
helium

Core of silicates,
minerals and ices

figure 9.20

The internal structure of Saturn is similar to that of Jupiter.

region where gaseous hydrogen changes into a liquid. The shell of liquid molecular hydrogen continues to a depth of 30,000 km to a region of liquid metallic hydrogen. At this level, the temperature is estimated to be 8500 K. The base of the liquid metallic hydrogen is above a core 12,600 km from the center of the planet where the temperature is 10,600 K. The core may consist of two parts: a dense inner region of metals and silicates, and an outer core of water, methane, and ammonia liquid/ice.

The liquid metallic hydrogen region is probably the source of the planet's magnetic field. As in the case of Jupiter, the dynamo action of the electrically conductive metallic zone generates the intrinsic magnetic field. Saturn's magnetosphere is formed by the interaction of the magnetic field and the solar wind. In one respect, the magnetic field of Saturn is unique in that the magnetic and rotational axes of the planet nearly coincide. Moreover, the polarity of Saturn's magnetic field is reversed in the same manner as the polarity of Jupiter's field.

Infrared experiments aboard the spacecraft indicate that Saturn radiates more heat than it receives from the Sun. Some of the thermal radiation is attributed to the gradual cooling of the planet and the continuous compression of its core. The remainder of the interior heating is believed to be caused by separation of the hydrogen and helium mixture in the liquid molecular layer. The more massive helium rains down to the top of the metallic hydrogen shell and in the process releases heat to the atmosphere and space.

## Atmosphere and Clouds

Voyager infrared spectrometer and radio occultation experiments revealed the vertical structure of Saturn's atmosphere from the high stratosphere to the lower cloud levels (fig. 9.21). The conditions within the lowest levels, or troposphere, can only be inferred from theoretical studies. There is evidence that the energy from the interior causes warm gases to rise by convection to the upper atmosphere where clouds condense at different levels. The tropopause, or boundary

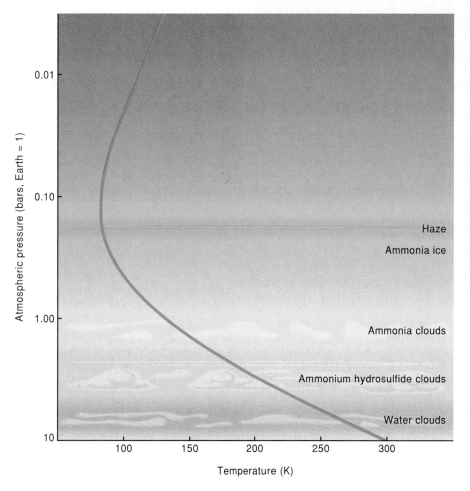

**figure 9.21**

Instruments aboard the Voyager spacecraft measured pressure and temperature variations in Saturn's upper atmosphere. Clouds of water, ammonium hydrosulfide, and ammonia condense at different altitudes.

between the troposphere and the stratosphere, marks the altitude of the uppermost clouds. Here the temperature is 93 K and the pressure about 100 mb, or one-tenth the atmospheric pressure on the Earth's surface.

Three layers of clouds in the upper troposphere are distinguished by their composition and altitude. The uppermost layer consists of white crystals of ammonia which condense at an altitude of 100 km, below the 100-mb level. Other cloud layers are found at lower altitudes: a clear atmosphere of hydrogen and helium; a middle cloud layer of ammonium hydrogen sulfide ($NH_4SH$); a lower level of water ice clouds; and a second clear layer of hydrogen and helium. The convective flow from the lower troposphere produces bright zones of rising

high pressure and darker belts of descending low pressure. Combined with rapid rotation, the clouds assume the prominent banded structure found in the atmosphere of Jupiter. However, Saturn's clouds are located deeper below the atmospheric haze and do not show the subtle contrasts seen on Jupiter. High-resolution false-color images are used to enhance the circulation patterns and other fine details (see fig. 9.22).

There is a fundamental difference in the relative zonal velocities in the counterflowing winds of the two planets. Contrary to the Jovian wind patterns, which alternate between high and low pressure regions, the winds of Saturn are dominated by westerly flows, in particular a single equatorial jet stream. The equatorial jet extends as much as 35°

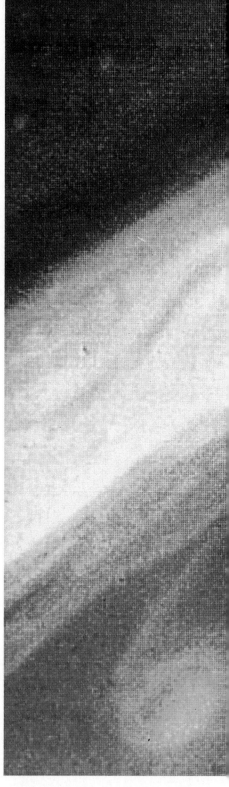

**figure 9.22**

Voyager images reveal a variety of patterns and eddies in Saturn's banded atmosphere.

north and south latitude and approaches supersonic speeds of 500 m/sec at the equator. Alternating east-west winds occur above 40° latitude in each hemisphere.

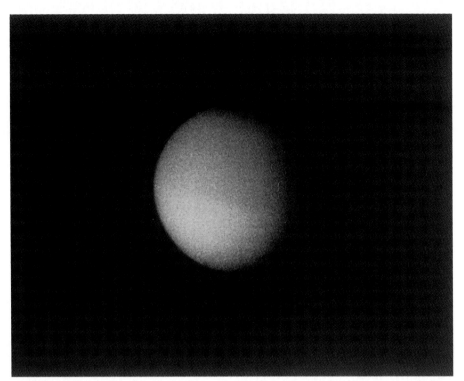

**figure 9.23**

The surface of Saturn's largest satellite, Titan, is hidden by a thick atmosphere.

There is a considerable variety of smaller patterns and eddies in the light and dark bands. Close-up Voyager images reveal puffy convective clouds of ammonia crystals across the middle latitudes. At higher latitudes, interacting brown and white ovals spin counterclockwise between alternating wind currents.

A feature peculiar to Saturn is a long, wavy, ribbonlike structure carried by the prevailing wind (fig. 9.22).

## Magnetosphere

The magnetic field of Saturn is smaller than Jupiter's and contains fewer ionized particles. The density of the particles trapped in the field lines is reduced by their interaction with the ring system and the inner satellites. The main region of the ring system extends from Saturn to a distance of about 2.3 $R_S$ ($R_S$ = radius of Saturn). Here the ions of the inner magnetosphere have been stripped, leaving only a few trapped particles in the magnetic field. Beyond the ring system, the plasma density increases to a maximum between 5 and 10 $R_S$ from the center of the planet. Moreover, the rapid rotation of Saturn creates a plasma sheet in the plane of the equator extending more than 15 $R_S$ into the outer magnetosphere.

From inside the orbit of the satellite Rhea to beyond Titan, the magnetosphere contains a torus-shaped gas cloud composed of neutral hydrogen atoms. Early in the history of Titan, hydrogen was separated from the gases in the satellite's primitive atmosphere and escaped into the magnetosphere. The magnetopause and bow shock in the outer magnetosphere change in distance between 20 and 30 $R_S$ as pressure changes in the solar wind.

## Satellites

Saturn has a retinue of at least 18 large and small satellites grouped into three categories. The largest, Titan, is a terrestrial body that will be treated separately. The remaining satellites are mainly composed of ice. The second group consists of six *major satellites* ranging in diameter between 400 and 1500 km. Finally, there are eleven *small satellites,* some of which share orbits or are associated with particles in the ring system.

### *Titan*

Saturn's largest satellite is of planetary proportions; it is larger than Mercury but second in size to Jupiter's Ganymede (fig. 9.23). Titan resembles Ganymede and Callisto in density (1.8 gm/cm³) and is believed to have their internal

**figure 9.24**

A false-color image of Titan from Voyager 1. The main constituent of Titan's atmosphere, molecular nitrogen, may have been produced by photodissociation of ammonia from the satellite's surface.

structure. Titan is differentiated into layers: a solid core of silicates about 3400 km in diameter, a mantle of ice almost 800 km thick, and a crust about 100 km deep.

Titan was detected by Huygens soon after Galileo discovered the four large Jovian satellites. But very little was known about Titan until 1943 when Gerard Kuiper identified methane in its spectrum and proved that the satellite had an atmosphere. Voyager 1 found the main constituent of Titan's atmosphere to be molecular nitrogen. The presence of an atmosphere can be explained by Titan's low surface temperature of 90 K. At one time, methane, ammonia, and water ices in the interior were heated and vented to the surface. Since gas molecules move more slowly at low temperature, the methane and ammonia molecules were unable to escape Titan's

relatively weak gravity. Later, the action of sunlight separated the ammonia into nitrogen and hydrogen. The lighter hydrogen escaped and formed the torus cloud in the magnetosphere of Saturn. Nitrogen and methane remained as the constituent gases of the present atmosphere of Titan (fig. 9.24).

An alternate explanation suggests that intense meteoric bombardment could have separated nitrogen from ammonia in the early atmosphere of Titan. Impacts would have raised the temperature sufficiently to liberate nitrogen and release hydrogen into the magnetosphere of Saturn.

Titan may have a surface covered by a sea of methane. At 90 K, methane can exist as a solid as well as a liquid. Thus, Titan may have sheets of methane ice across the polar regions and liquid methane covering the remainder of its surface.

### Major Satellites

This category contains most of the satellites known before the Voyager missions. In order of distance from Saturn, they are Mimas, Enceladus, Tethys, Dione, Rhea, and Iapetus. Titan's orbit lies between Rhea and Iapetus. These satellites and Titan have synchronous periods of rotation, keeping one hemisphere in the direction of Saturn.

Mimas has a diameter of 392 km and revolves in 22.6 hours. Voyager images show craters down to 2 km in diameter. The most prominent feature on Mimas is a large 130-km crater that covers about one-third the diameter of the satellite (fig. 9.25a).

Enceladus is 500 km across and revolves about Saturn in 1d 9h. Unlike Mimas, Enceladus has extensive smooth areas almost free of craters. These terrains contain ridges, faults and crevasses generally believed to be flow marks caused by recent geological activity (fig. 9.25b).

More than twice as large as Enceladus, Tethys is a heavily cratered satellite 1060 km in diameter, revolving in a period of 1d 21h at a distance of 294,660 km from Saturn. Its most prominent crater extends 400 km and is much larger than any crater on the Moon. There is a distinct boundary between ancient cratered regions and more recent terrain where fewer craters are found. Past surface activity is indicated by an enormous trench extending 2000 km, about two-thirds of the satellite's circumference. The canyon is about 100 km wide and 3 to 5 km deep and is comparable in size to the Valles Marineris on Mars (fig. 9.25c).

Dione has a diameter of 1120 km and completes its revolution in 2d 18h at a distance of 377,400 km from Saturn. Its higher density, 1.4 gm/cm³, indicates a greater ratio of silicates to ice than found on the other satellites. Moreover, Dione has highly varied surface features. The side opposite Saturn is as bright as other icy satellites, its leading hemisphere is heavily cratered, and the trailing hemisphere has curvilinear streaks of ice that may have oozed from cracks in the surface (fig. 9.25d).

Rhea has a diameter of 1530 km and takes 4d 12h to revolve at a mean distance of 527,000 km from Saturn. The

chapter 9

astronomy: through space and time

178

a.

d.

**figure 9.25**

The major satellites of Saturn: *a.* Mimas, *b.* Enceladus, *c.* Tethys, *d.* Dione, *e.* Rhea, *f.* Iapetus.

b.

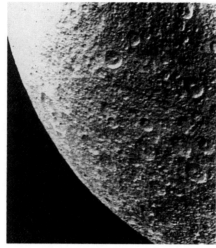

e.

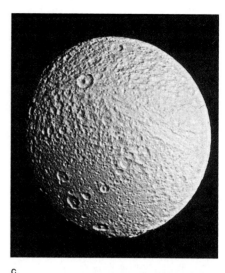

c.

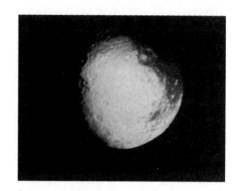

f.

heavily cratered surface of Rhea has the appearance of the highland region on the far side of the Moon. The bright streaks found on its trailing hemisphere were probably caused by internal activity at an earlier period in its history (fig. 9.25e).

The last major satellite, Iapetus, has a diameter of 1460 km, an orbital period of 79d 8h, and a mean distance of 3,561,300 km from Saturn. This satellite has a most unusual appearance. Its leading hemisphere has a dark layer distributed uniformly across the surface. In contrast, the trailing hemisphere has a bright surface of water ice (fig. 9.25f).

### Small Satellites

Hyperion is found between Titan and Iapetus, circling Saturn in about 21d. It is an irregular body composed of water ice mixed with dust, making Hyperion darker than other nearby satellites (fig. 9.26a). Phoebe, the outermost satellite, is in a highly tilted, retrograde orbit almost 13 million km from the planet. It is dark in color and may be composed of

the solid grains that formed the dust disk of the solar nebula.

Another group of small satellites occupy the same orbit and form an equilateral triangle with Saturn. Telesto and Calypso are at such equilibrium, or Lagrangian, points about 295,000 km from the planet. The two satellites are also located at the Lagrangian points of the major satellite Tethys. The satellite Helene is at the leading equilibrium point of Dione's orbit (refer to the Trojan asteroids of Jupiter).

Two **co-orbital satellites,** Janus and Epimetheus, revolve at different speeds in nearly the same orbit about 151,400 km from the center of Saturn. Every four years, when the satellites arrive at opposition, the faster one cannot pass because their separation is less than their diameters. Instead of colliding, they switch

orbits and keep going in the same direction around Saturn.

**Shepherd satellites** apparently keep particles of the ring system from scattering. Atlas, the innermost satellite, occupies an orbit on the outer edge of the A Ring. Other satellites, Prometheus and Pandora, bracket the F Ring and keep its particles restricted to a thin band (fig. 9.26b). The tiny satellite Pan is located inside the A Ring at a distance of 133,570 km from the center of Saturn. Its orbit lies within the **Encke division.** Apparently, the gravitational influence of the shepherd satellites confine the particles to a narrow zone. The irregularities in the orbital motion of the ring material are damped out by the passage of the moons along the inner and outer boundaries of the ring.

### The Ring System

Saturn's rings were first observed by Galileo in 1610 as ear-like bulges on the planet's disk. In 1659, Huygens

a.

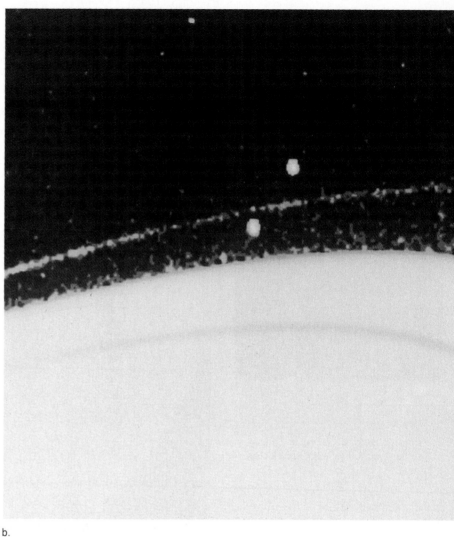

b.

**figure 9.26**

*a.* Small satellites of Saturn. *b.* Shepherd satellites Prometheus and Pandora.

explained the enigma as a ring encircling the planet. In the 1670s, Cassini discovered the dark gap that separates the bright portion of the ring into two components, the A Ring and B Ring. In 1850, Bond identified the third faint C Ring inside the B Ring. By the 1900s, occultations of stars by Saturn proved the rings to be a swarm of solid particles in orbit about the planet. Moreover, the inner portion of the ring revolves at a greater rate than the outer rim, which is possible only if the system were composed of particles. In 1966, Kuiper identified an additional tenuous ring outside

**figure 9.27**

A computer-enhanced, false-color image of Saturn's rings.

the principal rings. But the awesome beauty of Saturn's dynamic rings was unknown until the flights of the Voyager spacecraft (see fig. 9.27).

The principal rings extend from about 6700 km above Saturn's clouds to a distance of 73,600 km. The particles vary in size from boulders tens of meters in diameter down to fine microscopic grains. The material is grouped in narrow bands or ringlets no more than 100 km wide.

The ring system contains gaps that divide the rings into regions of different particle density and size. The bright A Ring and B Ring are separated by the **Cassini division,** 5000 km wide and located 119,000 km from the center of Saturn. From the Cassini division, the A Ring extends to the boundary of the narrow F Ring. The A Ring contains the Encke division, which is about 12,500 km from the inner edge. The Voyager spacecraft revealed fainter ringlets contained in both the Cassini and Encke divisions. Previously, the divisions were believed to be gaps between the rings. The F Ring, discovered during the Pioneer flyby, is a thin wavy ringlet only a few hundred kilometers wide. The ring is confined by the gravitational influence of its shepherd satellites. Far from the principal rings are the G Ring, 170,000 km from Saturn, and the E Ring extending from 210,000 to 300,000 km from the planet.

Moving inward from the Cassini division, we approach the prominent B

**figure 9.28**
B Ring of Saturn with "spoke" features.

Ring, the dominant region of the ring system. It is the brightest ring and contains the greatest density of particles. Its opaque surface casts a dark shadow onto Saturn's upper atmosphere. The B Ring contains strange radial **spokes** 10,000 km in length pointing outward across the ringlets (fig. 9.28). These mysterious structures do not share in the differential motion of the particles that make up the ring. Astronomers believe that the spokes are composed of tiny charged particles suspended a few meters above the orbiting ringlets by the action of Saturn's magnetic field.

The almost transparent C Ring, or Crepe Ring, is visible through a telescope but is very faint and more difficult to see than the brighter A and B Rings. The much fainter D Ring consists of a number of sparsely populated ringlets.

# SUMMARY

Jupiter and Saturn are characterized by their size, chemical composition, rapid rotation, many satellites, and rings. They are composed of hydrogen and helium as the main constituents. Their atmospheres contain striated clouds of ammonia and water ice crystals.

Pioneer and Voyager spacecraft successfully explored the environments of both planets. The missions were designed to transmit detailed images of the planets, satellites, and ring systems, and to investigate their physical properties.

Models of the internal structure of Jupiter and Saturn imply that their hydrogen and helium atmospheres extend to a liquid molecular hydrogen shell. Beneath the liquid hydrogen is an inner shell of liquid metallic hydrogen and a rocky central core.

The total radiation emitted by each Jovian planet exceeds the amount received from the Sun. Thermal radiation is produced in the interiors of the planets and transported by convection to their atmospheres. Gases from below rise, cool, and form the clouds observed at various layers of their upper atmospheres.

The convective circulation coupled with rapid rotation deflects the atmospheres into high-speed east and west winds at different latitudes. In the process, clouds are distributed in parallel zones and belts. Cyclonic circulation produces features such as the Great Red Spot on Jupiter, and colored ovals, eddies, and swirls in the atmospheres of both planets.

The metallic hydrogen shells are the source of the magnetic fields surrounding the planets. Jupiter and Saturn have strong dipolar magnetic fields of reverse polarity generated by the dynamo action of the rapidly spinning conductive fluid. In the magnetospheres of Jupiter and Saturn, the rotating magnetic field lines are warped into flat current sheets. Some satellites of both planets and the ring system of Saturn interact with and modify the magnetic fields. Io revolves inside a torus of ionized sulfur and oxygen emissions from the volcanoes found on its surface. The torus-shaped cloud about Titan is composed of hydrogen that separated from the primitive atmosphere and escaped into the magnetosphere.

Jupiter has 16 satellites: the Galilean satellites and 12 smaller bodies grouped at different distances from the planet. The four satellites in the outermost group have retrograde revolution. Saturn has at least 18 satellites: Titan, of terrestrial proportions; six major satellites; and eleven smaller bodies, some of which share the same orbit or are associated with particles in the ring system.

Saturn's ring system consists of narrow ringlets grouped in bands or rings of different density. The brightest B Ring is separated from the A Ring by the Cassini division. The principal rings extend outward from the A Ring to the narrow F Ring, which is confined by shepherd satellites. Beyond the F Ring are the faint G Ring and E Ring. Inside the B Ring, there are sparsely populated ringlets that form the C Ring and D Ring.

# KEY TERMS

belts

Cassini division

co-orbital satellites

current sheet

Encke division

Galilean satellites

Great Red Spot

grooved terrain

Lagrangian points

liquid metallic hydrogen

liquid molecular hydrogen

ring system

shepherd satellites

spokes

tidal flexing

Trojan asteroids

zones

# PROBLEMS

1. Why do the clouds of Jupiter appear brighter and more colorful than Saturn's clouds?

2. If the interior of Jupiter and Saturn cannot be studied directly, how can the internal mass distribution of the planets be determined?

3. How are the magnetic fields of Jupiter and Saturn similar? How are they different?

4. Discuss the sources of thermal energy in the lower atmosphere of Jupiter, Saturn, and Earth. How are they similar? Different?

5. How do the surface features of the Galilean satellites differ? What factors are responsible for these differences?

6. Give reasons why Saturn's ring system must be composed of particles and cannot be a solid disk.

7. Explain why Io and Callisto differ in density and internal composition.

8. If Titan resembles Ganymede and Callisto in size and density, why is Titan the only one of the three to possess an atmosphere?

9. What fundamental differences are there between the cloud structures in the atmospheres of Jupiter and Earth?

10. Why is Io the only Jovian satellite to have volcanoes?

11. Describe the significant features of Saturn's six major satellites.

12. In what manner do the Galilean satellites have a remarkable similarity to the planetary system about the Sun?

13. If Io's distance from Jupiter is about the same as the Moon's distance from Earth, why does Io complete 15 revolutions about Jupiter in the time it takes the Moon to make one revolution about the Earth?

14. What is the surface composition of Europa? Why does the satellite lack impact craters?

15. How do the impact basins on Callisto differ from those found on other terrestrial bodies?

16. During one synodic period, Jupiter changes in brightness from a maximum magnitude −2.7 to a minimum magnitude −1.9. Explain.

17. Find Jupiter's distance in kilometers when it is nearest to the Earth.

18. Determine how much brighter the Sun will appear at Jupiter compared to its brightness at Saturn.

19. During eclipse, when Jupiter's satellites emerge from the planet's shadow, are they seen to the east or west of Jupiter? Why?

20. Find the mass of Saturn using the distance and orbital period of one of its satellites.

# REFERENCES

Allison, Michael, and Larry D. Travis, eds. 1986. *The Jovian Atmosphere.* Washington, D. C.: NASA.

Audouze, Jean and Guy Israel. 1985. *The Cambridge Atlas of Astronomy.* Cambridge: Cambridge University Press.

Cuzzi, Jeffery N. 1985. Ringed Planets: Still Mysterious II. *Sky and Telescope* 69, no. 1 (January).

Dunham, David W., Carolyn C. Porco, and Douglas J. Mink. 1989. Saturn to Occult a Bright Star. *Sky and Telescope* 77, no. 6 (June).

Fimmel, Richard O., James Van Allen, and Eric Burgess. 1980. *Pioneer First to Jupiter, Saturn, and Beyond.* Washington, D.C.: NASA.

Lanzerotti, Louis J. 1989. The Planets' Magnetic Environments. *Sky and Telescope* 77, no. 2 (February).

Moore, Patrick, and Garry Hunt. 1984. *Atlas of the Solar System.* Chicago: Rand McNally and Company.

Morrison, David. 1982. *Voyages to Saturn.* Washington, D.C.: NASA.

———. 1985. The Enigma Called Io. *Sky and Telescope* 69, no. 3 (March).

Morrison, Nancy D., and David Morrison. 1984. The Volcanoes of Io: Still Erupting. *Mercury* (Astronomical Society of the Pacific) 13, no. 1 (January/February).

Murray, Bruce. 1989. A Triumphant Beginning. *The Planetary Report* (The Planetary Society) 9, no. 3 (May/June).

News Notes. 1988. Pounding the Gas Out of Titan. *Sky and Telescope* 76, no. 3 (September).

Peek, Bernard M. 1958. *The Planet Jupiter.* London: Faber and Faber Limited.

Sanchez-Lavega, Agustin. 1989. Saturn's Great White Spots. *Sky and Telescope* 78, no. 2 (August).

Soderblom, Laurence A. 1980. The Galilean Moons of Jupiter. *Scientific American* 242, no. 1 (January).

Wolfe, John H. 1975. "Jupiter." Chap. 9 in *The Solar System: A Scientific American Book.* San Francisco: W. H. Freeman and Company.

Yeates, C. M., T. V. Johnson, L. Colin, P. Fanale, L. Frank, and D. M. Hunten. 1985. *Galileo: Exploration of Jupiter's System.* Washington, D. C.: NASA.

chapter

10

the outer worlds: Uranus, Neptune, and Pluto

In August 1989, Voyager 2 reached Neptune and
revealed a planet with a deep blue atmosphere
filled with methane clouds.

At a distance of 2.8 billion km from Earth, twice as far as the giant planet Saturn, Voyager 2 made its brief rendezvous with Uranus, then changed course and continued on to Neptune. Mission designers had planned a trajectory that used the gravitational attraction of Saturn to point Voyager 2 toward its next destination. When Uranus was reached in 1986, the same technique was applied to steer the spacecraft to Neptune. Thus, in 1989, Voyager 2 completed its grand tour of the Jovian planets (fig. 10.1). Only tiny Pluto, twice as distant as Uranus, remains the last planet to be explored at some future time.

Uranus and Neptune are about the same size as each other and represent another set of twin planets along with Jupiter and Saturn. They have extensive atmospheres of hydrogen and helium but should not be thought of as smaller versions of the Jovian planets discussed in chapter 9. Uranus and Neptune have higher densities and contain water, methane, and ammonia ices in their interiors rather than the liquid and metallic hydrogen found in Jupiter and Saturn. Indeed, Uranus and Neptune form a distinctive group unlike the hydrogen- and helium-rich Jovian planets, or the rocky terrestrial planets found nearer to the Sun.

## Uranus

Estimates for the diameter, mass, and density of Uranus were obtained by timing stellar occultations by the planet and measuring the orbital period and distance of one of its satellites. A stellar **occultation,** or an eclipse of a star by a planet, is useful in a number of ways. A star can be considered as a point of light and, during an occultation, any variation of the light can be attributed to a characteristic of the planet. Since the orbital velocity of the planet is known, its diameter can be determined by the length of time the star remains hidden from view. Knowing the radius, we can compute the planet's volume (see Methods and Understandings

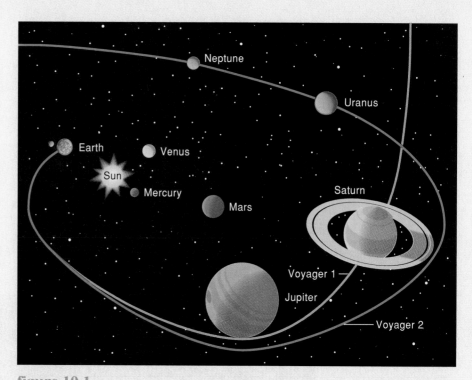

**figure 10.1**

The exploration of the outer solar system was made possible by a unique alignment of the giant planets.

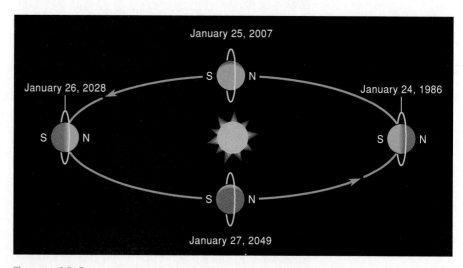

**figure 10.2**

Uranus takes 84 years to complete one revolution. Each pole of the planet faces the Sun every 42 years because the spin axis lies almost in the plane of the orbit. When Voyager 2 reached Uranus in January 1986, the south pole pointed toward the Sun.

9.1). From its mass and volume, Uranus's density is found to be 1.30 g/cm$^3$.

One of the remarkable features of Uranus is the 98° inclination of its equator to the plane of its orbit. The plane of the equator and the axis of rotation alternately point in the direction of the Sun every 21 years (fig. 10.2). At present, the pole of counterclockwise rotation (the

north pole on the Earth but the south pole on Uranus) is nearly in line with the Sun.

When Uranus is in opposition with the Earth, the unusual alignment of the axis can be detected by the motions of its satellites. At two points in the orbit of Uranus, when the plane of its equator appears edge-on, the satellites revolve

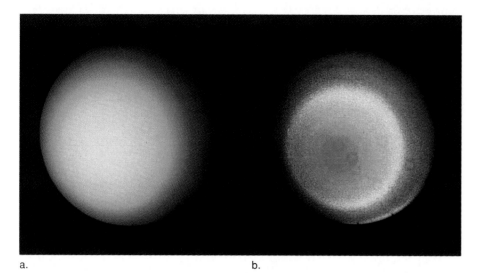

a.                                    b.

**figure 10.3**

*a.* A true-color image of Uranus from Voyager 2 shows the planet's atmosphere to be almost featureless. *b.* A false-color image reveals cloud bands in the upper atmosphere.

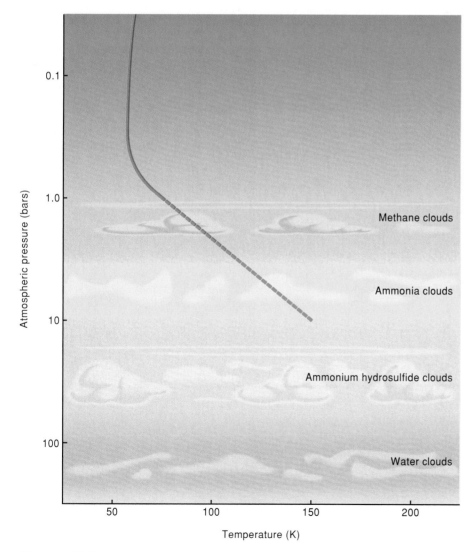

**figure 10.4**

Cloud structure and temperature profile of the troposphere of the Uranian atmosphere.

almost perpendicular to the ecliptic and appear edge-on, moving up and down. After 21 years, the axis of Uranus points toward the Earth and the satellites are seen to revolve in circular orbits. Five satellites were known before the Voyager 2 encounter.

The trajectory of Voyager 2 at Uranus was entirely different from the path followed during the previous encounters with Jupiter and Saturn. The inclination of Uranus's rotational axis to its orbit caused the Voyager 2 to cross the system perpendicular to the planet's equatorial plane. In its brief encounter of less than a day, the spacecraft photographed the satellites and rings, passed 28,000 km above the twisted face of Miranda, crossed the equatorial plane of Uranus 81,560 km from the cloud tops, and raced toward its next target, Neptune.

## Atmosphere and Clouds

The composition (by volume) of the Uranian atmosphere consists of 85% hydrogen mixed with about 15% helium. In addition, traces of methane absorb the longer red and reflect the shorter green and blue wavelengths that give the planet its distinctive aqua blue color, which extends deep into the lower atmosphere (fig. 10.3a).

The atmosphere of Uranus may be divided into two parts. The lower level contains the troposphere and stratosphere where constituent gases are mixed (fig. 10.4). In the troposphere, the uppermost cloud layer consists of methane ice at a pressure level of 1.6 bars and a temperature of 82 K. At greater depths and higher temperatures there are probably strata of ammonia and water clouds. At the tropopause above the 1000-mb level the temperature reaches a minimum of 51 K. In the stratosphere the temperature stops decreasing and begins to rise with increasing altitude.

Above the stratosphere, the atmosphere is no longer a mixture of gases but is composed almost entirely of hydrogen atoms and molecules. At 6000 km above the methane clouds, the pressure is reduced to about one microbar (one-millionth of the atmosphere at the Earth's surface). The breakdown of the hydrogen by sunlight produces an ionosphere of charged particles at a temperature of 750 K.

The Voyager 2 mission provided the first opportunity to investigate the circulation of the Uranian atmosphere. Black and white images of the cloud structure were transmitted through various filters: violet, orange, and in a red wavelength absorbed by methane gas. False-color enhanced images showed cloud bands concentric with the rotational axis of the planet (fig. 10.3b). Smaller cloud features at constant latitudes and bright and dark markings are carried around the planet by westerly winds in 17 hours at the equator and in 14 hours near the pole.

One of several surprises provided by Uranus is the east-west zonal circulation of its atmosphere. At the time of observation, the Sun was almost directly above the south pole and researchers expected the temperature gradient between the equator and the pole to produce a north-south circulation. Instead, Voyager 2 measurements indicated the temperature to be almost uniform at all latitudes in spite of the extreme axial tilt. It is evident that, although the Sun supplies most of the energy, atmospheric circulation is controlled by the rotation of the planet. Large-scale winds moving in a north-south direction veer into streams flowing parallel to the equator (fig. 10.5).

## Internal Structure and Magnetic Field

The internal structure of Uranus can be inferred from theoretical models based upon information about the planet's gravitational field and period of rotation. These and other physical quantities were derived from ground-based and Voyager 2 experiments. The most acceptable model based upon spacecraft data has two layers: a central core of iron and silicates, and an envelope of fluid water/ice extending from the core to and including a gaseous atmosphere of hydrogen and helium (fig. 10.6).

We will explore the interior by starting at the methane cloud deck where the pressure is about 1.6 bars and the temperature 82 K. Probing deeper, the temperature reaches a comfortable 290 K at a pressure hundreds of times greater than at the Earth's surface. At a depth of

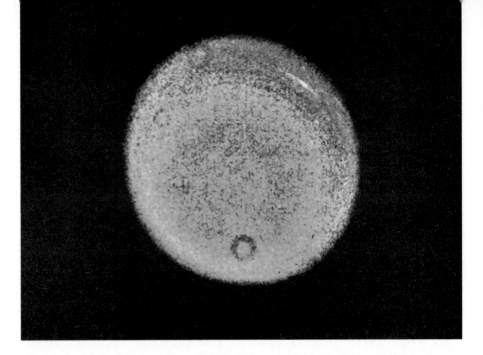

**figure 10.5**

False-color image of the south pole of Uranus, showing circumpolar methane clouds. The ringlike structure is a camera artifact.

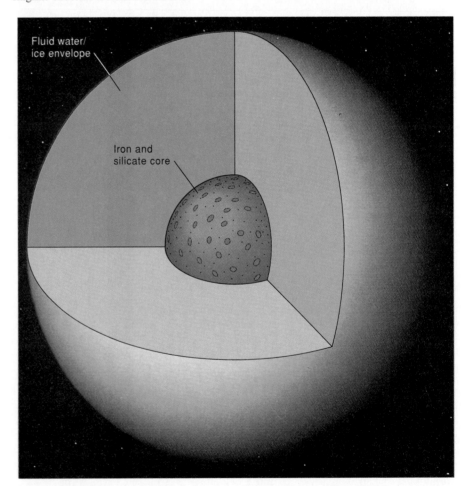

Fluid water/ice envelope

Iron and silicate core

**figure 10.6**

The internal structure of Uranus.

11,000 km, the separation between the atmosphere and the denser interior becomes indistinct as they merge into a hot, dense fluid. The pressure reaches millions of bars and the temperature thousands of kelvins at a molten core as

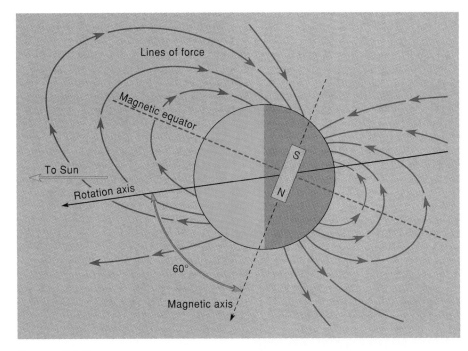

**figure 10.7**
The magnetic field of Uranus.

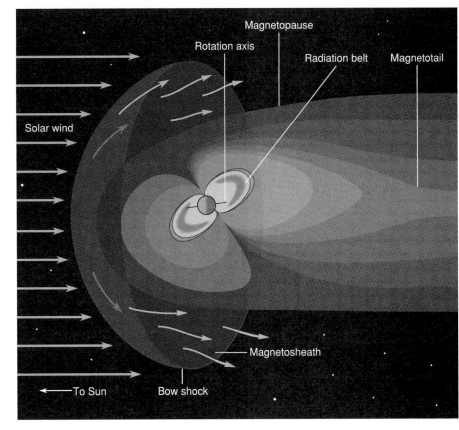

**figure 10.8**
The magnetosphere of Uranus.

large as the Earth. Moreover, the fluid in the interior is believed to be ionized, thus a good conductor of electricity. The dynamo action of the spinning fluid generates Uranus's magnetic field.

Only hours before encounter, Voyager detected radio emissions and charged particles in a remarkably different and complex magnetic environment. On other planets, the rotational and magnetic axes are tilted at a small angle to each other. For example, on Saturn the two axes almost coincide; on the Earth the difference is less than 12°. By contrast, the Uranian magnetic axis is tilted at an angle of 60° to the spin axis and is offset about one-third of the distance from the center of the planet (fig. 10.7).

The interaction between the magnetic field and the solar wind creates a magnetosphere consisting of a sunward lobe at a distance of about 18 radii from the planet. A magnetotail extends millions of kilometers in the opposite direction (fig. 10.8). The internal rotation rate of 17.24 hours was determined by radio bursts from charged particles in the twisting magnetic field.

The magnetosphere of Uranus contains radiation belts of ionized particles similar to the Earth's Van Allen belts. The Uranian satellites and rings are within the boundary of the radiation belts and provide the particles that become trapped in the magnetic field. As the satellites sweep through the spinning radiation belts, their surfaces are darkened by collisions with charged particles.

### Satellites and Rings

There are 15 known bodies and at least 10 rings of particles in orbit around Uranus. Five of these bodies are major satellites: Oberon and Titania were first seen by Herschel in 1787 six years after he discovered the planet; two more, Umbriel and Ariel, were found by Lassell in 1851; and Miranda was discovered by Kuiper in 1948. When Voyager 2 reached Uranus, 10 more were found, bringing the total to 15 satellites (see appendix C.3).

The five major satellites are distinguished from the minor satellites by their reflectance, size, and greater distance from Uranus (fig. 10.9). As a group, they

a.

b.

c.

d.

e.

▲ **figure 10.9**

The major satellites of Uranus. *a.* Titania, *b.* Oberon, *c.* Umbriel, *d.* Ariel, *e.* Miranda.

◄ **figure 10.10**

Miranda's rough surface is characterized by fault blocks and steep cliffs.

are much brighter and range in albedo from 0.18 for Umbriel to 0.34 for Ariel. Evidently, these larger bodies differentiated during accretion and formed a rocky core surrounded by an icy mantle and crust. The minor satellites are a mixture of dark grains and ice that reflect only 7% of the total radiation received from the Sun.

The largest Uranian satellite, Titania, has a surface scarred by many impact craters, deep rifts, and faults that extend for several hundred kilometers (fig. 10.9a). At one time, the interior of Titania was hot enough for water to exist as a liquid. Extensive intrusions of water onto the surface formed an icy layer over a primitive cratered crust. Eventually the interior cooled and the water froze into an icy mantle that expanded and cracked the surface into rift valleys.

Although Titania and Oberon are nearly the same size, there are significant differences in the way they evolved. Oberon has a heavily cratered, ancient surface that has remained practically unchanged since its formation (fig. 10.9b). A number of craters have floors with dark markings that indicate past internal activity. Water mixed with dark grains may have seeped through fissures and formed a layer of ice inside the craters.

Umbriel has the lowest albedo, 0.18, of all the large satellites and shows no significant variation in brightness from one region to another (fig. 10.9c). Umbriel is covered by ancient craters indicating little change since its origin.

Ariel is the brightest satellite (albedo = 0.34) and shows evidence of intensive tectonic activity during its history. Extensive fault valleys meander hundreds of kilometers in length (fig. 10.9d). As the crust separated, molten material welled up and covered ancient craters. Large, half-submerged craters rise above a relatively smooth surface scarred by sinuous grooves and ridges.

The smallest major satellite, Miranda, has a surface characterized by densely cratered terrain divided by oval regions of alternating light and dark ridges and grooves. One of the strangest landforms is a bright V shape that resembles a numeral 7 inside a dark rectangular area (fig. 10.9e). High-resolution images from Voyager 2 revealed a region of few craters, parallel ridges, grooves, and steep cliffs at tortuous angles reaching 15 km above the twisted landscape (fig. 10.10).

Eight of the minor satellites discovered by Voyager 2 occupy nearly circular orbits between the innermost major satellite, Miranda, and Uranus's **ring system.** The largest, Puck, was discovered by Voyager's cameras more than a month before the encounter in January 1986.

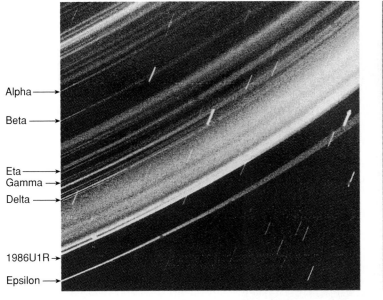

Alpha →
Beta →
Eta →
Gamma →
Delta →
1986U1R →
Epsilon →

a.

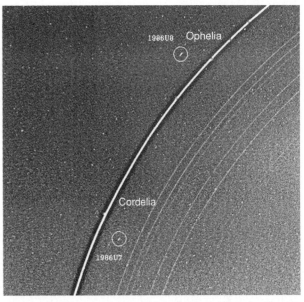

1986U8    Ophelia

Cordelia

1986U7

b.

## figure 10.11

*a.* Uranus's ring system recorded by Voyager 2. Materials in the rings range in size from large blocks of ice and boulders to fine dust particles. The short streaks are images of star trails made as the spacecraft tracked the planet. *b.* Shepherd satellites maintain orbits on either side of the Epsilon Ring.

## T a b l e   1 0 . 1

### rings of Uranus and Neptune

| Ring | Distance from Planet Center (km)[a] |
|------|--------------------------------------|
| *Uranus* | |
| 1986U2R | (38,000) |
| 6 | 41,840 |
| 5 | 42,230 |
| 4 | 42,580 |
| Alpha | 44,720 |
| Beta | 45,670 |
| Eta | 47,190 |
| Gamma | 47,630 |
| Delta | 48,290 |
| Lambda | 50,020 |
| Epsilon | 51,140 |
| *Neptune* | |
| 1989N3R | 41,900 |
| 1989N2R | 53,200 |
| 1989N4R | 53,200–59,100 |
| 1989N1R | 62,930 |

[a]Values in parentheses are uncertain by more than 10%.

From Carolyn Collins Petersen, "Uranus and Neptune, Satellites" in *The Astronomy and Astrophysics Encyclopedia.* Copyright © 1992 Van Nostrand Reinhold Company, New York, NY. Reprinted by permission.

The rings of Uranus were unknown until 1977, when a system of orbiting bands was found by astronomers while engaged in stellar occultation experiments. Rings can be detected by periodic changes in the brightness of a star prior to and after its disappearance behind a moving planet. Before ingress, the star's light diminishes in brightness each time it passes behind a ring. When the star emerges from behind the planet, the rings cause the light to fade again, but this time the minima occur in reverse order. Altogether, nine rings were discovered prior to the Voyager 2 mission. During the Voyager encounter in 1986, the known rings were confirmed; more rings were detected; and a multitude of ringlets composed of fine particles, as well as several partial ring-arcs, were revealed (table 10.1, and fig. 10.11).

## Neptune

Through a telescope, Neptune looks like a faint, aqua-colored ball. As discussed in chapter 6, the location of the planet was determined by theoretical calculations

**figure 10.12**

A false-color image of Neptune shows upper-atmospheric haze in red along the planet's limb. White plumes of methane form above the highest cloud deck.

based upon the observed deviations of Uranus from its predicted position. Once Neptune's distance was known, its physical and orbital quantities were computed. The planet's mean distance from the Sun is about 4.5 billion km and its period of revolution almost 164 years. Its diameter of 48,600 km is slightly less than the diameter of Uranus, making Neptune the fourth largest planet. Neptune has a mass equal to 17.2 Earth masses; its density is 1.76 gm/cm³; and its period of rotation, based on Voyager data, is estimated at 18.4 hours.

The physical structure of Neptune is similar to Uranus and is described by a two-layer model: an iron/silicate core; and a mantle of liquid/ices extending from the core to and including a hydrogen and helium atmosphere enriched by methane ice.

Two satellites of Neptune were known before the Voyager 2 flight. Triton, discovered by Lassell in 1846, is 2700 km in diameter and comparable in size to the Galilean satellites of Jupiter. Nereid, only 340 km across, was discovered photographically by Kuiper in 1949. Six more bodies were detected during the Voyager flyby.

## The Voyager 2 Mission

In 1989, faint signals from the aging Voyager 2 were reassembled into long-awaited images of the Neptune system. Several months prior to encounter, measurements of the planet's atmosphere and swirling clouds were already underway. Preliminary results showed that Neptune, in contrast to placid Uranus, is an active planet with an atmosphere of dark rotating spots, bright plumes, and streamers (fig. 10.12).

As the spacecraft neared closest approach only 5000 km above the cloud tops, studies were made of the atmospheric structure and planetary winds. Sensors measured magnetic fields and radio emissions. Infrared and ultraviolet detectors scanned the planet and its satellites and ring system.

One of the objectives of the mission was to investigate Neptune's magnetism and determine the planet's internal structure. Investigators found the magnetic axis of Neptune tilted to the spin axis and offset from the center more than that of Uranus.

After closest approach, six tiny satellites were revealed and three narrow rings

confirmed. The spacecraft ended its grand tour of the outer solar system with stunning views of Neptune's largest moon (figs. 10.13 and 10.20). The pictures of Triton showed a mottled surface containing icy volcanoes or geysers, large rolling expanses, and large-scale ice flows. The icy satellite turned out to be one of the most intriguing objects in the solar system.

## Atmosphere and Clouds

Although Neptune and Uranus are similar in size and composition, Neptune is far more complex than its dull twin. Both planets have an atmosphere of hydrogen and helium mixed with a small quantity of methane. The methane in the atmosphere absorbs the red and reflects the shorter wavelengths of sunlight to give the planets their distinctive blue-green color. Neptune is conspicuous for the variety of its dynamic wind and weather patterns, which are driven by vast convective currents within the gaseous envelope (fig. 10.14). Indeed, on Neptune internal heating is still in progress and accounts for the release of three times more thermal energy than the planet receives from the Sun.

Voyager 2 cameras photographed Neptune in different colors to enhance the contrast between distinct features in the atmosphere. The images sent to Earth revealed a prominent dark oval at 20° south latitude that has a structure similar to the Great Red Spot on Jupiter. This object, called the **Great Dark Spot,** is 2500 km wide and 6000 km long (fig. 10.15). Other features include striated dark belts and bright clouds. A broad, dark temperate belt is separated from a light tropical belt by a thin, bright band. A bright hood caps the south polar region. The atmospheric features of Neptune are surprisingly similar to the dark and light bands and circulating storms characteristic of the Jovian planets.

The highest clouds observed are represented by cirrus-type narrow streaks extending thousands of kilometers in an east-west direction (fig. 10.16). These upper clouds throw shadow bands onto a lower cloud deck of methane ice crystals. By measuring the shadow widths and computing the angle of the Sun on

**figure 10.13**

Voyager 2 image of Triton, Neptune's largest satellite, shortly after closest approach and passage into Triton's shadow on August 25, 1984. Only a thin crescent of the bright south polar region can be seen.

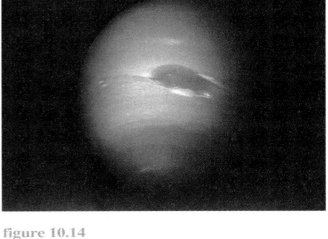

**figure 10.14**

A composite image of Neptune through green and clear filters. Voyager 2 revealed the Great Dark Spot and several cloud systems in Neptune's active atmosphere.

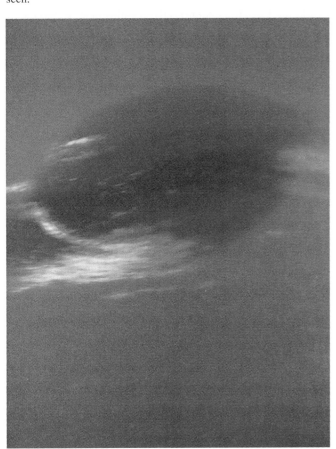

**figure 10.15**

Neptune's Great Dark Spot.

**figure 10.16**

Bands of clouds near the terminator cast long shadows on the methane cloud deck below.

the cirrus clouds, the distance to the methane cloud level was found to be about 50 km.

Bright white cirrus clouds extend 50 km above the southern rim of the Great Dark Spot (fig. 10.15). Images taken at intervals of slightly more than one revolution of the planet reveal that the GDS is moving westward at about 1000 km/hr retrograde with respect to the planet's rotation. As the spot drifts across the planet, the bright clouds form along its edges and stretch out 50 to 200 km. In one revolution, the clouds will dissipate and be replaced by new ones rising from below.

The explanation for the cloud formation is found in the nature of the Great Dark Spot. The GDS is a huge, rotating

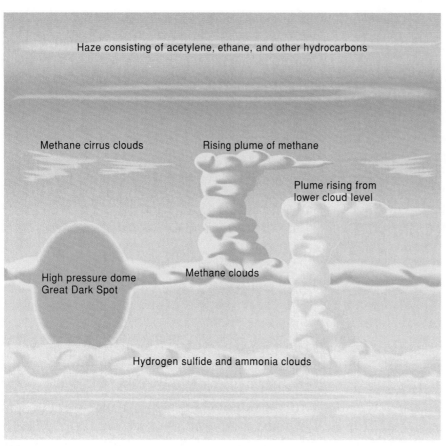

Haze consisting of acetylene, ethane, and other hydrocarbons

Methane cirrus clouds

Rising plume of methane

Plume rising from lower cloud level

High pressure dome Great Dark Spot

Methane clouds

Hydrogen sulfide and ammonia clouds

**figure 10.17**

The cloud structure in Neptune's upper atmosphere. Heat from the planet's interior causes vertical uplift of gases that produces cloud layers, rising plumes, and strong planetary winds.

high-pressure dome as large as the planet Earth (fig. 10.17). What appears to be a dark oval is a gaping hole in the methane cloud layer that exposes a deeper and darker blue-green region of Neptune's gaseous envelope. The high-pressure dome represents a barrier to the horizontal circulation of the methane-rich atmosphere. The result is a vertical uplift of the air to considerably higher levels. As the gases cool and expand, methane condenses and forms the white, feathery upper clouds that trail many kilometers behind the GDS. On Earth, a similar process occurs when warm moist air, forced aloft on the windward side of steep mountains, cools and condenses into clouds.

To the south of the GDS at about 51° south latitude, there is a smaller but darker formation called *Dark Spot Two.* In its center, a white cloud has condensed from a plume originating in the methane

cloud deck. The continuous upwelling provides the high concentration of methane found in the stratosphere. These methane molecules interact with sunlight, break down, and recombine into layers of diacetylene, acetylene, and ethane clouds.

Other white clouds are not associated with dark rotating vortices. The largest, known as *Scooter,* moves around the planet in about 16 hours (the same rotation rate as the planet's magnetic mantle) and may lie over a hot spot deep in the interior. The cloud may have condensed from material rising into the stratosphere from a denser lower cloud layer. Deeper in the atmosphere, ammonia, hydrogen sulfide, and water probably condense into clouds at various levels below the methane cloud deck. The hydrogen sulfide does not directly condense but combines with ammonia to form ammonium hydrosulfide clouds (see figs. 10.4 and 10.17).

## Internal Structure and Magnetic Field

Neptune and Uranus have the same structure and composition, but there are significant differences between the two planets. We have seen how active Neptune's atmosphere is, and the mechanism by which thermal energy is transported from the interior. Neptune has a greater mean density ($1.76 \text{ g/cm}^3$) and is smaller in size, but it is more massive than Uranus. Thus, if both planets are similar in structure (an icy mantle and rocky core), Neptune must contain a greater fraction of silicates.

Far below the lowest cloud level the atmosphere and icy mantle become indistinguishable and merge into a hot, dense fluid. At the center, the molten core reaches a temperature of thousands of kelvins and a pressure of several million bars.

The Voyager 2 magnetometer and charged-particle experiments revealed the magnetic fields of Neptune and Uranus to be remarkably similar. The magnetic axis of Neptune is tipped no less than 47° and offset from the center about half the radius of the planet (fig. 10.18a).

The explanation for the unusual alignment of the magnetic fields of Neptune and Uranus is found in the planets' internal composition. As previously described, the Earth has a magnetic field generated by a spinning, conductive liquid-metallic core. In contrast, the magnetic fields of Uranus and Neptune are produced by rapidly spinning ionized mantles. Thus the origin of the fields is at a distance from the core, which may explain the eccentric alignment and tilt of the planets' magnetic axes.

Of all the giant planets, Neptune has the lowest density of charged particles in its magnetosphere. The particles in the field consist of hydrogen and helium ions that originate in the planet's upper atmosphere. There are also nitrogen ions believed to come from the atmosphere of the large and active satellite Triton. The rotation rate of the magnetic mantle at 16h 3m was measured by radio bursts emitted from the charged particles trapped in the twisting magnetic field (fig. 10.18b).

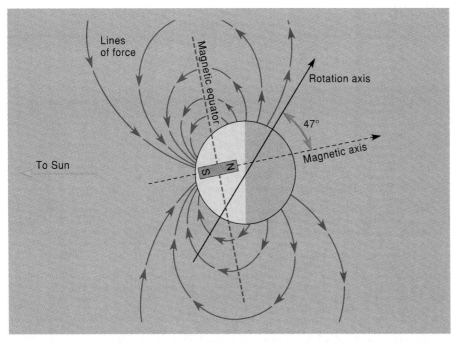

a.

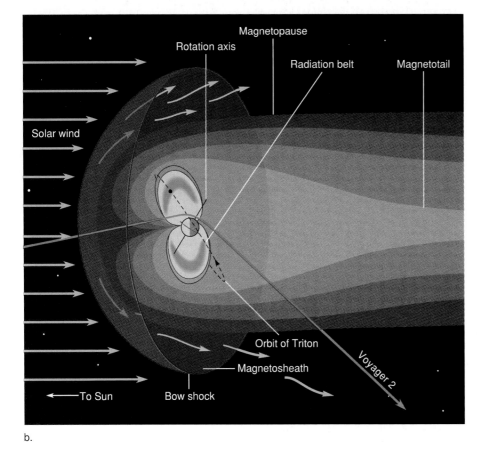

b.

**figure 10.18**

*a.* The magnetic axis and magnetic equator of Neptune are offset from the center of the planet. *b.* Model of Neptune's magnetosphere showing Voyager 2 crossing the bow shock and entering the radiation belt, which is bounded by the orbit of Triton.

## Satellites and Rings

In the 1980s, ground-based stellar occultation observations revealed a partial ring system surrounding Neptune. The light from the occulted stars failed to dim uniformly on both sides of the planet, indicating that the planet had **ring-arcs** rather than complete rings. The Voyager images identified the arcs as denser segments of a tenuous ring that had escaped detection from the Earth. Later pictures revealed two more rings closer to the planet (fig. 10.19). In addition, four of six satellites detected by Voyager 2 occupy orbits between the outer and innermost rings; two more lie beyond the outer ring.

All the satellites identified during the Voyager flight are small, irregular bodies ranging in size from 400 down to 50 km in diameter. All revolve in the plane of Neptune's equator except Naiad, which has an orbital inclination of 4.5°. They are frozen, inactive dark bodies that show evidence of meteoric impact. The largest satellite discovered by Voyager, Proteus, has a diameter of 415 km. It is slightly larger than Nereid, but was not detected earlier in ground-based telescopes because of its proximity to Neptune.

The outermost ring, 1989N1R, has a radius of about 63,000 km and is only 17 km in width. There are three bright segments that constitute the ring-arcs identified from the Earth. The ring-arcs appear as points of light that probably are unresolved fragments no more than 10 to 15 km in size. Ring 1989N2R is located 53,200 km from Neptune and is also about 17 km wide. A broad dusty third ring about 1700 km wide is located 42,000 km from Neptune. 1989N4R is nearly 6000 km wide and extends as far as 59,000 km from Neptune's center. About 2000 km inside the rim of this wide ring is a narrow, bright arc designated 1989N5R. Throughout the ring system, a diffuse disk of tiny dust particles extends from the outer rings almost to the atmosphere of the planet (table 10.1).

Nereid, one of the two satellites known before the Voyager mission, is the outermost moon of Neptune. Its orbit is the most elliptical of any satellite

**figure 10.19**
Voyager 2 image of a crescent Neptune and its ring system.

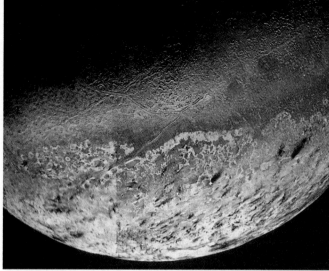

**figure 10.20**
Voyager 2 close-up photograph of Triton, showing a wrinkled polar cap of frozen nitrogen extending over most of the bright hemisphere.

in the solar system; thus Nereid ranges from 1.39 million to 9.63 million km from the center of Neptune. The satellite is only 340 km in diameter and its 360-day rotational period is the same as its orbital period. During the flight, Voyager did not come close enough to resolve the details of Nereid's surface.

### Triton

Triton moves in a nearly circular orbit with a radius of 355,000 km from the planet. It revolves in a period of 5d 21h at an inclination of about 157° to Neptune's equator. A unique feature of Triton is its retrograde motion from east to west, while its orbit precesses, or gyrates, in the opposite direction owing to the equatorial bulge of Neptune. The combined effect of Neptune's axial tilt of 30° to its orbit and the precession of Triton's orbit causes an unusual inclination of the satellite with respect to the Sun. Indeed, like Uranus, Triton alternately points polar and equatorial regions toward the Sun. When Voyager 2 arrived in 1989, the Sun was shining on Triton's south pole.

During its encounter, Voyager 2 passed within 38,400 km of Triton. The composition of its atmosphere was found to consist of nitrogen and a small fraction of methane. The atmosphere is very tenuous and has a surface pressure no more than 1/100,000 of the Earth's atmosphere. A thin haze extends from the surface to an altitude of 5 to 10 km.

The Voyager 2 images disclosed an exceedingly bright polar cap of frozen nitrogen mixed with methane ice that gives the cap a pale pink color (fig. 10.20). Of particular interest is its wrinkled appearance, indicating that freezing, melting, and refreezing occurred during an earlier era. The polar cap covers the southern hemisphere almost to the equator. At the time of encounter, most of the northern hemisphere was in darkness on Triton's night side.

Although the temperature is a low 37 K, the sunlit polar cap seems to be evaporating and disintegrating into strange markings and contours. The region has only a few craters, indicating that the surface is of recent origin. There are dark patches, each surrounded by a bright fringe. Near the south pole are dark, wind-blown streaks believed to be eruptions of liquid nitrogen, dust, and methane compounds from below the surface. Plumes from these "ice volcanoes" are carried by winds in a northerly direction for as much as 75 km. One of the Voyager images showed eruptions of dark material. A geyserlike plume extended to a height of 8 km and spread as a dark cloud over a distance of 140 km.

In the equatorial region there are large areas resembling the mottled surface of a cantaloupe. Some time ago, the crust fractured into long intersecting fissures where watery slurry gushed to the surface and froze into polygonic ridges. In addition, flat circular regions 200 km across are basins that were flooded when fluid welled up from the interior.

## Pluto

In contrast to the almost circular orbits followed by Uranus and Neptune, Pluto revolves in a highly elliptical orbit. Pluto has a mean distance of 5900 million km (39.5 AU) from the Sun. Owing to its orbital eccentricity of 0.25, the planet reaches 7376 million km at aphelion and 4424 million km at perihelion. At its closest approach, Pluto is nearer to the Sun than Neptune, but because of Pluto's high inclination of 17°, the orbits do not intersect and the planets cannot collide.

At the time of its discovery in 1930, Pluto was near mean distance and approaching perihelion. In 1979, it passed inside Neptune's orbit and lost the distinction of being the most distant planet from the Sun. Perihelion was reached in 1989, and by 1999 Pluto will again resume its role as the remotest planet (fig. 10.21).

### The Discovery of Pluto

In the years following the discovery of Neptune, astronomers were engaged in the search for a trans-Neptunian planet. Among the researchers who addressed the problem was Percival Lowell. At the Lowell Observatory in Flagstaff, Arizona, he used a modified version of the ana-

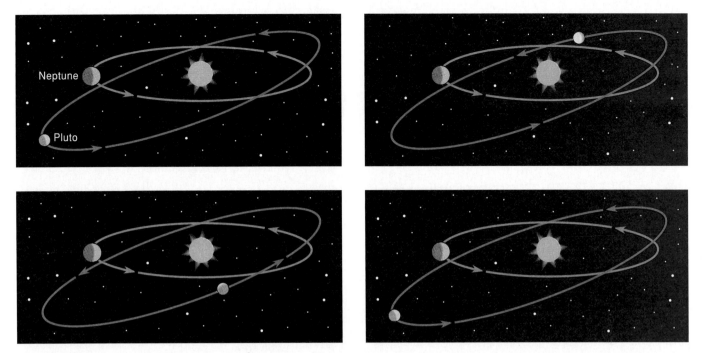

**figure 10.21**

The orbital periods of Pluto and Neptune are in resonance. Neptune completes three revolutions in the same time that Pluto makes two.

lytical procedure followed by Adams and Leverrier in their quest for Neptune. Lowell began his unsuccessful search for the new planet in 1905 and made an extensive photographic survey of the ecliptic region until his death in 1916. Lowell believed his "Planet X" to be several times larger than the Earth; and to have a mass between Neptune and Earth, a brightness of 12th or 13th magnitude, and an orbital inclination of 10° to the ecliptic plane.

In 1929, a new telescope and research camera began operation at Lowell Observatory to resume the search for Planet X. The work was carried out by Clyde Tombaugh, who made one-hour exposures of the sky with photographic plates covering an area of 12° by 14°. A *blink comparator* was used to examine two photographs of the same part of the sky taken several days apart. In the comparator eyepiece, the plates are viewed alternately in rapid succession so that an object in motion can be recognized by its displacement among the background stars.

To distinguish between the suspected planet and foreground asteroids in the same line of sight, observations were restricted to star fields opposite the Sun. At opposition, the shift in position of a nearer object such as an asteroid is much

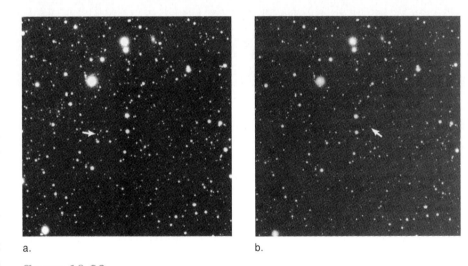

a.     b.

**figure 10.22**

The discovery of Pluto. In 1930, Clyde Tombaugh photographed the same part of sky on *a.* January 23 and *b.* January 29. In the following month, he identified a faint image (*arrows*) as a suspected new planet by its displacement among background stars.

greater than a planet suspect located deeper in space. At other configurations an asteroid may be near a stationary point where it can be mistaken for a more distant object.

Early in 1930, Tombaugh detected a faint image with the correct rate of motion (fig. 10.22). For several weeks, the object was observed on successive nights with different telescopes. Then on March 13, the 149th anniversary of Herschel's discovery of Uranus, the discovery of a

trans-Neptunian planet was made public. The new planet was named Pluto after the mythological god of the underworld.

Although Pluto was found near the position predicted by Lowell, it is too faint to be Planet X. Pluto is only as bright as a 14th-magnitude star and has an angular diameter no more than a fraction of an arc second. Indeed, Pluto is too small to be resolved into a disk and does not have sufficient mass to cause the observed deviations in Uranus's and

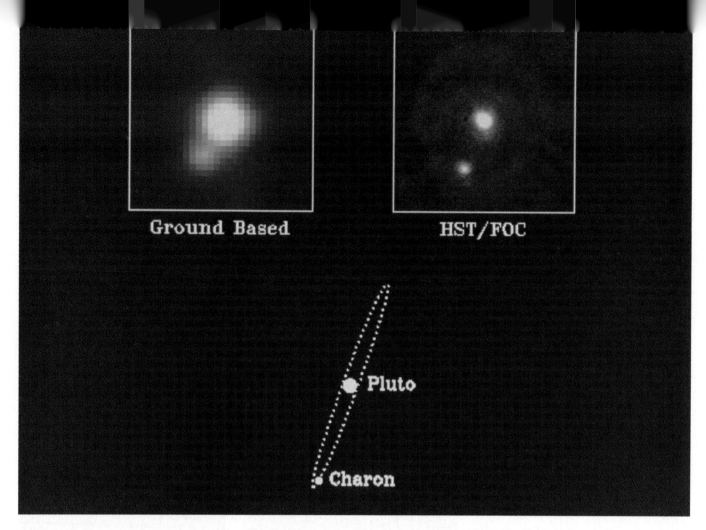

**figure 10.23**

An image of Pluto and Charon recorded by the Hubble Space Telescope in September 1990.

Neptune's orbital motions attributed to Planet X.

## Pluto and Charon

Pluto remained a mystery planet for many years after its discovery. Using measurements based upon its visual magnitude, investigators estimated the diameter of the planet to be about 5900 km. Photometric measurements of changes in reflectivity established Pluto's axial spin. The planet is partially covered by bright patches, and analysis of the light variations gave a rotational period of 6.39 days. When methane ice was discovered on Pluto's surface, the albedo was revised upward to 0.4 and its diameter was reduced to that of Triton.

A breakthrough occurred in 1978 when James W. Christy discovered the satellite of Pluto while observing at the

U.S. Naval Observatory in Flagstaff, about six kilometers from Lowell Observatory. Christy was examining photographs taken during astrometric observations when he detected a pronounced bulge in Pluto's image, while on the same plates background stars looked perfectly round. An examination of the *Palomar Sky Atlas* ruled out the possibility that the bulge was caused by the grazing occultation of a distant faint star. As further evidence, the bump was identified and measured on plates taken of Pluto in previous years. These and subsequent observations by other astronomers found the greatest angular separation of Pluto and the bulge to be 0.8 arc second, and that changes in its elongation and position angle took place over a period of six to seven days.

Christy reasoned that the bulge represented a satellite revolving clockwise

in a highly inclined orbit nearly 20,000 km from Pluto. The orbital and rotational periods of the satellite turned out to be 6.39 days, the same as the rotational period of the planet. Pluto and its satellite are tidally locked and always keep the same hemisphere facing each other. Pluto's moon was named **Charon** after the mythological ferryman who carried the dead across the river Styx to Pluto's foreboding realm (fig. 10.23).

By fortunate circumstance, Charon was discovered when the plane of its orbit is seen edge-on from the Earth. Such an event takes place every 124 years, or twice during Pluto's period of revolution. (See chapter 6, section on the orientation of Saturn's rings; and, in the present chapter, discussion of the edge-on view of Uranus's satellites.) As seen from Earth, Pluto and Charon eclipse one another and cause a change

## The Search for Additional Planets

Great discoveries in science frequently raise more questions than they provide answers to vexing problems. A case in point is the discovery of Pluto from calculations intended for a much more massive planet. Pluto is much too small to cause the perturbations of Uranus and Neptune that started the search for a trans-Neptunian planet.

Its orbital eccentricity and inclination aside, Pluto's mass is about the same as a large satellite—in particular, Triton—not an independent planet about the Sun. Yet Pluto has its own satellite like other planets. Some astronomers suggest that Pluto was a satellite of Neptune that got away. The orbital periods of Pluto and Neptune are in resonance; Neptune makes three revolutions in the same time that Pluto completes two (fig. 10.21).

Is Pluto a large asteroid? Like Pluto, there are a number of minor planets traveling in eccentric orbits that cross the paths of the Jovian planets. Asteroid 944 Hidalgo, for example, passes inside Jupiter's orbit at perihelion and swings beyond Saturn at aphelion. Another distant asteroid, 2060 Chiron, is 8.5 AU at perihelion, which is inside Saturn's orbit. At aphelion, Chiron reaches 18.9 AU, nearly as far as Uranus.

Pluto may be small, but it is much larger than an asteroid. Chiron is one of the larger asteroids but does not exceed 400 km in diameter. Pluto is about six times greater in size. Moreover, Hidalgo and Chiron may be nuclei of comets.

Is there possibly another planet beyond Pluto to account for the variations in Neptune's and Uranus's orbits? An unsuccessful hunt for a 10th planet was carried out from the time Pluto was discovered in 1930 to the 1950s. Evidently, no object of planetary size exists within 17° of the ecliptic out to 60 AU from the Sun.

Some of the answers to these perplexing questions may be found in the study of accretion disks surrounding young stars. The disks extend as far as 3000 AU from the central star. This is about 75 times greater than the radius of Pluto's orbit. In addition to a cloud of comets thousands of AU from the Sun, our solar system may also contain larger bodies too distant to be detected from Earth. Whatever the cause, the perturbations of Neptune and Uranus remain one of the mysteries of the solar system.

in brightness. The event is called a transit when Charon passes across the disk of Pluto, and an occultation when it disappears behind the planet. Transits and occultations began in 1985 and continued into the early 1990s (fig. 10.24).

The large discrepancies in previous estimates of Pluto's physical and orbital properties were rectified by various occultation and transit experiments. The mass of the Pluto-Charon system was determined from values derived for the period and mean distance of the satellite. From Kepler's third law, Pluto's mass was found to be astonishingly low—only $1.5 \times 10^{22}$ kg, or about 1/400 the mass of the Earth. In contrast, the Earth's Moon is five times more massive than Pluto.

The diameter of Pluto was also found to be less than the values arrived at from measurements of its albedo. New data were obtained by timing the duration of Charon's passage across Pluto's disk. Pluto is about 2300 km in diameter; Charon's diameter is 1200 km, about half that of its parent planet. The mean density of Pluto turned out to be 1.1 gm/cm³, indicating a composition of ice and silicates. At Pluto's low temperature of 59 K, the ices are likely to be a mixture of frozen water and methane.

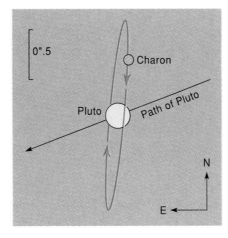

### figure 10.24

The orbit of Pluto's satellite, Charon, is viewed edge-on from the Earth every 124 years. The resulting transits and occultations have allowed astronomers to measure Charon's period and distance from Pluto as well as the mass of the system.

One of the mysteries explained by the discovery of Charon is the gradual decrease in Pluto's brightness. Because Charon revolves in the plane of Pluto's equator, the orientation of the planet's axis of rotation can be found by the inclination of Charon's orbit. Pluto is tipped 118°; thus the pole of counterclockwise rotation lies below the plane of the orbit in the same manner as Venus

(177°) and Uranus (98°). As a result, the poles and equator of Pluto alternately face the Sun every 62 years. At the time of its discovery, Pluto's south pole was in the direction of the Sun. When Charon was detected, Pluto's equator and Charon's orbit appeared almost edge-on (fig. 10.24).

The steady decrease in Pluto's brightness over the years is explained by differences in reflectivity of the polar and equatorial regions. Earlier, when a pole faced the Earth, its bright polar ice sheet gave the planet a higher albedo. By the 1960s, light and dark equatorial regions were observed from the Earth. They caused the periodic changes in brightness that identified the rotational period of Pluto.

The mutual eclipses by Pluto and Charon provided a way to map the light and dark surface features of the planet. During each transit, a different region of Pluto's surface will disappear and reappear as Charon gradually passes across the planet's disk. The markings and their location on Pluto's surface can be derived from these variations in brightness.

The surface composition of Pluto and Charon is determined from measurement of their spectra at different wavelengths. Data obtained between transits and

how  to  find  Uranus  and  Neptune

Most observers do not have a problem finding the five naked-eye planets known to the ancients. Binoculars or a low-power telescope are sufficient to reveal the phases of Mercury and Venus, the surface of Mars, the Galilean moons of Jupiter, and the rings of Saturn. But comparatively few sky watchers have located Uranus and Neptune. Yet the task of finding these planets is not as formidable as it might seem.

Uranus, the brightest of the outer planets, reaches 5.5 magnitude. If you accept the challenge and try to find Uranus without optical aid, the sky must be transparent and free of extraneous light. Moreover, the air must be steady; rapid changes in the density of the atmosphere will make the planet twinkle in and out of sight and be invisible for a good part of the time.

Star charts such as *Sky Atlas 2000.0* and *Uranometria 2000.0* are suitable for plotting the positions of planets. Various astronomy almanacs provide geocentric coordinates for the planets throughout the year. Popular astronomy publications give the times of opposition as well as star maps that show the paths of planets over a period of two to three months (fig. 10.25).

Uranus (magnitude 5.5 to 6.0) and Neptune (magnitude 7.8) can be seen with binoculars or a small telescope. First, become familiar with the bright stars in the constellation where the target planet is located. There may also be bright naked-eye planets in the same field to assist in finding the fainter object. Once the general area is fa-

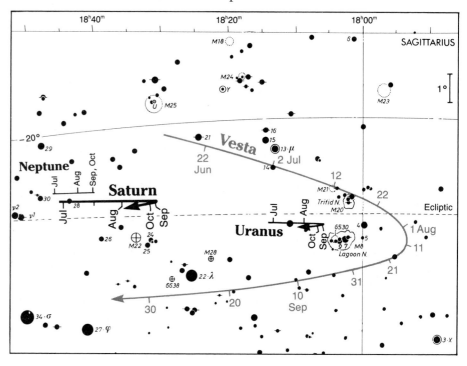

**figure 10.25**

Popular astronomy publications provide monthly star maps showing the positions of the planets and bright asteroids. This particular map shows positions of the planets Saturn and Uranus and the asteroid Vesta in 1989.

miliar to you, start from the nearest bright star and "star hop" until you reach the stars located where the planet is found on the chart. Compare the field stars in the telescope with the stars on the chart, paying attention to groupings such as conspicuous asterisms that are easy to identify. Knowing the magnitude of the planet you are seeking and the magnitudes of the background stars, look carefully for a planetary disk by com-

paring the image with stars in the field. If there is an "extra" object that shows a disk, you have found the planet. Uranus and Neptune move only a fraction of a degree per day, but their progress among the stars can be tracked by periodically observing the planets and marking their positions at intervals of about one month.

occultations include the combined spectrum of Pluto and Charon. During occultation only Pluto's spectrum is observed. Charon's spectrum is identified by comparing Pluto's spectrum with the combined spectrum.

The results confirmed the earlier discovery of methane ice on part of Pluto's surface. A model of Pluto based upon these findings indicate a light-colored layer of methane ice extending from the polar regions to the middle latitudes. A

darker, reddish terrain is found in the equatorial region. Charon's dark gray surface shows evidence of water ice.

## Pluto's Atmosphere

In 1988, while the mutual eclipses between Pluto and Charon were underway, Pluto occulted a 12th-magnitude star in Virgo. The gradual change in the star's brightness left little doubt that Pluto has an atmosphere. Before extinction, a sharp

decrease in light indicated an interface between two distinct atmospheric layers. There is a clear upper layer that extends down to about 1200 km from the center of Pluto. At this boundary there is an appreciable loss of light due to an opaque haze layer above the surface. Light extinction occurred at 1150 km from the center. This value may be the surface radius or the level where starlight is absorbed in the overlying haze.

# SUMMARY

Uranus and Neptune have atmospheres of hydrogen and helium mixed with small quantities of methane. The methane absorbs red and reflects shorter wavelengths of sunlight to give the planets a blue-green color.

Uranus appears bland and lacks the prominent cloud structure of the Jovian planets. Faint details indicate that winds are controlled by rotation and move parallel to the equator.

Neptune has conspicuous atmospheric features and weather patterns that are driven by convective currents. Internal heating is still in progress and accounts for Neptune's dynamic atmosphere of dark and light bands, cirrus-type clouds, and spinning ovals.

Although Neptune and Uranus are alike in structure and composition, the planets differ in several ways. Neptune has a greater density and is smaller but more massive than Uranus. Neptune's mantle has a greater fraction of silicates, allowing more heat from the core to escape into the atmosphere.

The magnetic fields of Uranus and Neptune are tilted at a high angle to their spin axes and are offset a distance from the center of each planet. The fields are generated by spinning, ionized, icy mantles rather than metallic cores. The magnetosphere of Uranus contains radiation belts of ionized particles deposited by its satellites and rings. Neptune has a low-density magnetosphere composed of hydrogen and helium ions derived from its upper atmosphere.

There are 15 satellites and 10 rings in orbit around Uranus. Five major satellites were found using ground-based telescopes. Titania, the largest, is scarred by craters, rifts, and faults, indicating a history of tectonic activity. The smallest major satellite, Miranda, is characterized by a terrain filled with craters, parallel ridges, grooves, and steep cliffs.

Neptune has eight satellites and three rings. Two satellites, Triton and Nereid, were known prior to the Voyager 2 mission. The largest, Triton, revolves retrograde while its orbit precesses prograde. The combined effect of precession and Neptune's axial inclination causes Triton to alternately point its polar and equatorial regions toward the Sun. Triton has a tenuous atmosphere of nitrogen and a small amount of methane. The satellite has polar ice caps and a strange, mottled surface. There are volcano-like eruptions of liquid nitrogen, dust, and methane compounds that form plumes extending kilometers above the surface.

Pluto, the outermost planet, is very similar to Triton in diameter and composition. Its bright surface regions were discovered to be sheets of methane ice.

When Pluto's satellite Charon was discovered, the mass of the system was determined by means of Kepler's third law. Data were obtained during mutual eclipses of Pluto and Charon. Pluto was found to be smaller than the Earth's Moon and composed of ice and silicates. The planet is covered by a light-colored layer of methane ice extending from the poles to the middle latitudes. A darker, reddish terrain covers the equatorial region. Charon is about half the size of Pluto and dark grey in color.

# KEY TERMS

Charon

Great Dark Spot

occultation

ring-arcs

ring system

# PROBLEMS

1. What observed characteristics of the magnetic fields of Uranus and Neptune are consistent with models of their interior compositions?

2. Why was the orientation of Charon's orbit important to astronomers during the time Pluto reached perihelion?

3. Compare the three outer planets in terms of their physical and orbital properties. Why might Pluto be considered to be a large asteroid?

4. Uranus and Neptune are classified as Jovian planets. Describe how they differ significantly from Jupiter and Saturn.

5. Explain why the plane of Charon's orbit is presented toward the Earth at different angles over time.

6. How do the magnetic fields of Uranus and Neptune differ from that of the Earth?

7. Explain why Pluto's atmosphere may be seasonal and exist only when the planet is nearest to the Sun.

8. Describe and compare the atmospheres of Uranus and Neptune.

9. In what respect is Pluto similar to Neptune's satellite Triton?

10. Explain the importance of stellar occultations in the investigations of the outer planets.

11. What is the surface structure and composition of Triton? Why does the satellite have such varied terrain?

12. How much fainter is the Sun at Pluto compared to its brightness at the Earth?

13. The second largest satellite of Neptune was unknown before the Voyager 2 flight. Explain.

14. Describe the interior structures of Uranus and Neptune based upon the two-layer model. How are they similar? How are they different?

15. Summarize the characteristics and compare the ring systems of Jupiter, Saturn, Uranus, and Neptune.

16. How long would it take an automobile traveling nonstop at 100 km/hr in a straight line to go from the Earth to Neptune?

17. If Pluto makes two revolutions for every three revolutions of Neptune, how often are the planets in line with the Sun?

18. Compute the greatest elongation of the Earth as seen from Uranus.

19. You observe a faint object that has an eastward motion among the stars of 42 arc seconds per day. If the object is a planet, which one is it likely to be?

20. Determine the mass of the Pluto-Charon system if the period of Charon is 6.39 days and its distance from Pluto is 19,130 km.

# REFERENCES

Beatty, J. Kelly. 1985. Pluto and Charon: The Dance Begins. *Sky and Telescope* 69, no. 6 (June).

———. 1986. A Place Called Uranus. *Sky and Telescope* 71, no. 4 (April).

———. 1986. Voyager 2's Triumph. *Sky and Telescope* 72, no. 4 (October).

———. 1987. Pluto and Charon: The Dance Goes On. *Sky and Telescope* 74, no. 3 (September).

———. 1989. Welcome to Neptune. *Sky and Telescope* 79, no. 4 (October).

Berry, Richard. 1986. Voyager: Discovery at Uranus. *Astronomy* 14, no. 5 (May).

———. 1989. Searching for the Real Triton. *Astronomy* 17, no. 2 (February).

———. 1989. Running Rings Around Neptune. *Astronomy* 17, no. 5 (May).

———. 1989. Approaching Neptune. *Astronomy* 17, no. 8 (August).

———. 1989. The Colors of Neptune. *Astronomy* 17, no. 9 (September).

———. 1989. First Discoveries at Neptune. *Astronomy* 17, no. 10 (October).

———. 1989. Triumph at Neptune. *Astronomy* 17, no. 11 (November).

———. 1989. Neptune Revealed. *Astronomy* 17, no. 12 (December).

Binzel, Richard P. 1990. Pluto. *Scientific American* 262, no. 6 (June).

Brown, Robert Hamilton. 1986. Exploring the Uranian Satellites. *The Planetary Report* (The Planetary Society) 6, no. 6 (November/December).

Chaikin, Andrew. 1986. Voyager among the Icy Worlds. *Sky and Telescope* 71, no. 4 (April).

Chapman, Clark R. 1986. Voyager 2 Explores the Uranian System. *The Planetary Report* 6, no. 2 (March/April).

———. 1989. Voyager at Neptune: Sorting Out the Early Results. *The Planetary Report* 9, no. 6 (November/December).

Croswell, Ken. 1986. Pluto: Enigma on the Edge of the Solar System. *Astronomy* 14, no. 7 (July).

Cuzzi, Jeffrey N., and Larry W. Esposito. 1987. The Rings of Uranus. *Scientific American* 257, no. 1 (July).

Flaser, F. Michael. 1992. "Uranus and Neptune, Atmospheres." In *The Astronomy and Astrophysics Encyclopedia*, edited by Stephen P. Maran. New York: Van Nostrand Reinhold.

Grosser, Morton. 1979. *The Discovery of Neptune*. New York: Dover Publications, Inc.

Hunt, Garry, ed. 1982. *Uranus and the Outer Planets*. Proceedings of the IAU/RAS Colloquium no. 60, Cambridge: Cambridge University Press.

Ingersoll, Andrew P. 1987. Uranus. *Scientific American* 256, no. 1 (January).

Johnson, Torrence V., Robert Hamilton Brown, and Laurence A. Soderblom. 1987. The Moons of Uranus. *Scientific American* 256, no. 4 (April).

Kaufmann, William J. 1989. Voyager at Neptune—A Preliminary Report. *Mercury* (Astronomical Society of the Pacific) 18, no. 6 (November/December).

Kinoshita, June. 1989. Neptune. *Scientific American* 261, no. 5 (November).

Morrison, Nancy D., and Stephen Gregory. 1987. Voyager Discoveries at the Rings of Uranus. *Mercury* 16, no. 2 (March/April).

News Notes. 1988. Why is Pluto Rocky? *Sky and Telescope* 76, no. 6 (December).

———. 1989. Pluto at Perihelion. *Sky and Telescope* 78, no. 4 (October).

Newswire. 1993. Pluto and Charon Weigh In. *Sky and Telescope* 85, no. 1 (January).

Simpson, Richard A., and Ellis D. Miner. 1989. Uranus: Beneath That Bland Exterior. *The Planetary Report* 9, no. 4 (July/August).

Tombaugh, Clyde W. 1986. The Discovery of Pluto, Parts 1, 2. *Mercury* 15, no. 3 (May/June), 4 (July/August).

Tombaugh, Clyde W., and Patrick Moore. 1980. *Out of the Darkness: The Planet Pluto*. Harrisburg, Pa.: Stackpole Books.

Whyte, A. J. 1980. *The Planet Pluto*. Toronto: Pergamon Press.

chapter

11

asteroids,    comets,    and    meteoric    fragments

Comet West. The yellow dust tail forms a wide
curve that lags behind the straight blue ion tail.

As we have seen, the planets move in their orbits accompanied by lesser bodies such as satellites and rings composed of smaller particles of ice and rock. In addition to these planetary attendants, the solar system contains innumerable smaller bodies such as asteroids (also called minor planets), meteoric fragments, and dust; and a swarm of comets with millions of members that extends far into space. Finally, the Sun and its family are enclosed in a vast region of charged particles formed by the outward flow of the solar wind, which marks the boundary between the solar system and interstellar space.

## Asteroids

When Kepler derived his famous laws of planetary motion, he noted that the wide gap between the orbits of Mars and Jupiter might contain an unknown planet. The idea was further advanced in the eighteenth century by J. E. Bode of the Berlin Observatory, who proposed an empirical rule for the planets' distances from the Sun. The relationship was first recognized by Johann Titius in 1766 and formulated as a mathematical expression by Bode in 1778. According to the so-called Titius-Bode law, when the mean distances of the planets are expressed in astronomical units, the values follow a regular progression of numbers. To complete the progression, Bode suggested an additional planet to fill the gap between Mars and Jupiter. Moreover, Bode carried the progression to hypothetical planets beyond Saturn. The discovery of Uranus in the place predicted by Bode's law encouraged astronomers to make a systematic search for the "missing" planet between Mars and Jupiter.

The discovery of the first asteroid was made by Giuseppe Piazzi on January 1, 1801. At first, Piazzi believed he saw a comet moving westward, or retrograde, in the constellation Taurus. Later, the planetary nature of the object was confirmed when it reached a stationary point, reversed direction, and proceeded in an easterly (prograde) direction. Named Ceres, in honor of the Sicilian goddess of grain, the asteroid was hailed as the missing planet in Bode's series.

After Ceres, other asteroids were found. Heinrich Olbers discovered the second, named Pallas, in 1802, and Vesta in 1807 (Juno was found by another astronomer in 1804). Vesta is the brightest of the asteroids and at opposition can barely be seen with the naked eye. When Olbers discovered Pallas, he found its mean distance from the Sun to be nearly the same as that of Ceres. The coincidence led him to wonder if the two asteroids were fragments of a larger body that at one time had been broken up by a collision with another object. Juno was discovered near the ascending node of Pallas but is 15 million km closer to the Sun than Ceres and Pallas. For almost 40 years only four asteroids were known. Then in 1845 the fifth and in 1846 the sixth were added; hundreds were catalogued by the end of the century.

In 1891, astronomer Max Wolf introduced photography in the search for minor planets. His more efficient method replaced the task of visually identifying the faint image of a suspect asteroid among the stars seen in the field of a telescope. During long camera exposures, a properly mounted telescope will track the stars and record their images as points of light. Finding an intruding asteroid was reduced to scanning photographs for a telltale streak of light.

Asteroids are detected by the same technique followed by Tombaugh in his search for Pluto. In a blink comparator, two photographs of the same part of the sky taken at different times are viewed alternately in rapid succession. An asteroid in orbit can be identified by its shift in position among the background stars.

Today, thousands of minor planets are listed by the Institute for Theoretical Studies in St. Petersburg, Russia. In the United States, the Minor Planet Center at the Smithsonian Astrophysical Observatory publishes orbital elements, provisional designations, and other information. Positions, opposition dates, and visual magnitudes are published each year in *The Astronomical Almanac* for 147 of the largest asteroids. Geocentric positions for every day of the year are provided for Ceres, Pallas, Juno, and Vesta.

When a minor planet is found, it is identified by the year and letters designating the month and order of discovery. After an orbit is computed and the asteroid is detected in later apparitions, it is assigned a permanent number: 1 Ceres, 2 Pallas, 3 Juno, 4 Vesta . . . 2060 Chiron, and so forth. Generally, the discoverer designates a new asteroid; at first, they were identified by names taken from classical mythology. However, as more asteroids were catalogued, the rule was modified to include names from opera (211 Isolda), places (136 Austria, 232 Russia, 341 California, 434 Hungaria), and famous people (742 Edisona, 1123 Shapley, 1815 Beethoven).

After a reliable orbit is computed, the physical properties of an asteroid are derived by several observational techniques. Mass can be determined when two asteroids have close encounters. Every 18 years, the more massive Vesta and smaller Arete are separated by a distance ranging between 2.7 and 5.2 million km. At nearest approach Vesta causes measurable perturbations in the motion of Arete. The mass of Vesta is determined by calculations based upon the gravitational effects. In the same manner, the masses of Ceres and Pallas are found owing to their similar mean distances and periods.

A number of indirect methods are used to find the small diameters of asteroids. One technique combines optical and infrared photometric measurements. Another is to time the disappearance and reappearance of a star behind the asteroid during an occultation. Observed changes in an occulted star's brightness may reveal double asteroids revolving around each other; a secondary dip in light intensity occurs as the star passes behind the minor satellite.

Spectrophotometric observations are used to determine the chemical properties of minor planets and classify them according to surface composition. Most asteroids belong to two major groups, *type C* and *type S*. Type C asteroids have low albedos and contain silicates and opaque minerals similar to dark meteorites called carbonaceous chondrites. They are found in the central and outer re-

## The Titius-Bode Law

To find the mean distances to the planets, begin with the following series of numbers.

0   3   6   12   24   48   96   192   384

With the exception of 0 and 3, each number is double the value of the preceding number. Now add 4 to each member in the series.

4   7   10   16   28   52   100   196   388

Divide by 10 and obtain the following sequence.

0.4   0.7   1.0   1.6   2.8   5.2   10.0   19.6   38.8

These are close approximations of the mean distances of the planets from the Sun measured in AU.

| Planet | Distance | |
|---|---|---|
| | *Bode's Law* | *AU* |
| Mercury | 0.4 | 0.39 |
| Venus | 0.7 | 0.72 |
| Earth | 1.0 | 1.00 |
| Mars | 1.6 | 1.52 |
| Ceres (asteroid) | 2.8 | 2.77 |
| Jupiter | 5.2 | 5.20 |
| Saturn | 10.0 | 9.54 |
| Uranus | 19.6 | 19.19 |
| Neptune | — | 30.06 |
| Pluto | 38.8 | 39.53 |

Expressed as an equation, Bode's law (see table) becomes

$$a = 0.4 + 0.3 \times 2^{n-2}$$

where

$a$ = mean distance from the Sun;

and

$$n = -, 2, 3, 4, 5, \ldots$$

For the Earth (third from the Sun),

$$a = 0.4 + 0.3 \times 2^{3-2}$$
$$a = 1.0 \, \text{AU}.$$

When this empirical rule was first proposed, all the known distances of the planets from Mercury to Saturn fit the series with the exception of the gap at 2.8 AU. The series was extended when Herschel detected Uranus in 1781. After the discovery of Ceres, Herschel suggested the name **asteroids** for the smaller bodies that fill the gap between Mars and Jupiter. Neptune proves to be the exception since no values in the series represent a planet at 30.06 AU.

gions of the main belt. Dark asteroids are also assigned to *type P* and *type D* groups found at distances beyond 3.3 AU from the Sun. Types C, P, and D asteroids contain the primitive matter that made up the solar accretion disk.

Type S or stony asteroids have higher albedos and contain silicate-metallic minerals found in chondrite meteorites. Figure 11.1 shows 951 Gaspra, a type S asteroid. Others known as *type M* asteroids resemble iron meteorites. Both S and M types are located in the inner region of the asteroid belt.

### Distribution of the Minor Planets

The greatest number of asteroids are located in a broad belt between Mars and Jupiter centered at about 2.8 AU, which is the distance predicted in Bode's series (fig. 11.2). They are not uniformly distributed; most are concentrated in bands situated from 2.1 to 3.3 AU from the Sun. The innermost main-belt asteroids are in highly inclined orbits about 60 million km from Mars. Others stray out of the belt and reach perihelion nearer to the Sun than the Earth. The remote asteroid Chiron follows a highly eccentric orbit in the vast expanse between Saturn and Uranus.

In 1867, Kirkwood explained the sparsely populated regions in the main belt as resonance gaps. These so-called **Kirkwood gaps** are the result of perturbations of asteroid orbits by the gravitational influence of Jupiter. This effect may have hindered the accretion of a planet between Mars and Jupiter. The gaps occur where asteroids would revolve in periods equal to fractions of Jupiter's period (1/4, 1/3, 2/5, 1/2, . . .). When the ratio of the orbital period of an asteroid is a fraction of the orbital period of Jupiter, the asteroid and the planet will periodically line up in the same configuration with the Sun in corresponding periods of time. At each configuration, their mutual gravitational attraction will produce perturbations in the asteroid's orbit which cause the divisions within the asteroid belt. An asteroid revolving at 1/2 Jupiter's period would pass Jupiter twice during each revolution of the planet. For example, the asteroid Hestia at a mean distance of 2.53 AU is near a Kirkwood gap. Its period of revolution, 4.02 years, is about one-third that of Jupiter.

asteroids, comets, and meteoric fragments

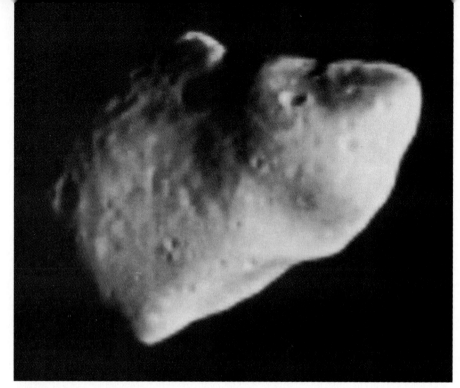

**figure 11.1**

The first close-up image of an asteroid was made by the Galileo spacecraft on October 29, 1991. The irregular asteroid named 951 Gaspra measures about 19.3 × 11.9 × 11.3 km. Compare this asteroid with the satellites of Mars.

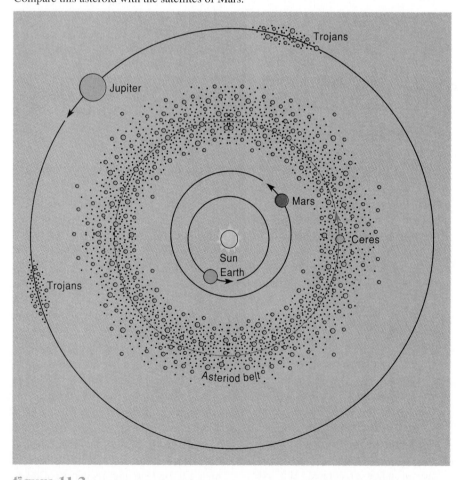

**figure 11.2**

The asteroid belt between Mars and Jupiter. Silicate-metallic asteroids are found in the inner region of the belt. More-primitive types of bodies, such as carbonaceous chondrites, are located in the central and outer regions. Trojan asteroids occupy libration points ahead of and behind Jupiter in its orbit.

Altogether, about 5000 minor planets have been identified in the main belt between Mars and Jupiter. They are small bodies with diameters less than most of the major satellites. The largest asteroid, Ceres, is approximately 1000 km across, about one-third the diameter of the Moon (fig. 11.3). Pallas, the second largest (diameter about 600 km), is between Saturn's satellites Enceladus and Tethys in size. The vast majority of asteroids in the main belt are no more than a few km across; the total population down to 1 km exceeds 500,000 members. The largest members—Ceres, Pallas, and Vesta—represent about one-half the total mass of the asteroid belt.

Olbers' idea of minor planets as fragments of larger bodies was reinforced when associations of common origin were identified. In 1918, the Japanese astronomer Hirayama showed that clusters of main-belt asteroids have the same orbital elements. Called **Hirayama families,** these objects are debris left by collisions of parent bodies. Later collisions reduced them to irregular blocks of iron-nickel and silicates. As collisions continued, the blocks were reduced to smaller fragments. The Infrared Astronomical Satellite (IRAS) discovered dust lanes in the asteroid belt, supporting the theory that collisions reduced larger bodies into smaller fragments and particles (fig. 11.1). Only the larger asteroids Ceres, Pallas, and Vesta retained their spherical shapes.

A number of minor planets at 2.0 AU form a group known as the Hungarias after their prototype Hungaria. Another group, the Hildas, are at 4.0 AU, corresponding to an orbital-period ratio of 3:2 with respect to Jupiter.

At one time, dark type D asteroids called the Trojan group were considered as the most distant from the main belt. As introduced in chapter 9, the Trojans represent two sets of minor planets that precede and trail Jupiter in its orbit about the Sun. Generally, the preceding members bear Greek names and the trailing members Trojan names of the warriors in Homer's Iliad (fig. 11.2). There are 14 members situated at the two libration points located approximately 60° from Jupiter. The eighteenth-century mathematician and astronomer Lagrange showed

Diameter = 3,476 km

Ceres

Diameter ≈ 1,000 km

**figure 11.3**

Ceres, the largest asteroid, is about one-third the diameter of the Moon.

that three bodies located at the vertices of an equilateral triangle will remain in equilibrium as two (Jupiter and an asteroid) revolve about a center of mass (the Sun). As a rule the Trojans remain at the libration points, but, owing to the influence of other planets, in particular Saturn, a Trojan can oscillate as much as 20° from its libration point.

Other asteroids stray out of the main belt in eccentric orbits beyond the Trojans. The first, Hidalgo, was discovered in 1920. At perihelion, Hidalgo is less than 2.0 AU, or about 300 million km, from the Sun. At aphelion, the asteroid reaches the orbit of Saturn.

The asteroid Chiron follows a highly eccentric orbit in the vast expanse between Saturn and Uranus. When Chiron reaches perihelion in 1996, it will be 8.5 AU from the Sun, inside Saturn's orbit. Then the asteroid sweeps out to 18.9 AU at aphelion, about 43 million km from the orbit of Uranus. Studies based upon its visual magnitude and albedo show

the diameter of Chiron to be 200–400 km. The low albedo of about 0.1 indicates it has a surface similar to carbonaceous chondrite meteorites and the dark, icy nuclei of comets.

Observations of Chiron in 1989 and 1991 showed sudden changes in brightness; they may be due to the sporadic deposition of volatile frosts on the surface. Volatiles are substances that vaporize at low temperatures. Methane, carbon monoxide, carbon dioxide, and molecular nitrogen may exist a few meters below the surface. As Chiron approaches perihelion, its temperature increases sufficiently to permit the volatiles to sublimate and form a gaseous envelope above the surface. Chiron becomes cometlike as a coma of dust particles and gases is blown by the solar wind into a tail extending more than 2 million km into space.

The presence of volatiles suggest that Chiron is not merely an asteroid in an unusual orbit. Perhaps Chiron formed at

a greater distance from the Sun and has been in its present location for a relatively short period of time. There is evidence for many Chiron-type bodies in addition to the innumerable comets that populate the outer region of the solar system. The most distant known asteroid (1993) is a faint 5-km object temporarily designated 1991 DA that reaches 22.2 AU at aphelion and within the orbit of Mars at perihelion.

## Earth-Approaching Asteroids

On March 20, 1989, a body perhaps 400 m in diameter crossed the ecliptic plane at an inclination of 5° and tumbled in the direction of the Earth. Two days later, the asteroid passed 690,000 km above the Earth, about twice the distance to the Moon. The newly discovered minor planet designated 1989 FC is a member of a group that travels between the main asteroid belt and the inner region of the solar system. Do asteroids collide with the Earth? The Moon, Earth, and other terrestrial planets show ample evidence of earlier collisions with asteroid-type bodies. An impact by 1989 FC would have formed a crater between 5 and 7 km in diameter. From time to time, the Earth is struck by large metallic and rocky meteorites, but none the size of an asteroid has scarred the planet in recent history. At present, the nearest and smallest asteriod to graze Earth was 1991 BA. This 5–10 m object passed within 170,000 km of our planet in January 1991.

The first Earth-approaching minor planet was discovered as early as 1898. Named Eros, the asteroid is inclined over 10° to the ecliptic in an orbit that takes it as near as 22.4 million km from the Earth to as far as the inner boundary of the main asteroid belt.

The shape and spin of Eros have been determined from measurements of periodic changes in its brightness. As the asteroid spins, variations in the observed brightness occur as different surface areas reflect the Sun's light. Eros is an elongated, rough cylinder about 35 km long and 16 km in diameter rotating in a period of 5h 17m. When the spectrum of Eros was studied, the surface was found to be composed of a mixture of stony-iron and chondritic material found in type S asteroids.

Eros belongs to a class of minor planets that approach or cross the Earth's orbit. **Aten** asteroids cross the Earth's orbit at perihelion but remain inside the orbit of Mars at aphelion. **Apollo** asteroids have perihelion distances less than 1.0 AU and aphelion distances greater than the orbit of Mars. **Amor** asteroids have perihelion distances between 1.0 and 1.3 AU. Eros is a member of the Amor group.

The greatest number of Earth-crossing asteroids belong to the Apollo and Amor classes. Icarus, an Apollo member, passes inside Mercury's orbit to within 28 million km of the Sun. In 1937, another Apollo object, Hermes, approached the Earth at only twice the distance of the Moon. An Apollo member designated 1989 PB may be a binary asteroid. The object is composed of two irregular blocks less than 1 km in diameter in contact or revolving around a common center of mass.

According to present estimates, there are about 1000 Earth-crossers and 500 Amor asteroids larger than 1 km. Of this population, three or four are expected to collide with the Earth every million years. This small number may be reassuring, but the lifetime of an Earth-crossing body is relatively short when compared to the age of the solar system. There must be a point of origin from which these objects are periodically ejected and placed into orbits grazing the Earth. Two likely sources are fragments from the main asteroid belt near the Kirkwood gaps, and the nuclei of extinct comets.

There are a number of asteroids with diameters of 50 to 200 km and low inclinations located in the main belt between 2.0 and 2.5 AU from the Sun. These are type S bodies such as Hebe (201 km diameter) and Flora (151 km), along with thousands of fragments that may be the source of Earth-crossers as well as the iron and silicate meteorites that reach the Earth. At present, the fragments in the Hebe and Flora groups are in stable orbits near the 3:1 Kirkwood gap.

## Comets

Very few celestial objects evoke more interest than the appearance of a bright comet. Some have been seen in daylight, even at noon when the Sun is at the meridian. As a rule, the best time to view comets is in the east before dawn and in the west shortly after sunset. Then the comets are near the Sun and reveal the spectacular features that distinguish these wanderers from other members of the solar system.

Only about 30 comets per century are bright enough to arouse the interest of the public. Most comets are telescopic objects that appear as faint, nebulous images on photographic plates. Many comets are discovered visually by amateur astronomers who sweep the sky with binoculars and telescopes. When a sighting is confirmed, the comet is identified by the name of the discoverer followed by the year and order of discovery. Thus Comet Austin 1989e represents the fifth comet found in 1989. Periodic comets are also identified by the letter P; **Comet Halley** is referred to as P/Halley.

The **nucleus,** or central body, of a comet appears to the unaided eye as a starlike point of light. Surrounding the nucleus is a nebulous atmosphere called the **coma** that gradually dims towards the edges, making its size difficult to determine. Together, the nucleus and coma form the *head* of the comet. If the coma is bright, the nucleus is generally undetectable.

By far, the greatest attraction is the **tail,** which is an extension of the coma. Solar radiation and the solar wind exert a force on the coma and push particles and gases away in the direction opposite the Sun. The tail varies in length from none at all to one stretching in a long arc across the heavens. When the comet passes close to the Sun, the tail is more developed and may extend longer than 1 AU.

### Orbits of Comets

The motion of a comet is determined by the size and form of the orbit, the orientation of the orbit in space, the inclination to the ecliptic, and the time of perihelion passage. Once these values are known, the comet's trajectory can be studied.

The largest number of comets observed have nearly parabolic orbits (eccentricity almost 1.0). These are **long-period comets** with periods greater than 200 years and aphelia of thousands of astronomical units. Many of the bright, spectacular comets belong to the long-period group.

Long-period comets approach the Sun from nearly every direction north and south of the ecliptic plane. Almost half revolve retrograde, moving clockwise about the Sun. In the inner solar system, the orbits of comets are changed by the gravitational influence of the planets, Jupiter and Saturn in particular. Some comets are accelerated by the planets into outbound orbits that allow them to escape into interstellar space. Most incoming comets are in closed elliptical orbits and have always been members of the Sun's family. Many have periods of longer duration than recorded history and are discovered as "new" comets when they approach perihelion.

The disturbing influence of the massive planets may also bring a number of comets into orbits of small eccentricities as **short-period comets.** Some have orbits similar to Earth-crossing and Mars-crossing asteroids discussed earlier. Investigations show that only a fraction of the known Earth-crossing bodies originate as fragments of the main asteroid belt. The rest are probably short-period comets in orbits that were altered by the attraction of the more massive planets.

One such comet, P/Encke, has the shortest period (3.3 years) of any comet, in an orbit nearer to the Sun than Jupiter. At perihelion, the comet reaches 0.34 AU, as near as Mercury's distance from the Sun (fig. 11.4).

P/Encke and other comets are subject to loss of material through the action of the Sun. In 1845, the Earth-crossing comet P/Biela divided in half, and in the 1970s Comet West (photo at opening of chapter) broke into several large pieces. When a cometary nucleus breaks up, clumps are scattered along the orbit; eventually an extended stream of small fragments is left in the comet's wake. If the swarm crosses the Earth's orbit, the particles are swept up and enter the upper atmosphere of our planet.

Some comets may decay into bodies similar in size and appearance to small asteroids. Indeed, since their discovery, two comets, P/Arend-Rigaux and P/Neujmin 1, no longer show a nebulous coma but appear as starlike points of light.

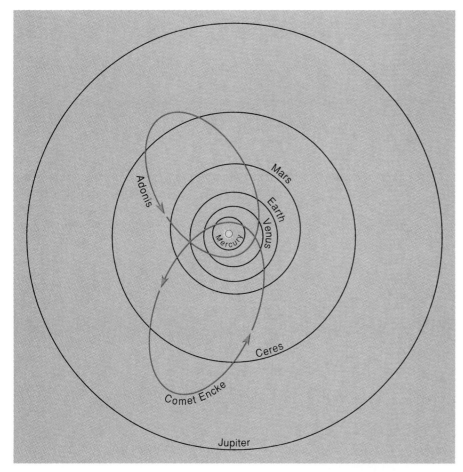

▲ figure 11.4

The orbits of the short-period comet Encke and the Earth-crossing asteroid Adonis.

## Comet Halley

Comet Halley has the distinction of being the most celebrated comet among astronomers and the general public (fig. 11.5). A description of a comet by the Chinese in 240 B.C. may be the earliest sighting. Reliable records of the comet are found on Babylonian clay tablets dated to 164 and 87 B.C. The comet changes in appearance at each return. In A.D. 1456, its tail extended from the horizon to the zenith. On another occasion, the comet remained faint until after perihelion passage.

Modern investigation began when Edmond Halley determined the orbital elements and successfully predicted the return of the comet that now bears his name. He established the identity of the 1682 comet with other well-documented appearances of comets in 1456, 1531, and 1607. The similarities of the comets in their inclination, perihelion distance, and retrograde motion left little doubt that they were the same object. Since the interval between appearances amounted to 75–76 years, Halley predicted the next return in 1758. Comet Halley reached perihelion in March 1759.

The next appearance in 1835 was greeted with equal enthusiasm by astronomers. It was a triumph for Newton's gravitational theory as well as the calculus used to compute the return to perihelion within a day of prediction. In 1910, a sensation was created when the Earth passed through the comet's extensive tail.

The latest return of P/Halley began in 1948 at aphelion beyond Neptune, 35.31 AU from the Sun. The comet approached the inner solar system in an elongated orbit inclined 162° to the ecliptic. In November 1985 Comet Halley passed the Earth at a minimum distance of 0.62 AU. Perihelion was reached in February 1986; closest approach occurred in April 1986 when Earth and the comet were separated by 0.42 AU (fig. 11.6).

◀ figure 11.5

Comet Halley, photographed by Arturo Gomez at Cerro Tololo Observatory in the Andes Mountains on April 15, 1986. The complex ion tail and diffuse dust tail are formed by material blown off the comet's head by the solar wind. The tails stretch "downstream"—away from the Sun. The galaxy NGC 5128 in Centaurus is seen to the left and below the comet.

asteroids, comets, and meteoric fragments

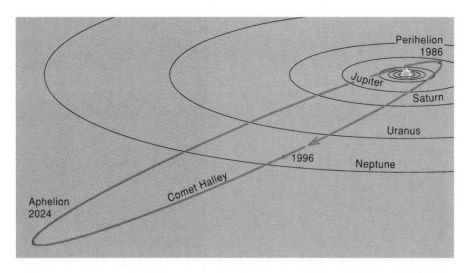

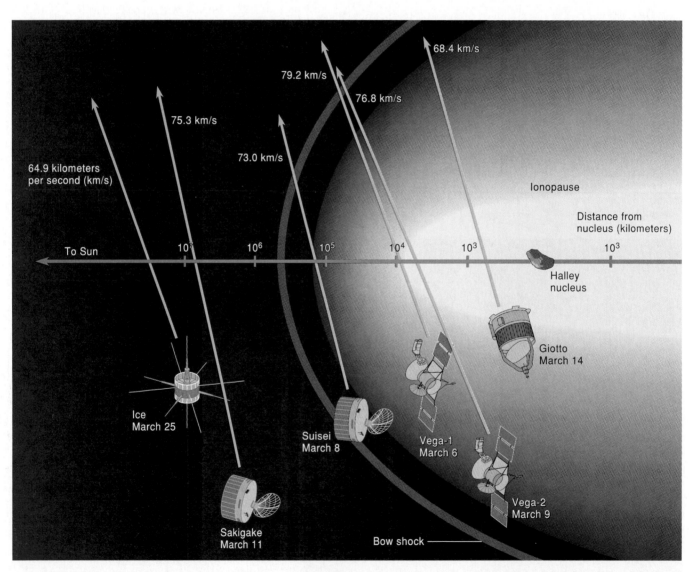

In 1986, a historic achievement was realized when six international space probes intercepted Comet Halley. The Soviet Vega-1 and Vega-2, the European Giotto, and the Japanese Suisei entered the coma. The Japanese Sakigake and American ICE passed between the comet and the Sun. For the first time, astronomers had a close-up view of a comet's main components: the frozen nucleus shrouded by a bright coma of dust and gas, and the tail composed of dust and ionized particles blown away from the comet by the solar wind (fig. 11.7).

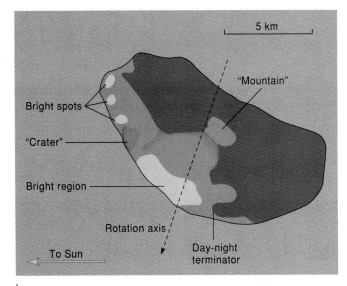

a.

b.

**figure 11.8**

***a.*** A composite image of the nucleus of Comet Halley from photographs taken by the Halley Multicolor Camera aboard the European Space Agency's Giotto spacecraft. ***b.*** Diagram of the nucleus of Halley's comet.

## The Structure of Comets

The nature of the nucleus of a comet was explained by Fred Whipple in the "dirty snowball" model proposed in the 1950s. According to the model, the nucleus consists of dust and small meteoric particles held together by frozen ices of water, methane, ammonia, and carbon dioxide. Because all astronomical bodies have axial spin, the nucleus can be expected to rotate as the comet revolves in an eccentric orbit around the Sun. The icy surface exposed to solar radiation will increase in temperature, sublime, and release molecules and dust that form the cometary atmosphere, or coma, surrounding the nucleus.

The spacecraft encounters with P/Halley confirmed that the surface of the nucleus is dark, and that a "snowy dirt ball" model is a plausible description of a comet's nucleus. The images of the nucleus taken by cameras aboard the Giotto spacecraft revealed an irregular elongated body resembling a potato 14.9 km long and 8.2 km in diameter (fig. 11.8a). The surface shows depressions, elevations, and an undulating terrain containing a number of bright spots and possibly craters (fig. 11.8b). The nucleus is one of the darkest objects in the solar system, similar to coal dust with a black velvet sheen. Evidently the surface is covered by a crust that insulates the interior from the action of the Sun.

Jets of dust and gas erupt from a few regions on the sunward side of the nucleus. When the comet rotates the active surface areas away from the Sun, the flares subside. The action of the jets sublimates volatiles, leaving the dark material to form a crust. In the vicinity of the Sun, crevices and a vesicular texture form in the crust. Sometimes huge cracks appear that may cause the nucleus to disintegrate.

In the cometary atmosphere, sunlight is scattered by tiny dust grains while a number of processes and reactions change more complex molecules from the nucleus into simpler molecules, atoms, and ions. There are many collisions between molecules as well as dust particles released during sublimation. Molecules are dissociated and ionized by ultraviolet radiation from the Sun. Finally, the gases form a visible cloud ranging from 10,000 to more than 1 million km in diameter.

Spectrometers aboard the Vegas and Giotto probes found that the dust particles in the coma are a mixture of light and heavy elements. The combination of the light substances carbon, hydrogen, oxygen, and nitrogen is referred to as CHON. The heavier materials are those found in silicate rocks, including magnesium, silicon, and iron. The particles vary in size from a grain of sand down to 1/1000 of a millimeter.

One of the investigations carried out aboard Giotto determined the nature of the neutral and ionized gases in the coma. The instruments indicated that about 80% of the molecules are water vapor, 15% carbon monoxide, and the remainder carbon dioxide, methane, and ammonia.

The inner region of the coma contains neutral molecules and atoms. At a greater distance from the nucleus, solar ultraviolet radiation breaks down the molecules into fragments called free radicals. Some of the radicals remain electrically neutral while others become positively ionized. The Vegas and Giotto identified ions related to water and carbon ($H_3O^+$, $H_2O^+$, $OH^+$, $CO_2^+$, $CO^+$). Before becoming ionized, atomic hydrogen moves rapidly outward into a tenuous *halo* 20 million km across (fig. 11.9b).

Let us consider how the action of the Sun accelerates dust and ionized particles from the coma into the billowing tail that gives a comet the appearance of a "long-haired star." We have described the solar wind as a continuous stream of ionized gas, or plasma, consisting of protons and electrons emitted by the Sun. These particles reach supersonic speeds (400 km/sec at the Earth's distance) as they rush past the planets and comets. The outgoing solar wind encounters a planet, forms a bow shock, and is deflected into an ionized tail. There is an analogous interaction of a comet with the solar wind.

COMET HALLEY

Pioneer Venus Orbiter
2–6 February 1986

a.

b.

**figure 11.9**

**a.** Comet Halley approaching perihelion in 1986, showing a bright coma surrounding the nucleus and a tail swept away by solar radiation and the solar wind. **b.** Color-enhanced image of the hydrogen halo around the nucleus of Comet Halley.

A solar magnetic field is associated with the solar wind and, as the Sun rotates, the magnetic field lines curve into spirals of increasing size and distance. The outgoing field lines are found in four sectors of alternating polarity (fig. 11.10).

When the solar wind and magnetic field encounter a comet, the coma acts as a barrier and slows down the solar wind. The magnetic field lines are compressed and sweep around the coma in a narrow tail opposite the Sun (fig. 11.11).

The Vegas and Giotto probes passed through the coma of Comet Halley at various distances from the nucleus (fig. 11.7). Giotto first detected the bow shock more than 1 million km from the comet. In the direction of the Sun, the bow shock extends about 400,000 km from the nucleus. Inside the bow shock, the solar wind continues into a turbulent region explored by the Suisei probe. Within a distance of about 100,000 km from the nucleus, the ionized particles in the coma exert an outward pressure that opposes the inward pressure of the solar wind. The Vegas analyzed this inner region within 9000 and 8000 km of the nucleus. Here the solar wind and its magnetic field make the deepest penetration into the comet.

Giotto crossed 535 km from the nucleus where no magnetic field lines or solar plasma are found. The boundary of this magnetic cavity marks the contact

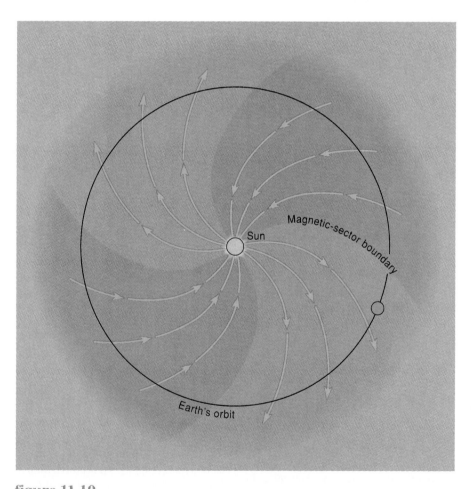

**figure 11.10**

The magnetic field associated with the solar wind.

surface where the pressure between the solar wind and the cometary ions are in balance. At the contact surface, the ions

and dust captured in the coma are accelerated by the solar wind plasma and solar radiation into two main types of

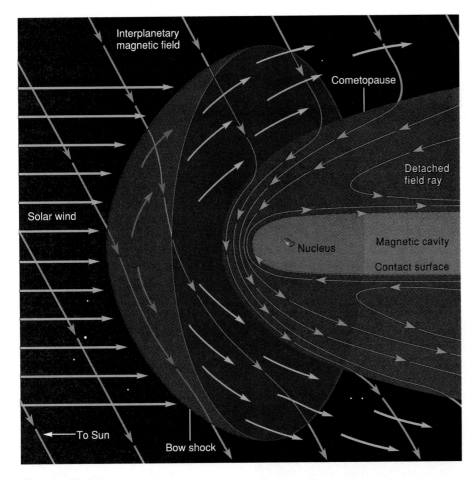

## figure 11.11

The major features of a comet's magnetosphere, including the bow shock, the turbulent cometopause, and the magnetic cavity inside the contact surface.

March 20          March 21          March 22

cometary tails (see photo at opening of chapter).

A *type I tail* consists of ionized molecules of carbon monoxide, carbon dioxide, nitrogen and water vapor. This **ion tail** is narrow, blue in color, and contains condensations and wavelike or spiral features flowing downstream away from the Sun. The magnetic field lines within the tail are divided into two sections of opposite polarity separated by a neutral channel through the center of the tail.

Occasionally, the ion tail disconnects from a comet and is blown away by the solar wind (fig. 11.12). Such an event is believed to occur when a comet crosses the sector boundaries of the solar wind's magnetic field where polarity is reversed. During its flyby through the solar wind between Comet Halley and the Sun, Sakigake crossed a sector boundary and recorded the predicted change in polarity.

A *type II tail* is yellow in color and composed of dust particles accelerated by solar radiation pressure. As a comet revolves in its orbit, this **dust tail** forms in a wide curve that lags behind the nearly straight ion tail. The particles range in size from microscopic dust to sand grains. When the particles are ejected into the tail, radiation pressure carries the dust to a greater distance and the larger grains are deposited nearer to the coma. As the comet advances, differences in velocity cause the particles to flair out into a tenuous fan made visible by reflected sunlight. Shortly after perihelion passage, the tail of a bright comet may extend from the horizon and gradually fade into the dark background sky at the zenith.

As a comet recedes from the Sun it grows fainter, and eventually only the nucleus remains. The nucleus continues its journey and is lost from view by the time it reaches the outer planets. Indeed, only the few comets that pass near the Sun can be investigated, while a countless number lie beyond our range of perception.

## The Oort Cloud and the Origin of Comets

Investigations of the orbits of long-period comets suggest that a vast cloud of comets exists far beyond the Sun and planets.

## figure 11.12

Disconnection of the ion tail of Comet Halley on March 21, 1986; photographed by William Liller with a small Schmidt camera at Easter Island.

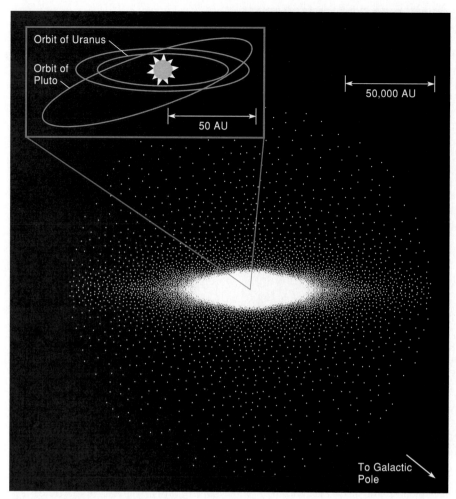

Orbit of Uranus

Orbit of Pluto

50,000 AU

50 AU

To Galactic Pole

**figure 11.13**
Depiction of the Oort Comet Cloud.

In 1950, astronomer Jan Oort proposed that a spherical cloud containing one trillion or more comets extends 200,000 AU from the Sun (fig. 11.13). The majority are believed to be located much nearer to the planets and revolving in orbits of small inclinations with respect to the plane of the ecliptic. The inner boundary of the so-called **Oort cloud** may be just beyond the orbit of Neptune.

Comets are believed to be primitive fragments of the solar accretion disk that extended hundreds of astronomical units into space. The evidence for a large disk of matter is provided by the IRAS discovery of accretion disks around the stars Beta Pictoris and Vega. The rings of particles about these stars extend about 1000 AU in diameter. (The IRAS discoveries show the presence of dust particles; a population of comets is inferred.) Beyond Neptune, the planetesimals of the solar accretion disk may have formed

the inner boundary of the Oort cloud. The primitive bodies near Uranus and Neptune were ejected into the outer Oort cloud by the gravitational influence of these planets.

In the outer region of the Oort cloud, there are a number of external sources capable of modifying the orbit of a comet. Perturbations of a passing star might cause a comet to lose energy and return to the inner solar system in a long-period orbit.

A different scenario is required to explain the present distribution of short-period comets. These comets follow orbits of small inclination to the ecliptic, and most revolve in a prograde direction similar to the planets. In 1951, Kuiper suggested that a disk of comets, too distant to be seen, lies beyond the orbit of Neptune between 35 and 50 AU from the Sun. The perturbations in the orbital motion of Neptune attributed to a trans-

Neptunian planet may be caused by this so-called *Kuiper belt* of comets extending to the inner boundary of the Oort cloud. The belt may be a remnant of the disk of planetesimals that surrounded the protosun. Evidence for the existence of the Kuiper belt came with the discovery of a small icy body designated 1992 QB1, which measures about 200 km in diameter and is located between 37 and 59 AU from the Sun. More research is needed before astronomers can conclude that a new class of solar-system objects exists beyond Pluto.

## Meteoric Fragments

On any clear night, a patient observer will be greeted by streaks of light commonly called falling stars or shooting stars. The bright flashes are **meteors** caused by fine particles, called **meteoroids,** that enter the atmosphere of the Earth. These high-speed particles are heated to incandescence and ionize the air into a glowing tube of light along the path of descent. Generally, meteors become visible in the ionosphere at about 100 km altitude. Up to six isolated or **sporadic meteors** can be seen hourly moving in all directions.

During the year, the Earth encounters streams of meteoroids left in space as debris of disintegrated comets. At such times the number of meteors observed each hour is substantially increased to a **meteor shower.** While in space, the particles move in parallel paths following the orbit of the parent comet, but, owing to perspective, in the atmosphere the meteors seem to come from one point in the sky called a **radiant.**

Occasionally there are exceptionally luminous meteors called *fireballs* (fig. 11.14). Brilliant fireballs are called *bolides;* they sometimes disintegrate in a celestial fireworks display. Fragments may fall into the lower atmosphere but seldom reach the ground.

### Types of Meteorites

Larger chunks of rock and iron that appear much brighter than bolides may survive passage through the atmosphere and reach Earth's surface as **meteorites.**

## observing meteor showers

Annually, Earth passes several meteoroid swarms at particular regions in space, producing meteor displays at the same dates each year. Generally, such showers are designated by the constellation found in the direction of the radiant.

The best time to observe a meteor shower is after midnight, when the hourly rate of meteors is at a maximum. The frequency of impact by bright meteors is increased by the motions of the Earth. As the Earth passes through a swarm of meteoroids, the leading hemisphere collides with all incoming particles regardless of their velocities. The motions of the meteoroids and the Earth are additive and give the meteors a greater relative speed through the atmosphere. On the trailing hemisphere, the Earth is moving away from incoming meteoroids and only high-velocity particles can overtake the Earth. The total number of meteors are reduced in brightness as well as in number.

Begin your observing program several days prior to the predicted maximum hourly rate given in table 11.1 and continue until after the shower has reached its peak. The procedure to follow requires no special equipment or setup. Sit in a lawn chair facing toward the radiant, relax, and become

## Table 11.1

### major visual meteor showers

| Shower | Shower Maximum | Radiant | | Single Observer Hourly Rate | Speed of Encounter with Earth | Normal Duration to 1/4 Strength of Max. |
| | | Position at Max. | | | | |
| | | R.A. | Dec. | | | |
|---|---|---|---|---|---|---|
| | | h    m | ° | | km/s | days |
| Quadrantids | Jan.  3 | 15  28 | +50 | 40 | 41 | 1.1 |
| Lyrids | Apr.  22 | 18  16 | +34 | 15 | 48 | 2 |
| η Aquarids | May  4 | 22  24 | 00 | 20 | 65 | 3 |
| S. δ Aquarids | July  28 | 22  36 | −17 | 20 | 41 | 7 |
| Perseids | Aug.  12 | 03  04 | +58 | 50 | 60 | 4.6 |
| Orionids | Oct.  21 | 06  20 | +15 | 25 | 66 | 2 |
| S. Taurids | Nov.  2 | 03  32 | +14 | 15 | 28 | – |
| Leonids | Nov.  17 | 10  08 | +22 | 15 | 71 | – |
| Geminids | Dec.  14 | 07  32 | +32 | 50 | 35 | 2.6 |
| Ursids | Dec.  22 | 14  28 | +76 | 15 | 34 | 2 |

Source: Data from Peter M. Millman, "Meteors, Fireballs and Meteorites" in *Observer's Handbook*, The Royal Astronomical Society of Canada, 1989, p. 157.

familiar with the faint background stars in the direction of the meteor display.

Knowing the stars is important when recording your data because they are used to estimate the brightness and color of the meteor trails. Record the time, number, and

magnitude of meteors seen every 15 minutes; tabulate how many occur per hour for each night of observation. Graph your results and determine the total duration of the shower and the date the shower reached maximum.

### figure 11.14

An exceptionally bright fireball, or bolide, photographed near Lost City, Oklahoma, on January 3, 1970. A stony meteorite weighing 9.8 kg was the only specimen recovered from the event.

Accidental discoveries or "finds" of individual meteorites occur from time to time, but very few people have witnessed the rare event of a meteorite fall. The sonic boom of entry is deafening; sometimes thousands of pieces fall as separate bodies and add to the fusillade. When the meteorites are recovered, they are identified by a thin outside layer called the *fusion crust,* which is formed by ablation during descent through the atmosphere. Surface irregularities resulting

from uneven fusion resemble thumb prints in plastic dough.

Meteorites are classified according to their chemical composition. **Iron meteorites** are composed principally of iron and nickel. Intermediate **stony-iron meteorites** are made of silicate minerals and iron-nickel. **Stony meteorites** are composed of various silicates and oxides. Many stony and some iron meteorites are *brecciated,* consisting of sharp fragments welded together in a matrix. Indeed, there is a correlation between meteorite classes and the major types of asteroids introduced earlier in the chapter.

Stony meteorites are most abundant and represent 93% of the total number in a fall (fig. 11.15). They contain plagioclase feldspar, olivine, and pyroxine, which are minerals found in the crusts

asteroids, comets, and meteoric fragments

**figure 11.15**
Stony-iron meteorite, subclassification Pallasite, from Springwater, Saskatchewan, Canada.

and mantles of terrestrial planets. About 86% of the stony meteorites are known as **chondrites** because of their granular structure. Chondrites contain *chondrules,* tiny spheres peculiar to meteorites and not found in terrestrial rocks.

**Achondrites** make up 8% of the stony meteorites and are very similar in composition to terrestrial basalts. They lack chondrules, which were destroyed during a slow cooling process. Astronomers believe that some achondrites discovered in Antarctica were blasted from the lunar surface during impact of an asteroid-type body. These specimens are similar in structure to the Moon rocks returned by Apollo astronauts. Moreover, a small number of achondrites may be fragments ejected during crater formation on the planet Mars. These meteorites contain trapped gases that are nearly identical in chemical composition to the Martian atmosphere.

Another group of chondrites, representing 6% of the stony meteorites, is composed of silicate chondrules, carbon, carbon compounds, water, and amino acids. **Carbonaceous chondrites** are similar in composition to type C asteroids found in the outer region of the asteroid belt. The close relationship between the abundances of elements in carbonaceous

chondrites and the Sun testify to their pristine nature. These meteorites are remnants of the earliest period of the solar system.

Of particular interest to astronomers are two carbonaceous chondrites recovered in 1969. The **Murchison meteorite** contains amino acids similar to terrestrial amino acids that are necessary for life to exist (fig. 11.16a). The existence of this type of meteorite suggests that extraterrestrial amino acids were present in the solar accretion disk during the birth of the terrestrial planets, before primitive life appeared on the Earth. The **Allende meteorite** has a composition similar to the solar accretion disk (fig. 11.16b). The presence of a decay product of Al-26, an aluminum isotope, provides a way of looking back in time to events leading up to the formation of the planetary system. The source of the radioactive elements may have been a nearby exploding star that triggered the collapse of the solar nebula almost five billion years ago. In time, the radioactivity provided the thermal energy required to melt and differentiate the asteroids and planets.

The largest meteorites recovered are huge specimens of iron-nickel alloy weighing many tons. When cut surfaces

of iron meteorites called *octahedrites* are polished and etched with acid, the crystalline structure of the iron-nickel alloys forms geometric figures called **Widmanstätten patterns** (fig. 11.17). Systems of parallel plates, or lamellae, up to several millimeters thick form Widmanstätten figures and irregular inclusions. The crystalline patterns are believed to be the result of slow cooling.

Iron meteorites are relatively small bodies and therefore unable to retain the heat required for slow cooling. Experiments with cooling rates show that these meteorites must have been located inside a 100- to 200-km differentiated parent body. In the core, minerals were exposed to the high temperatures and gradual cooling needed to precipitate the Widmanstätten patterns.

Small glassy objects called **tektites** are found in major strewn fields and small groups in various parts of the world. They are named after the place of discovery: *moldavites* (Czechoslovakia), *australites* (Australia), and *irghizites* (Kazakhstan). The North American strewn field of tektites extends along the eastern United States from Martha's Vineyard south across the Caribbean Sea to the northern coast of South America.

Tektites vary in shape from contorted, irregular irghizites to symmetrical moldavites and australites (fig. 11.18). Small spherules less than a 1 mm in diameter, called *microtektites,* have been discovered in core samples from the floor of the Caribbean Sea.

Tektites from all parts of the world have similar composition. They contain oxides of silicon, aluminum, iron, calcium, and other elements. Their colors vary from dark green to black.

So far, the origin of tektites remains a mystery. Some scientists believe tektites represent terrestrial rock melted by the impact of incoming meteorites. The fragments solidified into glassy tektites which scattered over a large area of the Earth's surface. Other investigators favor an extraterrestrial origin for tektites. Rock fragments may have been expelled from the Moon or perhaps the asteroid belt. Such material would ablate while passing through the Earth's atmosphere to form the characteristic shapes found in tektites.

a.

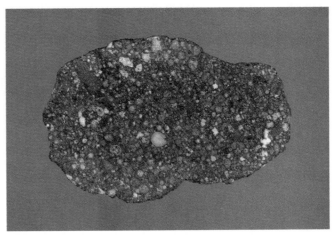

b.

**figure 11.16**

Examples of carbonaceous chondrites. *a.* The Murchison meteorite contains extraterrestrial amino acids. Many such specimens were recovered from a 1969 fall near Melbourne, Australia. *b.* A specimen from a 1969 fall near Pueblito de Allende, Mexico. This primitive meteorite is believed to have a composition similar to the solar accretion disk.

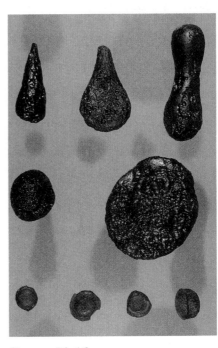

**figure 11.17**

An iron meteorite sliced, polished, and acid-etched to show Widmanstätten patterns.

**figure 11.18**

An assortment of tektites.

## The Meteorite-Asteroid Connection

For over a century, astronomers have regarded meteorites as fragments of larger parent bodies. More recent studies of the physical properties and chemical compositions of meteorites point to the asteroid belt as the source region. Indeed, the spectra and albedos of asteroid families show the members were at one time part of the core, mantle, and surface of a much larger body or bodies. Fragments probably were ejected into Earth-crossing orbits and eventually fell to the surface as meteorites.

Compelling evidence points to Earth-crossing asteroids and comets as the sources of heavy meteoric bombardment found in the inner solar system. Collisions with Apollo-type objects must have created the vast formations such as the Caloris Basin on Mercury, Mare Orientale and Mare Imbrium on the Moon, and the Argyre Planitia on Mars. The Earth shows vestiges of fossil meteorite craters almost eradicated by persistent weathering (fig. 11.19).

Not all meteorites are former asteroids. Geologists have discovered 11 meteorites in Antarctica believed to have been blasted from the surface of the Moon. These rock fragments range in mass from 6 to 663 grams. The composition of three specimens suggest that they originated in the lunar maria; the remaining eight meteorites have

215

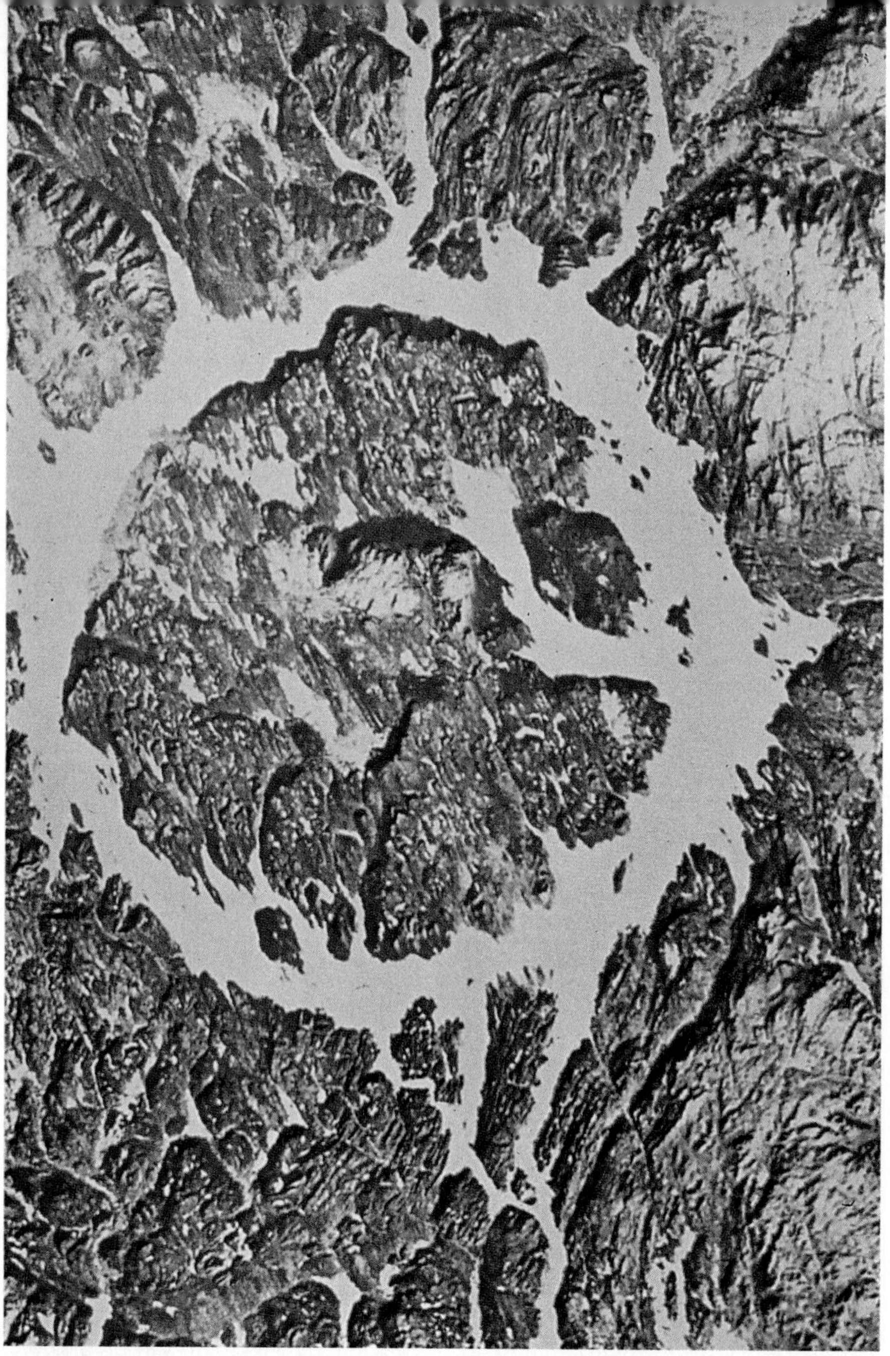

figure 11.19
An impact crater in northeastern Quebec, 70 km in diameter, was excavated by an asteroid-sized body about 3 km in diameter. Water filled the depression and formed a circular lake surrounding the central peak.

compositions similar to rocks found in the Moon's highlands. Other Antarctic meteorites crystallized only 1.3 million years ago and contain minerals indicating a volcanic origin. Astronomers believe these specimens were ejected into space from the Tharsis region of Mars during a meteoric impact.

**Barringer Crater (Meteor Crater)** in north central Arizona is a bowl-shaped formation produced during a meteorite fall (fig. 11.20). The 1260-m depression was blasted out of the Colorado Plateau as recently as 25,000 years ago. The crater rim rises 50 m above the surrounding desert; the floor is 170 m deep. Iron-nickel fragments were scattered over a wide area at the time of impact.

Picture an iron-nickel body 25 m across weighing over 63,000 tons approaching northern Arizona at a velocity of 15 km/sec. When the meteorite enters the ground, surface rocks are compressed and a shock wave spreads away from the initial cavity, marking the point of impact. The cavity expands and fragments of meteoric and terrestrial rock are ejected radially from the enlarged depression. Some of the expelled debris falls back and forms a raised circular rim. Fragments in higher trajectories reach greater distances from the newly created crater.

A remarkable explosive meteorite fall occurred on June 30, 1908, in central Siberia near the Podkamenaia Tunguska River. According to eyewitness accounts, a brilliant fireball trailing a long plume of dust crossed the sky in a matter of seconds; then a flash of light brightened the horizon. The explosion was heard as a deafening roar as far away as 1000 km. One witness located 60 km away was knocked down by the shock wave generated by the blast. Aerial inspection made over 20 years later revealed a region of forests blown over radially to a distance of 15 km from the point of impact.

Subsequent investigations determined that the **Tunguska meteorite** penetrated the lower atmosphere, probably at 30 or more kilometers per second velocity. Since no crater formed, the explosion occurred in the atmosphere above the site. The devastation on the surface was caused by the resulting detonation wave in the air (fig. 11.21).

The nature of the mysterious cosmic visitor is unknown. In 1930, Whipple (and, later, Soviet astronomers) explained the Tunguska event as an example of a small comet colliding with the Earth. More recent investigations have revealed concentrations of the element **iridium** in core samples taken at the site. These discoveries suggest that a huge stony object or perhaps a comet preceding a trail of particles may have caused the explosive encounter.

## Meteorites and Life on Earth

An issue under investigation is whether the impact of large meteorites may have influenced the course of evolution of life on Earth. In 1979, Luis and Walter Alvarez and associates identified an excess of iridium in the sediments between two geological time periods at what is called the Cretaceous-Tertiary boundary. The Cretaceous period marks the end of

**figure 11.20**
Meteor Crater near Winslow, Arizona.

the Mesozoic era, when giant land and marine reptiles were the principal animal groups. The Tertiary is the first period of the Cenozoic era, when archaic mammals and birds came to dominate the Earth.

Iridium, a silver-white metallic substance, is found as a trace element in the Earth's crust. Since the iridium content of meteorites (and therefore asteroids) far exceeds the amount found in the Earth, Alvarez proposed that the iridium discovered at the interface separating the two geological periods is of cosmic origin. The iridium concentrations suggest that a major impact by a meteorite perhaps 10 km in diameter occured about 70 million years ago. The explosion caused a dense layer of dust to form in the atmosphere that blocked the Sun's light and plunged the Earth into perpetual

**figure 11.21**
The site where the Tunguska meteorite fell in Siberia on June 30, 1908.

night. Green plants died out and the interrupted food chain caused many kinds of animals to become extinct.

The discovery of an impact site would be a strong argument that a collision with an asteroid triggered the mass extinction of life at the end of the Mesozoic era. Scientists have studied various sites around the world in search of evidence for the location of such an impact crater. During impact, debris would have been ejected and deposited around the destruction site. Iridium-rich dust and quartz particles suspended in the atmosphere

gradually would have settled as a thin layer and covered the material scattered by the impact.

By the 1990s, the possible impact sites had been narrowed down to the Caribbean basin. Scientists found layers of debris in Haiti and Cuba that were deposited by seismic sea waves kilometers high; they may have been caused by a large body falling into the Caribbean Sea. Several sites were investigated off the coasts of Cuba, Colombia, and the Yucatan peninsula. The most promising evidence was found along the northern

coast of Yucatan, where an 180-km circular depression lies buried beneath the surface. Core samples confirmed that the deposits are of extraterrestrial origin.

Was the Yucatan encounter a single event? There are sites in Iowa and north-central Siberia that contain large craters estimated to be about 65 million years old. Perhaps the Earth was struck by several fragments of an asteroid or comet which destroyed the plants and animals that had flourished for millions of years.

## SUMMARY

The asteroids, or minor planets, represent thousands of small bodies in the solar system, most of which are found in orbits between Jupiter and Mars. Ceres, the largest and first asteroid discovered, is about 1000 km in diameter. The larger asteroids are spherical, while the majority are irregular chunks of rock and metal.

The minor planets are not uniformly distributed in the main asteroid belt but are concentrated in bands from about 2.1 to 3.3 AU from the Sun. The sparsely populated regions known as Kirkwood gaps are the result of the gravitational influence of Jupiter. Differentiated type S and M asteroids of silicate and metallic composition are found in the center and inner edge of the main belt. Primitive type C asteroids containing carbonaceous chondrites are located in the outer region of the main belt.

Some asteroids have appreciable orbital eccentricities and reach perihelion inside Earth's orbit. The remote asteroid Chiron follows an orbit to a distance beyond Saturn.

That some asteroids are fragments of larger bodies was shown by the discovery of Hirayama families, which are clusters of main-belt asteroids sharing the same orbital elements. Collisions between asteroids in the inner main belt produce smaller bodies that are ejected into Earth-crossing orbits. These silicate and iron fragments are believed to be the source of meteorites recovered on the Earth's surface.

The dirty snowball model explains a comet as a nucleus of small meteoric matter held together by frozen ices of water, ammonia, and carbon compounds. When a comet approaches the Sun, the exposed icy surface will sublime and form an atmosphere, or coma, about the nucleus. The solar wind and magnetic field strike the comet, causing ions and dust in the coma to accelerate into ion and dust tails in a direction away from the Sun.

Encounters by six spacecraft provided data and close-up views of Comet Halley. The nucleus is about 15 km long and 8 km in diameter. The surface is covered by a crust of dark, porous nonvolatile substance. Jets of dust and gas stream from vents on the sunward side of the nucleus. Water and carbon monoxide ices sublime and leave deep crevices in the crust.

The source of long-period comets is thought to be the Oort cloud, where trillions of comets exist in orbits extending as far as 200,000 AU from the Sun. In the outer region of the cloud, oscillations in their orbits cause comets to fall in elongated paths toward the Sun. Short-period comets originate in the inner region of the Oort cloud at 35 to 50 AU from the Sun. Periodically, members are ejected into the inner solar system in orbits of small eccentricity.

Meteors are streaks of light caused by cometary particles burning in the atmosphere. Sporadic meteors are isolated grains that approach from any direction. Particles of a swarm fall together in a meteor shower. Bright meteors, or fireballs, may disintegrate into bolides.

Meteorites are metallic and stony bodies that survive the passage through the atmosphere and fall to the Earth's surface. They vary from small fragments to huge blocks weighing many tons. Chemically, a meteorite is composed of the same elements in similar proportions as the asteroids.

Most of the stony meteorites are chondrites containing chondrules not found in terrestrial rocks. Carbonaceous chondrites are primitive bodies that contain amino acids. The presence of the isotope Al-26 in these primitive meteorites provides a means to study the early history of the solar system.

Iron meteorites contain iron-nickel alloys. When the surface of a specimen is polished and etched, Widmanstätten figures are produced. The geometric patterns indicate that the alloy was formed inside the core of a parent asteroid and cooled very slowly.

Asteroids and comets are the sources of heavy meteoric bombardment of the Earth. Barringer Crater was formed by a huge iron body about 25,000 years ago. The Tunguska explosion in 1908 may have been caused by a stony fragment or a small comet.

## KEY TERMS

| | |
|---|---|
| achondrites | meteor |
| Allende meteorite | meteor shower |
| asteroids | meteorite |
| Aten-Apollo-Amor asteroids | meteoroid |
| Barringer Crater (Meteor Crater) | Murchison meteorite |
| carbonaceous chondrites | nucleus (comet) |
| chondrites | Oort cloud |
| coma | radiant |
| comet | sporadic meteors |
| Comet Halley | short-period comets |
| dust tail | stony meteorites |
| Hirayama families | stony-iron meteorites |
| ion tail | tail (comet) |
| iridium | tektites |
| iron meteorites | Tunguska meteorite |
| Kirkwood gaps | Widmanstätten patterns |
| long-period comets | |

# PROBLEMS

1. Explain how the distribution of asteroids in the main belt provides clues to the composition of the solar accretion disk.

2. A periodic comet does not follow the same orbit each time it approaches perihelion. Why?

3. Explain the relationship between certain comets and annual meteor showers. Why do they occur about the same time each year? Why does the rate per hour change from year to year?

4. According to Bode's law, a planet should occupy the gap between Mars and Jupiter. Why, then, are there asteroids instead of a planet? (Review the ring systems of the giant planets.)

5. If a reservoir of comets exists beyond the orbit of Neptune, why haven't they been resolved with ground-based telescopes?

6. Which type of meteorite is more difficult to distinguish from surface rocks? Why?

7. How are meteors distinguished from background stars on a long-exposure photograph made using a telescope equipped with a clock drive? How are asteroids identified?

8. What changes take place in a comet during pre- and post-perihelion passage?

9. What evidence can you give to support the view that meteorites are fragments of a large parent body?

10. Explain why the discovery of asteroid families is important in the investigation of meteorites.

11. Some comets develop two types of tails. Why do they form? How do they differ? Which type might detach from the comet?

12. Verify the following statement: Carbonaceous chondrites are more primitive than iron meteorites.

13. Do any asteroids have periods equal to that of Jupiter? If so, where are they located?

14. How do astronomers explain the continuous inflow of new comets every year? Where are the comets located? How did they originate? What evidence is there that comets are members of the solar system?

15. Explain why the Earth does not appear as heavily cratered as the Moon, Mercury, and Mars.

16. Comets are usually named after the person making the discovery. Explain why Comet Halley, which was first seen in ancient times, is named after the seventeenth-century astronomer Edmond Halley.

17. Why are more iron meteorites found and placed on display when a greater number of stony meteorites fall to Earth?

18. What action is taking place in the nucleus to cause a sun-grazing comet to explode and disintegrate?

19. Explain why a shower of meteors seems to emanate from a radiant.

20. What are the origin of and differences between meteoroids, meteors, and meteorites?

21. What steps would you follow to determine if a suspected stony meteorite is a genuine specimen or merely a terrestrial rock?

22. Compute the angular diameter of Ceres when the asteroid is in opposition. Use the mean distances in your calculations. Why do astronomers use indirect methods rather than micrometer measurements to determine the linear diameters of asteroids?

23. P/Encke has a perihelion distance of 0.34 AU and an aphelion distance of 4.09 AU. Find the period of the comet.

24. What is the mean distance of an asteroid with a period of revolution equal to 1/2 that of Jupiter? Would you expect to find a large population of asteroids with this period? Explain.

# REFERENCES

Balsiger, Hans, Hugo Fechtig, and Johannes Geiss. 1988. A Close Look at Halley's Comet. *Scientific American* 259, no. 3 (September).

Beatty, J. Kelly. 1991. Killer Crater in the Yucatan? *Sky and Telescope* 82, no. 1 (July).

Berry, Richard, and Richard Talcott. 1986. What Have We Learned From Comet Halley? *Astronomy* 14, no. 9 (September).

Binzel, Richard P., M. Antonietta Barucci, and Marcello Fulchignoni. 1991. The Origins of the Asteroids. *Scientific American* 265, no. 4 (October).

Bortle, John E. 1990. An Observer's Guide to Great Comets. *Sky and Telescope* 79, no. 5 (May).

Brandt, John C. 1981. "The Astronomy of Comets." In *Comets. Readings from Scientific American*, edited by John C. Brandt. San Francisco: W. H. Freeman and Company.

Brandt, John C., and Malcolm B. Niedner, Jr. 1986. The Structure of Comet Tails. *Scientific American* 254, no. 1 (January).

Brown, Peter Lancaster. 1973. *Comets, Meteorites and Men.* New York: Taplinger Publishing Company.

Chapman, Robert D., and John C. Brandt. 1985. Comets and Their Origin. *Mercury* (Astronomical Society of the Pacific) 14, no. 1 (January/February).

Chebotarev, G. A., E. I. Kazimirchak-Polonskaya, and B. G. Marsden, eds. 1972. *The Motion, Evolution of Orbits, and Origin of Comets.* International Astronomical Union Symposium no. 45. New York: Springer-Verlag.

Cristescu, Cornelia, W. J. Klepczynski, and B. Milet, eds. 1972. *Asteroids, Comets, Meteoric Matter.* International Astronomical Union, 22nd Colloquium. Bucharest, Romania: Editura Academiei Republicii Socialiste Romania.

———, ed. 1977. *Comets, Asteriods, Meteorites.* Toledo, Ohio: University of Toledo.

Delsemme, A. H. 1985. *The Nature of the Cometary Nucleus.* Publications of the Astronomical Society of the Pacific vol. 97, no. 596 (October). San Francisco: Astronomical Society of the Pacific.

———. 1989. Whence Came Comets? *Sky and Telescope* 77, no. 3 (March).

Gehrels, Tom, ed. 1979. *Asteroids.* Tucson: The University of Arizona Press.

Gingerich, Owen. 1986. Newton, Halley, and the Comet. *Sky and Telescope* 71, no. 3 (March).

Knacke, Roger. 1984. Cosmic Dust and the Comet Connection. *Sky and Telescope* 68, no. 3 (September).

———. 1987. Sampling the Stuff of a Comet. *Sky and Telescope* 73, no. 3 (March).

Mendia, D. Asoka. 1987. The Science of Comets: A Post-Encounter Assessment. *The Planetary Report* (The Planetary Society) 7, no. 2 (March/April).

Middlehurst, Barbara M., and Gerard P. Kuiper, eds. 1969. *The Moon, Meteorites and Comets*. The Solar System, vol. 6. Chicago: The University of Chicago Press.

Morrison, David. 1990. Target Earth: It Will Happen. *Sky and Telescope* 79, no. 3 (March).

Morrison, David, and William C. Wells, eds. 1978. *Asteroids: An Exploration Assessment*. NASA Conference Publication 2053. Washington, D.C.: NASA.

Morrison, Nancy D., and David Morrison. 1982. An Eocene Asteroid Impact; Radar Detection of a Comet; and Geography of the Asteroid Belt. *Mercury* 11, no. 6 (November/December).

Neugebauer, Marcia. 1984. The Comet Fleet. *Mercury* 13, no. 3 (May/June).

News Notes. 1985. Lifetimes of Comets. *Sky and Telescope* 69, no. 5 (May).

———. 1987. New Evidence Unearthed at Tunguska Site. *Sky and Telescope* 74, no. 5 (November).

———. 1988. A Comet Reservoir Just Beyond Neptune? *Sky and Telescope* 76, no. 2 (August).

O'Keefe, John A. 1978. The Tektite Problem. *Scientific American* 239, no. 2 (August).

Ostro, Steven J. 1985. *Radar Observations of Asteroids and Comets*. Publications of the Astronomical Society of the Pacific vol. 97, no. 596 (October). San Francisco: Astronomical Society of the Pacific.

Sagdeev, R., and A. Galeev. 1987. Comet Halley and the Solar Wind. *Sky and Telescope* 73, no. 3 (March).

Stern, S. Alan. 1989. *Implications of Volatile Release from Object 2060 Chiron*. Publications of the Astronomical Society of the Pacific vol. 101, no. 635. San Francisco: Astronomical Society of the Pacific.

Stewart, Glen R. 1990. Source of Short-Period Comets. *Nature* (London) vol. 343, no. 6253 (4 January).

Weissman, Paul R. 1987. Realm of the Comets. *Sky and Telescope* 73, no. 3 (March).

Wetherill, George W. 1979. Apollo Objects. *Scientific American* 240, no. 3 (March).

Whipple, Fred L. 1981. "Trans-Neptunian Comet Belt." In *Comets. Readings from Scientific American*, edited by John C. Brandt. San Francisco: W. H. Freeman and Company.

———. 1986. Discovering the Nature of Comets. *Mercury* 15, no. 1 (January/February).

———. 1987. The Black Heart of Comet Halley. *Sky and Telescope* 73, no. 3 (March).

Yeomans, Donald K. 1985. *Advanced Missions to Primitive Bodies*. Publications of the Astronomical Society of the Pacific vol. 97, no. 596 (October). San Francisco: Astronomical Society of the Pacific.

chapter

12

the sun as a star

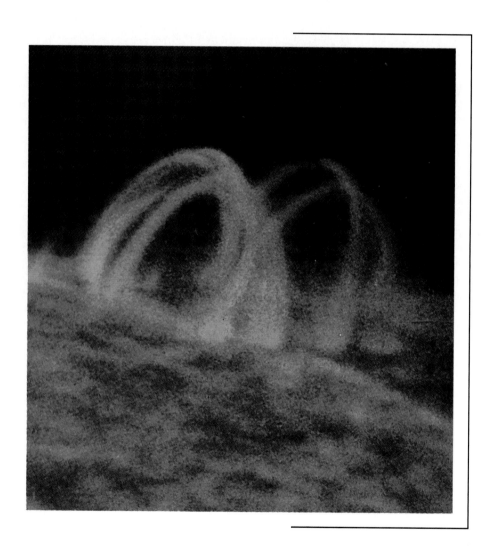

A photograph of the Sun in action.

V ery few celestial experiences available to everyone rival the beauty of the rising Sun. Day begins as twilight sweeps away the darkness, leaving the bright stars, a late crescent moon, and perhaps a bright planet to enhance a multicolored sky. The spectacle was expressed by Homer in the *Iliad* when he paused in his description of battle between the Trojans and Greeks to admire the saffron hues of the sky at dawn.

But the constant Sun in its diurnal journey reveals little of its true nature. On the cosmic scale, the Sun is an average star of middle age and similar to countless other stars found in the Galaxy. To us it dominates the sky as the nearest star, only one astronomical unit from the Earth. The Sun is an immense body containing more than 99% of the mass in the entire solar system. To appreciate its size, imagine a sphere almost 1.4 million km in diameter, large enough to contain more than one million Earths and require more than 300 Earths to ring its circumference. Despite its huge bulk, the mean density of the Sun is only 1.41 gm/cm$^3$, compared to 5.52 gm/cm$^3$ for the Earth.

The picture we have of a blazing Sun is merely the image of a visible layer called the **photosphere.** The photosphere represents the thickness of atmosphere commonly referred to as the Sun's surface. But we must keep in mind that the Sun is gaseous throughout and does not possess a surface in the same sense as the Earth. The bright photosphere is opaque and conceals the seething internal activity that makes the Sun a star. Yet the photosphere is only a few hundred kilometers thick and is so tenuous that it can be considered a vacuum. Above the photosphere, more rarified layers called the **chromosphere** and **corona** blend with the photosphere into a canopy without distinct boundaries. (See fig. 12.1.)

## Luminosity of the Sun

The amount of solar radiation reaching the Earth is only a very tiny fraction of

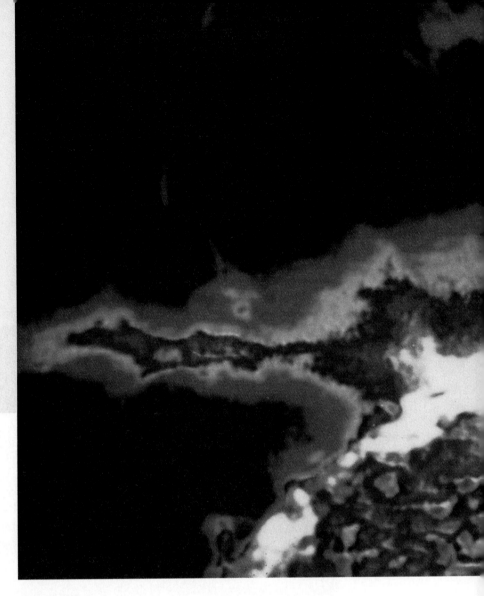

**figure 12.1**

A computer color enhancement of a solar prominence taken from Skylab.

the total quantity emitted. The total energy output per second in all directions is called the **luminosity** of the Sun. To find the Sun's luminosity, we must first determine how much radiation is intercepted by the Earth. The **solar constant** is the measure of the energy received per second at an area of one square centimeter placed outside the Earth's atmosphere in the direction of the vertical rays of the Sun. Its value is equal to 1.95 calories per square centimeter per minute, or $1.36 \times 10^6$ ergs $\cdot$ cm$^{-2} \cdot$ sec.

Now consider a sphere centered on the Sun with a radius $R = 1$ AU so that its surface extends to the Earth's orbit. If the surface of the sphere is divided into units equal to one square centimeter, then each unit will receive an amount of solar energy equal to the solar constant. By simply computing the area ($A$) of the

sphere and multiplying that area by the solar constant, the luminosity of the Sun ($L\odot$) can be found.

$$A = 4\pi R^2$$

where

$$R = 1.50 \times 10^{13} \text{ cm, or 1 AU}$$
$$A = 2.83 \times 10^{27} \text{ cm}^2$$
$$L\odot = 2.83 \times 10^{27} \text{ cm}^2 \times 1.36 \times 10^6 \text{ ergs} \cdot \text{cm}^{-2} \cdot \text{sec}$$
$$L\odot = 3.85 \times 10^{33} \text{ ergs/sec.}$$

Stellar luminosity can be derived from the solar luminosity once the intrinsic brightness of a star is known (see chapter 13).

## Source of Solar Energy

The first scientific explanation for energy production within the Sun was set

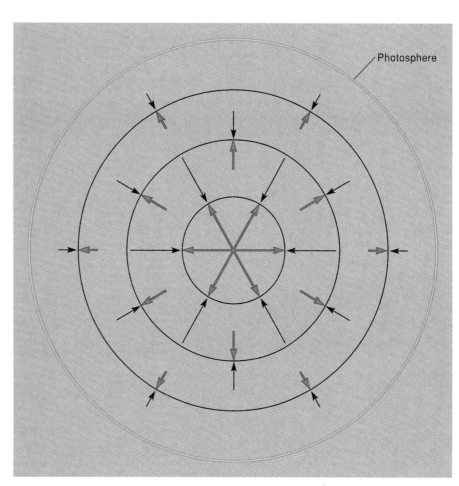

Photosphere

**figure 12.2**

Hydrostatic equilibrium in the Sun. At each successive layer from the photosphere to the core, the outward force balances the inward force of gravity.

forth by Hermann von Helmholtz in 1853. He proposed that the Sun could keep shining for 50 million years by slowly shrinking and converting gravitational energy to radiant energy. In the nineteenth century this time span seemed reasonable, but not long after Helmholtz made his calculations, advancements in other sciences provided evidence against the contraction theory. Fossil remains of animals and plants found in ancient rock attested to a much earlier origin for the Earth and Sun. The discovery of radioactive elements proved the Earth and therefore the Sun to be billions rather than millions of years old. Later came the development of atomic theory with protons, neutrons, and electrons as the building blocks of matter. In the twentieth century came the discovery that the Sun and stars shine by converting matter into energy.

But contraction does serve as an energy source; gravitational energy is vital

at the beginning as well as in several later stages in stellar development. Indeed, the Sun represents a balance between the outward force produced by thermal energy in its core and the inward force of gravity produced as the body of the Sun squeezes down toward the core.

## Hydrostatic Equilibrium

Beginning at the photosphere of the Sun, let us probe its interior down to the core. What takes place inside is determined by the physical properties of the Sun—its mass, density, volume, pressure, and temperature. The inward force of gravity produced by the mass causes the density of the Sun to increase toward the center. Temperature is also higher at the core than at the photosphere.

The Sun will remain stable at the same size and surface temperature as long as a

balance exists between thermal pressure and the weight of the solar substance at any given point from the center. Where does this internal pressure come from? Consider the pressure inside a balloon. Just as molecules of air collide with each other and the balloon's rubber surface, fast-moving protons and electrons trapped in the Sun are in constant agitation. If this pressure rises, gravity cannot keep the Sun at its present size and it will expand until a new balance is attained. If the internal pressure drops, gravitational contraction will squeeze the Sun into a smaller volume of space. To keep the Sun in balance, the outward force at any distance from the core must equal the inward force of gravity at that point. From the photosphere to the core, the pressure increases enough to balance the weight of each successive layer. Thus every adjacent layer of the Sun is at rest in **hydrostatic equilibrium** (fig. 12.2).

## Thermal Equilibrium

Whether on the Earth or inside the Sun or other stars, thermal energy flows from a substance of higher temperature to one of lower temperature. We see this at work whenever we heat water on the stove. Cold water in a pot standing on a hot burner gets heat from the burner and eventually will boil.

From this we must conclude that in the Sun, thermal energy deep inside the core is carried layer by layer to the relatively cooler surface where it radiates into space. To keep a balance, the Sun must radiate into space the same amount of energy it produces in the core. We call this balance **thermal equilibrium.** As energy leaves the core and passes through progressively cooler shells, at each point the energy gained must balance the amount lost to the succeeding layer. If the Sun produced more energy than its surface area could radiate, it would expand to a greater volume and gain a greater surface area. If the Sun emitted less energy, it would contract until equilibrium returned.

## Nuclear Fusion Inside the Sun

Our modern concept of energy production in the Sun and stars began with Sir Arthur Eddington's investigation of stellar interiors in the 1920s. He proposed that the enormous energy necessary to fuel the Sun and stars for billions of years comes from the transmutation of matter to energy as given by Einstein's predicted relationship, $E = mc^2$. According to this equation, a small unit of mass is converted into a huge amount of energy needed to maintain equilibrium. Particle accelerators in the 1930s were smashing high-speed nuclear particles into atomic nuclei to release energy in the form of gamma rays, thus supporting Eddington's hypothesis. Although this nuclear *fission,* or splitting of the atom, did release the predicted energy, another atomic process takes place inside the Sun and stars.

Solar energy is produced by combining the nuclei of lighter hydrogen atoms to form the nucleus of a heavier helium atom. In this **fusion** process, the hydrogen nuclei (protons) are used as building blocks that add up to a helium nucleus.

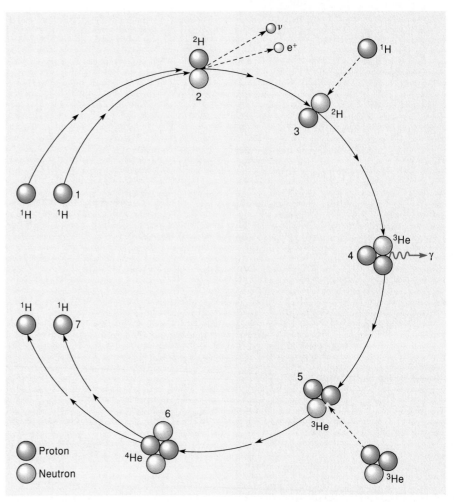

**figure 12.3**

The proton-proton chain, in which hydrogen nuclei, or protons, combine to create a helium nucleus and release energy. *1.* Two protons combine to form *2.* a deuterium nucleus, a positron, and a neutrino. *3.* The deuterium nucleus, or deuteron, and a proton join to yield *4.* a helium isotope $^3$He and a gamma ray. *5.* Two $^3$He nuclei combine to form *6.* $^4$He, and *7.* two protons.

A helium nucleus is almost but not quite four times as massive as a proton. Why isn't the mass of helium equal to *exactly* four protons? Because a fraction of the mass is converted to the enormous energy needed to drive the Sun. Since protons are chiefly involved, the process is called the **proton-proton chain,** which occurs in sunlike stars with core temperatures below 15 million K (fig. 12.3).

The nature of the Sun's interior composition, structure, and energy production must be inferred from theoretical models. The models are derived from physical laws dealing with the behavior of gases under extreme pressure and temperature. Deep in the Sun's core where hydrogen is converted to helium by thermonuclear fusion, a part of the solar mass is changed into energy in the form of gamma radiation.

In the dense interior, gamma ray photons are absorbed and re-emitted many times in their outward journey to the surface (fig. 12.4). Thousands of years pass as the photons lose energy by their constant interaction with solar matter. When the energy finally reaches the surface and is radiated into space, most of the original gamma rays have been supplanted by radiant energy of longer wavelengths: X-rays, and ultraviolet, visible, infrared, and radio-frequency radiation.

## Helioseismology

At one time the opaque surface of the Sun seemed an impenetrable barrier to

## The Proton-Proton Chain

Nuclear fusion is the combining of two lighter nuclei into a new heavier nucleus containing a greater number of particles. In the proton-proton chain, four hydrogen nuclei, or protons, combine and, in a series of transformations, create an alpha particle, or helium nucleus. However, the mass of the original four protons is slightly greater than the mass of the end-product helium. A small amount of matter is converted to radiant energy.

The reaction begins as a hydrogen proton combines with another to form heavy hydrogen, or deuterium:

$$^1H + {}^1H \rightarrow {}^2H + e^+ + \nu.$$

Deuterium consists of a proton and a neutron. In the process, a positron and a neutrino are released. Then the deuterium nucleus, or deuteron, joins with another proton to yield the helium isotope, $^3He$, and a photon of gamma radiation:

$$^2H + {}^1H \rightarrow {}^3He + \gamma.$$

$^3He$ contains two protons and a neutron. In time, two $^3He$ nuclei combine to form $^4He$ and two protons:

$$^3He + {}^3He \rightarrow {}^4He + {}^1H + {}^1H.$$

The end product will be a new element, helium-4, the second most abundant element in the universe (fig. 12.3).

The net amount of energy produced can be determined from the mass balance:

|      | mass of four hydrogen nuclei | 4.0319 $u$ |
|------|------------------------------|------------|
| less | mass of final helium nucleus | − 4.0026 $u$ |
| equals | mass converted into energy | = 0.0293 $u$ |

(The atomic mass unit, $u$, is defined as 1/12 of the mass of the carbon atom $^{12}C$.) The lost mass converted to energy, 0.0293 $u$, represents 0.73% of the initial hydrogen mass. Thus, in order for the Sun to maintain its present luminosity, about four million tons of hydrogen must be converted into energy every second. The Sun has consumed hydrogen at this rate for almost five billion years.

**figure 12.4** ▶

The structure and energy production of the Sun. In the core, thermonuclear fusion converts hydrogen to helium and to energy in the form of gamma rays. As it moves outward, this radiation is absorbed and emitted by atoms. Energy is lost through these collisions and gamma rays are reduced to X-rays, ultraviolet rays, and other longer-wave radiation. In the convection zone, turbulent currents carry energy to the photosphere and finally to the active solar atmosphere.

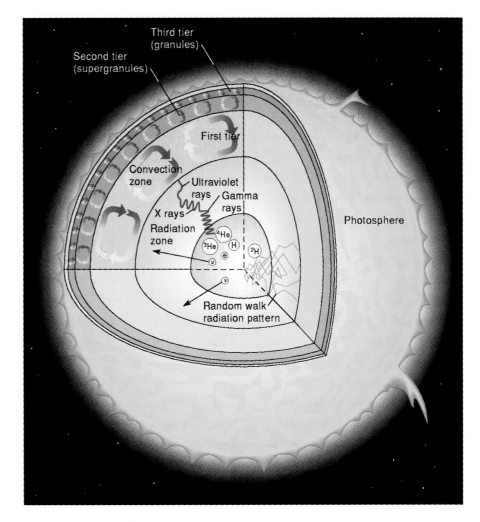

further study of the solar interior, but, in 1960, astronomers began to investigate a rapid periodic motion of the photosphere caused by oscillations in the Sun's convective region. There is a continuous up-and-down movement throughout the solar surface that raises and lowers photospheric gases up to 2000 km in about five minutes. The pulses are detected by observing Doppler shifts of the photospheric absorption lines when the gases rise and fall. The spectral lines of the rising (approaching) gases are shifted toward blue (shorter) wavelengths while the returning (receding) gases are shifted toward the red (longer) wavelengths. These solar vibrations are analogous to the compression waves produced by an earthquake.

Since the Sun is a fluid body, its internal oscillations are acoustic and therefore behave as sound waves do in the Earth's atmosphere (fig. 12.5). The pressure wave inside the Sun is alternately compressed and rarified in the direction of propagation. **Helioseismology,** the study of the internal wave motion of the Sun, provides astronomers with a method to probe solar as well as stellar interiors.

The speed and direction of acoustic wave motion depend upon the internal temperature and density at different depths within the Sun's convective region. When a compression wave approaches the photosphere, the sudden decrease in density causes the wave to reflect and turn back in the direction of the interior. The photosphere serves as a barrier to further upward wave movement, while the encounter causes the oscillation we observe as a Doppler shift in the absorption spectrum. The descending reflected wave passes through regions of increasing temperature and density that cause the wave fronts to refract and curve back again toward the surface. The depth at which the wave changes direction represents the lower limit of penetration. The depth of penetration and number of oscillations made by each wave depend upon the angle of incidence at the photosphere; shorter waves have a greater angle of incidence and do not extend as far into the interior. Thus waves are confined to the upper and lower limits of a spherical shell as they travel in a series of arcs below the solar surface.

## The Photosphere

The photosphere provides evidence for a turbulent convection zone below the visible surface. In the interior above the radiative core, convective currents transport globs of hot gas to the photosphere. On reaching the surface, this thermal agitation produces a uniform granular structure resembling a vast expanse of boiling water (fig. 12.6). The **granulation** represents convection cells averaging about 700 km across that rise upward at a velocity of 2 km/sec. A granule may

**figure 12.5**

A computer-generated simulation of one mode of solar acoustic oscillation. The red areas represent gas moving outward, the blue areas gas moving inward. The speckled region indicates the convection zone below the photosphere. The bright center represents the core below the radiation zone.

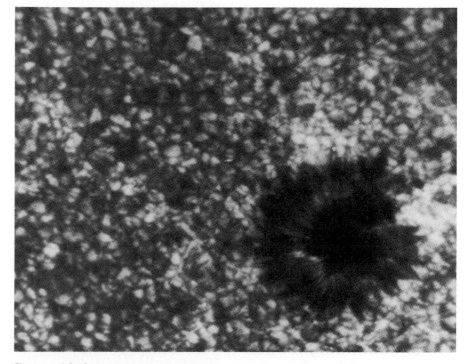

**figure 12.6**

A sunspot surrounded by solar granulation, photographed from the space shuttle Challenger in 1985. The smallest features are about 200 km across.

## The Elusive Neutrino

According to the standard model of the Sun, two particles are released when hydrogen is fused into helium during the proton-proton reaction. The first is a photon of electromagnetic radiation in the form of a gamma ray. The photons are absorbed and scattered a countless number of times before they reach the photosphere and radiate in all wavelengths.

The second particle, the neutrino, interacts weakly with matter and is not absorbed and re-emitted as in the case of the photon. Neutrinos are believed to have little if any mass and travel unimpeded through the Sun at or near the speed of light. Therefore, the particle can be used to probe the Sun's helium-producing core.

The neutrino is a member of a group of particles called leptons. In the lepton family, there are three sets of two particles. Each pair contains a charged particle and an associated neutral particle—an electron and an electron neutrino; a muon and a mu neutrino; and a tau particle and a predicted tau neutrino.

Solar neutrinos present a problem to investigators because they pass through the Earth as readily as they do the Sun. Atoms have little effect on the motions of neutrinos, but occasionally neutrinos do interact with atoms and are detected.

How can a neutrino encounter be distinguished from that of another particle? One method is to place detectors deep underground where only neutrinos can reach the apparatus. In 1968, Raymond Davis, Jr., began neutrino experiments inside the deep Homestake gold mine in South Dakota. The Homestake detector used a large tank filled with cleaning fluid containing the stable isotope chlorine-37. Neutrinos can easily pass through the overlying bedrock to the tank of fluid, and occasionally a particle will react with a chlorine-37 nucleus. The encounter changes a neutron in the chlorine nucleus into a proton to form a radioactive isotope of argon-37. The amount of radioactive decay represents a measure of the rate of neutrino interaction. The experiments detected only one-third as many neutrinos as had been predicted by the standard solar model.

The Irvine-Michigan-Brookhaven (IMB) and the Japanese Kamiokande II are detectors that consist of huge tanks of highly purified water. When neutrinos enter the tanks and interact with atoms in the water, the resulting radiation is recorded by photocells attached to the walls of the tanks (see chapter 16 on the detection of neutrinos from Supernova 1987A). The Homestake, IMB, and Kamiokande detectors "see" only the high-energy neutrinos released during proton-proton fusion inside the Sun.

Gallex and SAGE are gallium detectors in which electron neutrinos combine with gallium-71 to yield an electron and the radioactive isotope germanium-71. The electron neutrino is the type produced in the proton-proton reaction. The Gallex solar neutrino laboratory is located beneath a mountain peak in the Apennines near Rome, Italy. SAGE is an acronym for Soviet-American Gallium Experiment located underneath a peak in the Caucasus Mountains in the former U.S.S.R. The Gallex experiment has detected less than half the quantity of neutrinos predicted by the standard solar model.

The results from these experiments have not resolved the solar neutrino problem raised by astrophysicists. Discrepancies between the neutrino count and the standard model challenge our understanding both of the Sun's internal processes and the behavior of neutrinos when passing through the solar interior. Perhaps helioseismology and future studies in the physics of neutrinos may help solve the mystery.

last from 5 to 15 minutes while it radiates energy, cools, and returns to the underlying convective zone. Each cell is separated by narrow lanes of cooler descending gases that appear darker in contrast to the bright granules rising from below the surface.

When viewed in white light, the photosphere appears brighter in the center than along the limb. The decrease in light intensity is called **limb darkening.** The center is brighter because we see light originating from lower and therefore hotter layers of the photosphere. The light observed along the limb is emitted from higher and cooler layers (fig. 12.7).

figure 12.7

The Sun's photosphere appears brighter in the center. The decrease in brightness along the limb is called limb darkening.

Thus far we have described how gases in the interior of the Sun absorb radiation and make the Sun opaque. Recall our discussion in chapter 4 of a blackbody in thermal equilibrium that absorbs and radiates all energy it receives. Blackbody radiation is an idealized condition not found in nature, although the Sun and stars can be thought of as approximate blackbodies. Let the Sun's interior represent an insulated enclosure absorbing the incident radiation, reaching thermal equilibrium, and radiating the same amount of energy into space. In chapter 4 we saw how the wavelength of the maximum-intensity radiation is inversely proportional to its absolute temperature (Wien's law). A continuous spectrum of the Sun extends from the near ultraviolet through the visible region to the infrared. Maximum intensity is at about 500 nm, and the photospheric (surface) temperature is 5800 K. The visible spectrum of the photosphere is a continuum of colors covered by many Fraunhofer absorption lines. Each line represents the signature of an element found in the photosphere. As we might expect, the bulk of the Sun is composed of hydrogen and helium, but most of the heavier elements found in the Earth's crust are present in the Sun.

## The Chromosphere

The portion of the Sun's atmosphere called the chromosphere is a transparent layer of ionized gases extending several thousand kilometers above the photosphere. From the photosphere, the atmospheric temperature decreases from 5800 K to a minimum of 4400 K at a few hundred kilometers altitude. At this level there is an inversion where the temperature slowly rises to 7000 K at 2000 km above the photosphere. The upper chromosphere is characterized by irregular spikes of glowing gas called *spicules* (fig. 12.8).

Monochromatic photographs of the upper chromosphere show a blotched region of spicules surrounding a bright network covering the entire Sun. The spicules appear as narrow jets rising and falling at about 30 km/sec to altitudes of 6000 km and higher in a period of 10 minutes. The spicule network encloses

**figure 12.8**

Monochromatic image of solar spicules photographed in the Hα wavelength.

**supergranules,** which are similar to photospheric granules but 30,000 km across. The spicules are tilted at various angles in the direction of local magnetic fields (fig. 12.9).

The emission spectrum, or *flash spectrum,* of the chromosphere can be viewed during a solar eclipse an instant before the onset and after the end of totality. When the photosphere is obscured by the Moon's disk, the photospheric absorption spectrum is suddenly replaced by the chromospheric emission spectrum.

When a flash spectrum is photographed, the emission lines appear as a series of concentric arcs representing the visible portion of the chromosphere in different wavelengths (fig. 12.10 ). From this, the distribution of elements can be determined. In fact, the element helium was first discovered in the chromosphere before it was identified on Earth as a decay product of radioactivity.

Today, there are a number of instruments designed for solar investigation. A *spectroheliograph* is a spectrograph

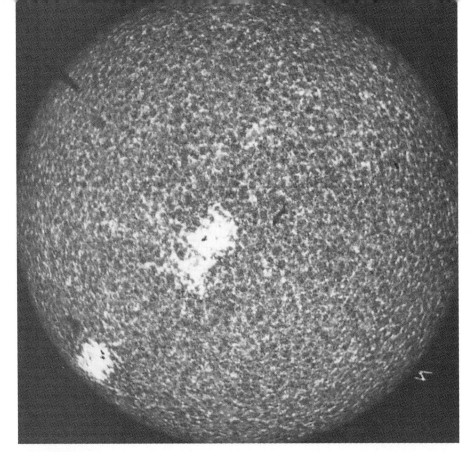

**figure 12.9**

A calcium K image showing supergranuals across the Sun's upper chromosphere.

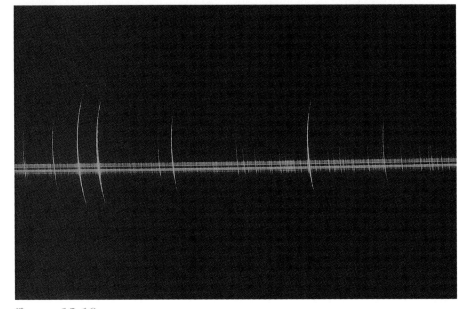

**figure 12.10**

A flash spectrum obtained during a total eclipse of the Sun. The emission spectrum appears as a series of concentric arcs representing the chromosphere at different wavelengths.

equipped with a second slit to isolate a specific spectral line so that solar features may be photographed in the wavelength of one selected line. Another method to obtain monochromatic photographs uses polarizing filters that isolate a specific wavelength such as the Hα line. A *coronagraph* is used to study the chromosphere and corona in full daylight without a total solar eclipse. In the coronagraph, the image of the photosphere is obscured by an occulting disk that produces an artificial eclipse.

Beginning in the 1930s, high-altitude balloons and rockets carried instruments aloft to examine the Sun. Later, orbiting solar observatories scanned the Sun in wavelengths not obtainable from the Earth's surface. Finally, in the 1970s, manned *Skylab* missions made it possible to study the Sun in all wavelengths over a period of several months.

The most ambitious solar exploration planned for the 1990s is the Ulysses mission. Its purpose is to investigate the solar wind and magnetic fields associated with the polar regions of the Sun. So far, solar observations have been made from spacecraft within the ecliptic plane. Ulysses is designed to fly out of the ecliptic plane and into a polar orbit around the Sun. The launch vehicle was not sufficiently powerful to place the spacecraft into an inclined solar orbit without a gravity assist from Jupiter, so Ulysses rounded the giant planet in February 1992 and was boosted into a new orbit back toward the Sun. In 1994, the spacecraft will pass about 2 AU below the Sun's south pole, cross the ecliptic at about 1.2 AU in February 1995, and swing around the Sun's north pole in June-September 1995 before proceeding back to aphelion near Jupiter's orbit. The mission will allow scientists to investigate the Sun's activities from all solar latitudes.

## The Corona

The awesome spectacle of the Sun's corona can be viewed with the unaided eye during a total solar eclipse. At totality, the outer atmosphere of the Sun appears as a diffuse, pearly-white halo surrounding the occulted solar disk while coronal streamers pierce the darkened sky. At every eclipse the tenuous corona reveals subtle changes in appearance. During periods of maximum sunspot activity, the corona spreads symmetrically around the solar limb and a sunburst of long streamers stretches out to 10 solar radii (fig. 12.11a). At sunspot minimum, the streamers form at the Sun's equator as delicate coronal plumes follow magnetic

a.

b.

**figure 12.11**
*a.* Solar corona photographed during sunspot maximum, when the corona is spread symmetrically around the Sun. Prominences may appear as arches and loops along the solar limb. *b.* Solar corona photographed during sunspot minimum, when streamers form near the equator and plumes at the poles.

field lines emanating from the poles (fig. 12.11b).

Close to the solar limb, the corona is as bright as the full Moon, but its brightness decreases sharply outward from the Sun. Most of the coronal light originates in a continuous spectrum produced by photospheric light scattered by free electrons. Called the *K corona,* this spectrum is similar to that of the photosphere except the Fraunhofer lines are not in evidence. The lines have been spread and dimmed by the rapid motions of the electrons. An outer *F corona* is produced by photospheric light scattered and reflected by interplanetary dust. The F corona spectrum is superimposed on the continuous spectrum and is distinguished by dark absorption lines. Scattering begins several solar radii from the photosphere where dust particles are no longer vaporized by the Sun. The F corona extends to great distances beyond the Sun where it merges into the **zodiacal light;** i.e., sunlight reflected by the meteoric dust found in the plane of the ecliptic. From Earth, the zodiacal light can be seen as a conelike glow above the western horizon at sunset in spring, and above the eastern horizon at sunrise in autumn.

## The Active Solar Atmosphere

It has been demonstrated that transitory and cyclic phenomena in the Sun are

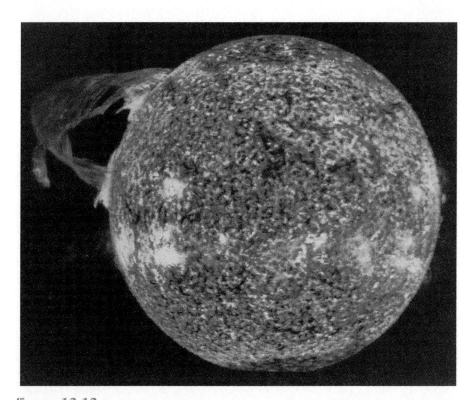

**figure 12.12**
This Skylab image of the Sun in ultraviolet light shows a number of bright flares and a huge prominence.

examples of interactions between atmospheric gases and solar magnetic fields. The formation of **sunspots** in the photosphere represents the most conspicuous evidence of the periodicity of solar activity. In the chromosphere, huge gaseous eruptions called **prominences** reach high altitudes in the form of columns and arches that follow magnetic field lines (fig. 12.12). Energetic electrons trapped in magnetic field lines produce radio bursts in the active corona. Moreover, the magnetic field carried by the solar wind produces the tails of comets, magnetospheres about planets, and the boundary between the solar system and interstellar space.

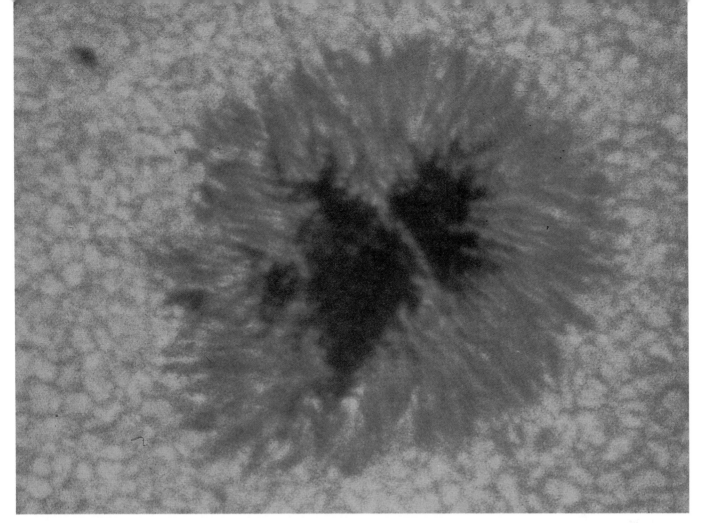

**figure 12.13**

The structure of a sunspot as seen in the Hα wavelength. The dark central umbra is surrounded by the lighter fibrous penumbra.

Dark markings on the photosphere of the Sun were reported by Galileo and Fabricus as early as 1611. In fact, solar observations may have contributed to Galileo's blindness in his old age. By the 1840s, Heinrich Schwabe had completed over a decade of observations that established a cyclical change in the number of sunspots over an average period of 11 years (fig. 12.16).

Small sunspots with diameters of a few hundred kilometers are called *pores* and appear in the photosphere as dark regions between bright granules. Most of the pores last for several days, but a few increase in size to diameters above 25,000 km and are visible for months.

The complex structure of a sunspot includes a dark central region called the *umbra,* which is surrounded by a lighter-colored *penumbra* showing threadlike filaments aligned radially away from the center (fig. 12.13). The umbra looks dark in contrast to the surrounding

photosphere, which is about 2000 K higher in temperature.

A **sunspot cycle** begins when a few spots appear in the higher solar latitudes. Eventually these fade as more numerous sunspots are seen at lower latitudes. The procedure continues until a maximum number of spots is found at approximately 15° north and south of the solar equator. A few spots may appear at lower latitudes.

Strong magnetic fields associated with sunspots are measured by means of the **Zeeman effect,** the splitting of spectral lines of atoms in a magnetic field. When the lines are measured, their displacement establishes magnetic polarity and field strength. A *magnetogram* is a graphic representation in which different levels of magnetic field intensity are shown as changes in brightness across the solar disk (fig. 12.14).

In 1960, H. W. Babcock described how sunspots and related phenomena are

produced by the combined actions of the Sun's *differential rotation* and magnetic fields. The Sun does not spin as a solid but has a shorter period at the equator than at the poles. At higher latitudes, one rotation takes about 30 days compared with 25 days near the equator. According to Babcock's model, the differential rotation deflects a weak north-south magnetic field into a strong east-west field parallel to the equator.

The Sun's magnetic field is believed to originate by the dynamo action of the electrically conducting interior. At the start of a solar cycle, the magnetic field lines emerge from the photosphere at about 60° latitude in one hemisphere and enter the photosphere at the same latitude in the other hemisphere. This dipole magnetic field is evidenced by the formation of coronal plumes over the north and south polar regions during minimum solar activity (fig. 12.11b). Inside the Sun, the magnetic field lines extend to about 70,000 km below the photosphere.

As the Sun rotates, the section of the internal field lines near to the equator are carried along faster than those at higher latitudes (fig. 12.15a). The effect causes the magnetic field lines to stretch laterally, squeeze together, and wrap around the Sun (fig. 12.15b). The convective action beneath the photosphere twists and distorts the magnetic lines into braided, ropelike tubes. The magnetic tubes, buoyed by the surrounding gases, break through the photosphere as swirling loops that form bipolar magnetic regions composed of two sunspots (fig. 12.15c). The field lines emerge at a trailing spot that has a higher latitude than the leading spot. Moreover, the trailing spot has a polarity opposite that of the hemisphere from which the sunspot pair originated. The leading sunspot has the same polarity as its hemisphere.

After maximum activity, sunspots become mixed and diminish in number, with some closer to the equator. The magnetic field reverses polarity and returns to a north-south circulation. About 11 years have passed, and *half* of the cycle has been completed. Now a new set of sunspots appears in the higher latitudes. Like the Sun, the new spots also have reversed polarity. What had been a north magnetic pole in the previous cycle becomes a south magnetic pole in the new cycle. After another 11 years, or a total of 22 years, the solar cycle is complete and the Sun's bipolar magnetic field is restored to its initial polarity.

Ever since Heinrich Schwabe discovered variations in sunspot numbers, scientists have tried to find a correlation between conditions on the Sun and cyclic changes on the Earth (fig. 12.16). In 1890, E. W. Maunder made a study of the number of sunspots observed between the years 1645 and 1715 when no sunspot maxima were reported. Named the *Maunder minimum* by John Eddy in the 1970s, it was a time of climatic change throughout the world. Europe suffered an extended cold period called the "little ice age." In the southwestern United States, cliff-dwelling people experienced severe droughts that left their cultivated lands arid.

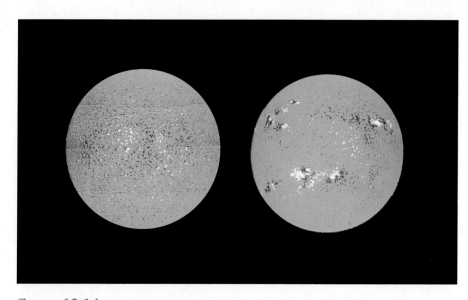

**figure 12.14**

Magnetograms of the sun during maximum (**left**) and minimum (**right**) solar activity. White indicates north polarity; dark blue represents south polarity.

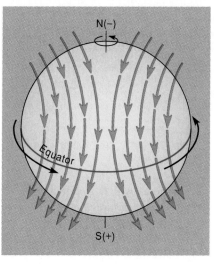

a.

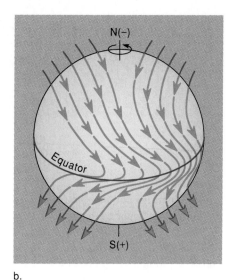

b.

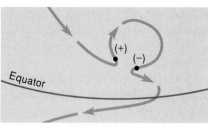

c.

**figure 12.15**

Formation of bipolar regions. **a.** The Sun's weak north-south magnetic field is deflected into **b.** a strong east-west field parallel to the equator. **c.** Convective action twists the magnetic lines into ropelike tubes that break through the photosphere and form magnetic regions of two sunspots with opposite polarities.

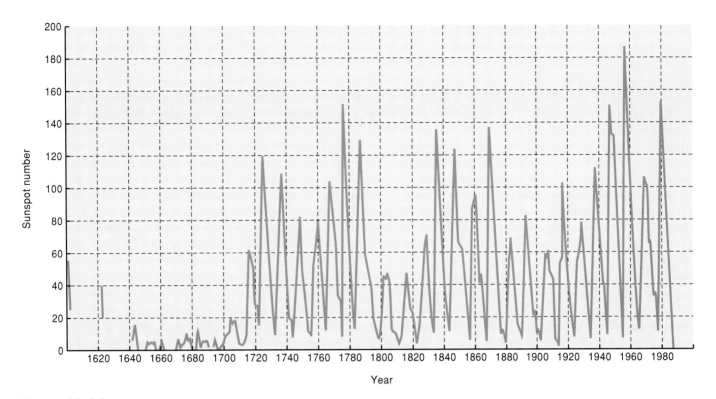

**figure 12.16**

The sunspot cycle. A maximum number of sunspots occurs about every eleven years.
From "The Solar Cycle in Pre-Cambrian Time" by George E. Williams. Copyright © 1986 by Scientific American, Inc. All rights reserved.

Investigators have looked for connections between the solar cycle and climatic changes in seemingly unrelated fields: in the growth patterns of tree rings, core samples of the Antarctic ice sheet, and layers of sedimentary rock over 500 million years old. Another possible link in solar activity and climate is the rise and fall of temperature in the polar stratosphere in step with the sunspot cycle. The upper atmosphere was found to be coldest during sunspot minima. Although correlations seem to exist, evidence from such studies remains inconclusive.

## Faculae and Plages

The bright, active regions of high temperature called **faculae** are associated with sunspots. They have a granular structure, but they are larger and have a longer lifetime than the ordinary granules characteristic of the solar surface. Faculae are absent from the bright central region of the solar disk but are conspicuous along the limb where smaller granules fade out due to limb darkening.

Moreover, spectroheliograms of the chromosphere show bright, cloudlike regions above the sunspots that are related to faculae.

The bright chromospheric regions called **plages** are caused by magnetic fields associated with sunspots. They are most prominent in monochromatic photographs taken in the ultraviolet K line of ionized calcium, and the red Hα line. Plages are composed of gases of higher density and temperature that form a torchlike expanse across the entire chromosphere.

## Prominences

A total eclipse reveals another intriguing feature of the Sun. From the chromosphere, huge gaseous eruptions called prominences tower more than 100,000 km into the corona. They appear in a variety of shapes. Some surge upward as spectacular twisted columns. Others hang suspended as giant red clouds and rain tenuous fibers back into the lower chromosphere.

Total eclipses are brief encounters and provide precious little time to study prominences. Most of what we know has been obtained outside eclipses by means of ground-based instruments and orbiting observatories. The spectroheliograph, monochromator, and coronagraph are used for visual and photographic investigations. The Skylab space laboratory carried six principal solar instruments: two X-ray telescopes, an ultraviolet spectroheliograph, an ultraviolet spectroheliometer, an ultraviolet spectrograph, and a visible-light coronagraph. Prominences and other solar phenomena were studied in wavelengths ranging from short X-rays through the visible spectrum (fig. 12.17).

The Hα line is the best spectral line to use to observe prominences. Coronagraphs and hydrogen-alpha telescopes fitted with a filter monochromator centered on the Hα line are used to obtain time-lapse photographs of prominences in action. Along the limb of the Sun, they appear as delicate loops, eruptive arches, and sometimes streamers pouring downward from higher altitudes. When

the sun as a star

# SKY WATCHERS 12.1

## observing sunspots

We have viewed the stars as distant points of light; now let us examine the only star close enough to be resolved into a disk. When observed with a telescope, sunspots show up in distinct groups scattered across the central regions of the photosphere. Usually the spots are small, but during a peak in the solar cycle, they may become large enough to be visible to the unaided eye.

Before we proceed, you must understand the dangers associated with solar observing. Don't take chances while observing the Sun; *the penalty may be total loss of sight.* **NEVER** look at the Sun through photographic film, dark glasses, camera filters, or *any* darkening device. The light may be subdued, but ultraviolet and infrared radiation will pass through and take their toll. **AT NO TIME** should you look at the Sun through a telescope that is not properly adapted for solar work.

The following procedure is recommended for safe solar observing with a telescope. The telescope aperture need not be larger than 10 cm (about 4 in); a large telescope will heat up and produce a scintillating image that is difficult to focus and observe. The same effect occurs when a distant object is seen through the turbulent air over hot pavement. Find a shady spot or construct a canopy over the telescope. Direct sunlight on the telescope will cause excessive heating and additional convection inside the tube.

The aperture of the telescope should be fitted with a solar filter. One of the more effective and inexpensive filters is made of aluminum bonded to a Mylar sheet. Be sure that the filter is secure but not too tight. Mylar will warp when heated, and you must take care to prevent pinholes, tears, or wrinkles in the filter surface.

A projection screen mounted behind the eyepiece of the telescope allows a number of people to observe the Sun at the same time. Many small commercial telescopes can be purchased with fittings and rods for mounting a solar screen to the tube. Remove the Mylar filter and substitute a severely stopped-down aperture, which allows only a fraction of the Sun's light to enter the telescope. **DO NOT** focus the telescope by sighting along the tube or through the small finder scope attached to the main instrument. As a precaution, cover the aperture of the finder scope so other people do not unknowingly look at the Sun. Point the telescope toward the Sun by adjusting the tube until the shadow of the eyepiece on the screen is minimum size. Focus the eyepiece to form an image of the Sun on the screen large enough to view the sunspots.

When sunspots are observed over a period of two weeks, they will advance across the solar disk from the eastern to the western limb. At each observation, sketch the shape and location of prominent spots on a diagram representing the Sun. Repeat this procedure on succeeding days and determine the rotational period of the Sun. Keep in mind that the Earth is not stationary in space. Will the Earth's orbital motion have any effect on your measurements of the Sun's rotation? Discuss this question with your instructor.

The paths followed by the spots across the disk are seldom seen as straight lines. The Sun's axis of rotation is inclined about 7° to the ecliptic and, as the Earth revolves, the Sun alternately points its north and south poles in our direction. Thus sunspot paths curve northward in spring when the Sun's south pole is facing the Earth, and southward in autumn when the Sun's north pole is in our direction. The spots move in straight lines in the beginning of June and December when the Sun's axis is perpendicular to our line of sight. You can estimate the inclination of the Sun's axis by plotting the paths taken by sunspots over a period of a year.

**figure 12.17** ▶

A huge eruption on the Sun called a loop prominence. The arch followed by the prominence is caused by interaction of charged particles with magnetic fields.

prominences are observed in Hα light against the bright solar disk, they appear as dark, threadlike markings called *filaments* (fig. 12.18).

Various types of prominences are found on the Sun. *Quiescent prominences* appear as sheets of gas extending up to 100,000 km. They have a slender, ribbonlike structure supported by large-scale magnetic fields and last several weeks before fading away. Short-lived *active prominences* are more spectacular and most frequently observed on the Sun. Sometimes two prominences interact and exchange streams of gas. Another com-

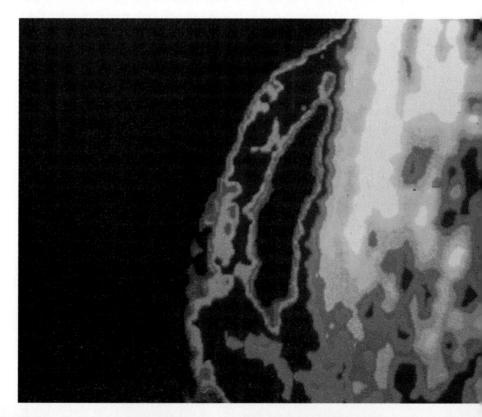

**figure 12.18**

An image of the Sun in the Hα wavelength. Prominences appear as dark threadlike markings above the bright solar disk.

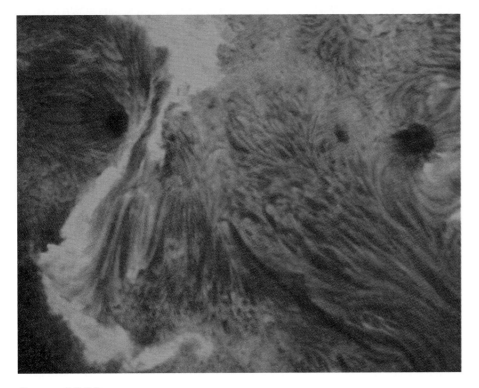

**figure 12.19**

A solar flare over a sunspot region, photographed in Hα light. Flares appear suddenly as rapid brightenings in the chromosphere.

mon type has streamers that extend outward and curve back again into the Sun.

*Eruptive prominences* rise suddenly and fade away. The sequence begins when the lower region of the prominence brightens. The gases erupt in a rising arch that separates into two parts; one returns to the chromosphere while the other continues outward into space. Most eruptives are found in sunspot regions.

The arches and loops followed by prominences are the result of interactions with magnetic fields. During an eruption, charged particles spiral around and are held aloft by field lines. They are cooler regions insulated from the high-temperature corona by the magnetic field.

## Flares

The most powerful short-lived eruptions of energy on the Sun are called **flares.** Associated with sunspots, these catastrophic events appear suddenly and spread rapidly above a sunspot region. Flares emit radiation in all frequencies from intensive X-rays to long radio waves. The shortwave X-rays reach Earth and may produce fade-outs of radio communication. Moreover, there is an increase in *corpuscular radiation* consisting of atomic nuclei (mostly protons) called **solar cosmic radiation.** These high-energy particles produce brilliant displays of auroras seen in the polar regions of the Earth's ionosphere.

When photographed in the Hα line, flares are among the brightest phenomena seen on the Sun. They are observed as rapid brightenings in plage areas in the chromosphere. Flares are connected with strong magnetic fields extending above sunspot regions (fig. 12.19).

Astronomers at ground-based observatories have engaged in continuous surveillance of flares for many decades. Activities are recorded by solar cinematography. Frames photographed every 15 seconds provide a time-lapse motion picture sequence of an event from its inception to dissipation into space. Presently videotape is used as an alternative to film.

Investigations show a correlation between the frequency of flares and the

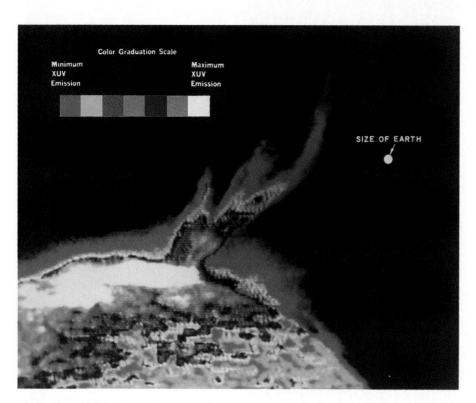

Color Graduation Scale

Minimum XUV Emission

Maximum XUV Emission

SIZE OF EARTH

**figure 12.20**

A false-color image of a solar flare photographed from Skylab. Note the size of the Earth in comparison.

solar cycle. A greater number of flares can be expected to erupt during a sunspot maximum, when small flares can occur every hour and a spectacular flare erupts about every month. Why flares explode is not fully understood, but astronomers believe the sudden upsurge of energy and particles is related to the behavior of magnetic fields. The energy release is staggering—the burst of a large flare is equivalent to several million hydrogen bombs exploding every few minutes. These behemoths extend as far as 300,000 km beyond the Sun.

In the 1970s, one prime objective of the Skylab missions was to observe flares in X-ray and ultraviolet wavelengths. Onboard experiments showed that the initial disturbance leading to a flare occurs at the crests of magnetic loops extending into the chromosphere. When flares occur, temperatures soar to as much as 20 million K, which is higher than the temperature inside the Sun's energy-producing core. Thus energy released in the X-ray and ultraviolet range is greater than that detected in the visible wavelengths (fig. 12.20).

The corpuscular radiation associated with flares consists of protons, electrons, and alpha particles (helium nuclei). The particles are accelerated to high energies by the flare and carried away from the Sun at speeds approaching 1500 km/sec. When these solar cosmic rays reach the Earth, the ionosphere is buffeted by violent magnetic storms as the high-energy particles spiral along the Earth's magnetic field lines. Only a fraction of the total energy is intercepted by the Earth, but it is sufficient to create the luminous arcs, rays, and streamers of the aurora. Auroral displays are more common during sunspot maximum, when frequent flare eruptions take place.

## The Active Corona

The action of the Sun extends above the chromosphere to the corona where high-energy particles raise temperatures to millions of degrees. When high-resolution X-ray telescopes are trained on the Sun, the corona appears as a tangle of loops and arches supported by magnetic field lines. The most energetic X-rays are detected in the upper part of the corona where temperatures soar to 4 million K. In the lower corona above the transition region, temperatures are about 2 million K.

Extensive X-ray and ultraviolet observations of fundamental coronal features were made aboard Skylab missions in 1973 and by the Solar Maximum Mission (SMM) spacecraft launched in 1980. There are **coronal holes,** extended regions that appear dark in X-ray and ultraviolet wavelengths. *Bright points* are seen across the entire solar disk. Large bright areas appear to be associated with active regions in the photosphere and chromosphere. Extensive loops connect active coronal regions of concentrated magnetic fields, some of which are separated by thousands of kilometers. Finally, the corona on the far side of the Sun extends as a diffuse halo beyond the solar limb.

Coronal holes are important features of the Sun, first discovered during X-ray investigations using high-altitude rockets. From orbiting observatories, in particular Skylab, X-ray and ultraviolet photographs show holes as dark expanses where densities and temperatures are reduced to about half that of the surrounding area. Moreover, the separation between a hole and the rest of the corona is quite steep and looks like the face of a cliff extending into the Sun (fig. 12.21). Coronal holes in the polar regions are essentially permanent features of the Sun that resemble dark caps. Coronal holes appear dark because X-ray and ultraviolet emissions are less intense or entirely missing.

The vast coronal holes are not limited to polar regions. A wide gap in the corona may open up and form a sinuous dark canyon extending from a polar hole as far as 2 million km in a north-south direction. As the corona parts, the magnetic field lines no longer arch across the hole as they do over other regions of the corona. Instead, the field lines open up and turn radially away from the Sun as they do at the poles. After a few months, nearby coronal arches gradually extend across and remove all traces of the north-south gap.

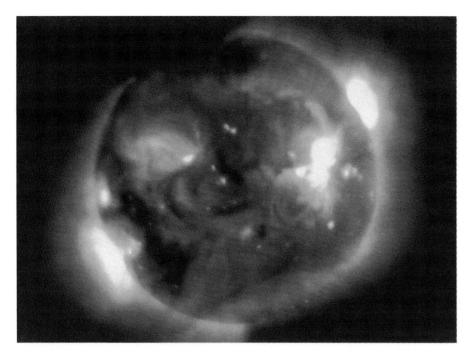

**figure 12.21**

An X-ray image of the Sun's corona taken from Skylab. The dark gap is a coronal hole extending more than 1 million km in a north-south direction.

Skylab made possible the continuous observation of coronal holes for an extended period of time. These experiments confirmed an important discovery—the relationship between coronal holes and the particles of the solar wind. Because the magnetic field lines are open, protons, electrons, and nuclei of heavier elements in the lower atmosphere of the Sun are allowed to escape through the coronal holes. Elsewhere, ionized particles are forced to spiral in closed loops of the solar magnetic field.

X-ray photographs show scores of bright points that cover the solar disk like glittering rubies. These points are magnetic concentrations that contribute to the Sun's general magnetic field. Some points last for only a few minutes; others persist for several days.

In the polar regions, bright points are found at the bases of polar plumes, which are filaments of gas that escape into space along open magnetic field lines. Bright points in ultraviolet are seen in the cooler lower corona above the transition region. They are associated with magnetic fields found between supergranules in the chromosphere.

## The Solar Wind

Charged particles of the solar wind recede from the polar coronal holes at supersonic speeds measuring 400 km/sec. The ionized stream and its associated magnetic field continue outward in undulating spirals beyond the planets, diminishing in strength until they are balanced by the weak pressure of the interstellar medium. Some of the field lines leave the poles and curve back toward the solar equator to form a neutral magnetic sheet in the equatorial plane. Owing to the 7° inclination of the Sun's axis to the ecliptic, the magnetic sheet extends above and below the Earth's orbital plane. Thus during each revolution, the Earth alternately passes through regions of opposite magnetic polarity (fig. 12.22).

The spiral structure can be explained by considering one point of origin for the solar wind. If the Sun were stationary, the solar wind particles and magnetic field would move radially away from the source. But, as we know, the Sun rotates in a period of 25 days, which translates into an angular displacement of the solar wind source by about 14°

per day. The situation is analogous to that of a rotating garden sprinkler sending a jet of water across a lawn. In the solar wind, particles reach the Earth in four days and cross our planet's orbit at an angle of about 45°.

As described in previous chapters, the solar wind interacts with the upper atmospheres and magnetic fields of the Earth and other planets. It causes the ion and dust tails of comets to point away from the direction of the Sun. Moreover, the steady wind carries meteoric dust, gas, and minute particles away from the inner solar system. Occasionally the eruption of flares induces surges in the solar wind that cause wavelike motions in the Earth's magnetic field. Most frequent during sunspot maxima, these magnetic storms play havoc with electric power generation and communication systems.

How far does the solar wind extend into space? To find the answer, astronomers study signals from distant space probes such as Pioneer 10, attempting to identify the **heliosphere,** the region of space around the Sun where the solar wind meets the interstellar medium. Launched in 1972, the Pioneer 10 was the first spacecraft to travel beyond the asteroid belt and explore Jupiter. Now the probe is beyond Pluto (over 50 AU distant) and still sending faint signals that have allowed astronomers to extend the known dimensions of the heliosphere. The Voyager 1 and 2 spacecraft continue their passage beyond the planets to the boundary of the Sun's magnetic realm. The theoretical limit is placed at 160 AU, which is four times the distance to Pluto.

Astronomers postulate two models to describe the heliosphere. In the first, the pressure of the solar wind creates a bow shock in the direction in which the solar system is moving through space. "Downwind," the heliospheric boundary has a teardrop shape similar to a planetary magnetosphere (fig. 12.23). A shell of turbulent plasma lies at the interface region outside the heliosphere. The outer boundary of the interface is called the *heliopause.* Astronomers estimate the distance to the heliopause at between 60 and 100 AU from the Sun. In 1993,

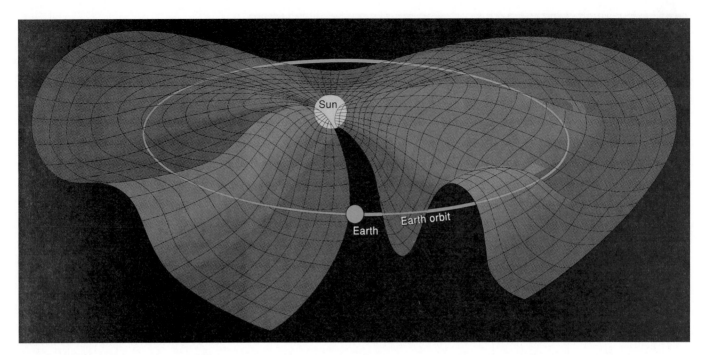

**figure 12.22**
A model of the Sun's neutral magnetic sheet.

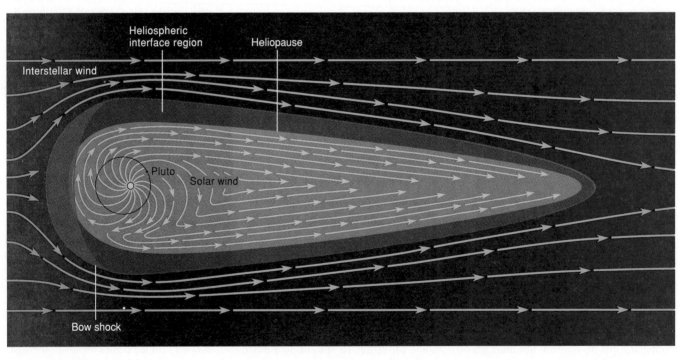

**figure 12.23**
A model of the boundary between the solar system and interstellar space. A teardrop-shaped heliospheric interface region is formed by the collision of interstellar charged particles and the solar wind.

signals from Voyager 1 and Voyager 2 spacecraft at distances of 53 and 38 AU place the heliopause between 82 and 130 AU. The spacecraft should detect changes when they leave the heliosphere and enter the interface region.

In the second scenario, there is no distinct boundary marking the heliosphere. Instead, the solar-wind plasma gradually merges with the galactic magnetic field.

# SUMMARY

The Sun is an average star of middle age, similar to countless others found in the Galaxy. It is an immense, gaseous body containing more than 99% of the mass in the solar system.

The visible layer of the Sun, called the photosphere, represents the lowest atmosphere commonly referred to as the Sun's surface. Above the photosphere are more rarified layers called the chromosphere and corona.

The Sun represents a delicate balance between the outward force produced by the energy in its core and the inward force of gravity produced by its mass. In the core, hydrogen is converted to helium and radiant energy by the proton-proton chain reaction.

The photosphere consists of granules representing rising convection cells averaging about 700 km across. Each cell is separated by cooler gases descending below the surface. On the photosphere, there is a fluctuation in the number of sunspots over a period of about 11 years, part of a 22-year solar cycle. A well-developed sunspot has a dark central umbra surrounded by a lighter penumbra. Spots are associated with the Sun's magnetic fields.

The chromosphere is characterized by supergranules and spikes of glowing gases called spicules, which rise 6000 km and higher. Huge prominences reach high altitudes in the shape of columns and arches along magnetic field lines. The most powerful eruptions are called flares.

During a solar eclipse, the solar corona is seen as a pearly-white halo surrounding the Sun. It contains extensive regions called coronal holes that appear dark in X-ray and ultraviolet wavelengths. A permanent feature at the poles, the holes may form gaps extending as far as 2 million km in a north-south direction. Charged particles of the solar wind recede from the coronal holes at supersonic speeds. Magnetic field lines are carried by the solar wind in spirals to distances beyond the planets.

# KEY TERMS

| | |
|---|---|
| chromosphere | photosphere |
| corona | plages |
| coronal holes | prominences |
| faculae | proton-proton chain |
| flares | solar constant |
| fusion | solar cosmic radiation |
| granulation | sunspot |
| helioseismology | sunspot cycle |
| heliosphere | supergranules |
| hydrostatic equilibrium | thermal equilibrium |
| limb darkening | Zeeman effect |
| luminosity | zodiacal light |

# PROBLEMS

1. Describe the features and characteristics of the Sun revealed by studies in each region of the spectrum.

2. How are solar activities and terrestrial phenomena related?

3. Explain how the strength of solar magnetic fields is determined.

4. The interplanetary magnetic field is spiral in structure. Why?

5. Explain why the temperature of the solar atmosphere increases from the photosphere to the corona.

6. How do astronomers obtain monochromatic photographs? What solar features do they reveal?

7. In white light the limb of the Sun appears darker than the center of the disk. Why?

8. List the steps required to produce solar energy by the proton-proton reaction.

9. What methods are used by astronomers to probe the interior of the Sun? What discoveries have been made?

10. Describe the features of the inner and outer coronas observed at optical wavelengths.

11. What are coronal holes? How are they related to the solar wind?

12. What are solar flares? How do they affect the Earth and our lives?

13. Explain how solar activity may have long-term effects on the Earth's climate.

14. Describe the stages in the development of sunspots during the 22-year solar cycle. Explain the effects of differential rotation and changes in the Sun's dipolar magnetic field.

15. Most of the chemical elements found on the Earth have been detected in the Sun. How were these elements identified in the Sun?

16. Why do sunspots appear darker than the surrounding photosphere when viewed in optical wavelengths?

17. If a sunspot advances 14° per day across the Sun's disk, what is the Sun's rotational period at that latitude?

18. You measure a sunspot with a micrometer and find its angular diameter to be 17.6 arc seconds. What is the linear diameter of the sunspot? How does the sunspot compare with the diameter of the Earth? Assume the Sun's distance to be one astronomical unit.

# REFERENCES

Aldhous, Peter. 1990. Ulysses Treads a Lonely Path. *Nature* (London) 347, no. 6293 (October 11).

Audouze, Jean, and Guy Israel, eds. 1985. *The Cambridge Atlas of Astronomy.* Cambridge: Cambridge University Press.

Bahcall, John N. 1990. Neutrinos from the Sun: An Astronomical Puzzle. *Mercury* (Astronomical Society of the Pacific) 19, no. 2 (March/April).

———. 1990. The Solar Neutrino Problem. *Scientific American* 262, no. 5 (May).

Bennett, Gary L. 1987. Voyage into the Third Dimension. *Astronomy* 15, no. 5 (May).

Bray, R. J., and R. E. Loughhead. 1974. *The Solar Chromosphere.* London: Chapman and Hall, Ltd.

Dyer, Alan. 1992. Ulysses Meets a Giant. *Astronomy* 20, no. 7 (July).

Eddy, John A. 1979. "A New Sun." In *The Solar Results from Skylab,* edited by Rein Ise. Washington, D.C.: NASA.

Foukal, Peter V. 1990. The Variable Sun. *Scientific American* 262, no. 2 (February).

Franco, Anna, and D. H. Smith. 1987. Vanishing Solar Neutrinos. *Sky and Telescope* 73, no. 2 (February).

Harvey, John W., James R. Kennedy, and John W. Leibacher. 1987. GONG: To See Inside Our Sun. *Sky and Telescope* 74, no. 5 (November).

Hill, Richard, 1989. Equipped for Safe Solar Viewing. *Astronomy* 17, no. 2 (February).

Kanipe, Jeff, Richard Talcott, and Robert Burnham. 1988. The Rise and Fall of the Sun's Activity. *Astronomy* 16, no. 10 (October).

Leibacher, John W., Robert W. Noyes, Juri Toomre, and Roger K. Ulrich. 1985. Helioseismology. *Scientific American* 253, no. 3 (September).

Lindsay, Sally. 1976. The Turbulent Sun. *Natural History* (November).

LoPresto, James Charles, 1989. Looking Inside the Sun. *Astronomy* 17, no. 3 (March).

Nichols, Robert G. 1989. Solar Max: 1980–89. *Sky and Telescope* 78, no. 6 (December).

Norton, Arthur P. 1986. *Norton's Star Atlas.* 17th ed. Revised and rewritten by Christopher R. Kitchin et al. New York: John Wiley & Sons, Inc.

Paresce, Francesco, and Stuart Bowyer. 1986. The Sun and the Interstellar Medium. *Scientific American* 255, no. 3 (September).

Robinson, Leif J. 1987. The Sunspot Cycle: Tip of the Iceberg. *Sky and Telescope* 73, no. 6 (June).

Schwarzchild, Bertram. 1992. Gallex Data Can't Quite Lay the Solar Neutrino Problem to Rest. *Physics Today* (American Institute of Physics) 45, no. 8 (August).

Smith, David H. 1990. The Solar Neutrino Mystery Deepens. *Sky and Telescope* 80, no. 4 (October).

Smith, Elske v. P., and Kenneth C. Jacobs. 1989. *Introductory Astronomy and Astrophysics.* Philadelphia: W.B. Saunders Company.

Williams, George E. 1986. The Solar Cycle in Precambrian Time. *Scientific American* 255, no. 2 (August).

Wolfson, Richard. 1983. The Active Solar Corona. *Scientific American* 248, no. 2 (February).

Xanthakis, John N. 1967. *Solar Physics.* London: John Wiley & Sons.

Zirin, Harold. 1988. *Astrophysics of the Sun.* Cambridge: Cambridge University Press.

The Sagittarius-Scorpius region of the
Milky Way.

The Sun, an average star, is the only star we can examine close-up. Other stars, many of which exceed the Sun in size and luminosity, are seen as mere points of light. What we have learned about the Sun can be applied to the stars, while the study of stars provides a better understanding of the Sun.

Even a casual glance at the sky on a clear night reveals differences in the brilliance of the stars. The brightest are scattered across the night sky as solitary beacons separated by thousands of lesser lights of diminishing intensity. Today we know that stars vary in distance as well as intrinsic or actual brightness. Indeed, most of the stars near our solar system are too faint to be seen without a telescope. The majority of the brightest stars we see are hundreds of times more distant and tens of thousands of times more luminous than the feeble neighbors of the Sun.

Moreover, stars emit light in all colors of the spectrum: hot stars are blue-white, cooler stars are red. Sunlike stars radiate more effectively in the middle range and appear yellow. Stars vary in diameter even more than they do in temperature. Most stars are only a fraction of the size of the Sun, while others are large enough to occupy the inner region of the solar system.

## Measuring Distances to the Stars

Before investigating the properties of these diversified stars, let us focus on the measurement of stellar distances. The term **parallax** describes the slight apparent shift in position of the nearer stars when viewed from opposite points in the Earth's orbit. Bifocal vision is the most common example of how the parallax effect helps you distinguish between objects near and far. Hold a finger about 15 cm beyond your nose and focus on a distant object. Now alternately blink each eye and see how parallax makes your finger appear to move back and forth

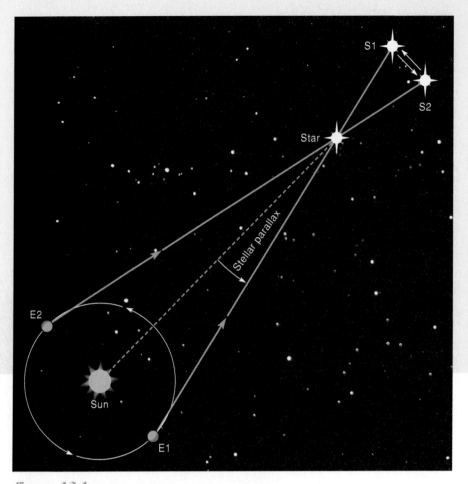

**figure 13.1**

The revolution of the Earth causes an apparent shift in the positions of nearby stars. Stellar parallax is defined as one-half of the angular displacement of a star.

against the distant object. Nearby objects have a greater parallactic shift than distant objects.

### The Parsec

Picture the Earth revolving about the Sun. In the sky, the motion of the Earth causes an apparent displacement of the nearest stars in a path called a *parallactic ellipse*. A star located in the direction of the ecliptic pole will trace out an almost circular path; at the ecliptic, a star will seem to move back and forth in a line. The size of the parallactic ellipse decreases with distance so that the displacements of remote stars become increasingly more difficult to measure.

Consider the star shown in figure 13.1. A photograph of the star field is taken in January when the Earth is at *E1*; the star appears in the star field at *S1*. In July, six months later, the Earth has advanced

to *E2*, and a second photograph shows the star at *S2*. The two photographs are compared and the apparent displacement measured. The maximum change in position represents the major axis of the parallactic ellipse. From this the *annual parallax,* or **stellar parallax,** is defined as the semimajor axis of the parallactic ellipse. Think of the parallax as the angle made by the radius of the Earth's orbit (1 AU) observed at the star's distance (fig. 13.2). Accordingly, if the parallax is known, the distance to the star can be computed.

In chapter 6, the distance between the Earth and the Moon was found using the radius of the Earth as a baseline and the angular displacement, or parallax, of the Moon seen from two points on the Earth's surface.

$$d = \frac{206265 \times \text{radius of the Earth}}{\text{parallax of the Moon}}$$

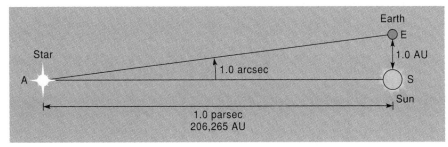

**figure 13.2**

A parsec is a distance having a stellar parallax equal to one arc second.

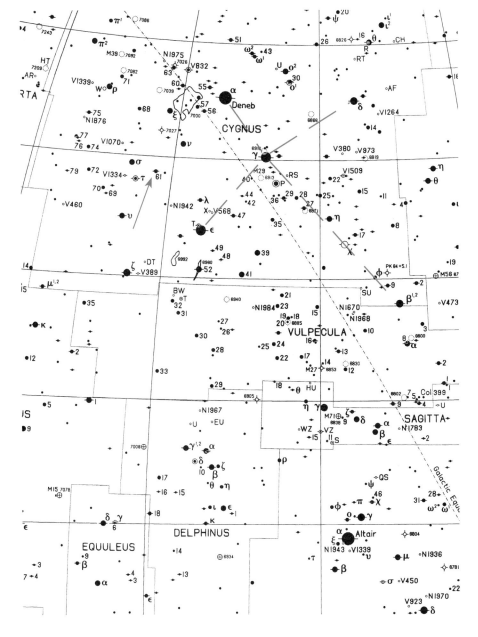

**figure 13.3**

The annual parallax of the fifth-magnitude star 61 Cygni (*arrow*) was determined in 1838. The bright stars in the region outline the Northern Cross in the constellation Cygnus.

From *Norton's 2000.0 Star Atlas and Reference Handbook,* 18th ed. Copyright © 1991 Longman Group UK Ltd. Reprinted by permission.

By substituting terms, the equation may be used to find the distance to a star.

$$d = \frac{206265 \times \text{radius of the Earth's orbit}}{\text{parallax of the star}}$$

In figure 13.2, let $E$ and $S$ represent the Earth and Sun; the distance $ES$ is the radius of the Earth's orbit, 1 AU. Let $A$ represent a star with a stellar parallax, $p$, equal to one arc second. The distance to the star is

$$d = \frac{206265 \times 1 \text{ AU}}{1.0''} = 206265 \text{ AU}$$

There are no stars near enough to the Sun to have a parallax as large as one arc second. Moreover, measuring in astronomical units is entirely too cumbersome, much like trying to measure distances between cities in centimeters rather than kilometers. A more suitable scale would be to define the unit of measure as the distance at which the *parallax* is equal to one arc *sec*ond. A **parsec** is the unit of length equal to the distance where the radius of the Earth's orbit subtends an angle of one arc second; thus one parsec = 206265 AU. To find the distance in parsecs,

$$d_{pc} = \frac{206265 \times 1 \text{ AU}}{\text{parallax of } 1.0''} \times \frac{1 \text{ parsec}}{206265 \text{ AU}}$$

$$d_{pc} = \frac{1}{p},$$

where

$d_{pc}$ = The distance in parsecs,

and

$p$ = The stellar parallax in arc seconds.

A more familiar astronomical measurement, the *light-year,* is equal to the distance that light travels in the course of one year. There are about 3.26 light-years in one parsec. To find the distance to a star in light-years,

$$d_{ly} = \frac{3.26}{p}.$$

In 1838, Friedrich Wilhelm Bessel was the first to successfully determine the parallax of 61 Cygni, a nearby star located 3.4 parsecs from the Sun (fig. 13.3). Soon afterward Thomas Henderson measured the parallax of

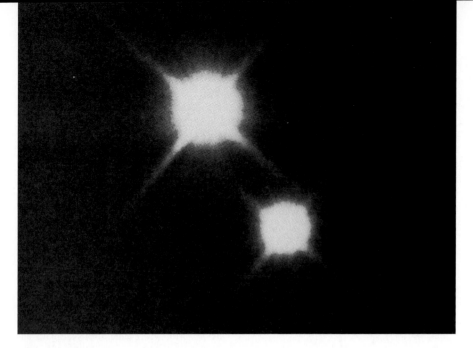

### figure 13.4
The overexposed image of Alpha Centauri A **(top)** and B **(bottom)**.

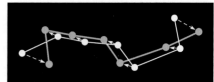

### figure 13.5
In 100,000 years, proper motions of the stars that make up the Big Dipper will change its familiar shape to the configuration shown in yellow.

Alpha Centauri and Friedrich Wilhelm Struve determined the parallax of Vega. The Alpha Centauri system has a parallax of 0.75 arcsec (fig. 13.4). Proxima Centauri, the nearest star to the Sun, has a parallax of 0.767. The distance of Proxima Centauri in parsecs and light-years is determined by

$$d_{pc} = \frac{1}{0.767} = 1.30 \text{ parsecs}$$

$$d_{ly} = \frac{3.26}{0.767} = 4.25 \text{ light-years}$$

The second brightest star in Centaurus, Beta Centauri, has a parallax of 0.009 arcsec, which is about the smallest angle capable of being measured by the trigonometric method. How far is Beta Centauri from the Sun?

## Measurement of Stellar Motion

How did Bessel, Struve, and Henderson know which stars to choose for their experiments? When Bessel selected 61 Cygni for his distance experiment, he had reason to believe the star is close to the Sun and possesses a measureable annual parallactic motion. Stars have a continuous small displacement on the celestial sphere that partly represents their space motions (see fig. 13.5). *Proper motion* is the angular rate of a star's change in position after corrections have

been made for parallax, aberration, and precession. Most stars have proper motions amounting to less than 1.0″ per year. Generally, nearer stars show a greater displacement than more distant stars. It was known to Bessel that 61 Cygni has a large proper motion (5.22″ per year), indicating its proximity to the Sun.

## Other Methods of Finding Distances

Trigonometric parallax is the most direct method used to measure distances to relatively nearby objects within a few hundred parsecs of the Sun. Astronomers derive distances by alternative methods when measurements involve remote objects in our Milky Way system and other galaxies billions of light-years from the Earth. Following are brief descriptions of distance-determination methods described later in this chapter. Other methods are treated elsewhere in the text.

### Moving clusters

The distance to a nearby star cluster can be measured by the proper motions and radial velocities of the member stars. The stars move in parallel paths through space, but owing to perspective, they seem to converge to or diverge from a point on the sky. The distance to the cluster is determined geometrically from the rate of convergence and radial velocity.

The famous Hyades cluster in Taurus is the nearest moving cluster. Its distance is fundamental because it serves as a reference standard for distance determination by other methods. Measurements to remote galaxies are based upon such distance indicators. The distance to the Hyades is estimated to be 145 to 155 light-years from the Sun.

### Luminosity criteria

There is a relationship between the intensity of the lines in a star's spectrum and its temperature. The intrinsic brightness of a star can be found by its characteristic spectral signature. The distance to the star can be computed from the difference between the observed brightness and intrinsic brightness determined from its spectrum.

### Period–luminosity relation

The period of light variation of a cepheid variable star is related to its intrinsic brightness. The longer the period, the higher the luminosity of the star. The distance to a cepheid star is determined from the difference between its observed brightness and luminosity.

## Apparent Magnitude

In the *Almagest*, Ptolemy describes the brightness of naked-eye stars according to six classes, or magnitudes, introduced by Hipparchus in the second century B.C. The 20 brightest stars are grouped as first-magnitude stars; the next category, second magnitude, contains about 60 stars; the faintest stars are classed as sixth magnitude. Note that the magnitude scale is inverse, so that the numerical value of the magnitude *increases* as stellar brightness *decreases*.

## Finding the Space Motion of a Star

The vast majority of stars are either moving toward or away with respect to the Sun. The so-called *space velocity* of a star can be computed by separating its motion into two components, *tangential velocity* and *radial velocity*. The space velocity can be treated as the hypotenuse of a right triangle, which can be found by applying the Pythagorean theorem—the square of the hypotenuse is equal to the sum of the squares of the two sides ($a^2 + b^2 = c^2$). Figure 13.6 illustrates the method.

Knowing the proper motion and distance allows astronomers to compute the tangential velocity, which represents the star's motion in km/sec across our line of sight. The radial velocity is the star's motion in km/sec in the line of sight. Radial velocity is determined by the Doppler displacement in the positions of the lines in the star's spectrum (fig. 5.12). The star is approaching if the spectral lines are blueshifted and receding if the lines are redshifted.

When the tangential and radial velocities are known, the space velocity can be found. Space velocity is important in astronomy because it represents a star's apparent speed and direction through the Galaxy relative to the Sun (see fig. 17.4).

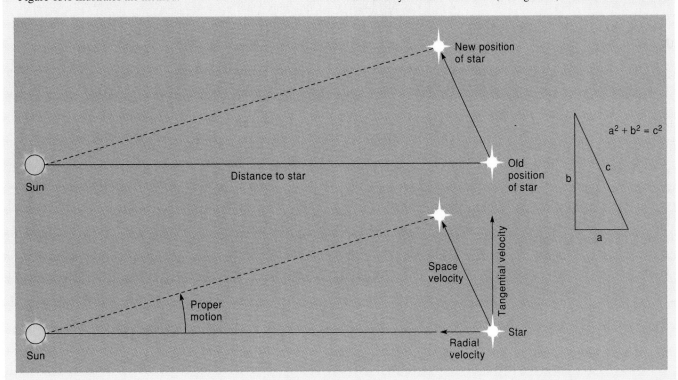

**figure 13.6**

Space velocity is a star's motion relative to the Sun, computed from the tangential velocity and the radial velocity. The tangential velocity is determined from the star's distance and proper motion. Radial velocity is measured by shifts in the positions of the lines in the star's spectrum.

The magnitude categories refer to the appearance and not the actual brightness of stars. A less luminous star nearer to the Sun might appear brighter than a more luminous star at a greater distance just as a pocket flashlight held close to the eye is brighter than a distant automobile headlight. A given star removed to a greater distance will be reduced in brightness and appear fainter. Thus the observed bright-ness of a star is dependent upon two quantities: actual or intrinsic brightness, and distance from the Sun. Two stars with the same observed magnitude may vary significantly in luminosity. For the present, let us investigate the **apparent magnitude (m)**—the observed brightness of a star. Intrinsic brightness and luminosity will be treated later in this chapter (see fig. 13.7).

### Pogson's Scale

The nineteenth-century English astronomer John Herschel noted that a first-magnitude star appears about 100 times brighter than a sixth-magnitude star. In 1856, Norman R. Pogson proposed a system in which magnitudes are measured in explicit terms while the original brightness ratio based upon visual response is retained. On Pogson's scale, a first-magnitude star is defined as *exactly* 100 times brighter than a sixth-magnitude star. Thus the ratio of brightness between two successive magnitudes will equal 2.512 to 1, which is the fifth root of 100 ($100^{1/5} = 10^{2/5} = 2.512$).

Accordingly, a first-magnitude star is $(2.512)^1$ times brighter than a second-magnitude star; $(2.512)^2$ or 6.310 times brighter than a third-magnitude star; and $(2.512)^5$ or 100 times brighter than a sixth-magnitude star. The power to which the constant 2.512 is raised and the difference in magnitude between the stars are numerically equal. Table 13.1 presents Pogson's scale.

Apparent magnitudes of stars are determined by comparing their brightness with designated standard stars. On Pogson's magnitude scale, zero and negative values are given to stars brighter than first magnitude. Moreover, the scale provides magnitude values for the Sun, Moon, planets, and comets.

Sirius, the brightest star in the sky, has an apparent magnitude $m = -1.46$. Vega ($m = +0.03$), Arcturus ($m = -0.04$), Rigel ($m = +0.12$), and Aldebaran ($m = +0.85$) are among the stars of zero magnitude. The apparent magnitude of the Sun is $-26.73$, compared to the $+23.50$ magnitude of the faintest telescopic star. At opposition the magnitude of the Moon is $-12.74$. Venus, the brightest planet, reaches $-4.70$ magnitude; faint Pluto is only $+15.12$ magnitude at mean opposition. Familiar first-magnitude stars include Pollux, Antares, and Deneb; Hamal and Polaris are examples of second-magnitude stars. (See table 13.2.)

### Types of Apparent Magnitude

The magnitude resolved with the eye is called *visual magnitude*, $m_v$; the eye is more sensitive to yellow-green wavelengths than red or blue. By using a photometer and filters in agreement with the visual scale, *photovisual magnitude* can be determined. The magnitude measured from blue-sensitive photographic plates, emulsions, or filters is called *photographic magnitude* (fig. 13.8).

*Photoelectric magnitude* is derived with a photoelectric photometer. Various photometric systems in use today are based upon the wavelength intervals

**figure 13.7**

Differences in magnitudes of stars in the Praesepe or Beehive cluster (M44) in the constellation Cancer. The stars vary in magnitude from +6.6 to +15.

## Table 13.1

### Pogson's magnitude scale

| Magnitude Difference | Brightness Ratio |
|:---:|:---:|
| 0 | 1:1 |
| 1 | 2.512:1 |
| 2 | 6.310:1 |
| 3 | 15.851:1 |
| 4 | 39.818:1 |
| 5 | 100:1 |
| 10 | 10,000:1 |
| 15 | 1,000,000:1 |

transmitted by suitable filters. The **UBV system** devised by Johnson and Morgan gives magnitudes in ultraviolet ($U$) centered at 350 nm, blue ($B$) at 430 nm, and visual ($V$) at 550 nm. Other systems extend into the infrared range.

The magnitudes obtained by photometric systems are limited to wave-

### Using Pogson's Magnitude Scale

By definition, Pogson's ratio is expressed as

$$\frac{b_1}{b_2} = 10^{2/5(m_2 - m_1)}$$

where $b_1$ represents the brightness of star 1 and $b_2$ the brightness of star 2; and the terms $m_1$ and $m_2$ their respective magnitudes. The logarithm of the expression to the base 10 is

$$\log\left(\frac{b_1}{b_2}\right) = \frac{2}{5}(m_2 - m_1).$$

Simplify and solve for the difference in magnitude,

$$m_2 - m_1 = 2.5 \times \log\left(\frac{b_1}{b_2}\right).$$

For example, two stars are measured photometrically and found to have a brightness ratio of 100:1. Find the difference in magnitude.

$$\frac{b_1}{b_2} = 100 = 10^2$$

$$m_2 - m_1 = 2.5 \times \log 10^2$$

$$= 2.5 \times 2$$

$$m_2 - m_1 = 5 \text{ magnitudes}$$

What is the brightness ratio of two stars when the magnitude difference is seven? Refer to table 13.1. Multiply the brightness ratios of any magnitude entries that add up to seven (2 + 5; 3 + 4).

$$6.310 \times 100.0 = 631:1$$

$$15.851 \times 39.818 = 631:1$$

This equation, $m_2 - m_1 = 2.5 \times \log(b_1/b_2)$, is fundamental in computing apparent magnitudes. One star in the equation ($b_1$) may be used as a comparison star to find the magnitude of the second star ($b_2$). In the example, let $b_1$ represent a standard star of $m_1 = +2$. The magnitude of star $b_2$ is found to be $m_2 = +7$.

## Table 13.2

### apparent magnitudes of bright objects

| | |
|---|---|
| Sun | -26.73 |
| Moon | -12.74 |
| Venus | -4.70 |
| Jupiter | -2.70 |
| Mars | -2.01 |
| Sirius | -1.46 |
| Canopus | -0.72 |
| Alpha Centauri | -0.01 |
| Arcturus | -0.04 |

**figure 13.8**

The photovisual magnitude (*left*) and the photographic magnitude (*right*) of a red star. The difference in the two magnitudes is called the color index of the star.

lengths transmitted by the filters. Each spectral band carries only a fraction of the light and does not represent the radiation emitted in all wavelengths. Moreover, there are invisible emissions at radio, infrared, ultraviolet, X-ray, and gamma wavelengths that must be included to account for all the radiation leaving a star. Measurement of the total radiation of a star is called apparent bolometric magnitude, $m_{bol}$. **Bolometric magnitude** will always be numerically less than visual magnitude because the former represents the total brightness of a star over the entire spectrum.

### The Inverse Square Law

In the eighteenth century, Pierre Bouguer demonstrated what Kepler had stated theoretically—that the intensity of starlight behaves according to the **inverse square law** and decreases inversely as the square of the distance between the source and the observer. Consider a distant star radiating in all directions. As shown in figure 13.9, the energy from the star spreads into concentric spheres of light. At distance $d_1$ from the star, the radiant energy covers a square with sides equal to one unit and an area $A_1$ of $1 \times 1$ or 1 square unit. When the light has reached distance $d_2$ and is twice as far from the star, the sides of the square

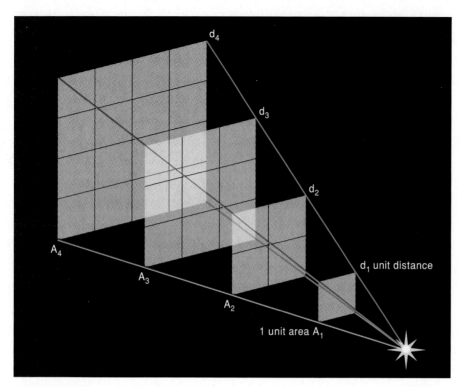

**figure 13.9**

The inverse square law of radiation.

## Table 13.3

### apparent and absolute magnitudes of selected stars

| Star | $m_v$ | $M_v$ | $(m_v - M_v)$ | $d_{pc}$ |
|------|-------|-------|---------------|----------|
| Sun | −26.73 | +4.84 | −31.57 | — |
| Proxima | +11.05 | +15.49 | −4.44 | 1.3 |
| Cen A | −0.01 | +4.37 | −4.38 | 1.3 |
| B | +1.33 | +5.71 | −4.38 | 1.3 |
| Sirius | −1.46 | +1.42 | −2.88 | 2.7 |
| Procyon | +0.37 | +2.65 | −2.28 | 3.5 |
| Altair | +0.76 | +2.28 | −1.52 | 5.0 |
| Vega | +0.03 | +0.65 | −0.62 | 7.5 |
| Canopus | −0.72 | −3.50 | +2.76 | 35.7 |
| Spica | +0.97 | −3.20 | +4.17 | 67.5 |

covered by the radiation are now two units in length and the area $A_2$ has increased to $2 \times 2 = 4$ square units. If the energy emitted each second by the star is constant, the amount of light that falls on one square unit at distance $d_1$ must cover four times as much area at distance $d_2$. Each unit area at $d_2$ will receive one-fourth as much energy as a unit area at $d_1$; at three times the distance, $d_3$, one-ninth as much.

## Absolute Magnitude and Luminosity

Since stars vary in apparent brightness as well as distance, we cannot determine their intrinsic brightness unless the distance factor is removed. The **absolute magnitude (M)** is defined as the apparent magnitude a star would have at a standard distance of 10 parsecs from the Sun. Absolute magnitudes are obtained in various wavelengths from apparent

magnitudes. Absolute visual and absolute bolometric magnitudes represent the visual and bolometric magnitudes of a star at 10 parsecs. If the star's true distance, $d$, and apparent magnitude, $m$, are known, its absolute magnitude, $M$, can be computed.

Suppose a star of magnitude +6 is located at 100 parsecs. What is its absolute magnitude? At 100 parsecs, the star is ten times more distant than the standard 10 parsecs. According to the inverse square law, the star would appear $10 \times 10$ or 100 times brighter at 10 parsecs than it appears at 100 parsecs. Earlier we learned that an increase in brightness by a factor of 100 ($10^2$) corresponds to a difference of five magnitudes. Since the star measures +6 magnitude at 100 parsecs, its absolute magnitude is $M = +1$.

### The Distance Modulus

In table 13.3, $(m_v - M_v)$ represents the difference between apparent visual and absolute visual magnitude of each star. The relationship defines the **distance modulus,** which is a measure of relative distance. If the distance modulus is negative, the star is nearer to the Sun than the standard distance of 10 parsecs. The smaller negative number identifies the nearer star. Our Sun has the smallest distance modulus of −31.57.

A star at 10 parsecs will have a zero distance modulus since apparent and absolute magnitudes are equal in value. A star located beyond 10 parsecs has a positive distance modulus.

### Stellar Luminosity

In chapter 12, we defined the luminosity of the Sun as the rate at which energy is emitted per second ($3.8 \times 10^{33}$ ergs/sec). Luminosity can also be expressed as the absolute brightness of the Sun or any other star, and therefore is related to the bolometric magnitude, which is the measure of the total radiation.

So far, our discussion has centered on apparent bolometric magnitude, which is related to the apparent visual magnitude of the stars. The measurement of the actual intensity of light—the quantity of surface radiation per unit of time—involves the absolute visual magnitude,

## Finding the Luminosity of Vega

The luminosity of the bright star Vega can be computed using the equation introduced in Methods and Understandings 13.2.

$$\log\left(\frac{L_*}{L_\odot}\right) = \frac{2}{5}(M_{\odot\,bol} - M_{*bol})$$

where $L_*$ = luminosity of the star; $L_\odot$ = the luminosity of the Sun ($L_\odot = 1$); and ($M_{\odot\,bol} - M_{*bol}$) = difference between the absolute bolometric magnitudes of the Sun and star ($M_{\odot\,bol} = +4.8$).

To find the absolute bolometric magnitude of Vega, we begin by measuring its apparent visual magnitude ($m_v$) and stellar parallax ($p$), which are found to be $m_v = 0.03$ and $p = 0.133$ arcsec. To find the distance to Vega in parsecs,

$$d = \frac{1}{0.133}$$

$$d = 7.5 \text{ parsecs.}$$

To find the absolute magnitude $M_v$, use the equation derived in Methods and Understandings 13.4 and solve for $M_v$.

$$M_v = m_v + 5 - 5\log d$$
$$M_v = 0.03 + 5 - 5\log 7.5$$
$$M_v = 0.65$$

The value of the bolometric correction is a function of the star's temperature. For Vega, which has an intrinsic temperature of about 10,000 K, the bolometric correction is −0.68.

$$M_{*bol} = M_v + BC$$
$$M_{*bol} = 0.65 - 0.68$$
$$M_{*bol} = -0.03$$

Since the luminosity of the Sun is unity ($L_\odot = 1$),

$$\log L_* = \frac{2}{5}(4.8 + 0.03)$$
$$\log L_* = 1.93$$
$$L_* = 90\, L_\odot.$$

The luminosity of Vega is 90 times that of the Sun.

and from this the absolute bolometric magnitude ($M_{bol} = M_v + BC$). The *bolometric correction* (*BC*) is defined as the difference between a star's bolometric magnitude and its visual magnitude. It is the same value for both apparent and absolute magnitudes since the distance between a star and the Sun does not change a star's spectral characteristics.

The luminosity of a star, $L_*$, may be found in terms of the Sun's luminosity as unity, $L_\odot = 1$. To determine the star's luminosity, we must first compute its absolute bolometric magnitude. The difference between the absolute bolometric magnitudes of the Sun and the star is a function of the ratio of their luminosities.

## Spectral Classification

The dark absorption lines and bands in the solar spectrum identified by Joseph von Fraunhofer were also observed in the spectra of stars. The discovery left little doubt that the Sun is also a star, and only one of uncounted billions found in our galaxy. Indeed, stellar spectra show the same abundances of hydrogen and helium in the stars as well as the Sun.

But Fraunhofer and, later, in 1863, the astronomer Angelo Secchi discov-ered differences in the appearances of the spectral lines. Secchi devised a classification scheme in which class I and II represented spectra with very strong absorption in the Balmer series of hydrogen; class III contained spectra of sunlike stars; and class IV consisted of spectra with prominent molecular bands.

## The Harvard Spectral Classification

In 1890, Edward C. Pickering and Williamina P. Fleming at Harvard Observatory classified the stars using capital letters from A to Q. The letter A designated the stellar spectra showing maximum strength of the hydrogen absorption lines. Later, Annie Jump Cannon modified the series to one that, in the 1920s, was recognized as a temperature sequence. The hottest stars O and B were placed before A, while other letters were omitted entirely. In order of decreasing temperature, the final sequence became O B A F G K M. The sequence can be remembered through the mnemonic, "Oh, Be A Fine Girl/Guy, Kiss Me."

Between 1911 and 1914, Cannon completed the Harvard classification by identifying the spectra of 225,300 stars.

Each category in the series was further subdivided by numbers from 0 to 9; an A5 star is between A0 and F0; a G0 star has a higher temperature than a G9 star. The Sun is classified as a G2 star. The spectral system was published in nine volumes as the *Henry Draper Catalogue* (1915–1924). By 1948, a total of 350,000 stellar spectra were represented.

During the time Cannon was compiling the Harvard classification system, research in the theory of stellar absorption lines was underway. An important advance took place in 1913 when absorption and emission of energy within an atom were explained by means of the Bohr model. In the 1920s, astronomers showed that ionization and excitation taking place within atoms were dependent upon temperature and pressure in the atmospheres of the Sun and stars (fig. 13.10).

## Stellar Temperatures and Color Index

The elements present in stellar atmospheres exhibit various degrees of ionization at different temperatures. (A singly ionized atom has lost one of its electrons; a doubly ionized atom has lost

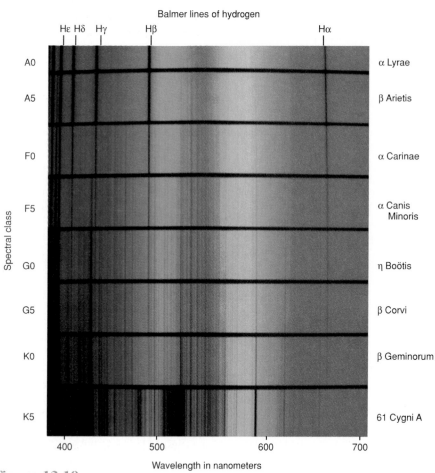

Balmer lines of hydrogen

Hε Hδ Hγ   Hβ                    Hα

A0                                        α Lyrae

A5                                        β Arietis

F0                                        α Carinae

F5                                        α Canis
                                          Minoris

G0                                        η Boötis

G5                                        β Corvi

K0                                        β Geminorum

K5                                        61 Cygni A

400        500        600        700

Wavelength in nanometers

**figure 13.10**

The spectra of several stars and their classification according to temperature. The elements present in a star's atmosphere show various degrees of ionization at different temperatures.

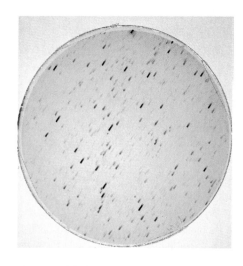

**figure 13.11**

An objective-prism spectrogram. A prism placed in front of the objective lens of a telescope produces spectra of many stars in one photographic exposure. These spectra do not have much detail, but they can be used to roughly classify stars.

two.) The strength of each absorption line is dependent upon the excitation-ionization temperature of each element. A helium atom is ionized at extremely high temperatures. Singly ionized helium (He II) exists in the stars of spectral type 0 in the Harvard classification. These are blue-white stars of very high photospheric temperature (50,000 K). In addition to ionized helium that identifies the stars' spectral type, the hydrogen Balmer lines appear less prominent than in cooler stars. Spectral type B stars are also blue-white in color, at temperatures of about 20,000 K. Their spectra are characterized by lines of neutral helium (He I), and ionized silicon and magnesium. The hydrogen Balmer lines gradually increase in strength from spectral types B0 to B9. White A-type stars are at temperatures of about 11,000 K, and their spectra are dominated by the Balmer lines. Lines of singly ionized silicon and magnesium are present. Type F are yellow-white stars at

7000 to 8000 K; they have spectra defined by lines of singly ionized calcium. Balmer lines appear weaker than those found in A stars. The spectra of G stars are characterized by a great number of metallic lines; temperatures are about 6000 K. Type K stars are orange (5000 K) with intense metallic lines and the beginning of molecular bands. Red stars of spectral type M are identified by lines of neutral metals and molecular bands of titanium oxide. Temperatures reach about 3000 K (see figs. 13.10 and 13.11).

Stellar temperatures may be expressed in terms of **color index,** the difference between a star's blue ($B$) and visual ($V$) magnitudes (fig. 13.8). Color index ($B - V$) is devised so that a spectral type A0 star has a color index of 0.00. Blue-white stars have negative color indices; yellow, orange, and red stars have positive values. Color index is always defined as the difference between the magnitude of shorter wave-

length and the magnitude of longer wavelength: for example, ultraviolet minus blue ($U - B$) or blue minus visual ($B - V$).

According to Wien's displacement law, the peak wavelength of a star's thermal radiation is inversely proportional to its absolute temperature; the wavelength of maximum intensity is shifted to the shorter wavelengths for stars of higher temperature. Thus in this UBV system high-temperature stars have brighter blue magnitudes ($B$) than visual magnitudes ($V$). The spectral type B star Rigel has a blue magnitude $B = +0.09$, a visual magnitude $V = +0.12$, and color index ($B - V$) = $-0.03$. A star of lower temperature radiates more intensely in the longer wavelengths and will appear brighter in visual magnitude. For the K-type star Aldebaran, $B = +2.39$, $V = +0.85$, and color index is equal to $+1.54$. High-temperature stars are identified by negative color indices; cooler stars have positive color indices. White stars such as Vega ($B = +0.03$, $V = +0.03$), are equally bright in blue and visual magnitudes and have color indices equal to zero.

## The Hertzsprung–Russell Diagram

Research on the distribution of spectral classes and intrinsic brightness was ad-

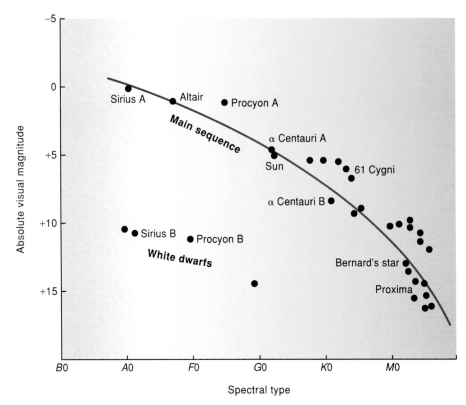

**figure 13.12**

A graph of the absolute magnitudes and spectral classes of stars within five parsecs of the Sun.

vanced by Hertzsprung in 1905 through a systematic study of stars to within 10 parsecs of the Sun. He graphed absolute magnitudes against spectral types and found that the majority of the nearest stars followed a sequence of decreasing luminosity and temperature from spectral types A through M. Near the Sun, there are no stars intrinsically brighter than type A.

In figure 13.12, each point represents one of the stars nearest to the Sun listed in appendix E.1. Four stars, Alpha Centauri A, Sirius A, Procyon A, and Altair, are more luminous than the Sun. The remaining stars are cooler G, K, and M stars. Our Sun ranks as one of the more luminous stars in its immediate neighborhood. More than half are spectral type M; the luminous O and B stars are very rare and not found in the Sun's vicinity.

The large percentage of nearby M stars of low luminosity seems to contradict observation. There are type G (Capella), K (Pollux), and M (Antares) stars that are more distant than 10 parsecs yet appear much brighter than nearby stars of the same spectral class;

the nearest M stars, for example, are telescopic objects. This observational incompatibility suggests that there are highly luminous giant stars of spectral class G through M in addition to dwarf stars.

In 1913, Henry Norris Russell extended the investigation by following procedures he and Ejnar Hertzsprung developed independently. The results were graphed as the Hertzsprung-Russell (H-R) diagram, which depicts each star in terms of its absolute magnitude and spectral class (fig. 13.13).

## Sequences of Stars

On the **H-R diagram,** the magnitude scale extends from −10 for the most luminous stars down to +15 for the least luminous stars. Spectral class is measured horizontally from left to right from the hottest O stars to the coolest M stars. The H-R diagram confirms the existence of branches containing separate sequences of stars. Most stars belong to the **main sequence,** which includes O-type **blue giant stars** down to intrinsically faint M-type **red dwarf stars.** To

find the position of the Sun on the diagram, move horizontally from +5 on the absolute magnitude scale and vertically from spectral class G2. The Sun is on the main sequence where the lines meet. All main-sequence stars are classified as dwarfs and subdwarfs to distinguish them from the more luminous giant and subgiant stars (see the following section on Morgan-Keenan luminosity classes).

The **giant branch** of stars extends from above the center of the main sequence to the upper right. In contrast to lower main-sequence stars, the stars represented on the giant branch increase in luminosity as their temperatures decrease. Above the giants are **supergiant stars** of higher luminosity than members of the giant branch.

Stars of similar spectral class on the giant branch and the main sequence have the same temperature and surface brightness per unit area. If the stars on the giant branch are more luminous, they must also be greater in diameter. You can visualize the sizes of *red giants* and *red supergiants* if you mentally place them in the center of the solar system. Betelgeuse would be twice as large as the orbit of Mars (fig. 13.14). Other supergiants would extend beyond the orbits of Jupiter and Saturn. By contrast, main-sequence red dwarfs are smaller than the Sun.

A grouping in the lower left region of the H-R diagram contains stars many times fainter than main-sequence stars of the same color. Called **white dwarf stars,** they are hot stars of average absolute magnitude of only +12. No larger than a planet, white dwarfs have twice the photospheric temperature of the Sun but only a fraction of the Sun's intrinsic brightness.

## The Morgan-Keenan Luminosity Classes

The atmosphere of a star on the giant branch is significantly less dense than that of a main-sequence star of the same spectral class. The low density causes certain lines to appear narrower and brighter in the spectra of giant stars. Thus measuring strengths and widths of spectral lines provides a way to distinguish

*Brightness = size*

Absolute visual magnitude

bright

dim

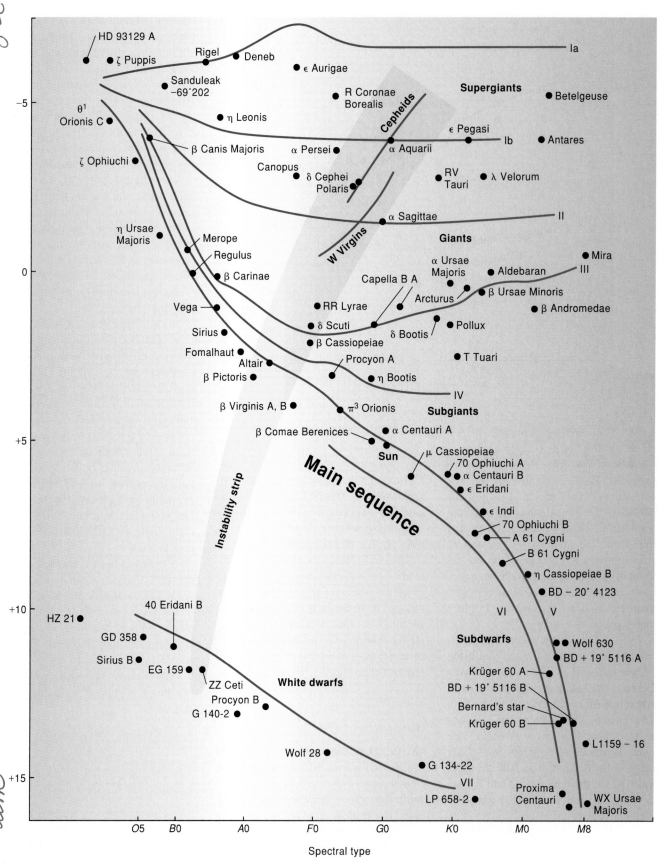

HD 93129 A
ζ Puppis
Rigel
Deneb
ε Aurigae
Sanduleak –69°202
R Coronae Borealis
**Supergiants**
Betelgeuse
θ¹ Orionis C
η Leonis
ε Pegasi
Ib
Antares
ζ Ophiuchi
β Canis Majoris
α Persei
α Aquarii
Canopus
δ Cephei
Polaris
RV Tauri
λ Velorum
η Ursae Majoris
Merope
α Sagittae
II
Regulus
**Giants**
Mira
β Carinae
α Ursae Majoris
Aldebaran
III
Capella B A
β Ursae Minoris
Vega
Arcturus
β Andromedae
RR Lyrae
δ Scuti
δ Bootis
Pollux
Sirius
β Cassiopeiae
Fomalhaut
T Tuari
Altair
Procyon A
β Pictoris
η Bootis
IV
β Virginis A, B
π³ Orionis
**Subgiants**
β Comae Berenices
α Centauri A
**Main sequence**
**Sun**
μ Cassiopeiae
70 Ophiuchi A
α Centauri B
ε Eridani
ε Indi
70 Ophiuchi B
A 61 Cygni
B 61 Cygni
η Cassiopeiae B
BD – 20° 4123
VI
V
HZ 21
40 Eridani B
**Subdwarfs**
Wolf 630
GD 358
BD + 19° 5116 A
Sirius B
Krüger 60 A
EG 159
BD + 19° 5116 B
ZZ Ceti
**White dwarfs**
Bernard's star
Procyon B
Krüger 60 B
G 140-2
L1159 – 16
Wolf 28
G 134-22
VII
Proxima Centauri
WX Ursae Majoris
LP 658-2

Instability strip
Cepheids
W Virgins

Spectral type

**figure 13.13**
The Hertzsprung-Russell (H-R) diagram.

*temperature*

hi

lo

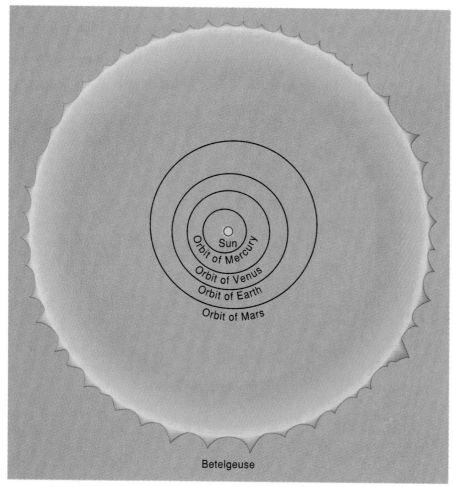

**figure 13.14**

The red supergiant star Betelgeuse in the constellation Orion, compared in size to the orbits of the terrestrial planets. The radius of the star is equal to 800 solar radii.

## T a b l e   1 3 . 4

### the M–K system

| Luminosity Class | Star |
| --- | --- |
| Ia: Supergiants | (Rigel, Deneb) |
| Ib: Supergiants | (Canopus) |
| II: Bright giants | (Alpha Sagittae) |
| III: Giants | (Capella, Aldebaran) |
| IV: Subgiants | (Procyon) |
| V: Main-sequence dwarfs | (Altair, Sun) |
| VI: Main-sequence subdwarfs | (Kruger 60) |
| VII: White dwarfs | (Sirius B, Procyon B) |

between stars of similar temperature but different luminosity.

In the late 1930s, Morgan, Keenan, and Kellman added a second dimension to spectral classification by grouping stars according to luminosity differences. Stellar temperatures follow the spectral classes as on the H-R diagram, while **luminosity classes** are indicated by Roman numerals (see fig. 13.15). In this M-K system, the most luminous stars in each spectral class are categorized as luminosity class I stars; main-sequence stars are luminosity class V (see table 13.4).

Earlier in the chapter, we described how distances to nearer stars are computed by the trigonometric parallax method. The correlation between luminosity and spectral type provides a way to determine absolute magnitudes of stars beyond 100 parsecs. Once absolute magnitude is known and apparent magnitude is measured, stellar parallax and distance can be computed (see Methods and Understandings 13.4).

## Stars of Varying Brightness

Most of the stars described so far emit energy consistently and remain unchanged in magnitude. However, there are others designated as *variable stars* that fluctuate from maximum to minimum brightness in a given period of time. They are grouped into two general categories: **intrinsic variable stars,** in which variability is caused by internal changes; and **eclipsing variable stars,** with light variations due to stars eclipsing one another in a binary system.

Variable stars are designated by Roman letters followed by the possessive name of the constellation where the star is found. The first variable star discovered in a constellation is assigned the capital letter R, the second S, and so forth to Z; then RR, RS, . . . to ZZ. After ZZ, the stars are named AA, AB, . . . AZ; BB, BC, . . . BZ; and finally to QZ for a total of 334 combinations. If more stars are discovered they are designated V and numbered consecutively beginning with V335. Examples include RR Lyrae, T Orionis, and V711 Tauri. Some prominent variables have proper names or Greek letter identification: for example, Algol (β Persei), δ Cephei, Mira (o Ceti). Variables are also identified by the prototype star in each class. Thus cepheid variable stars have characteristics of their namesake, δ Cephei.

Intrinsic variable stars are grouped into classes. *Periodic variables* pulsate with clocklike regularity. *Irregular, semiregular,* and *long-period variables* lack uniformity in their periods. When plotted on the H-R diagram, the periodic

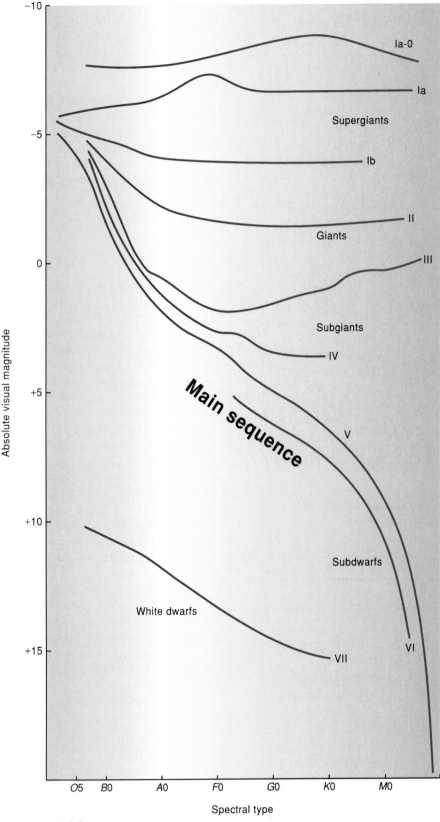

**figure 13.15**

The Morgan-Keenan luminosity classes are designated by Roman numerals.

variables occupy a vertical region called the *instability strip.* The others are found among the giant stars in the upper right region of the diagram (refer to figure 13.13).

## Types of Variable Stars

The majority of the stars found on the instability strip are **cepheid variable stars.** They are highly luminous stars that have periods ranging from 1 to 70 days. The prototype for the group, δ Cephei, was identified as a periodic variable by John Goodricke in 1784. They are yellow giant stars of spectral class F at maximum brightness; they pass to G and K at minimum brightness. These stars have luminosities between 300 to 40,000 $L_\odot$ and surface temperatures about $T_\odot$ . Another group, called **RR Lyrae variable stars**, includes luminous stars of spectral class A with periods from a few hours to 1.5 days.

Variable stars are studied by means of a **light curve,** a graph of the change in the star's magnitude with respect to time. Figure 13.16 graphs the light curve of δ Cephei. Apparent magnitude is represented by the vertical scale, while time is plotted on the horizontal scale. Increasing brightness is plotted from bottom to top on the vertical scale, and elapsed time (usually measured in days) from left to right. The difference in magnitude between maximum and minimum is the amplitude of the curve. The period of the star is defined as the interval between two successive maxima of light variation.

Let us follow the changes in magnitude and spectral class of δ Cephei for a complete cycle. The time of maximum brightness is marked 0.0 on the horizontal time scale, measured in divisions of the period called *phase*. One phase represents one cycle from maximum back to maximum brightness. From maximum there is a gradual decline in brightness until minimum is reached in about four days. After minimum, the light curve shows a more rapid rise to maximum again. The cycle is completed in a period of 5.37 days. During this time the

## Distances Derived from Luminosity Criteria

Distances greater than 100 parsecs can be obtained from a star's apparent and absolute magnitudes by the method of *spectroscopic parallax*. Earlier we found that the relationship between the difference in magnitude and brightness ratio of two stars is

$$\frac{b_1}{b_2} = 10^{2/5\,(m_2 - m_1)}.$$

Instead of two stars, consider one star where $M$ and $B$ represent the absolute magnitude and brightness at 10 parsecs; and $m$ and $b$ the apparent magnitude and brightness at $d$, the actual distance from the Sun.

$$\frac{B}{b} = 10^{2/5\,(m - M)}$$

According to the inverse square law, brightness is inversely proportional to the square of the distance. Therefore,

$$\frac{B}{b} = (d\,/\,10)^2.$$

Substituting terms,

$$\left(\frac{d}{10}\right)^2 = 10^{2/5\,(m - M)}$$

$$\left(\frac{d}{10}\right) = 10^{1/5\,(m - M)}$$

$$\log d = \frac{5 + m - M}{5}.$$

*Example.* If a star has an apparent magnitude of +11 and an absolute magnitude equal to +1, find the distance.

$$\log d = \frac{5 + 11 - 1}{5} = 3$$

$$d = 10^3 \text{ or } 1000 \text{ parsecs}$$

The absolute magnitude of a star can be determined beyond 100 parsecs from its spectral type or color index in the H-R diagram. Refer to figure 13.14.

*Example.* A sixth-magnitude, spectral class B star is plotted on the H-R diagram and is found to have −4.0 absolute magnitude. How far is the star from the Sun?

$$\log d = \frac{5 + 6 - (-4)}{5} = 3$$

$$d = 10^3 \text{ or } 1000 \text{ parsecs}.$$

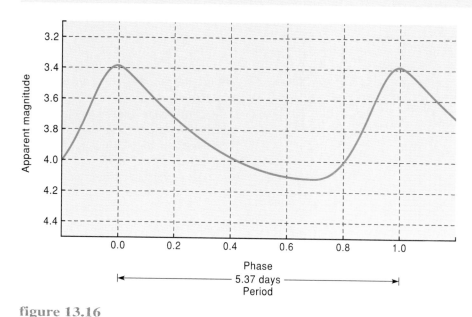

### figure 13.16

The light curve of δ Cephei.

Source: Data from J. A. Mattei, "Observations from the AAVSO International Data Base," private communication, 1993.

magnitudes and periods range from 30 to 1000 days. The subtype RV Tauri stars have light curves with a deep primary minimum followed by a more shallow secondary minimum. The period is measured as the interval between two successive primary mimima. **Mira variable stars** are long-period pulsating stars that vary several magnitudes from maximum to minimum. Omicron Ceti, or Mira, the prototype, varies from a minimum of 8th to 10th magnitude to a maximum between 2nd and 5th magnitude in a period of about 330 days.

### The Period-Luminosity Relation

The **period-luminosity relation** between the light variations and luminosities of cepheid stars was discovered by Henrietta Leavitt in 1908 while studying variable stars in the Magellanic Clouds. The Magellanic Clouds are the nearest galaxies to our Milky Way Galaxy, but far enough away for their stars to be considered equidistant from the Sun (fig. 13.17).

Leavitt graphed the stars and found that the periods of variability depended upon the apparent magnitudes; stars with longer

star changes its spectral class from F5 at maximum to G2 at minimum brightness.

Other pulsating stars have less-defined periods and show long-term cyclic variation. Irregular variables are characterized by changes in light amplitude from one period to the next. There are several groups distinguished as semiregular variables—giant and supergiant stars that have an appreciable periodicity accompanied by irregularities in brightness. Amplitudes do not exceed one or two

**figure 13.17**

*a.* The Small Magellanic Cloud and *b.* Large Magellanic Cloud. The variable stars in these nearby galaxies led to discovery of the period-luminosity relation.

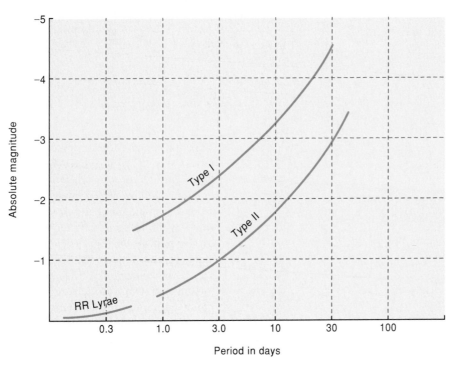

**figure 13.18**

The period-luminosity relation for population I and population II cepheid variable stars.
Source: Data from the American Association of Variable Star Observers.

Type II cepheids are distinguished from classical cepheids by differences in their light curves and spectra. A Type II variable star has a mass about equal to that of the Sun while Type I stars range between 3–9 solar masses. Moreover, Type II cepheids are found in the galactic disk among the older stars as well as in globular clusters, and in the halo of old stars surrounding the central bulge of our stellar system. The location of Type II cepheids shows that they are among the oldest stars in the Galaxy.

The total luminosity of a star is a function of its radius and surface temperature. Moreover, the mean density (mass per unit of volume) of a variable star will determine its period of pulsation. High-density stars will pulsate in shorter periods than low-density stars. From this we can conclude that giant stars will have the highest luminosities and the longest periods. In the case of cepheid stars, the differences in mass, luminosity, temperature, density, and age mean that a distinct period-luminosity law applies to each type. For any given period of oscillation, a Type I cepheid will be brighter than a Type II cepheid (fig. 13.18).

The distances to the stars may be computed from this important relationship. When the period of a cepheid is known, its absolute magnitude can be found from the period-luminosity relation. The apparent magnitude is observed and the distance computed from the distance modulus.

The period-luminosity relation makes it possible to measure objects located *kiloparsecs* (kpc), or thousands of parsecs, away in space. Pulsating stars are sufficiently luminous to be observed at vast distances. In later chapters, the distance to the center of our galaxy will be found by observing variable stars in globular clusters. Distances to the nearer galaxies are measured in the same way. After corrections, the distance modulus of the Small Magellanic Cloud is found to be about 18.9 and its distance approximately 60 kpc.

periods have brighter apparent magnitudes than stars with shorter periods. Later, Harlow Shapley calibrated the period-luminosity relation to an absolute magnitude scale derived from the observed motions of relatively nearby cepheids in the central plane of our galaxy.

There are two populations of cepheid stars: classical, or *Type I cepheids* (similar to δ Cephei), and *Type II cepheids,* which include W Virginis, BL Herculis, and RV Tauri stars. Classical cepheids are comparatively young stars found in the disk and the spiral arms of the Galaxy.

SKY WATCHERS 13.1

## observing variable stars

One of the more important and satisfying activities for Sky Watchers is the observation of variable stars. There are thousands of variables of all classes in need of constant surveillance over long periods of time. The selection of stars will depend upon the observer's experience, optical equipment available, and geographic location.

The beginner should select a long-period variable with an amplitude of one or more magnitudes. Owing to the range from maximum to minimum, the change in magnitude is more pronounced. Also, long-period variables change brightness slowly and require only weekly observations to establish a light curve.

Your first task will be to select a long-period variable. Star charts are available that distinguish variable stars from others in a given constellation. On the charts, a variable star may be shown as an open circle. Generally, a variable star is depicted by a dot enclosed in a circle, indicating the star's minimum and maximum magnitude. Select several stars in the same field to serve as comparison stars in estimating the changes in magnitude of the variable.

As the variable star changes brightness, compare its magnitude with one of the selected comparison stars. Keep an observing notebook and enter the date and time of observation, estimated magnitude of the variable, and name and magnitude of the comparison star. Include in your notebook any other data of interest and significance: sky condition, phase of the Moon, or event such as a bright meteor. Plot a light curve and graph your results. Let each point on the light curve represent one night of observation.

You might begin by observing the most famous long-period variable, Mira, "the Wonderful." Mira was discovered to be a variable by Johannes Fabricus in 1596. The star is elusive because most of the time it is too faint to be seen. Mira remains at maximum for about 10 days, slowly fades to minimum in about 240 days, and returns to maximum again in about 90 days. Observe the star in a low-power telescope or binoculars for several months before and after maximum. Mira is located in the constellation Cetus about seven degrees southeast of Al Rischa, the third-magnitude star in Pisces (fig. 13.19).

Fortunately, variable stars can be monitored with small telescopes and binoculars. Thus many amateur astronomers are dedicated observers and members of several variable-star organizations. Foremost is the American Association of Variable Star Observers, which was organized in 1911 by Edward C.

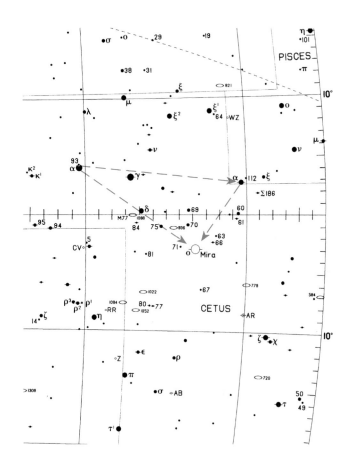

### figure 13.19

The long-period variable star Mira (Omicron Ceti) forms a triangle with Menkar (Alpha Ceti) and Al Rischa (Alpha Piscium).
*From Norton's 2000.0 Star Atlas and Reference Handbook*, 18th ed. Copyright © 1991 Longman Group UK Ltd. Reprinted by permission.

Pickering of Harvard Observatory and amateur astronomer William T. Olcott. Through the AAVSO, data is collected annually for thousands of stars and made available to professional astronomers. Variable-star observing is the most successful example of amateur-professional cooperation in astronomy.

## SUMMARY

Distances to the nearest stars are measured by the parallactic method. As the Earth revolves, the nearest stars follow elliptical paths in a period of one year. Stellar parallax defines the angle formed by the radius of the Earth's orbit observed at a given star's distance. Parallax decreases with distance so that remote stars have smaller displacements than nearer stars. Distances to the stars are measured in light-years and parsecs.

The measure of a star's observed brightness is called apparent magnitude. For over 2000 years, naked-eye stars have been grouped into six categories based upon brightness estimates. Today, magnitudes are measured quantitatively by Pogson's scale. The brightness perceived by the eye is called visual magnitude; photographic magnitude is derived from blue-sensitive photographic plates. In the UBV system, filters allow magnitude measurements in different colors. Color index is the difference between a star's magnitudes measured in two spectral bands ($U - B$; $B - V$).

Absolute magnitude is the apparent magnitude a star would have if it were at a distance of 10 parsecs. The difference between apparent and absolute magnitudes of each star defines the distance modulus ($m - M$). A star's luminosity is the rate at which a quantity of

the stars around us

257

energy is emitted per second. Absolute magnitude and luminosity measure the intrinsic brightness of stars.

At Harvard Observatory, stars were grouped into spectral types from A to Q according to the intensity of the hydrogen Balmer series and other characteristic lines and bands. From this evolved the Harvard spectral series, O, B, A, F, G, K, M, representing stars on a scale from high to low temperatures.

The Hertzsprung-Russell diagram is a graphic representation of stellar classification according to spectral type and absolute magnitude. Most stars plotted on the H-R diagram are on the main sequence from upper left to lower right. Other groups contain giant stars and a limited number of red supergiants. On the diagram, white dwarfs are found in the lower left.

Stars are classified according to luminosity in the Morgan-Keenan system. Temperature follows the Harvard classification while luminosity values are indicated by Roman numerals.

Variable stars change brightness from maximum to minimum in a given period of time. There are two main groups: intrinsic variables that change brightness because of internal conditions, and eclipsing variables where brightness changes when one star in a binary system blocks the light of the second component. A variable star is studied by means of its light curve, which depicts changes in magnitude with respect to time.

Intrinsic variables are grouped as periodic, irregular, semiregular, and long-period variables. There is a relationship between the light variation and luminosities of cepheid stars; the longer the period, the greater the luminosity. This period-luminosity relation permits cepheid stars to serve as standard candles to measure distances to remote star clusters and galaxies.

## KEY TERMS

| | |
|---|---|
| absolute magnitude (M) | luminosity classes |
| apparent magnitude (m) | main sequence |
| blue giant stars | Mira variable stars |
| bolometric magnitude | parallax |
| cepheid variable stars | parsec |
| color index $(B - V)$ | period-luminosity relation |
| distance modulus $(m - M)$ | red dwarf star |
| eclipsing variable stars | RR Lyrae variable stars |
| giant branch | stellar parallax |
| H-R diagram | supergiant stars |
| intrinsic variable stars | UBV system |
| inverse square law | white dwarf stars |
| light curve | |

## PROBLEMS

1. There are two apparent displacements in the positions of stars caused by the Earth's revolution. Describe how each provides proof of the Copernican system.

2. Consider two stars on the H-R diagram. One is an A2V star; the other an A2III star. Which star is more luminous? Explain.

3. The hydrogen Balmer lines do not have the same intensity or prominence in all stellar spectra. Why?

4. How much brighter is a first-magnitude star than a third-magnitude star? A first-magnitude star and a twelfth-magnitude star?

5. Two stars are at the same distance from the Sun. Star A has an apparent magnitude $m = +8$; star B has $m = +5$. Which star is brighter? By how much? Explain.

6. The Sun has an absolute magnitude $M = +5$. What would the apparent magnitude of the Sun be if observed from 100 parsecs?

7. Explain why the majority of the brightest stars in the sky are not among the nearest to the Sun.

8. How are variable stars used as distance indicators?

9. On the period-luminosity graph, how are classical Type I cepheids distinguished from Type II cepheids?

10. Betelgeuse, the brightest star in the constellation Orion, has a color index $C.I. = +1.85$; Rigel, the second brightest, has a $C.I. = -0.03$. Which star has a higher surface temperature?

11. An A0V star has an apparent magnitude, $m = +3$. What is its distance?

12. Find the distance to a star with a parallax of 0.1 arc second.

13. What is the distance and absolute magnitude of a star if its apparent magnitude $m = +7.0$ and its parallax is 0.004 arc second?

14. What is the ratio of brightness between the star in problem 13 and the Sun? (Let the Sun's absolute magnitude $M = +5$.)

15. What are the luminosity and spectral classes of a star with a color index $C.I. = +1.85$ if its parallax is 0.002 arc second and apparent visual magnitude $m = 1.5$?

16. If a classical cepheid star has a period of 10 days and an apparent magnitude $m = 11$, what is the distance?

17. Determine the luminosity classes of the stars listed below.

| Star | Spectral Class | M |
|---|---|---|
| 1 | G5 | +5.0 |
| 2 | F0 | +12.0 |
| 3 | K5 | 0.0 |
| 4 | A7 | −2.5 |
| 5 | A0 | −5.0 |

## REFERENCES

Bidelman, W. P. 1969. "Stellar Spectra and Spectral Types" and "Two-Dimensional Spectral Classification." In *Stellar Astronomy,* vol. 1, edited by Hong-Yee Chiu, Robert L. Warasila, and John L. Remo. New York: Gordon and Breach Science Publishers.

Harrington, Robert S., and Betty J. Harrington. 1987. Barnard's Star: A Status Report on an Intriguing Neighbor. *Mercury* (Astronomical Society of the Pacific) 14, no. 3 (May/June).

Henden, Arne A., and Ronald H. Kaitchuck. 1990. *Astronomical Photometry.* Richmond, Va.: Willmann-Bell, Inc.

Kaler, James B. 1986. Cousins of Our Sun: The G Stars. *Sky and Telescope* 72, no. 5 (November).

———. 1986. The K Stars: Orange Giants and White Dwarfs. *Sky and Telescope* 72, no. 2 (August).

———. 1986. M Stars: Supergiants to Dwarfs. *Sky and Telescope* 71, no. 5 (May).

———. 1987. The B Stars: Beacons of the Skies. *Sky and Telescope* 74, no. 2 (August).

———. 1987. The Spectacular O Stars. *Sky and Telescope* 74, no. 5 (November).

———. 1987. The Temperate F Stars. *Sky and Telescope* 73, no. 2 (February).

———. 1987. White Sirian Stars: *Sky and Telescope* 73, no.5 (May).

———. 1988. Journeys on the H-R Diagram. *Sky and Telescope* 75, no. 5 (May).

Keenan, P. C., and W. W. Morgan. 1951. "Classification of Stellar Spectra." In *Astrophysics,* edited by J. A. Hynek. New York: McGraw-Hill Book Company.

Levy, David. 1989. *Observing Variable Stars: A Guide for the Beginner.* Cambridge: Cambridge University Press.

Lovi, George. 1985. Rambling Through January Skies. *Sky and Telescope* 69, no. 1 (January).

Mattei, Janet Akyuz. 1986. "Visual Observing of Variable Stars." In *The Study of Variable Stars Using Small Telescopes,* edited by John R. Percy. Cambridge: Cambridge University Press.

MacRobert, Alan M. 1988. Six Million Variable Star Estimates. *Sky and Telescope* 76, no. 5 (November).

Motz, Lloyd, and Anneta Duveen. 1966. *Essentials of Astronomy.* Belmont, Mass.: Wadsworth Publishing Company.

Payne-Gaspochkin, Cecilia. 1951. "The Intrinsic Variable Stars." In *Astrophysics,* edited by J. A. Hynek. New York: McGraw-Hill Book Company.

Smith, Elske v. P., and Kenneth C. Jacobs. 1989. *Introductory Astronomy and Astrophysics,* Philadelphia: W.B. Saunders Company.

Soderblom, David R. 1987. The Alpha Centauri System. *Mercury* 16, no. 5 (September/October).

Strohmeir, W. 1972. *Variable Stars.* Oxford: Pergamon Press.

Tucker, Wallace, and Karen Tucker. 1982. Dwarf Stars: Red, Brown, and Black. *Mercury* 11, no. 3 (May/June).

Welther, Barbara. 1984. Annie Jump Cannon: Classifier of the Stars. *Mercury* 13, no. 1 (January/February).

chapter

14

binary stars, clusters, and stellar associations

The open cluster M16 and the Eagle nebula in
the constellation Serpens.

**B**illions of stars move endlessly in the Galaxy as members of various stellar aggregations. Some are double stars in binary systems that revolve about a common center of mass. Many belong to multiple systems that contain three or more components held in place by their mutual gravitational attraction. Another category, star clusters, may consist of a few scattered stars or up to as many as hundreds of thousands in an assemblage as large as 100 parsecs in diameter. Although the stars in a cluster are more widely separated than members of a binary system, they are of common origin and have the same velocity and direction. A stellar association is a sparsely populated group of stars separated by distances of up to 100 or more parsecs. Associations have fewer stars than clusters and are eventually dispersed by their random motion and galactic rotation.

## Binary and Multiple-Star Systems

Investigations show that **binary stars** are commonplace and represent more than half of the total stellar population. They are not to be confused with the so-called *optical double stars* that seem to be close pairs but are simply two stars at different distances in the same line of sight. Only *physical double stars* are true binaries in which each star is held in orbit around the other by the gravitational influence of the other component. Moreover, most members of binary systems are telescopic objects and cannot be separated into individual stars by the unaided eye. In the northern hemisphere, the most familiar optical double is formed by two stars in the middle of the handle of the Big Dipper. The brighter second-magnitude star, Mizar, is located about 23 parsecs from the Sun. Alcor, the second and fainter fifth-magnitude star, is at a distance of 26 parsecs. Mizar and Alcor also happen to be members of a true binary system.

Physical double stars are grouped as **visual, astrometric, spectroscopic,** and **eclipsing binary stars.** When the angular distance between two stars is more than 0.15 arc seconds, the components can be resolved in a telescope as a visual binary. Generally the linear distance separating the stars varies from about 5 AU to larger than Pluto's orbit; periods of revolution range from a few years to many centuries. As a rule, the orbits of visual binaries are elliptical and have greater eccentricities than the orbits of the planets in the solar system.

Astrometric binary stars are detected by the irregular motion of a visible component owing to the gravitational pull of an unseen companion. Astrometric binaries are among the nearest stars to the Sun.

Spectroscopic binaries cannot be resolved visually because the angular distance between the stars is less than 0.15 arc seconds. Such stars may be distinguished as binaries if their orbits are sufficiently inclined to the plane of the sky. The stars alternately approach and recede from the Earth as they revolve about a common center of mass. The motion produces a Doppler effect, which is detected as a periodic shift of the stellar spectral lines toward the blue and red portions of the spectrum. Spectroscopic binaries revolve in nearly circular orbits in periods ranging from a few hours to several years.

If the orbital plane of a binary system lies in the line of sight or nearly so, the revolving stars will eclipse each other and produce light variations. Eclipsing binaries, or eclipsing variable stars, are studied photometrically by means of light curves (see chapter 13).

### Visual Binary Stars

The first visual binary star to be discovered, Mizar, was found in 1650 by G. B. Riccioli. In the telescope, Mizar is resolved into two stars, Mizar A and Mizar B, separated by an angular distance of 14.5 arc seconds. It is customary to designate the brightest member in a binary system as the A or **primary star,** and the second brightest as the B or **second-**

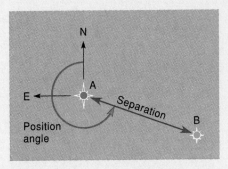

**figure 14.1**
The location of the secondary component B in a visual binary system relative to the primary star A is determined by the separation and position angle.

**ary star.** The secondary is also called the **companion star.**

Other binary stars were discovered, but for many years astronomers continued to believe these stars to be optical pairs separated by vast distances. In fact, by the late 1770s Herschel attempted to use double stars to detect their parallactic displacement. He reasoned that, as the Earth revolved, the nearer star would show a greater parallax and thereby provide a measure of its distance.

By 1803, Herschel's careful measurements confirmed that double stars are binaries and the long-term changes in their positions are due to orbital motion. They represent a physical system in which the motion of the secondary star is described as a relative ellipse about the primary star situated at a focal point of the elliptical orbit. Today, many thousands of binary stars have been catalogued and orbits have been determined for about 800 stars.

### Orbits of Visual Binary Stars

The determination of visual binary orbits requires a coordinate system projected onto the sky from which the changing positions of the stars can be measured. Consider two stars of unequal brightness; the brighter component serves as the primary and the fainter star as the secondary. (If the stars are of equal brightness, the observer who discovers the binary determines which star shall be designated as the primary.) Figure 14.1 shows the relative positions of the com-

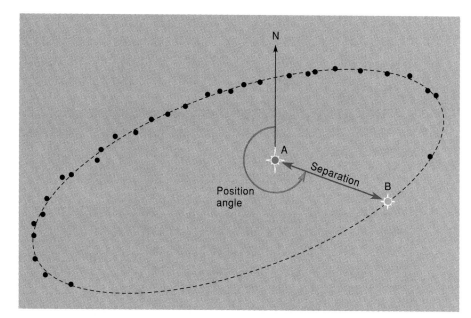

**figure 14.2**

The apparent orbit in a visual binary system is found by plotting the position of the secondary star during its period of revolution. The orbit is drawn after the secondary star has advanced enough for a satisfactory ellipse to be constructed.

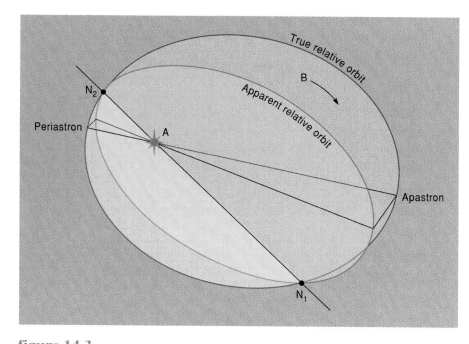

**figure 14.3**

The relationship between the apparent and true relative orbits of a binary system. The points $N_1$ and $N_2$ represent the ascending and descending nodes. The primary star A is on the line of nodes.

ponents projected to the plane of the sky in a polar coordinate system. The primary star, A, is at the point of origin. The angular distance between star A and the secondary star B is called the **separation.** The angle measured from north in an easterly direction to star B is the **position angle** of the secondary star B

relative to its primary, star A. An estimate of the shape of the orbit can be made after a sufficient number of positions have been obtained along the course of the companion star's **apparent relative orbit** (fig. 14.2).

Since the time of their discovery, binaries have been measured with filar mi-

crometers (see chapter 5). The instrument is rotated around the optical axis until the stars are aligned with the fixed thread in the reticle. The number of arc degrees turned represents the position angle of the secondary star. The angular separation is measured by bringing the movable thread to star B; the displacement is read on the graduated micrometer scale.

Today, photographic techniques supplement the programs carried out with micrometers. Multiple-exposure photographs are superior to visual observations where stars are separated by more than two arc seconds. Moreover, a photographic plate is a permanent record that can be studied by other astronomers, while a micrometer reading represents one recording made by a single observer. However, astronomers continue to use micrometers to observe close binaries.

## Determining the Orbits of Visual Binary Stars

One purpose of observing binary stars is to compute their orbits and from this find their masses. The mass of a binary system is determined from the semimajor axis and period of the companion stars's relative orbit. The orbit of the secondary star in its own plane is called the **true relative orbit.** We can consider the true orbit of the secondary star to be an ellipse with the primary star located at one focal point. The secondary star sweeps out equal areas as it revolves about the primary star. The apparent ellipse that results from plotting the positions of the companion star represents the true relative orbit of the star projected onto the plane of the sky (figs. 14.2 and 14.3). Generally, the true orbit is inclined to our line of sight and will project foreshortened as the apparent relative orbit. When the inclination is 0° the true orbit and apparent orbit coincide. If the inclination is 90° the true orbit will appear edge-on. The term *relative* is used when describing apparent and true orbits because both stars are revolving about a center of mass in the same manner as the Earth and Moon revolve about the barycenter. In our discussion, keep in mind that the primary star is not at the center of mass in a binary system.

## The Visual Binary System Sirius A and Sirius B

Sirius, the "Dog Star" in the constellation Canis Major, has been famous since antiquity. The ancient Egyptians worshipped the star as the god Sothis, which, at that time, appeared in the east at dawn when the Nile River overflowed its banks. Today, the brightest star remains a main attraction in the winter sky. Sirius became important to astronomy in the nineteenth century when Friedrich Bessel found evidence for an unseen companion. The secondary star turned out to be the prototype of the remarkable stars known as white dwarfs.

Shortly after measuring the distance to Sirius in 1834, Bessel found unexpected variations in its proper motion; the star followed a serpentine track along a straight line. He continued investigating the star's progress for ten years and was convinced that the irregularities were caused by the attraction of an invisible object. Finally, in 1862, the separation between the stars was sufficient for Alvan G. Clark to detect the faint companion previously lost in the glare of the brilliant primary star (fig. 14.4).

Since its discovery, Sirius B has completed more than two revolutions so that its true relative orbit and orbital elements are known with high precision (fig. 14.5). When the mean distance and period are known, the combined mass of the stars may be found. (See Methods and Understandings 6.3, Newton's Derivation of Kepler's Third Law; and Methods and Understandings 9.1, The Mass of Jupiter.) If the total mass of a binary is computed in terms of the Sun-Earth system as unity, and the distance between the stars given in astronomical units and the revolutionary period in years, the equation may be written as

$$(M_A + M_B) = \frac{a^3}{P^2}$$

where $(M_A + M_B)$ = the mass of the primary and secondary stars; $a$ = the semimajor axis of the true orbit measured in astronomical units; and $P$ = the period of the companion star measured in years.

Sirius has a trigonometric parallax, $p$, of 0.378 arc seconds. After its true orbit is determined, the companion star is found to revolve in a period, $P$, of about 50 years at a mean separation, $s$,

**figure 14.4**

The bright star Sirius A and its white dwarf companion Sirius B (**arrow**).

of 7.62 arc seconds. The mean distance, $a$, between the stars measured in astronomical units is expressed as

$$a = \frac{\text{mean angular separation}(s)}{\text{stellar parallax }(p)}$$

$$a = \frac{7.620}{0.378}$$

$$a = 20.16, \text{ or about 20 AU.}$$

$$(M_A + M_B) = \frac{(20)^3}{(50)^2} = 3.2 \text{ solar masses.}$$

Recall how the masses of the Earth and Moon were found from the ratio of their distances from the barycenter (see chapter 6). The masses of Sirius A and Sirius B are found in the same way. A comparison of their motions against the field stars shows that Sirius B revolves about 2.2 times as far from the center of mass as Sirius A. Thus Sirius A must be 2.2 times as massive as Sirius B. If the total mass of the system is 3.2 solar masses, then the

As shown in figure 14.3, the intersection of the plane of the true orbit and the plane of the sky is represented by $N_1 N_2$, the line of nodes. The primary star, A, lies in both planes on the line of nodes. *Periastron* is the point in the true orbit where the companion star is nearest to the primary; *apastron* marks the point where the stars are farthest apart. The period of the secondary star is measured in years and is of equal length in the true and apparent orbits.

As shown in figure 14.2, the apparent orbit is derived from the changing values of the angular separation and position angle at different times during the revolution of the secondary star. The orbit is determined by plotting the positions of the companion relative to the primary component, which is placed at the origin of a polar coordinate graph. Generally, the primary star does not project to a focal point of the apparent ellipse. The true orbit is obtained by ro-

tating the apparent orbit about the line of nodes by an angle equal to the inclination of the secondary star's orbit to the plane of the sky (fig. 14.3). The inclination and other elements of the true ellipse may be determined geometrically from the displacement of the primary star in the apparent ellipse.

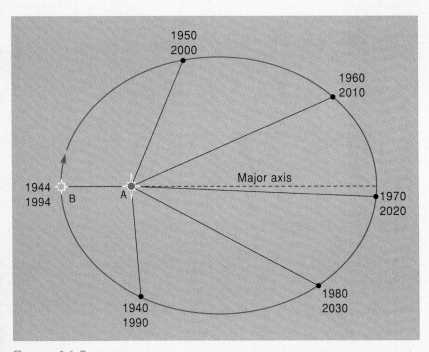

**figure 14.5**

The true relative orbit for the visual binary Sirius. In accordance with Kepler's second law, the companion Sirius B sweeps out equal areas in the same time interval.

masses of Sirius A and Sirius B must be 2.2 and 1.0 solar masses respectively (see fig. 14.5).

A point of interest concerning the system is that Sirius A and B are both spectral type A stars and have about the same temperature. Despite their similarity in temperature, they differ enormously in luminosity, size, and density. Sirius A is a main-sequence star of absolute magnitude +1.41, roughly 20 times brighter than the Sun. Sirius B is classified a white dwarf star and is about 10 magnitudes fainter, or 10,000 times as dim as Sirius A. Moreover, the dwarf companion is exceedingly small, about twice the size of the Earth. Inside Sirius B and other white dwarfs, atomic nuclei and free electrons are more closely packed together than the particles found in ordinary matter. The density of Sirius B is over 100,000 times greater than the density of the Sun. This class of dense objects represents the final stage in the evolution of stars like the Sun.

## Astrometric Binary Stars

There are 65 stars within five parsecs of the Sun. A study shows that as many as 30 of these stars are members of binary and multiple systems. Among them, no less than eight show perturbations in their proper motions caused by unseen companions. As described in Methods and Understandings 14.1, Bessel attributed the variability of Sirius's motion to the gravitational effect of an invisible companion. In 1850, he proposed that similar irregularities in the motion of Procyon were also caused by the presence of an unresolved star. In 1896, the discovery of a white dwarf companion, Procyon B, confirmed Bessel's prediction.

Consider a star in the Sun's neighborhood suspected of having an unseen companion. As a rule, unresolved components are discovered among nearby stars having large parallaxes and proper motions. If the visible star is without a companion, its proper motion will be rectilinear; if the star is an astrometric binary, its proper motion will follow a wavelike path. The image of the secondary star may be close to and blend into the light of the primary star, or it may have the necessary angular separation but is too faint to be seen.

Moreover, a companion may not have the mass and temperature needed to ignite its hydrogen core. Instead, the object may radiate in the infrared wavelengths by the conversion of gravitational energy to heat. Recall how thermal energy is produced within the planet Jupiter and transported to its atmosphere. There are several astrometric binaries where perturbations indicate the presence of an unseen companion less than 10 times the mass of Jupiter. Such planet-sized objects can be detected by the motion of the visible stars about the common center of mass.

The orbital motion of an astrometric binary is determined after thousands of observations are made over a period of many years. Analysis of the data yields the elements of the true relative orbit from which the mass of the unseen companion is derived.

## The Mass–Luminosity Relation

In his study of stellar interiors, Sir Arthur Eddington arrived in 1924 at a relationship between the masses and luminosities of main-sequence stars. The **mass-luminosity relation** is represented by a curve whose vertical componant is the bolometric absolute magnitude (luminosity) and horizontal component is the mass. As shown in figure 14.6, luminous giant stars are more massive than the Sun, and the Sun is more massive than faint red dwarfs. The direct method for finding the mass of a star is to measure its effect upon the motion of an orbiting companion. Thus relatively nearby visual binary stars were originally used to graph the mass-luminosity relation.

The mass-luminosity relation is a curve very similar to that of the main sequence of the H-R diagram. Note the location of the nonconforming white dwarf stars. Once established, the mass-luminosity relation was instrumental in finding the masses of single main-sequence stars.

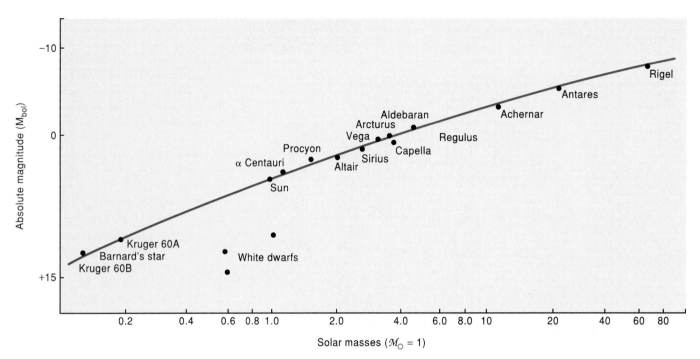

**figure 14.6**

The mass-luminosity relation.

For main-sequence stars, the mass-luminosity relation can be expressed as

$$\log \frac{L_*}{L_\odot} = 3.5 \log \frac{\mathcal{M}_*}{\mathcal{M}_\odot}$$

where $L_*$ = the luminosity of the star; $L_\odot$ = the luminosity of the Sun ($L_\odot$ = 1); $\mathcal{M}_*$ = the mass of the star; and $\mathcal{M}_\odot$ = the mass of the Sun ($\mathcal{M}_\odot$ = 1).

*Example.* If a blue giant star is 50,000 times more luminous than the Sun, what is its mass in solar units?

$$3.5 \log \mathcal{M}_* = \log 50,000$$

$$\log \mathcal{M}_* = \frac{4.7}{3.5}$$

$$= 1.3$$

$$\mathcal{M}_* = 10^{1.3}$$

$$= 22 \, \mathcal{M}_\odot .$$

## Spectroscopic Binary Stars

There are many binary stars that have small angular separations and cannot be resolved into separate points of light. Instead, these close pairs are identified by their spectral characteristics and are classified as double-line spectroscopic binaries. A spectrogram will show conspicuous and identifying features in the spectrum of each component. As the stars revolve, there is a periodic oscillation

and doubling of the spectral lines. If only the primary star is visible the system is called a single-line spectroscopic binary, in which the lines appear to oscillate about an average position. These motions reveal the mutual period of the stars and their relative distances from the center of mass. Spectroscopic binaries are as close to each other as the terrestrial planets are to the Sun and revolve in periods ranging from a few days to several months. In other systems the periods extend over several years.

The displacement of the spectral lines is a Doppler effect. It was first applied to electromagnetic radiation by French physicist Hippolyte Fizeau in 1848. According to the Doppler-Fizeau principle, the apparent change in the wavelength of light and other electromagnetic radiation is a function of the radial velocity between the source and the observer. If the source is approaching, the frequency of the waves increases and the spectral lines shift from their stationary position toward the blue region of the spectrum. If the source is receding, the frequency decreases and the spectral lines are shifted toward the red portion of the spectrum. If the source is neither approaching nor receding, the spectral lines remain in the position they would have if the lines were produced by a stationary

source in a laboratory or observatory (fig. 14.7).

As described in chapter 13, radial velocity is a star's motion toward or away from an observer, measured by the apparent displacement in frequency or wavelength of the star's spectral lines. The amount of spectral shift is compared to the spectrum of a source at rest relative to the observer. The comparison spectrum is made from the light of an incandescent source recorded in the spectrograph attached to the telescope.

The Doppler principle shows that the spectral shift is proportional to the radial velocity; a higher velocity produces a greater change in the positions of the lines. The radial velocity ($V$) is expressed as

$$V = \text{velocity of light} \times \frac{\text{change in wavelength}}{\text{wavelength at rest}},$$

or

$$V = c \, \frac{\lambda - \lambda_0}{\lambda_0}$$

where $c = 3.0 \times 10^5$ km/sec; $\lambda_0$ = the wavelength at rest relative to observer; and $\lambda$ = the observed wavelength.

The radial velocity is positive (+) when the star is receding from the observer and negative (−) when the star is approaching the observer. This equation

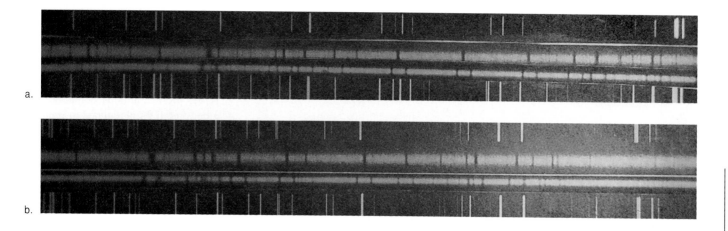

a.

b.

**figure 14.7**

Spectra of the spectroscopic binary Kappa Arietis. Above and below the stellar spectra are the bright lines of a stationary comparison spectrum. *a.* When the stars are approaching and receding, the absorption lines are separated and displaced by the Doppler effect. *b.* When the stars are moving across our line of sight, the absorption lines are single and stay in the same position as the lines in the reference spectrum.

is valid only when velocities are a small fraction of the velocity of light. At speeds approaching *c,* the equation is modified to account for the effects of relativity (see Methods and Understandings 19.1).

Figure 14.8a shows an idealized spectroscopic binary system where the primary star A and the companion star B revolve in circular orbits about a common center of mass C. The constant change in direction relative to the observer produces a periodic variation in the radial velocity of each star. Note that the stars are always at opposite ends of a radius vector passing through the center of mass.

At position 1 the stars are moving in opposite directions across our line of sight and no spectral shift due to orbital motion is observed. At position 2 the spectral lines are displaced. Star A is approaching and its spectrum will show a Doppler shift toward the shorter wavelengths. Star B is receding so its spectral lines will move toward longer wavelengths. Position 3 finds the stars moving across the line of sight and their radial velocities will be zero. At position 4 the spectral lines are doubled as the stars once again move in our line of

**figure 14.8** ▶

An idealized spectroscopic binary system. *a.* The primary star A and secondary star B revolve around a common center of mass, C. *b.* The velocity curve shows the changes in radial motion during one revolution.

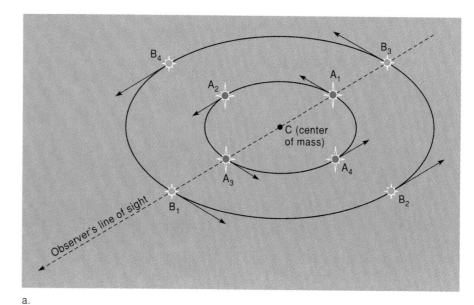

a.

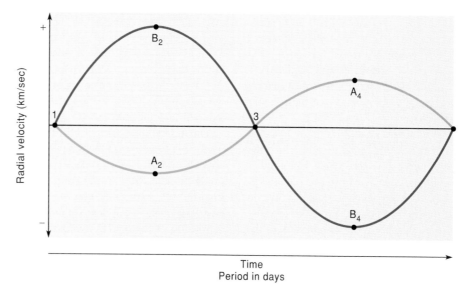

b.

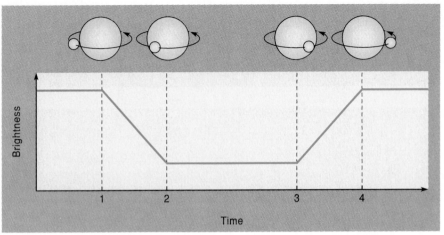

**figure 14.9**
An idealized eclipsing binary system with a central eclipse. The light curve shows the times of contacts, the reduction of light during minimum brightness, and the duration of the eclipse.

sight: star A is receding and star B approaching at their maximum radial velocities.

The changes in radial motion during one revolution are graphed as a **radial velocity curve** in which radial velocity is given in km/sec and the period in days (fig. 14.8b). Double-line binaries show two sinusoidal curves representing the primary and companion stars alternately approaching (−) and receding (+) from the observer. Maximum radial velocity occurs at positions 2 and 4 when the stars are in our line of sight. The curves cross at positions 1 and 3 where radial velocity is zero. Note that the companion star is revolving at a greater velocity but in the same period as the primary star. Since the periods are equal, the radial velocities may be used to find the ratio of the stars' distances from the center of mass, and the ratio of their masses. If the system is a single-line binary and only one spectrum is visible, the presence of the companion is confirmed by the radial velocity curve of the primary star.

The binary system in figure 14.8 represents a hypothetical case in which the stars move at constant speed in circular orbits inclined nearly 90° to our line of sight. Usually, binary stars revolve in elliptical orbits and produce velocity curves that are more complex than the simple, wavelike forms in our example. Moreover, their orbits are inclined at all angles to the plane of the sky and their radial velocities are merely projections of the actual orbital motions. The peri-

ods of spectroscopic binaries can be found by radial velocity observations, but the orbits and masses of these stars are determined through the analysis of many spectroscopic binary systems.

## Eclipsing Binary Stars

Several thousand spectroscopic binaries have orbits nearly edge-on to our line of sight and constitute the unique class called eclipsing binary stars. From Earth, these stars are seen to mutually eclipse one another and cause variations in brightness. To the unaided eye or through a telescope, close binaries appear as single variable stars; i.e., the eclipsing variables introduced in chapter 13. Most are identified by letters followed by the genitive name of the constellation where they are found: AR Lac, W Delphini, VV Cephei, W Ursae Majoris, RS Canum Venaticorum, and so forth. Like intrinsic variable stars, eclipsing binaries are studied by means of light curves in which the change in magnitude is plotted as a function of time.

During eclipse, the occulting star passes between us and the other component causing the light to fade rapidly to minimum and back to maximum again. Figure 14.9 shows the light curve and positions of the component stars during eclipse. First contact (1) marks the start of the eclipse. As the eclipse progresses, brightness decreases until second contact (2), when totality begins. The light curve shows that brightness remains at minimum during totality from second to

third contact (3). Totality ends when the eclipsed star emerges from behind the occulting star. The eclipse ends at fourth contact (4) when maximum light is received from both components.

If the more luminous component is occulted, the light is reduced to greatest minimum at **primary eclipse**. A **secondary eclipse** is reached when the fainter companion star is concealed. The secondary minimum shows less reduction in light. The time elapsed between two successive primary minima designates the period of the system. Moreover, the eclipse may be total, annular, or partial depending upon the diameters of the stars, their linear separation, and the inclination of their orbits to our line of sight (fig. 14.10).

Often the changing brightness of the binary system is compared with the magnitude of a nearby constant star. Then the magnitude plotted on the light curve is the difference in apparent brightness between the variable and comparison stars. It is convenient to graph the duration of the period as the phase or time from the middle of the primary eclipse rather than the date and time of observation (see fig. 14.14, phase axis).

Consider two spherical stars of equal luminosity and size in circular orbits where the plane of the orbit coincides with the line of sight (fig. 14.11a). The light curve shows that the minima of both stars have the same depth and occur at equal intervals of time.

Suppose the stars are not the same size and brightness. The minimum will be deeper when the more luminous star is eclipsed. During primary as well as secondary minimum, the amount of surface concealed by the eclipsing star is the same as the surface area of the smaller component. More light per unit area is cut off when the hotter star is eclipsed (fig. 14.11b).

## Algol, the First Eclipsing Binary Star

According to Chinese records dating back 2000 years, the light changes of Algol were believed to represent an ominous sign foreshadowing disaster. In Greek mythology, Algol represents the winking eye in the head of the legendary Medusa, one of the Gorgons slain by

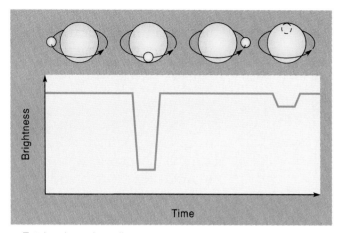

a. Total and annular eclipses

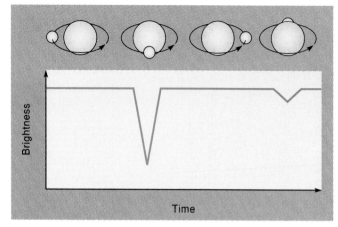

b. Partial eclipses

**figure 14.10**

Eclipsing binary stars. *a.* Total or annular eclipse. *b.* Partial eclipse. The type of eclipse depends on the diameters of the stars, their linear separation, and their inclination to our line of sight.

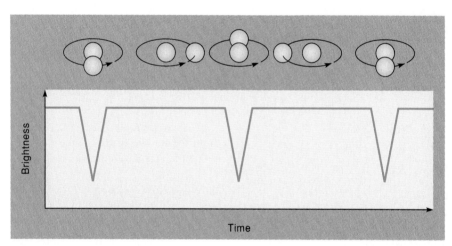

a.

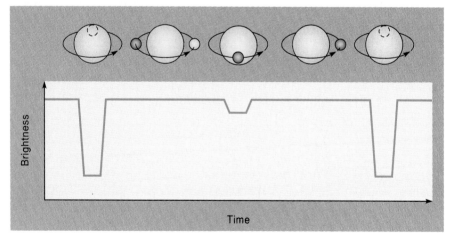

b.

**figure 14.11**

*a.* Hypothetical light curves of two eclipsing binary stars of equal luminosity and size.
*b.* Hypothetical light curve of two eclipsing binary stars of unequal luminosity and size shows a deeper minimum when the more luminous star is eclipsed.

Perseus. Modern observations began in 1669 when Geminiano Montanari made systematic observations of the star's varying light. Over a century later, in 1783, John Goodricke attributed the periodic changes in light to mutually revolving stars.

The hypothesis that Algol and other variables like it are eclipsing binaries was confirmed in 1889 through spectroscopic investigations. At the same time, photographic techniques supplanted visual estimates and provided more accurate measurements of magnitude changes. In 1910, Joel Stebbins pioneered the use of photocells to measure variations in light and later published a photoelectric light curve of Algol. Moreover, Stebbins was first to identify the secondary minimum of Algol A and B and to suggest a third component, Algol C, as the cause of observed deviations in the motions of the system. In the 1930s, A. E. Whitford and G. E. Kron introduced the use of the photomultiplier tube and the photoelectric techniques practiced today.

Algol A and B revolve in a period of 2.87 days during which time brightness varies from a maximum magnitude +2.1 between eclipses down to magnitude +3.4 at primary eclipse. The change in brightness during primary eclipse takes place in less than 10 hours. Thirty-five hours later, a brightness change of only 0.06 occurs at secondary eclipse (fig. 14.14a).

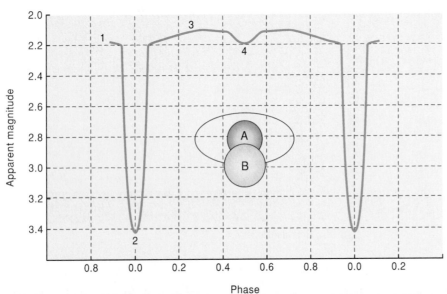

The light curve of Algol, the first eclipsing binary star system discovered.
Source: Data from Michele Gerbaldi, "Binary Stars" in *The Cambridge Atlas of Astronomy,* 2d ed., Jean Audouze and Guy Israel (eds.), Cambridge University Press, p. 284.

▼ **figure 14.13**

The multiple star system of Algol A, B, and C. Algol A and B form an interacting binary system. Astronomers believe that a stream of gases from the outer atmosphere of Algol B spirals down to form an accretion disk around Algol A. Eventually the gases splash down to the surface of the primary star.

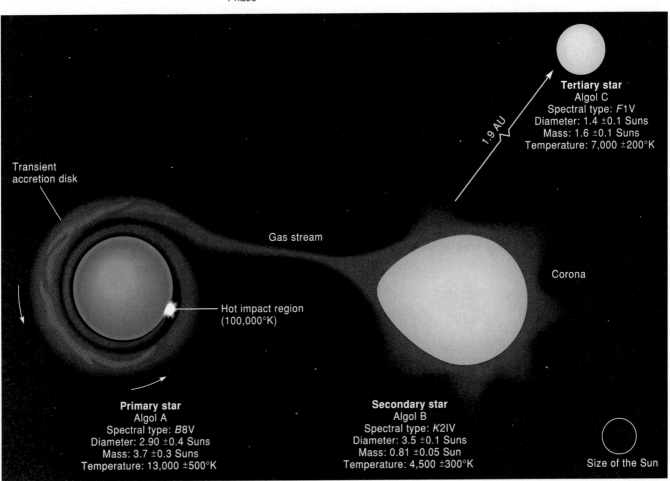

Figure 14.12 depicts the revolution and light curve for the Algol binary system. Star A, the primary component, represents the more massive and brighter star. The secondary, star B, is a cooler subgiant. At position 1, first contact, star B is approaching our line of sight. A deep primary minimum occurs at position 2 when the smaller but brighter star is partially eclipsed by the cooler companion. Position 3 shows the stars between eclipses when both are visible and the system is observed at maximum brightness. A shallower secondary eclipse takes place at position 4 when the fainter companion is partially eclipsed by the brighter primary star.

Figure 14.13 depicts the Algol system. The brighter component of the eclipsing pair, Algol A, is a spectral type *B*8V star about three times the size and about four times the mass of the Sun. Algol B is a spectral type *K*2IV subgiant with a mass nearly equal to the Sun, although its diameter is larger. The third component, Algol C, is a sun-sized spectral type *F*1V astrometric binary revolving in a period of 1.87 years at a distance of 1.9 AU. Streams of gas are ejected from the orange B component and swirl around the blue A component. The gas becomes ionized before colliding with the primary star. The impact causes a hot spot on the star's surface.

## Other Prominent Eclipsing Binary Stars

Some eclipsing binaries show anomalies or irregularities in their light curves that are caused by huge photospheric starspots. These are RS Canum Venaticorum stars containing a type F or G primary and a G or K secondary star. The spots cover large areas of the cooler star's surface. As the spots slowly migrate, the irregularities in the light curve identify the location of the spots on the star.

Beta Lyrae is the prototype of a group of binary stars consisting of a spectral class B8 luminous primary and a larger and cooler companion surrounded by a toroidal disk. The close pair are nearly in contact and are distorted into ellipsoidal shapes by their mutual gravitation. According to one interpretation, the B8 star expels a stream of gases into the disk about the secondary star. Owing to the distortion of the stars, the light curve shows a continuously curved maximum between the primary and secondary eclipses (fig. 14.14b).

Stars of the W Ursae Majoris class are in contact. The light curve has two minima of nearly equal depth indicating that the stars have about the same temperature (fig. 14.14c). The pair is surrounded by an extensive atmosphere.

## Star Clusters and Stellar Associations

The study of star clusters and associations provides essential information relating to the distribution in space, motions, and structure of stars. Of even greater signifi-

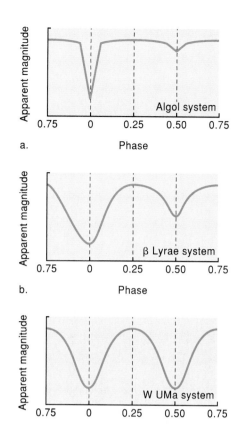

**figure 14.14**

Light curves of three types of close eclipsing binary stars.

cance is the importance of clusters and associations in determining how stars form, follow their respective evolutionary processes, and reach terminal stage. Clusters are stellar collections of common origin having the same motion in space and held together by their mutual gravitation. The member stars were formed together in the same nebula and are therefore of about the same age and chemical composition. Differences between the stars in a given cluster include their masses, luminosities, and temperatures.

There are two distinct types of clusters: the more sparsely populated **galactic** or **open clusters** (fig. 14.15) and the densely populated **globular clusters** (fig. 14.16) that are spherical formations of stars. The categories represent two separate classifications of stars found in different regions of the Galaxy. Our first concern will be the galactic clusters and their relationship with the transitory aggregates of young stars called *stellar associations*.

## Galactic Clusters

Some galactic clusters are associated with bright gaseous nebulae. An example is the Rosette Nebula in Monoceros, where clouds of hydrogen are ionized by the intense radiation from O and B stars contained in the cluster at the center of the nebula (fig. 14.17). Indeed, a comparison of the location of clusters shows that those containing high-luminosity O and B stars occupy the dust and gas lanes in the plane of the Milky Way.

Most open clusters are distributed in a narrow region in the spiral arms of the Galaxy. The highest concentration is found along the Milky Way in the direction of the galactic center. Another concentration of clusters, which includes the double cluster in Perseus, lies in a spiral arm more distant from the galactic center than the Sun. In addition, there are low-luminosity clusters outside the spiral structure where random motions have scattered the stars away from their place of origin in the Milky Way.

The differences in luminosities and distribution of clusters in our galaxy are related to the ages of the clusters. The most luminous O and B stars are found in very young clusters associated with nebulosity. The star cluster in the nebula NGC 6611 in Serpens is in this early period of stellar formation (see photo at opening of chapter). The oldest known open cluster, NGC 188 in Cepheus, is located more than 20° north of the galactic plane and has only a few spectral class F stars remaining as the most luminous main-sequence members.

## Stellar Associations

In the Milky Way, young open clusters are sometimes found among collections of highly luminous stars called **O associations.** These are sparsely populated aggregations containing fewer stars than the number found in the general field of stars. Associations are unstable formations influenced by their random motions, galactic tidal forces, and galactic rotation that eventually cause the stars to drift away from each other. But rather than stream out along the Milky Way, the stars show an unmistakable radial motion away from their place of origin

**figure 14.15**

The Jewel Box cluster (NGC 4755) is an example of an open cluster. It is located in the constellation Crux (the Southern Cross), visible from Earth's southern hemisphere. The stars in the cluster are about 2400 light-years distant.

▲ **figure 14.16**

The globular cluster M15 (NGC 5904) in the constellation Pegasus. This sixth-magnitude cluster is at a distance of about 35,000 light-years.

**figure 14.17** ▶

The Rosette nebula, about 2500 light-years away in the constellation Monoceros.

## The Enigmatic Epsilon Aurigae

Southwest of Capella, the brightest star in Auriga, there is a small triangle of third- and fourth-magnitude stars known as "The Kids." The 3.0-magnitude star at the apex of the triangle, Epsilon Aurigae, is a strange eclipsing binary that has baffled astronomers for many years. Epsilon Aurigae was discovered to be a variable star in 1821. Studies were made of the light changes during the next minimum, which took place in 1848. By 1904, astronomers explained the brightness variations as the periodic eclipse of a binary star by an invisible component.

Epsilon is not an ordinary eclipsing variable star but a complicated system that scientists find difficult to interpret. Its light curve is different from other eclipsing binaries. There is a prolonged primary eclipse lasting about one year, but no secondary minimum showing an eclipse of a companion star. Other eclipsing binary stars are in close orbits and revolve in periods lasting days or months; the stars in Epsilon Aurigae are far apart and require 27.1 years to complete one cycle.

There have been six eclipses of Epsilon Aurigae since its discovery. The last eclipse occurred during the years 1982–1984 (see fig. 14.18). The stars' brightness steadily declines to 3.8 magnitude at minimum light in about 192 days. Minimum brightness remains fairly constant except for a rise to about 3.6 magnitude in the middle of the eclipse and a return to 3.8 magnitude. The duration of the minimum phase is 330 days while the entire eclipse lasts 610 days.

What is the nature of the unseen object causing the eclipse? Astronomers who studied the 1983 minimum of Epsilon Aurigae generally agree that a large, opaque accretion disk surrounding the companion occults a type F2I supergiant primary star every 27.1 years. Electron scattering caused by ultraviolet radiation emitted by the star may be responsible for the opacity of the disk. Moreover, a circumstellar envelope consisting of many cloudlike formations may surround the system. A single-lined spectrum that identifies the primary is visible during the eclipse as well as between eclipses when the star is seen at maximum light. The companion that lies buried in the center of the accretion disk has never been detected and so its nature remains a mystery.

Some investigators have proposed that the secondary consists of a close pair of type A or F stars inside the revolving disk. According to this model, the disk was formed at an earlier stage when the F2I primary was a distended red supergiant star. The outer layers of the bloated star streamed off and spiraled around the companion stars, forming a thick rotating disk. As the binary companions circle the supergiant star, the accretion disk is carried across our line of sight and partially blocks the light from the primary star.

Margherita Hack designed a model of Epsilon Aurigae based upon infrared, visible, and ultraviolet observations. In her model, the supergiant primary is partially occulted by a ring of dust surrounded by flat shells of gas. A tenuous circumstellar cloud of gas envelopes the entire binary system. At the center of the disk formation, there is a single blue dwarf companion ejecting mass in bipolar jets. It is an irregular variable similar to the T Tauri protostars found in interstellar clouds. (See chapter 6, chapter 15, and the text on T associations in this chapter.) Since the T Tauri stage is a relatively short interval of time in the history of a star, if the model is correct, a system such as Epsilon Aurigae is a rare phenomenon. Which one of these models explains this remarkable star? Perhaps the next eclipse in 2010 will provide the answer.

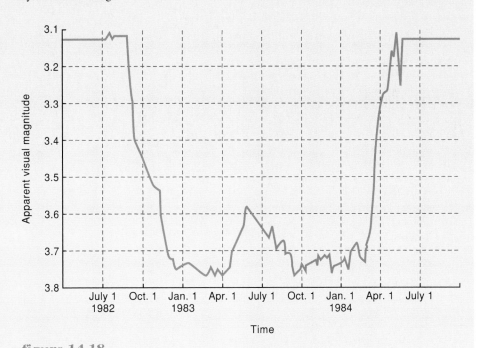

**figure 14.18**

The light curve of Epsilon Aurigae during the eclipse of 1982–1984.

Source: Data from J. L. Hopkins, Hopkins Phoenix Observatory, and S. I. Inquarsson, Tjornisland Astronomical Observatory, Sweden.

binary stars, clusters, and stellar associations

### the great cluster in Hercules

Hercules is a well-known northern constellation seen during the early evenings of spring and summer. The constellation lies above the northeastern horizon in late April, and by summer it appears overhead for Sky Watchers observing in the middle latitudes. Hercules can be recognized as a large letter H with a "keystone" formed by four bright stars, Epsilon, Zeta, Eta, and Pi (fig. 14.19). The keystone locates the most distinctive object in the constellation, the famous Great Cluster, M13. Edmond Halley was first to identify the cluster in 1716 as a faint patch of light. Our Sky Watchers' project will be to identify and observe M13 as a naked-eye object and then through binoculars and a telescope.

Your first task will be to find Hercules in the sky with the aid of a star chart. Locate the bright orange star Arcturus by following the curved handle of the Big Dipper. Now look eastward and identify the white star Vega. Arcturus and Vega are the brightest northern stars in the spring and summer sky. Find Hercules east of Arcturus about two-thirds of the distance to Vega. Locate the keystone in Hercules and then identify the stars Zeta and Eta Herculis. The Great Cluster is found about two-thirds of the distance between Zeta and Eta Herculis.

M13 is a sixth-magnitude object, barely visible to the unaided eye. Select an observing site away from extraneous light from street lamps or other sources that will interfere with your seeing. Moreover, the sky must be clear and completely dark. Having accepted the challenge, find the constellation and look with averted vision (through the corner of your eye) for the cluster. With some patience, you may see a hazy patch with a bright center.

With the help of binoculars, M13 appears as a tiny, smokelike cloud while the field

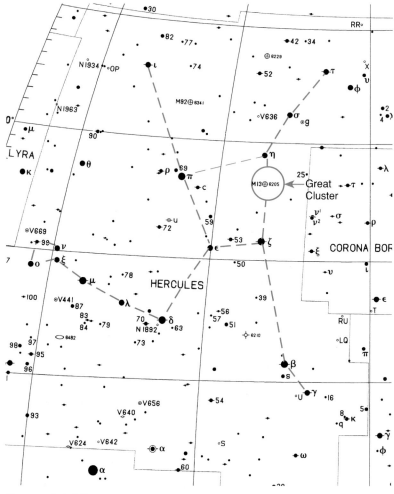

**figure 14.19**

The Hercules region. The Great Cluster, M13 (*arrow*), is located between the stars Zeta and Eta Herculis.

From *Norton's 2000.0 Star Atlas and Reference Handbook*, 18th ed. Copyright © 1991 Longman Group UK Ltd. Reprinted by permission.

stars are seen as sparkling points of light. A telescope of moderate aperture is needed to resolve member stars in the cluster. The view in a large-aperture telescope is breathtaking. Stars in the cluster can be seen from the periphery almost to the center before the images overlap into a bright glowing mass. There are over 100,000 stars in the cluster, which is located 21,000 light-years distant (fig. 14.20).

into a more or less spherical formation. Associations vary in size between 40 and 400 light-years and contain from 100 to 1000 stars. O associations are relatively short-lived compared to galactic clusters; their average age extends to about 30 million years.

O associations are found in the Milky Way together with bright nebulae. The stars in the region of Orion's belt and sword make up the Orion I Association. There are no less than six associations in the Scorpius-Sagittarius region at a distance of 1300 to 2300 parsecs from the Sun. The Perseus I Association is farther from the galactic center than the Sun by a distance of 2300 parsecs.

Individual associations cover large regions and often contain open clusters and multiple star systems. For instance, the double cluster h and χ Persei is found in the Perseus I Association. The Trapezium, a system of four stars, lies in the center of the Great Nebula which is a part of the Orion I Association (fig. 14.21).

**figure 14.20**
The Great Cluster in Hercules, M13.

**figure 14.21**
The highly luminous stars in the diffuse nebula M42 are a part of the Orion I Association.

Another globular cluster, M15 in Pegasus, can be observed in the fall and early winter. This cluster is about the same magnitude as M13, but is more compact. First locate the star Alpha Pegasi in the southwest corner of the Great Square of four bright stars that identifies the constellation. From Alpha, follow the line of stars Xi, Zeta, and Theta to Epsilon. Epsilon is the second-magnitude star northwest of Theta. M15 is located about 3° northwest of Epsilon. The cluster can be seen with binoculars as a hazy ball of light. The outer stars can be resolved in a telescope of moderate aperture.

Another category, a **T association,** is composed of pre-main-sequence T Tauri stars that are located in the dark dust lanes and molecular cloud complexes found in the Milky Way (see chapters 6 and 15). The prototype star, T Tauri, is located in the constellation Taurus. It was discovered more than a century ago and is believed to be a binary star or perhaps a multiple system. These unique variable stars are recently formed and do not have the internal temperature required to convert hydrogen to helium. The unpredictable light variations are linked to their interaction with surrounding nebulosity. Indeed, some stars remain at a maximum brightness followed by irregular periods of minimum light. Other T Tauri stars remain at minimum light except for sudden surges in brightness.

In 1946, Alfred H. Joy discovered that T Tauri stars have spectral characteristics unlike those found in stars outside the molecular cloud complexes. As described in chapter 13, cooler G, K, and M stars on the main sequence have spectra characterized by metallic lines and

**figure 14.22**
The globular cluster 47 Tucana is one of three globular clusters visible without optical aid. It is visible in the sky of the southern hemisphere.

molecular bands. T Tauri spectra show emissions in the hydrogen Balmer lines, ionized calcium, and ionized iron.

The Taurus, Auriga, and Perseus regions of the Milky Way are particularly rich in young T Tauri stars. Moreover, there are many examples of clustering within T associations.

Astronomers believe that T associations contain the youngest stellar objects. T Tauri protostars are still contracting and are always found embedded in dark interstellar clouds. The surface and atmospheric activities associated with T Tauri stars give ample evidence that star formation is a turbulent process. Polar jets of rapidly moving gas stream away from the star, causing the ejected stellar

matter to collide with nearby interstellar clouds. The resulting shock front produces small emission nebulae called *Herbig-Haro objects.*

Thus T and O associations provide a clear picture of early stellar evolution from collapsing protostars to the formation of the most luminous main-sequence stars. In time, hydrogen fusion will begin among the more massive T Tauri objects and form the luminous stars of the O associations.

## Globular Clusters

Thus far, we have discussed the distribution of comparatively young stars in galactic clusters and associations found in the dust and gas clouds of the Milky Way. Now we turn to another type of cluster that is entirely different in terms of stellar population, organization, and location in the Galaxy. Globular clusters rank among the most impressive objects viewed in a telescope. Of nearly 200 known globular clusters, only three are visible without optical aid: the Hercules cluster, M13, and Omega Centauri and 47 Tucanae (fig. 14.22) in the southern hemisphere sky. A telescope reveals a spherical formation over 100 parsecs in diameter containing from 10,000 to an estimated one million stars. Individual stars are seen at the outer limits as scattered points of light; stellar density increases toward the center until the images blend into a bright, glowing mass. The stars at the core of a globular cluster are much closer to each other than the stars found in the Sun's neighborhood. In a cluster, the time required for light to travel between stars is measured in weeks rather than years.

From our location, most but not all known globular clusters are seen in the direction of the galactic center. They are distributed in an almost spherical system extending from the center of the Galaxy to distances beyond the position of the Sun. Globular clusters revolve about the galactic center in elliptical orbits of high eccentricity and inclination. Globular clusters are distinguished by the kinds of stars they contain as well as their location. These stable formations date back to the beginning of the Galaxy.

## SUMMARY

Binary systems are composed of two stars mutually revolving about a common center of gravity. More than half the stellar population are members of binary or multiple-star systems.

Visual binary stars can be resolved into two stars by means of a telescope. Orbital motion is measured with filar micrometers and photographic techniques. Orbital periods of visual binaries vary from a few years to several centuries; linear distances between the stars range from 5 to more than 50 AU. When the orbital period and the size of the true relative orbit are known, the combined masses of the stars may be found.

If the angular separation between the stars is too small to be resolved, the stars may be observed as spectroscopic binaries. As the stars revolve, they alternately approach and recede from the direction of the Earth. The motion is observed as a Doppler effect in the spectra of the component stars.

The changes in radial velocity during one revolution are graphed as a velocity curve. The orbital period and size of the orbit are computed to determine the mass of the system. These values are uncertain because the inclination of the orbit is unknown.

When the orbits of spectroscopic binary stars lie in or near the line of sight, the stars will occult one another as eclipsing variable stars. A light curve illustrates the changes in brightness during one revolution. The characteristics of the eclipse, size of the orbit, and diameters of the component stars are determined from the shape of the light curve and the radial velocities of the stars.

Galactic or open clusters are irregular groups of stars found in or near the plane of the Milky Way. Some clusters are sparsely populated while others contain hundreds of stars in assemblages as large as 20 parsecs across.

Most open clusters are distributed along the Milky Way. Clusters containing high-luminosity type O and B stars are found in bright nebulae. Low-luminosity clusters are located above and below the Milky Way.

These differences in luminosity and distribution are related to the age of a cluster. Young open clusters are found in O associations. T associations are composed of pre-main-sequence T Tauri stars embedded in dark dust lanes and molecular clouds. Associations vary in size from 10 to 300 parsecs and contain as many as 1000 stars.

A globular cluster is a spherical formation of stars up to 100 parsecs in diameter that may contain from 10,000 to over one million stars. They are stable systems and contain the oldest stars in the Galaxy.

# KEY TERMS

| | |
|---|---|
| apparent relative orbit | primary eclipse |
| astrometric binary | primary star |
| binary stars | radial velocity curve |
| companion star | secondary eclipse |
| eclipsing binary | secondary star |
| galactic or open cluster | separation |
| globular cluster | spectroscopic binary |
| mass-luminosity relation | T association |
| O association | true relative orbit |
| position angle | visual binary |

# PROBLEMS

1. Refer to the light curve of Epsilon Aurigae. What evidence do you find that the obscuring object is not a dark nebula in the foreground?

2. Compare the light curve of an Algol-type eclipsing variable with the light curve of a cepheid variable star. Describe the distinguishing features of each.

3. What observational procedures would you follow in order to determine whether two stars make up a binary system or an optical double?

4. What are the colors of the brightest stars found in open clusters? In globular clusters? Explain.

5. The known astrometric binary stars are located in the Sun's neighborhood. Why haven't we discovered any at greater distances?

6. Explain how the luminosity and mass of main-sequence stars are related. What does this tell us about the relationship between temperature and mass?

7. Why is it more difficult to compute the orbital velocities for spectroscopic binaries than eclipsing binaries?

8. Explain how the diameters of eclipsing binary stars are determined.

9. Compare globular clusters and galactic clusters in terms of stellar population, appearance, and location in the Galaxy.

10. How is the velocity curve of a spectroscopic binary used to find the ratio of the masses of the stars?

11. Describe briefly how the true relative orbit of a visual binary star is determined.

12. Which cluster is stable—young galactic, old galactic, or globular? Give reasons for your answer.

13. Why are only young stars found in associations?

14. How do we differentiate between O and T associations?

15. The companion star in a visual binary system revolves in a period of 40 years. The mean separation between the stars is 4.26 arc seconds. The stellar parallax of the system is 0.31 arc seconds. Find the total mass of the system.

16. In problem 15, the companion revolves twice as far from the center of mass as the primary star. Find the mass of each star in solar mass units. Which star is more like the Sun?

# REFERENCES

Aitken, Robert G. 1964. *The Binary Stars.* New York: Dover Publications, Inc.

Arp, Halton C. 1965. "Globular Clusters in the Galaxy." In *Galactic Structure,* edited by Adriaan Blaauw and Maarten Schmidt. Vol. 5 of *Stars and Stellar Systems,* Gerard P. Kuiper, gen. ed. Chicago: The University of Chicago Press.

Battan, Alan H. 1973. *Binary and Multiple Systems of Stars.* Oxford: Pergamon Press.

Couteau, Paul. 1981. *Observing Visual Double Stars.* Translated by Alan Battan. Cambridge, Mass.: The MIT Press.

Goldstein, Alan. 1989. Split a Star in Two. *Astronomy* 17, no. 12 (December).

Haas, James. 1986. Galactic Clusters for Binoculars. *Astronomy* 14, no. 2 (February).

Hack, Margherita. 1984. Epsilon Aurigae. *Scientific American* 251, no. 4 (October).

Harrington, Phil. 1989. The Ten Best Double Stars. *Astronomy* 17, no. 7 (July).

Hodge, Paul. 1988. How Far Are the Hyades? *Sky and Telescope* 75, no. 2 (February).

Kopal, Zdenek. 1990. Eclipsing Binary Stars: The Story of Algol and its Celestial Relations. *Mercury* (Astronomical Society of the Pacific) 19, no. 3 (May/June).

Levy, David. 1989. *Observing Variable Stars: A Guide for the Beginner.* Cambridge: Cambridge University Press.

Limber, D. Nelson. 1962. The Pleiades. *Scientific American* reprint. San Francisco: W. H. Freeman and Company.

MacRobert, Alan. 1988. Epsilon Aurigae: Puzzle Solved? *Sky and Telescope* 75, no. 1 (January).

Morrison, Nancy D., and Stephen Gregory. 1986. The Puzzle of Epsilon Aurigae: Results from the Recent Eclipse. *Mercury* 15, no. 6 (November/December).

Sahade, Jorge, and Frank Bradshaw Wood. 1978. *Interacting Binary Stars.* Oxford: Pergamon Press.

Sharpless, Stewart. 1965. "Distribution of Associations, Emission Regions, Galactic Clusters, and Supergiants." In *Galactic Structure,* edited by Adriaan Blaauw and Maarten Schmidt. Vol. 5 of *Stars and Stellar Systems,* Gerard P. Kuiper, gen. ed. Chicago: The University of Chicago Press.

Tomkin, Jocelyn, and David L. Lambert. 1987. The Strange Case of Beta Lyrae. *Sky and Telescope* 74, no. 4 (October).

Van de Kamp, Peter. 1967. *Principles of Astrometry.* San Francisco: W. H. Freeman and Company.

chapter

15

t h e   l i f e   c y c l e s   o f   s t a r s

The Horsehead nebula in Orion is an extension
of an enormous dark cloud of gas and dust.
There is evidence of star formation between the
horsehead-shaped protrusion and the blue
reflection nebula NGC 2023 above it.

Two impressive things about stars are their visual impact on the observer and how they evolve over millions and billions of years. Sky watchers, poets, and philosophers agree that the stars are an inspiration and awesome to behold. Throughout history, people have wondered if the stars are eternal and immutable in the heavens. Today we know they are fragments of creation and follow prescribed life cycles from embryo to various terminal stages. How was this evolutionary puzzle solved? Like the astronomers who found the answers, we have probed beneath the glowing exterior of our Sun, the nearest star, and into its energy-producing core. What we have learned about the Sun's internal mechanism will be applied to the distant stars. Conversely, by learning how other stars evolve, the history of the Sun can be traced in the past and into the future. And we shall look for evidence of stellar creation in the dark dust lanes and glowing gas clouds of the Milky Way (fig. 15.1).

## A Tour of the Milky Way

Pretend you are outdoors away from all artificial illumination. The time is early evening in September; the sky is clear and, in the inky darkness, the Milky Way arches high overhead. Scorpius and Sagittarius hang above the southwestern horizon while the stars of autumn slowly drift across your meridian. As the hours pass, the winter stars of Taurus and Orion emerge above the eastern horizon. We shall follow the Milky Way from Scorpius to Orion and trace out the location of bright stars, clusters, and clouds of dust and gas, as well as some bizarre clues needed to unravel the mystery of the stars.

The Milky Way clouds are the breeding grounds for new stars. The region from Serpens to Sagittarius is exceptionally rich in dark and bright nebulosity. Of particular interest to us are the nebulae catalogued as M16, M17, M20, and M8 that seem to be connected into one

**figure 15.1**

A complex nebula associated with the cluster NGC 2264 in Monoceros. The cluster contains bright young stars and pre-main-sequence stars that are still embedded in the dusty nebula. Some of the brighter emission streaks in the red nebula are Herbig-Haro objects produced by T Tauri stars (see fig. 15.11).

huge interstellar formation. Also, the region is filled with a large number of galactic and globular clusters. The relative ages of clusters can be measured, so they are useful in determining how stars of the same age change with time.

Individual bright stars in the region are helpful, too. Most of the stars in Scorpius are the luminous blue giant variety. The exception is the red giant Antares. Recall from chapter 14 that a loose aggregation of hot stars is defined as an O association. These associations in Scor-

pius and elsewhere in the Milky Way contain young stars surrounded by nebulae. There must be a direct relationship between blue giants and nearby dust and gas clouds.

In the constellation Ophiuchus we find more dark and luminous clouds as well as the remains of **supernovae**—stellar explosions. Novae are designated by the year of discovery. Nova 1604 was the bright one seen and recorded by Kepler. Other novae in Ophiuchus were observed in 1848 and 1917. We are interested in

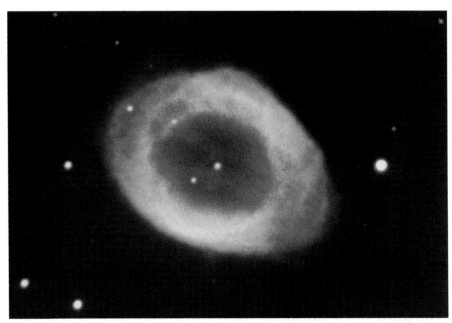

figure 15.2

The planetary nebula M57 in Lyra. The Ring nebula, as it is known, is an expanding spherical envelope of material shed by a star. The bright central core will eventually become a white dwarf star.

supernovae because they represent the "last hurrah" of behemoth red supergiant stars approaching terminal stage.

Eastward along the Milky Way we encounter dark dust and gas rifts in the neighborhood of Cygnus. Again we discover evidence of the birth of stars in nebulae, and their demise as supernovae. Of particular interest is the Cygnus Loop, a wispy stellar remnant expanding into the gaseous medium between the stars. In Vulpecula we find the Dumbbell nebula, and nearby, in Lyra, the famous Ring nebula. Both are examples of **planetary nebulae**, which represent a later evolutionary stage where stars reduce mass by moderately expelling their outer envelopes (fig. 15.2).

Our journey along the Milky Way brings us to the northern stars of Cepheus, Cassiopeia, and Perseus. The constellation Cepheus contains the star δ Cephei, the prototype of the cepheid variable stars. In chapter 13, we found these stars useful in measuring the distances to deep sky objects by means of the *period-luminosity relation.* Now we shall find out why they pulsate and how they fit into the evolutionary scheme. Tycho's star, Nova 1572 in Cassiopeia, was the first supernova to be studied systematically. Perseus is the location of a planetary nebula, M76, and the Double Cluster, h and χ Persei, two galactic clusters in the same line of sight.

The winter sky of Orion and its neighbors provides additional opportunity to see a variety of bright stars as well as find more evidence of stellar birth and death. With the exception of the red star Betelgeuse, the entire star field is an O association. South of the stars forming the belt of Orion lies the Great Nebula, a faint glowing patch of dust and gas where young blue giant stars ionize and illuminate the region. Nearby embryo stars lie hidden in their dark, dusty cocoons ready to emerge as hydrogen-burning stars (fig. 15.3).

An arc of varicolored stars—red, orange, yellow, white, and blue-white—form a halo around Orion. In chapter 13, we learned how color and magnitude are used to graph stars on the H-R diagram. There is a link between a star's position on the diagram and the evolutionary path it will follow. When clusters of different ages such as the Hyades and the Pleiades in Taurus are plotted on the same H-R diagram, the differences in the positions of the stars on the diagram suggest an evolutionary trend.

Taurus is also the location of two objects that represent the birth and death of stars. There is the unique variable called a **T Tauri star** that is the prototype for others like it found throughout the dust and gas clouds. They are the embryo stars we would expect to find after the collapse of a gas and dust globule. The *Crab Nebula, M1,* represents the remains of a dramatic supernova scattering heavy elements forged deep in its core. Someday these ashes will be recycled into a future generation of stars.

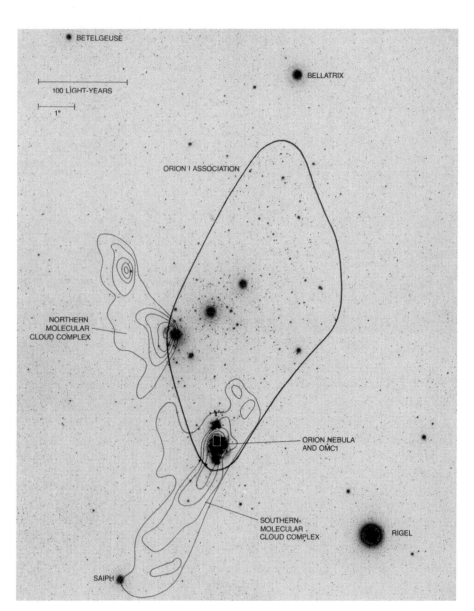

BETELGEUSE

BELLATRIX

100 LIGHT-YEARS

1°

ORION I ASSOCIATION

NORTHERN
MOLECULAR
CLOUD COMPLEX

ORION NEBULA
AND OMC1

SOUTHERN
MOLECULAR
CLOUD COMPLEX

RIGEL

SAIPH

**figure 15.3**
Negative print of the Orion I association, outlined in black. The isophotes (in red) show the
intensity distribution of carbon monoxide in the northern and southern molecular cloud
complexes. The Orion molecular cloud (OMC1) lies beyond the Orion nebula, M42.

## The Beginning of Star Formation

Thus far we have examined the Milky Way, which is part of the spiral structure of our galaxy. The spiral arms are the most recently formed component of the stellar system and, as one might expect, they contain the youngest stars. Since old stars are located elsewhere in the Galaxy, the first stars must have condensed out of hydrogen and helium before the spiral arms developed.

In a scenario proposed by Olin J. Eggen, Donald Linden-Bell, and Allan R. Sandage, the Galaxy began as a huge shapeless cloud. Eventually, this glob contracted and fragmented into smaller, compacted spherical bodies. Later, swarms of these fragments broke down into tens and hundreds of thousands of smaller spheres that became the stars of globular clusters. Today, the globular clusters, as well as single massive stars, form a halo from the center of the Galaxy to the outer limits of the spiral arms. According to the ELS theory, the halo was formed in a period of less than one billion years.

In an alternate theory by Leonard Searle and Robert J. Sim, the halo star clusters required a longer period of time to evolve. Complex interactions and accretion of fragments into stars delayed the process by several billion years. The remainder of this primordial galactic cloud continued to shrink and finally broke up into the old stars found in the center of the Galaxy.

A large number of the more massive stars must have exploded as supernovae that blasted heavy elements into the contracting hydrogen and helium cloud. As time progressed, the mixture of gas and dust moved around the center of the Galaxy and eventually formed a thin disk that wheeled around in the central plane. Spiral arms formed in the disk and provided the ingredients for the next generation of stars. The newcomers differed from the old stars in one important respect: they started out with the heavy elements and dusty mineral residue provided by their precursors. The main ingredients in virtually all stars, however, are still hydrogen and helium.

As we might expect, not all second-generation stars are the same age, nor are they located in the same region of the spiral arms. Only the very youngest stars are found in gas and dust clouds. In 1944, Walter Baade pointed out that blue stars are prodigious energy producers and cannot continue to radiate for more than a few million years. Luminous stars such as Rigel in Orion must be younger than sunlike stars that are known to be billions of years old. Rigel first appeared when our primitive ancestors roamed the Earth. The O- and B-type stars that ignited at the same time as the Sun are gone, having depleted their energy supply long before there were telescopes to observe them. Also, the O associations that contain the hot stars have more or less the same space motion as the nebulae in which they are found. Differences in motion exist but these are random motions of stars of common origin. The relationship between young stars and nebulae is firmly established, and our next task will be to confirm that such clouds of dust and gas are the incubators of embryo stars.

## From Collapsing Cloud to Pre-Main-Sequence Stars

The stars in the spiral arms travel in endless orbits around the center of the Galaxy. At the Sun's distance from the galactic core, stars require over 200 million years to complete one circuit. Since it was formed, the Sun has made about 20 trips around the Galaxy. It is difficult to realize that in only one galactic rotation, generations of the brightest short-lived stars have come and gone. The thousands of blue-white stars around us bear vivid testimony to a continuous process of star making. To maintain this constancy, an enormous reserve of raw material similar in composition to the stars must be present. We find this source in the diffuse dust and gas clouds of the *interstellar medium.*

Most atoms in the nebulae are simply neutral hydrogen. Some nebulae contain ionized hydrogen, which shines with a suffused fluorescent glow. (The most common example of such emission is the fluorescent lamp used in illuminating our homes.) In cosmic clouds, electrons are removed from atoms by energetic UV radiation from nearby high-temperature stars. Eventually, electrons and protons recombine at a lower energy level and emit photons of visible wavelengths. In addition to hydrogen, other elements have been detected, including oxygen, nitrogen, and iron.

The interstellar medium is also rich in solid specks of dust. In 1884, E. E. Barnard observed dark lanes and "holes" twisting through the star clouds and bright nebulae in Sagittarius and Ophiuchus. In those days, astronomers thought that the dark masses were voids and vacancies between the stars. But by 1910, Barnard had identified the dark spaces as clouds of obscuring matter. The chemical nature of the *dark nebulae* is not altogether certain; there may be particles of carbon imbedded in ice, dusty grains of iron, or perhaps tiny crystals of rock (fig. 15.4).

**figure 15.4**

A blue reflection nebula surrounds the star Rho Ophiuchi (***top***). IRAS satellite studies of the dark cloud of dust south of Rho Oph and northeast of Sigma Scorpii show evidence of early stellar evolution. Light from the red giant star Antares (***lower left***) illuminates dust particles ejected by the star.

## Mass Condensations in Molecular Clouds

As early as the 1930s, molecules made up of two or more atoms were found in the dust and gas lanes of the Milky Way. The first to be discovered were a few two-atom molecules, including cyanogen and methyladine. Existence of the molecules was confirmed by telltale absorption lines in spectrograms photographed with optical telescopes.

After the advances of radio astronomy in the 1950s, many molecules were added to the list. Among these are hydrogen, carbon monoxide, hydroxyl, water, sulphur dioxide, ammonia, formaldehyde, methanol, and ethyl alcohol. At present, nearly 80 molecules are known to exist in space.

Molecular hydrogen is the most plentiful substance in a molecule-rich nebula. Because it does not possess a strong spectral signature its presence is inferred by the detection of carbon monoxide, the second most abundant molecule in the cloud. Carbon monoxide is stable and remains nearly constant by a factor of one molecule for at least 10,000 hydrogen molecules. Scarce as it might be,

**figure 15.5**
A part of the giant molecular cloud in Sagittarius contains enough molecular hydrogen to produce millions of sunlike stars.

carbon monoxide allows radio astronomers to trace the most massive nebulous objects in the Galaxy: **giant molecular clouds,** or **GMC** (fig. 15.3).

The GMC occupy the dark rifts in the central plane of the Milky Way in a complete band around the sky. The GMC in Sagittarius contains enough molecular hydrogen to form three to five million sunlike stars (fig. 15.5). Clouds stretching 600 parsecs are not uncommon. The outer envelope of a GMC is exposed to radiation from nearby stars and, as we might expect, it consists of atomic hydrogen. In the dusty interior, molecular hydrogen, carbon monoxide, and a host of simple as well as complex molecules survive the effects of starlight.

It is clear that a relationship between dust clouds and molecules does exist. In a protected environment, molecules are formed when atoms combine on the surfaces of dust grains. Radio astronomers have discovered that embryo stars form in regions of greater density inside the huge, optically invisible GMC. They call these concentrations *molecular cloud cores* or *density cores*.

## The Initial Contraction

In 1947, prior to the discovery of molecular clouds, astronomer Bart Bok identified dark globules silhouetted against the glowing gas of ionized nebulae. These so-called Bok globules of interstellar gas and dust are small enough to occupy regions of space between stars, and they contain the elements found in second-generation stars. At that time, they were considered to be possible sites of star formation. Investigations in the 1980s confirmed that point sources of infrared radiation detected in IRAS images are the embryonic stars predicted by Bart Bok.

As advancements were made in radio and infrared astronomy, microwave and thermal radiation detected from concentrations within molecular clouds also were explained as emissions from protostars (figs. 15.6 and 15.7). A molecular cloud core can form and eventually become a protostar only if the cloud complex is sufficiently dense (about 30,000 hydrogen molecules per cubic centimeter) and cool (about 10 kelvins). Heat is an indication of molecular activity, and if the molecular motion is great enough to overcome gravity, the particles in the density core will disperse. Theorists believe the cores to be slightly unstable; the thermal pressure is less than the gravitational attraction provided by the particles in the density core. Complex mo-

**figure 15.6**
The Orion nebula is visible to the unaided eye as a fuzzy patch of light in the sword of Orion. Strong stellar winds from the Trapezium star cluster in the brightest portion of the nebula sweep away surrounding dust and gas. Pre-main-sequence stars behind the dust clouds are detected by infrared sensors.

**figure 15.7**
The Cone nebula in Monoceros is another region where star clusters are forming. Many of these newborn stars are hidden by a shell of dust that absorbs their visible light and radiates it as infrared. The presence of the stars is inferred from the radiation from the dust. The bright glowing cloud at the center casts a shadow that forms the conical structure.

tions of stars and interstellar particles create density waves in galactic spiral arms that contribute to the formation of stars. In regions of compression, molecular clouds are squeezed into density cores that become protostars (fig. 15.8).

A contracting protostar takes from several thousand to tens of millions of years to evolve into a hydrogen-burning, main-sequence star. For this reason, much of what astronomers know about stellar evolution, energy production, physical changes, and the subsequent ter-minal stages of stars is based upon models determined from theoretical calculations made with computers. In 1980, Steven W. Stahler, Frank H. Shu, and Ronald Taam made computer simulations of the evolution of protostars equal to the Sun in mass.

## The Birth of the Sun

Let us take an imaginary journey into one of the spiral arms of the Galaxy as it might have appeared about five billion years ago. As we enter one of the molecular clouds, we see one hundred or more density pockets that will form into stars. One of these density cores is of special interest to us because it is destined to become the Sun. We shall follow the progress of this formless glob of dust and gas until it emerges as a hydrogen-burning star.

At first, the outer layers of the core are diffuse and allow radiation from nearby stars to penetrate and heat the interior. Gravitational contraction begins from the inside out and, as density increases, the core becomes dark and opaque to light and ultraviolet radiation from other stars. Gravity relentlessly squeezes the material into a protostar. Dust and gas continue to fall toward the center from the outer regions of the density core for hundreds of thousands of years.

In the model described by Stahler and his associates, the infalling matter approaches the surface of the protostar at high speed and pressure, creating a shock

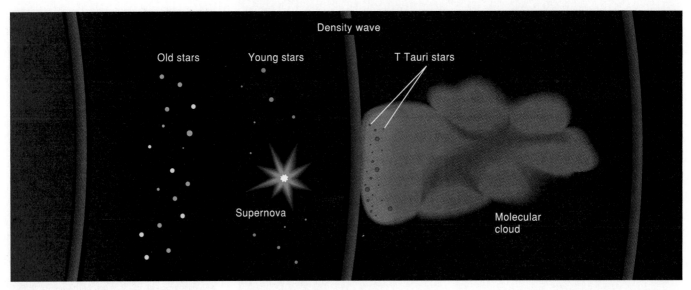

**figure 15.8**

Star formation might begin when a density wave in the spiral arms of a galaxy passes through a molecular cloud. The wave compresses the gas and dust into density cores. Supernovae in the wake of the density wave induce contraction and seed the molecular cloud with heavy elements.

front that heats the incoming gas to temperatures of one million kelvins. The high temperature drops as photons from the shock front are radiated and vaporize incoming dust above the protosun. The photons are absorbed and radiated at longer wavelengths in the cooler dust envelope situated at a greater distance from the protosun (fig. 15.9). Eventually, photons escape as infrared radiation in the tenuous outer region beyond the dust envelope.

At this point the protosun enters a new phase in its evolution. Not all of the gravitational energy is converted to heating the core. Some energy will be used to break down molecular hydrogen into atomic hydrogen. The process removes energy from the core, which in turn reduces thermal pressure. When internal pressure is diminished, gravity responds with increased compression. Rapid implosion begins, and the material in our embryo Sun continues in free-fall until thermal pressure gets high enough to balance the pull of gravity.

When these evolutionary changes in the Sun are plotted as points on the H-R diagram, the graph is an almost vertical line to the right of the main sequence called a **Hayashi track** (fig. 15.10).

The temperature has remained nearly constant during this runaway contraction. Finally, the obscuring dust around the

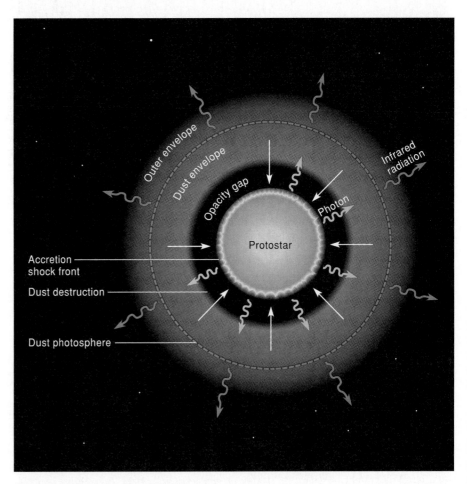

**figure 15.9**

A model of a protostar. Infalling matter forms an accretion shock front at the surface. Rapid deceleration heats the gas. Photons stream away from the shock front through a region of vaporized dust called the opacity gap. Photons are absorbed and re-emitted and eventually escape as infrared radiation.

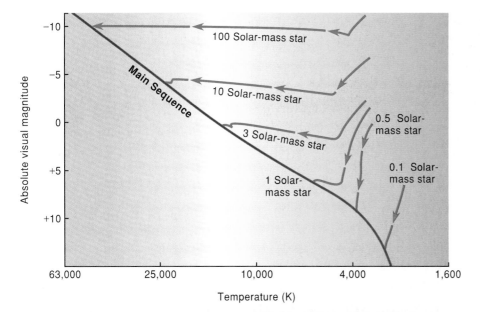

◀ **figure 15.10**
Theoretical pre-main-sequence tracks in the H-R diagram. Stars of different masses follow distinct vertical paths, called Hayashi tracks, prior to turning onto the main sequence.

▼ **figure 15.11**
Infrared emission from the bipolar outflow source L1551. **a.** The lobes extend about 1.5 light-years from the center. The source is believed to be a T Tauri star. **b.** The colors indicate blue-shifted and red-shifted gas approaching and receding at about 10 km/sec relative to the molecular cloud.

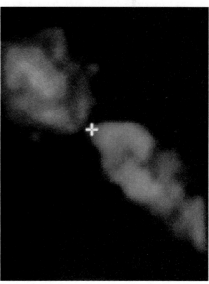

a.

b.

the life cycles of stars

protosun evaporates, allowing light to penetrate the outer envelope for the first time. Convective movement of material in and out of the core causes variations in brightness, which has been observed in T Tauri stars. Our protosun has reached another milestone as a huge, pulsating, pre-main-sequence star, or T Tauri object, as large as the orbit of Mercury.

Nebulae associated with T Tauri stars are located several parsecs from the protosun. These are called **Herbig-Haro objects** after the astronomers who first recognized the clouds as evidence of star birth. The clouds are formed when T Tauri stars eject bipolar flows of matter that become visible when they collide with the gas and dust surrounding the

star (figs. 15.11 and 15.12). Material is apparently moving toward as well as away from the collapsing central star. The bipolar flow is restricted in two opposing streams because a flat accretion disk has formed at right angles to the star's spin axis. The accretion disk as well as the jets are the result of the rapid implosion that took place prior to the T Tauri stage.

The temperature of the protosun continues to rise until it reaches about one million K, when nuclear fusion of deuterium takes place. Once the process begins, thermonuclear energy produced in the core is carried to the surface of the pre-main-sequence Sun by convection. More deuterium from the surface is

brought to the core during the return convective flow. The stepped-up energy production raises the temperature high enough for surface deuterium to ignite. The emerging star increases in size to five times the present Sun, while strong stellar winds drive away incoming gas and dust.

About 50 million years have elapsed since the beginning of contraction. By now the core temperature has reached 10 million K. Thermonuclear fusion of hydrogen begins and the Sun emerges as a **zero-age main-sequence** or **ZAMS object** in thermal and hydrostatic equilibrium (fig. 15.13).

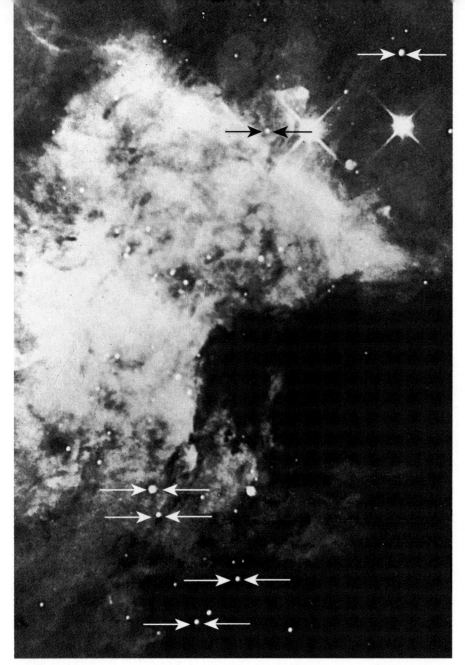

**figure 15.12**
Infrared images of T Tauri stars (*arrows*) in M42, the Orion nebula.

### The meaning of the main sequence

Imagine a nonrotating, nonmagnetic model star in hydrostatic equilibrium. Its chemical composition is uniform throughout, having recently evolved from a nebulous cloud. The core has reached fusion temperature and the star maintains thermal equilibrium as energy works its way up to the photosphere. Moreover, the energy of the core and, ultimately, the luminosity are a function of the mass of the star.

Consider many stars identical in mass and composition to the model star. Can we expect that they will all evolve in the same way? The answer is yes; the stars

are subject to the same physical laws. The structure of a star is determined by its composition and mass.

Suppose we select any number of stars of different mass but similar composition. These stars have evolved from gas and dust globules of unlike mass. If each star is to maintain equilibrium, the most massive, largest star will be the most luminous and will radiate at maximum intensity at the wavelength of highest temperature (Wien's displacement law). Conversely, the least luminous dwarf star will radiate at maximum intensity at the lowest temperature. When we graph luminosity versus temperature for these

stars, the result is a series of points generating the main sequence.

On the H-R diagram, the main sequence appears as a band rather than a line because (1) small differences in chemical composition do exist among these stars, and (2) differences show up in later stages of evolution that cause a "spreading" of the ZAMS.

### The Birth of Giant Stars

Let us suppose that part of a molecular cloud is made unstable by a shock wave and breaks up into collapsing dense globules. Each of these fragments represents a future blue supergiant found in an O association. As contraction continues, molecules in the center are packed closer together and heated by gravitational energy. Half of the potential gravitational energy heats up the cloud while the other half is radiated into space. Astronomers detect the emissions using antennae tuned to the microwave frequency of the carbon monoxide molecule.

As the core increases in density, the temperature becomes high enough for other molecules such as $H_2O$ to emit infrared radiation. The process continues, and in a few hundred thousand years, the core has reached temperatures over 10 million K, hot enough for nuclear fusion to begin. The star is now a hydrogen-burning main-sequence object with a surface temperature in excess of 20,000 K.

In the interior of massive stars, where temperatures exceed 15 million degrees, elements other than hydrogen and helium take part in the nuclear reaction. The so-called **carbon-nitrogen-oxygen cycle** was worked out by Hans Bethe in 1938. At various stages, carbon joins with hydrogen to produce the elements nitrogen and oxygen. Eventually, nitrogen and a proton combine to yield carbon and helium. As in the proton-proton chain, helium is the end product, while carbon acts as a catalyst, necessary to initiate the reaction but chemically unchanged. Other nuclear reactions at even higher temperatures transform helium to the heavier elements.

The newly evolved star is one of many in an O association. The stars are still buried in the molecular cloud; their presence is revealed by their effect on surrounding dust. Radiation from the stars

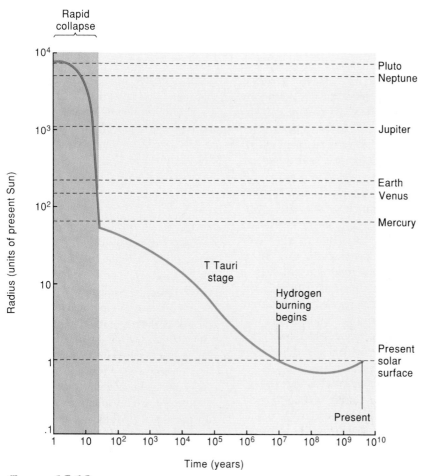

**figure 15.13**

Stages in evolution of the Sun from protostar to the main sequence.

**figure 15.14**

The Trifid nebula, M20, in Sagittarius is noted for its prominent dust lanes. The bright ionized region surrounding a hot star is called a Strömgren sphere.

is absorbed by the dust, which in turn emits energy in IR and radio wavelengths.

The stars also affect molecules in the gas cloud. The UV radiation emitted from hot O- and B-type stars forms shell-like regions within the molecular cloud. First the high-energy radiation breaks down hydrogen molecules into atoms. Then the hydrogen atoms are stripped of their electrons and become ionized. The glowing shell lies buried in the cloud and remains opaque to visible wavelengths, but it can be verified by radio-frequency radiation generated by free electrons. Inexorably, the bubble gnaws into the molecular cloud and sweeps away the dust grains. Finally, the glowing shell becomes visible as a bright *Strömgren sphere* associated with an emission nebula (fig. 15.14).

## On the Main Sequence

As we have learned, the position of a star on the main sequence depends upon its mass. Massive stars are brighter, have higher temperatures, and fall on the upper branch of the main sequence. The blue giant stars deplete their hydrogen and enter a new evolutionary stage long before the dim red dwarfs leave the lower branch of the main sequence.

For example, a star of 15 solar masses will burn hydrogen for only 10 million years, whereas the Sun and stars like it take 10 billion years to use up their available fuel. It is no surprise that hot O and B stars are rare since their time is all too brief. In contrast, more than half the stars around us are red dwarfs, indicating that dust and gas clouds are more apt to fragment into smaller globules than large. The abundance of binary and multiple-star systems provides further evidence of this tendency toward the formation of less massive stars. As a result, each cycle of star birth increases the number of red dwarfs that end their days by cooling into dark cinders that cannot be recycled into new stars.

The present population of young stars contain elements heavier than helium so that hydrogen burning can be sustained by the carbon-nitrogen cycle as well as the proton-proton chain. The proton-proton reaction occurs in all stars but is most important in the less massive, lower-main-sequence stars. The carbon-nitrogen cycle is restricted to the massive stars of the upper main sequence. Between these extremes there is a transitory region where both processes are in operation. The stars in this region are intermediate-mass stars (about one solar mass) that are hot enough to start the C-N cycle but not massive enough to make it the primary energy source.

## Upper-Branch Main-Sequence Stars

The massive stars on the main sequence have internal temperatures above 15 million K so that the C-N cycle is the source of energy production in the core. The size of the core depends upon the mass of the star; one as large as 30 solar masses will have over half its substance in the core. At such high temperatures, the core cannot maintain radiative stability, and in the turbulence, energy is transported away by convection. As the hydrogen at the center is converted to helium, additional hydrogen is brought down by the convective currents. This action is significant because it keeps the chemical composition the same throughout the core. Energy production ceases in the entire core when all available fuel for synthesis is used up.

The energy produced leaves the core and reaches the surface by radiating through the envelope. As hydrogen burning proceeds in the core, the star steadily increases in diameter and luminosity as surface temperature declines. Its H-R diagram graph will be a track up and to the right of its main-sequence position.

## Lower-Branch Main-Sequence Stars

Metal-rich stars of 1.5 solar masses and less have a lower rate of energy generation and remain on the main sequence for a longer time than more massive stars. Their energy production is confined to a small radiative region at the center. The size of the core is determined by the mass of the star. Beyond the core is an outer convective zone that extends to the surface. In stars with masses as low as 0.27 solar masses, the convective zone may reach down to the center. Thus the internal structures of upper- and lower-branch main-sequence stars are reversed: an upper-branch star possesses a convective core and a radiative envelope, and a lower-branch star has a radiative core and a convective envelope.

The smallest possible star on the main sequence will have a mass equal to 0.07 solar masses. Below this limit, a star cannot reach the temperature and density required for hydrogen to ignite. Instead, the star will contract into a dark sphere and emit its energy in the infrared range.

Sunlike stars develop a helium core that gradually increases in size. In the absence of convection, the hydrogen at the core is not replenished. In time, the hydrogen-burning region moves outward as the star increases in luminosity as well as surface temperature. Let us follow the progress of a sunlike star through its cycle of energy production.

In a star the size of the Sun, the energy-producing core is smaller than the planet Jupiter. Here, deep inside the star, matter is crushed together to a density greater than 100 times the density of water. The temperature has reached 13 million K and all known substances are in a gaseous state. This is low compared with the temperatures that will be attained later in the life of the star. As hydrogen is transformed into helium, energy leaves this turbulent core and enters the main body of the star. Now the energy is alternately absorbed, emitted, and scattered as it radiates to the outer convective shell where turbulent mixing takes place. Finally, the energy reaches the surface and radiates into space.

Energy production diminishes the number of protons available for the fusion process. You will recall that a star remains in hydrostatic equilibrium as long as core pressure and gravity are in balance. A reduction in one force tips the scales in favor of the other. A decrease in the number of colliding particles reduces the pressure and upsets the equilibrium. Gravity responds by compressing the core. As particles fall toward the center, the distance between them is reduced and collisions become more frequent. A transfer of energy occurs as kinetic energy of particle motion due to gravity is converted to thermal energy in the core. The star adjusts to the new situation by converting hydrogen to helium at a faster rate. But the increase in core temperature demands an adjustment in thermal equilibrium. The envelope of the star expands and provides a greater surface area to radiate additional energy into space. At this point, our star slowly increases in luminosity, temperature, and size, while deep in its core the available proton fuel is steadily depleted.

## To the Giant Branch

In chapter 13, we discussed how thousands of stars graphed on the H-R diagram fall into definite groupings and patterns. Most stars plotted on the diagram follow the main sequence (fig. 13.13). We are reminded that main-sequence stars differ in temperature, mass, and luminosity but are similar in one important respect—they all maintain equilibrium by converting hydrogen to helium.

Off the main sequence there are yellow, orange, and red giants on the branch situated above the middle and to the upper right of the diagram. Other luminous stars stretch horizontally from the tip of the giant branch toward the left. Finally, white dwarf stars are found clustered together in the lower left portion of the diagram.

This stellar distribution might suggest an evolutionary sequence, but we cannot be sure because the stars plotted in the diagram were selected at random and vary in age, composition, and origin. To discover how stars change over a long period of time it will be necessary to graph many stars of the same age. Then we can compare the diagrams of younger stars with others we know to be older. Our problem is to find many stars of the same age and common origin.

Fortunately, the task of selecting stars born at the same time and place is not as formidable as it might seem. In chapter 14 we found that most stars are not single, as the Sun is, but are gathered together in multiple systems, clusters, and associations. Our next task will be to examine in detail galactic and globular clusters for evidence of stellar evolution away from the main sequence.

## Galactic Clusters

Open clusters of different ages provide the information we need to determine

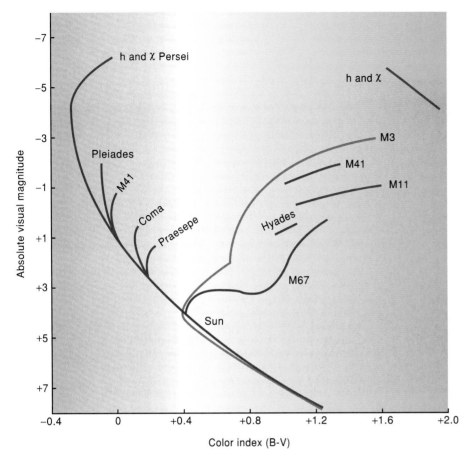

**figure 15.15**

Composite H-R diagram for star clusters of different ages.

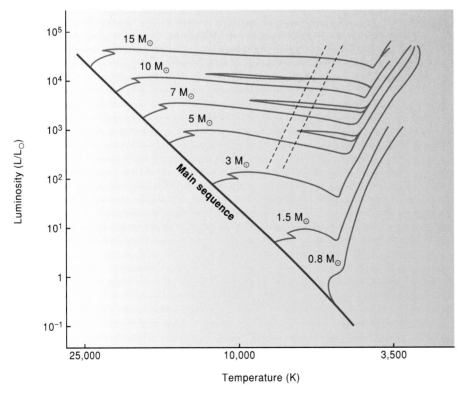

**figure 15.16**

Post-main-sequence evolutionary tracks of population I stars from the main sequence to the giant stage.

how stars evolve. These clusters are not permanent formations in the Galaxy but eventually will be dispersed by their random motions. Also, the shearing action of the rotation of the galactic arms tends to spread the stars apart.

When young open clusters are plotted on the H-R diagram, most of them are on the main sequence. Blue giant stars are an exception—they appear to have shifted slightly to the right of the position they occupied when they were zero-age main-sequence stars (fig. 15.15). An older galactic cluster will have stars of even lower luminosities than the blue giants, off and to the right of the main sequence. In these older clusters there are no blue giants at all. Instead we find red giant stars occupying the upper right portion of the graph. All the stars greater in luminosity than the Sun have peeled off to the right into a well-developed branch of giant stars. The less luminous yellow giants are above the Sun's position on the main sequence, and the most luminous red supergiants are at the top of the branch. The graph strongly indicates that the luminous, hydrogen-burning blue giant stars evolve into red supergiants (fig. 15.16).

## Globular Clusters

The evidence of evolution indicated by aging galactic clusters is supported by stars in globular clusters, which contain the oldest known stars (fig. 15.17). When

**figure 15.17**

The globular cluster Omega Centauri contains tens of thousands of stars concentrated toward the center of the cluster.

In this observing project our objective will be to estimate the relative ages of several well-known clusters that are bright enough to be resolved in binoculars. Our procedure will be to observe the clusters and compare the brightness and color of the member stars. Not all main-sequence stars are represented in galactic clusters. The luminous stars are absent in older clusters. Our selection includes some famous naked-eye examples: the Pleiades, the Hyades, h and χ Persei, and the Praesepe.

Let us begin our observations in late winter when the Pleiades and the Hyades in Taurus are seen in the early evening sky. Six bright stars in the Pleiades form a small asterism resembling a dipper. The best view of the group is through binoculars or a low-power telescope. The entire field is filled with stars of every magnitude, from Alcyone, a third-magnitude type B7 star, to fainter, less luminous main-sequence type G stars.

Altogether, there are more than several hundred stars in the Pleiades located about 400 light-years from the Earth. A long-exposure photograph of the region shows that the brightest stars are surrounded by nebulosity (fig. 15.18).

The Hyades is the nearest cluster, at a distance of 150 light-years from the Earth. Within the distinctive V formation, representing the head of Taurus, there are about 20 stars visible to the unaided eye. Low-power telescopes show a number of visual binary stars sparkling in contrasting colors. There are no bright O and B stars to be seen, indicating that the Hyades cluster is older than the Pleiades. The brightest main-sequence stars range in spectral class from type A7 to K0. The brightest star in the constellation, Aldebaran, is in the foreground about 60 light-years from the Earth. Over 300 stars make up the Hyades cluster.

Between the stars Delta Cassiopeiae and Alpha Persei, there is a hazy glow representing the clusters h and χ Persei (fig. 15.19). The clusters are visible through binoculars in the same field and are therefore referred to as the "double cluster." However, they are separated by a thousand light-years and appear together only because they lie in the same line of sight. The stars in both clusters include many very young, luminous B0 and B1 stars.

**figure 15.18**
The open cluster M45, the Pleiades, in the constellation Taurus.

**figure 15.19**
The double galactic cluster h and χ Persei.

The Praesepe cluster is found in the obscure constellation of Cancer. Barely visible to the unaided eye, the Praesepe, or Beehive, is a striking view in binoculars. The cluster is very similar to the Hyades in age and number of stars. Its brightest stars are spectral type A0 (fig. 15.20).

If we organize these clusters in order of the luminosity of the brightest member stars, h and χ Persei are the youngest clusters, followed by the Pleiades. The Hyades and the Praesepe are about the same age.

these aged stars in the Galaxy are graphed on the H-R diagram, they follow a track that is similar to the plot of an old galactic cluster. For both galactic and globular clusters, the turnoff point on the main sequence indicates the age of the group. The stars in the oldest clusters that are still on the main sequence have lower masses and fainter absolute magnitudes.

As further evidence that stellar distribution on and away from the main sequence is indicative of evolution, young galactic clusters have red giants that are more luminous than those found in globular clusters. This is so because in globular clusters the most luminous red supergiants have already passed on to later evolutionary stages. In younger galactic clusters, red supergiants represent the stars that have recently evolved from the most luminous blue giants. Consequently, they emerge as the brightest red supergiants.

In summary, the main sequence shows how stars of different mass produce energy by converting hydrogen to helium. How long the process continues depends upon the quantity of hydrogen contained in a star. A massive blue giant has a higher core temperature and will consume more hydrogen in a shorter period of time than a red dwarf star. Therefore, blue giants last for only a few million years while the red dwarfs will continue to shine for as long as 40 or 50 billion years. Our Sun's estimated time as a main-sequence star is about 10 billion years. We already know that our middle-aged Sun has been shining for about half that length of time. In another five billion years the Sun will leave the main sequence and follow an evolutionary track represented by stars located on other branches of the H-R diagram (fig. 15.21).

## Later Stages of Stellar Evolution

During the hydrogen-burning stage, a star slowly increases in luminosity as it builds up a helium core. Its graph on the H-R diagram runs above the main sequence and to the right toward the giant branch. At first a star's journey is slow, but the

**figure 15.20**
The open cluster M44 (NGC 2632) in Cancer. Called the Praesepe and the Beehive, this fourth-magnitude cluster is about 500 light-years distant.

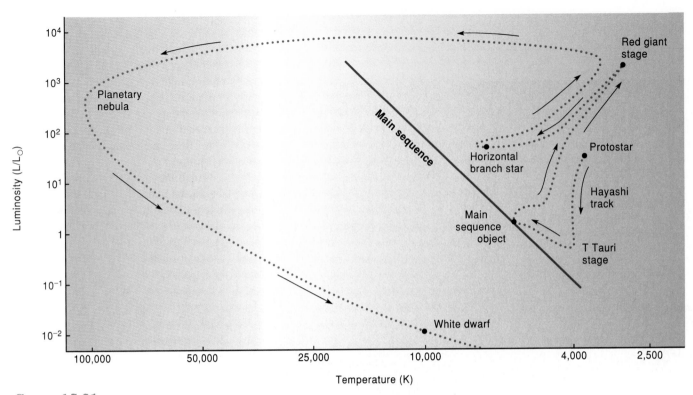

**figure 15.21**

The evolutionary track of a sunlike star in the H-R diagram.

tempo picks up as the hydrogen available for conversion to helium is depleted. Once the hydrogen is gone, the nuclear furnace shuts down and energy production in the core ends. Without thermal pressure, the helium core collapses and forces the particles together. The core contains protons and neutrons that took part in the fusion process as well as freely moving electrons. The free electrons are squeezed closer together and, as the distance between them decreases, their mutual repulsion increases. In this high-density state, Newtonian laws describing the behavior of particles in random motion no longer apply. Such a high-density substance is called a **degenerate electron gas.** Convection is no longer possible because the degenerate core behaves like a solid. Energy is now transmitted from the center by conduction, which equalizes the temperature throughout the core. Once again, hydrogen ignites and begins to produce helium, now in a thin shell above the core.

The star expands in size as interior temperature and the rate of energy production rapidly increase. On the H-R diagram, stars from 1.0 to 1.5 solar masses

are graphed as points on a steep track up the giant branch. The surface temperature is reduced as the expanding envelope provides the increased area needed for radiation. In a time span measured in a few billion years, a sunlike star will be transformed into a luminous red giant. A blue giant of 15 solar masses will make the change in only a few million years.

A sunlike star will have sustained a striking alteration in appearance and substance. It has a core only five times the Earth in diameter, yet its outer envelope stretches across a distance equal to the diameter of the Earth's orbit. As described in chapter 13, a red supergiant may become larger than the orbit of Mars. Its core is a ball of inert helium no bigger than the Earth but compressed to 100,000 times greater than the density of water. The central temperature of the helium core reaches 70 million K. Meanwhile, energy production continues in the narrow hydrogen-burning shell above the core. Some of the energy is conducted down to the inert helium while the remainder radiates into the body of the star and finally to the surface.

As the process continues, a dramatic event takes place. The core temperature has increased to 100 million K, causing the inert helium to ignite and start a new thermonuclear process. Helium is about to be converted to carbon, but the conditions are not the same as they were when the star was a hydrogen-burning main-sequence object. The degenerate core behaves like a dense solid that hardly expands as the temperature rises. Something must give way! It does when the temperature is high enough to trigger a sudden explosion that astronomers have coined the **helium flash.** The temperature soars to 300 million K, but then subsides to 100 million degrees as helium is transformed into carbon and oxygen.

This new reaction is called the **triple-alpha process** because helium nuclei, or alpha particles, are involved. As described by E. E. Salpeter in 1952, two helium nuclei combine to form the element beryllium. The beryllium will combine again with helium to create carbon. The carbon may also join with an alpha particle to form oxygen.

At this point, the star embarks on a new phase in its evolution. At its center

## The Carbon-Nitrogen-Oxygen Cycle

A star at the hydrogen-burning stage combines four protons into one helium nucleus by means of two types of reactions. The *proton-proton chain,* introduced in Methods and Understandings 12.1, combines three protons to form a $^3$He nucleus, which reacts with another $^3$He to obtain $^4$He and $2^1$H. In the second process, the *carbon-nitrogen-oxygen cycle,* four protons combine at different stages with carbon, nitrogen, and oxygen. In the process, the final outcome is $^{12}$C and $^4$He, so that $^{12}$C serves as a catalyst to set the mechanism in motion. The reaction begins as carbon combines with hydrogen to form the isotope of nitrogen, $^{13}$N, and release a photon of gamma radiation.

$$^{12}C + {}^1H \rightarrow {}^{13}N + \gamma$$

The unstable isotope $^{13}$N breaks down into carbon, $^{13}$C. In the process a positron and neutrino are released.

$$^{13}N \rightarrow {}^{13}C + e^+ + \nu$$

The $^{13}$C joins with a proton to form the stable nitrogen isotope, $^{14}$N.

$$^{13}C + {}^1H \rightarrow {}^{14}N + \gamma$$

At the next stage, $^{14}$N combines with a proton to build the unstable isotope of oxygen, $^{15}$O,

$$^{14}N + {}^1H \rightarrow {}^{15}O + \gamma,$$

which becomes an isotope of nitrogen, $^{15}$N, a positron, and a neutrino.

$$^{15}O \rightarrow {}^{15}N + e^+ + \nu$$

The cycle is completed when $^{15}$N joins with another proton to form $^{12}$C and a helium nucleus, $^4$He.

$$^{15}N + {}^1H \rightarrow {}^{12}C + {}^4He$$

The net result is a $^4$He nucleus from four protons, which is the same outcome as the proton-proton chain.

---

lies a helium-burning core covered by a hydrogen-burning shell. As carbon production continues, the helium-burning star slowly increases in temperature while its luminosity remains about the same. On the H-R diagram, these changes will graph as points extending to the left of the giant branch.

When the oldest globular clusters are graphed, they show a well-developed *horizontal branch* of stars from the tip of the giant branch to the left across the H-R diagram (fig. 15.21). These are believed to be stars that have evolved beyond the red giant stage. A one-solar-mass horizontal-branch star is reduced in size to about four times the Sun's diameter while its helium-burning center measures only twice the diameter of the Earth. The entire core is no more than one-tenth the size of the Sun, yet it contains almost 80% of the star's total mass. Energy is transported from the helium-burning center by convection and radiates from the core through the main body of the star to the surface.

When the helium core is depleted, the triple-alpha process continues in a helium-burning shell below the hydrogen-burning shell. The core consists of carbon and oxygen, the first elements heavier than helium to be synthesized

inside the star. The production of oxygen continues as more carbon unites with helium. In time, the carbon core will contract and raise the temperature to 500 million degrees.

Now the surface temperature alternately increases and decreases as successive ignitions of elements heavier than carbon take place inside the core. In more massive stars contraction continues, driving the temperature to one billion degrees. In these behemoths the temperature is high enough for carbon nuclei to fuse into magnesium and silicon. In the process, alpha particles are released to enter into further reactions that build up an inert iron core.

### Evolution and Variable Stars

At various times after its evolution from the main sequence, a star may undergo periods of instability and pulsate as an intrinsic variable star. Recall from the description of cepheids in chapter 13 that there are classical (Type I) and W Virginis (Type II) cepheid stars. Type I cepheids are rich in heavy elements and belong to the population of stars found in the spiral arms of the Galaxy. Type II cepheids and RR Lyrae stars are members of the old population of stars found

in the globular clusters located outside the Galaxy's spiral arms.

When stars between 2 and 10 solar masses leave the main sequence, they move horizontally to the right across the **instability strip** where cepheid and RR Lyrae variable stars are found. This first crossing of the instability strip takes place during the hydrogen-burning-shell phase as the stars approach the red giant stage. These are relatively young Type I cepheid stars found in the spiral arms (figs. 13.13 and 15.16). After helium burning begins, a massive star may cross the instability strip two or three times during later stages of evolution.

Not all main-sequence stars will become variables. Stars of 40 or more solar masses leave the main sequence as other stars do but never reach the instability strip. These heavyweights eject their outer layers and become the hottest stars known.

The instability strip extends far enough to allow low-mass stars called *dwarf cepheids* to become short-period variables after leaving the main sequence. Such stars are found in globular clusters and range in spectral type between A and F. Stars on the lower branch of the main sequence approach the giant branch

## The Alpha Particle and Nuclear Reactions

When a star has progressed to the red giant stage, core temperatures have reached 100 million K, which is high enough to begin other nuclear reactions. The stellar core consists of helium nuclei, or alpha particles, which are fundamental to the formation of elements beyond helium. Astronomers believe that all known elements were transmuted from simple hydrogen. The minerals that sustain all life, past and present, were produced inside the stars prior to the evolution of the Sun and planets.

The first reaction begins as two alpha particles unite to form an isotope of the metal beryllium.

$$^4He + {}^4He \rightleftharpoons {}^8Be + \gamma$$

In the process a gamma ray photon is released. The beryllium is unstable and reverts back to helium as indicated by the arrows shown in both directions. But the reaction continues because a number of the beryllium atoms last long enough to join with a third alpha particle to form carbon and release another gamma ray.

$$^4He + {}^8Be \rightarrow {}^{12}C + \gamma$$

The formation of a carbon nucleus by the synthesis of three helium nuclei is called the *triple alpha process.*

When $^{12}C$ reaches a higher concentration, the process may continue by combining $^{12}C$ with another alpha particle.

$$^{12}C + {}^4He \rightarrow {}^{16}O + \gamma$$

The end product is oxygen, $^{16}O$, which may join with $^4He$ to produce neon.

$$^{16}O + {}^4He \rightarrow {}^{20}Ne + \gamma$$

The process continues until the interior of the star consists of concentrated shells of elements above an inert iron core.

$$^{20}Ne + {}^4He \rightarrow {}^{24}Mg + \gamma, \text{ and so on.}$$

**figure 15.22**

The emission nebulae NGC 6164–6165. A massive central star violently ejects material that produces two nebulosities around the star. The rapid loss of mass may trigger the end of the star's life; it may become a supernova.

along a track below and to the right of the instability strip.

### How Stars Lose Mass

Our present understanding of the ultimate fate of stars is based upon the investigation of **mass loss** taking place during the later phases of their evolution. Mass loss occurs in a number of ways.

Huge supergiant stars have low surface gravity so that their outer layers may easily escape into space; and they have significant stellar winds that eject vast amounts of gas and dust into extensive clouds (fig. 15.22). Such stars expel as much as one solar mass in only a few hundred thousand years. Owing to their internal instability, horizontal-branch stars experience changes in brightness and temperature; in time, rhythmic undulations will cause the outer layers to be ejected into circumstellar shells of gas and dust.

Further evidence of mass loss is found among stars in clusters. Various open clusters, including the Hyades and the Pleiades, contain white dwarf stars along with main-sequence stars of masses greater than 3 $M_\odot$. However, we know that the more massive stars are first to leave the main sequence and reach the horizontal branch as helium-burning objects. If most of the white dwarfs we observe average between 0.5 and 0.7 $M_\odot$, how did the early main-sequence stars shed their mass? There must be a phase during which the stars lose most of their substance. How this takes place depends upon the original mass of the evolving star.

In less massive post-horizontal-branch stars, the temperatures are not high enough to ignite the carbon-oxygen core. Instead, the stellar core contracts and increases in temperature while energy continues to be produced in helium and hydrogen shells enclosing the core. Meanwhile, the outer layers expand, cool, and form an extensive nebulous shell about the exposed interior region. Many stars pass through this *planetary nebula* phase before reaching terminal stage. Keep in mind that a planetary nebula

**figure 15.23**

The Dumbbell nebula, M27, in Vulpecula. Loss of mass from these sunlike stars is much less violent than the type of mass loss experienced by supergiant stars (fig. 15.22).

may result when stellar winds have stripped away the outer layers of a red supergiant star and reduced its mass to about the mass of the Sun.

## Planetary Nebulae

When viewed in a telescope, a planetary nebula has the appearance of an oval or circular disk surrounding a blue-green central star. The simplest have shells of gas that superficially resemble the disks of the planets Uranus and Neptune. Herschel noted the similarity and named them planetary nebulae. Although many are spherical, most are a varied assortment of rings, dumbbells, hour glasses, or no shape at all (fig. 15.23). Some have been discovered in globular clusters, but most of them are concentrated in the plane of the Galaxy between the spiral arms. About 1000 planetary nebulae are known.

The central stars found in planetary nebulae have temperatures that range from 50,000 to over 100,000 K. They radiate strongly in the ultraviolet range and cause the gaseous envelope to fluoresce. Ultraviolet radiation from the star ionizes atoms in the gas. When the ions recombine with free electrons, radiation is emitted in the longer wavelengths of visible light. The spectra of planetary nebulae contain emission lines of doubly ionized nitrogen and oxygen. This gives a blue-green appearance to the inner region where the radiation is more intense. Ionized hydrogen provides the pink and red glow seen at the outer boundary of the visible region.

A planetary nebula extends far beyond the bright gaseous envelope. The portion we see represents the limiting distance of the emission region of the central star. How far the region extends depends upon the luminosity of the star and the density of the gas shell. At greater distances from the center, cooler and more tenuous neutral hydrogen in the nebula cannot be observed visually and is detected by means of radio telescopes.

The planetary nebula stage represents a brief period in the history of a star. In less than 100,000 years, the outer envelope will reach distances exceeding 10,000 AU. After the nebula dissipates and energy production subsides, the highly compressed center will become a white dwarf star.

## SUMMARY

Stellar evolution is a slow process beginning with the birth of stars in diffuse dust and gas clouds. The interstellar medium contains giant molecular clouds and dark nebulae composed of dust grains. Protected from radiation by the dust, atoms of the gas combine to form complex molecules. From this, a stellar association evolves when portions of a cloud become unstable and form into many density cores.

The molecular cloud cores contract, increase in density, and form protostars of different masses and temperatures. During rapid collapse, a protostar becomes a pre-main-sequence star, called a T Tauri star, that ejects matter into an accretion disk and extensive bipolar streams. At the end of the T Tauri stage, the star reaches thermal and hydrostatic equilibrium as a hydrogen-burning, zero-age main-sequence object.

The time spent by a star on the main sequence will depend upon its mass. Blue giants are the first to deplete their hydrogen and evolve to the supergiant stage. Less massive stars remain on the main sequence for a longer period of time. As available hydrogen is used up, the helium core collapses and increases in temperature. In time the star will be transformed into a red giant.

When the temperature in the core increases to more than 100 million K, the core ignites in a helium flash. Helium in the core is converted into carbon by the triple-alpha process. Now the star passes through successive stages of core ignition that form shells of heavier elements until iron is produced.

At various times after their evolution from the main sequence, stars may undergo periods of instability and pulsate as intrinsic variable stars. Variable stars are classified as Type I cepheids that belong to the population of young stars found in the spiral arms of the Galaxy; and as Type II cepheids and RR Lyrae stars, which are members of the old population of stars found in globular clusters and in the halo of stars surrounding the central bulge of the Galaxy.

Massive stars lose mass by expelling their outer layers into space. Less-massive stars expand into a planetary nebulae where the outer layers of the star form an extensive nebulous shell surrounding the exposed central region. The planetary nebula stage represents a brief period of time in the history of the star prior to reaching terminal stage as a white dwarf.

## KEY TERMS

carbon-nitrogen-oxygen cycle

degenerate electron gas

giant molecular clouds (GMC)

Hayashi track

helium flash

Herbig-Haro objects

instability strip

mass loss

planetary nebulae

supernovae

triple-alpha process

T Tauri star

zero-age main-sequence
(ZAMS) object

## PROBLEMS

1. Describe the evolution of a star of one solar mass from a dark nebula to the main sequence.

2. Explain how star clusters of different ages are useful in determining stellar evolution.

3. How do stars change in luminosity and temperature as they evolve from the main sequence to the tip of the giant branch?

4. Describe the events that mark the end of a star's time on the horizontal branch of the H-R diagram.

5. Explain why the less luminous stars found in globular clusters are still on the main sequence.

6. Why do the central stars in planetary nebulae have such high temperatures?

7. What important events are triggered by the rapid collapse of a protostar approaching the T Tauri stage?

8. Explain why more stars form inside molecular clouds than elsewhere in the spiral arms.

9. What evidence is there that energy is produced at the center of stars by nuclear reactions?

10. Type I cepheid stars are younger than Type II. Explain.

11. Why are red supergiants more likely to be found in galactic clusters than in globular clusters?

12. Explain why more Type I cepheid stars are found in the spiral arms than elsewhere in the Galaxy.

13. Main-sequence stars vary from luminous, hot blue giants to dim, low-temperature red dwarfs. Why are there no main-sequence stars above and below these limits?

14. When contraction stops and hydrogen burning begins, what determines the location of a star on the main sequence?

15. What does the location of the turn-off point on the main sequence indicate in terms of the ages of clusters?

## REFERENCES

Becker, S. A. 1985. "Cepheid Evolution." In *Cepheids: Theory and Observations,* edited by Barry F. Madore. Proceedings of the IAU Colloquium, no. 82. Cambridge: Cambridge University Press.

Bok, Bart J. 1977. "The Birth of Stars." In *The New Astronomy and Space Science Reader,* edited by John C. Brandt and Stephen P. Maran. San Francisco: W. H. Freeman and Company.

Demarque, Pierre. 1992. "Stellar Evolution." In *The Astronomical and Astrophysical Encyclopedia,* edited by Stephen P. Maran. New York: Van Nostrand Reinhold.

Gordon, M. A., and W. B. Burton. 1970. Carbon Monoxide in the Galaxy. *Scientific American* 240, no.5 (May).

Herbig, George H. 1979. "The Youngest Stars." In *New Frontiers in Astronomy: Readings from Scientific American.* San Francisco: W. H. Freeman and Company.

Herbst, William, and George E. Assousa. 1979. Supernovas and Star Formation. *Scientific American* 241, no. 2 (August).

Iben, Icko, Jr. 1977. "Globular Cluster Stars." In *The New Astronomy and Space Science Reader,* edited by John C. Brandt and Stephen P. Maran. San Francisco: W. H. Freeman and Company.

Kaler, James B. 1988. Journeys on the H-R Diagram. *Sky and Telescope* 75, no. 5 (May).

Reeves, Hubert. 1965. "Stellar Energy Sources." In *Stellar Structure,* vol. 8 of *Stars and Stellar Systems,* Gerard P. Kuiper, gen. ed. Chicago: University of Chicago Press.

Reipurth, Bo. 1984. Bok Globules. *Mercury* (Astronomical Society of the Pacific) 13, no. 2 (March/April).

Schramm, David N., and Robert N. Clayton. 1978. Did a Supernova Trigger the Formation of the Solar System? *Scientific American* 239, no. 4 (October).

Schwarzschild, Martin. 1958. *Structure and Evolution of the Stars.* Princeton: Princeton University Press.

Spitzer, Lyman. 1983. Interstellar Matter and the Birth and Death of Stars. *Mercury* 12, no. 5 (September/October).

Stahler, Steven W. 1991. The Early Life of Stars. *Scientific American* 265, no. 1 (July).

Struve, Otto. 1950. *Stellar Evolution.* Princeton: Princeton University Press.

Zeilik, Michael. 1978. The Birth of Massive Stars. *Scientific American* 238, no. 4 (April).

chapter

16

how stars perish

M1 (NGC 1952), the Crab nebula, in Taurus.
The supernova that was responsible for this
remnant was seen as a "visiting star" by Chinese
astronomers in 1054.

To reach one of several terminal stages, stars ranging in mass from about one to more than 20 solar masses must expel most of their substance into space. The greater number of stars, including the Sun, will ultimately end up as slow-cooling **white dwarf stars;** others will become smaller and denser **neutron stars.** A more massive star may become a **black hole** from which neither particles nor radiation can escape. The strong gravitational fields and the behavior of radiation associated with white dwarfs, neutron stars, and, in particular, black holes are described by Einstein's general theory of relativity. Before proceeding further, let us investigate how mass, gravity, space, radiation, and time are treated in Einstein's theory.

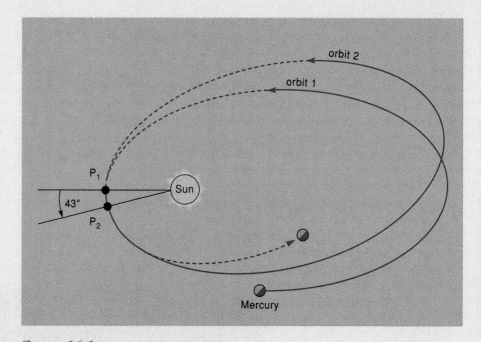

**figure 16.1**

The advance of the perihelion of Mercury was predicted by Albert Einstein in his general theory of relativity. The major axis of Mercury's orbit advances 43″ of arc per century.

## The Geometry of Space-time

In 1915, Einstein formulated the **general theory of relativity,** which considers accelerated motion and gives new meaning to gravitation. Einstein treats gravitation as an effect of the curvature of space rather than an attractive force between masses.

The universe is a four-dimensional continuum; there are three dimensions of space and one of time. All physical phenomena are measured in this four-dimensional **spacetime.** In spacetime, the interval between two events does not have absolute value, nor is it independent of the change in position of an object in motion.

Space is not merely a void between objects but has geometric properties that are dependent upon the distribution of the mass it contains. Just as a magnet affects the space around it by creating a magnetic field, a mass produces a corresponding gravitational field in spacetime.

As we have learned, bodies in a gravitational field experience the same acceleration regardless of their masses. Einstein interprets this in the following way.

According to Newton's second law of motion, force = inertial mass × acceleration. In a gravitational field, force = gravitational mass × intensity of the gravitational field. From this we find acceleration (*a*):

$$a = \frac{\text{grav. mass} \times \text{intensity of grav. field}}{\text{inertial mass}}.$$

By proper choice of units, the ratio of the gravitational mass to the inertial mass is unity, and the acceleration becomes independent of the mass of the body in motion. Thus we find acceleration to be a function of the intensity of the gravitational field that determines the curvature of spacetime. This **principle of equivalence** of inertial mass and gravitational mass is a fundamental law of relativity.

## Confirmation of the General Theory of Relativity

Perturbations are changes in a planet's orbital motion caused by the influence of the planets on one another. Newtonian theory accounts for all perturbations in the orbit of the planet Mercury except for one—an excess in the *advance of the perihelion* of Mercury that amounts to 43 arc seconds per century. In the mid-1840s, the French mathematician Leverrier had calculated perturbations in the orbit of Uranus that led to the discovery of Neptune. He proposed that Mercury's perihelial advance was the effect of perturbations caused by a hypothetical planet located between Mercury and the Sun. No such planet exists.

According to the general theory of relativity, the major axis of the orbit of a planet should slowly rotate as the planet revolves around the Sun. This relativistic effect is insignificant in the nearly circular orbits of most planets but is evident in the eccentric orbit of Mercury (fig. 16.1). Einstein's theory agrees with the observed value within the accuracy of the experiment of a few arc seconds.

When a light ray travels through a gravitational field, the ray will follow the curvature of spacetime in the same way as a planet in orbit. According to theory, if a light ray grazes the Sun, it should be displaced by an angle of 1.75 arc seconds from its true position (fig. 16.2). To prove this, Einstein proposed that photographs be taken during a solar eclipse when stars can be seen in the direction of the Sun; and, later in the year, that a comparison photograph of the star field be taken at night when the

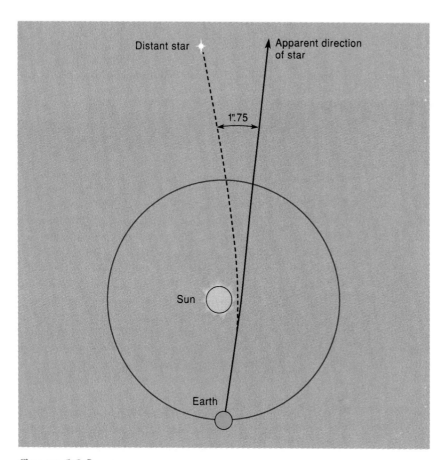

Labels within figure: Distant star, Apparent direction of star, 1".75, Sun, Earth

**figure 16.2**
Curvature of light in a gravitational field.

Sun is in another part of the sky. The first test of the effect came during the solar eclipse of 1919 and showed the predicted displacement. Today, radio telescopes are used to obtain values that are in close agreement with those predicted by the general theory.

Einstein's theory also predicts that in the presence of a strong gravitational field, a clock will run at a slower rate than a similar clock on the surface of the Earth. The frequency of vibration of an atom can serve as a clock. Consider an atom in the photosphere (the visible layer) of a star with a strong gravitational field. It will vibrate at a lesser frequency or a longer wavelength than an atom of the same element in the photosphere of a star with a weaker gravitational field. Verification of this "Einstein effect" has been found in the shift to longer wavelengths of the light from dense white dwarf stars.

## White Dwarf Stars

Studies show that white dwarf stars differ significantly from other stars. Recall the stellar distribution found in the mass-luminosity relation discussed in chapter 14. At that time it was noted how white dwarfs do not conform but show the greatest digression from the curve. They have low luminosities in relation to their masses (fig. 14.6). The temperatures of white dwarfs are high, but the surface area available for radiation has been drastically reduced. Thus white dwarfs such as the companion of Sirius have about the same mass as the Sun but only a fraction of its luminosity (see Methods and Understandings 14.1).

Several hundred white dwarfs are known, five of which are within five parsecs of the Sun. Three of the nearby white dwarfs are companions in binary systems. However, most of the stars listed

are single field stars. Owing to their low intrinsic brightness, less than 100 nearby white dwarfs have been observed in detail. Spectral studies of white dwarfs reveal broad lines that distinguish them from main-sequence stars with narrow lines. The widening is caused by the star's rapid spin. Unless the axis of rotation lies in the line of sight, one limb of the star will approach while the other limb will recede. Spectral lines will show a slight Doppler shift from which the dwarf star can be identified. Moreover, the rapid rotation of the stars generates magnetic fields more than one million times stronger than the magnetic field of the Earth.

The sizes of these stars are on the order of the Earth; they vary between 4800 to nearly 16,000 km in radius. The average mass of white dwarfs is about 0.6 solar masses. Their densities reach as high as 1000 $kg/cm^3$ compared with a mean density of 1.41 $gm/cm^3$ for the Sun. In some instances, their densities may be 10 million times that of the Sun. Newton's law tells us that the gravitational field of a massive object of small radius such as a white dwarf must be 100,000 times stronger than the Earth's.

Not all white dwarfs are white—i.e., spectral class A stars. Their temperatures range from as high as 20,000 down to 4000 K. Thus white dwarf stars occupy a broad region in the H-R diagram below main-sequence stars of similar temperature (fig. 16.3).

## Structure of White Dwarf Stars

How does a white dwarf maintain a stable configuration for billions of years after it has exhausted all its nuclear energy sources? Consider an idealized model white dwarf with a carbon-oxygen interior. The energy emitted into space is residual thermal energy remaining in the core after the nuclear processes have shut down. In several billion years this energy reserve will be depleted, and the star will fade out and become a black dwarf.

The unusual structure and conditions inside our model white dwarf cannot be explained by the simple ideal-gas laws that apply to ordinary stars. In solar-type

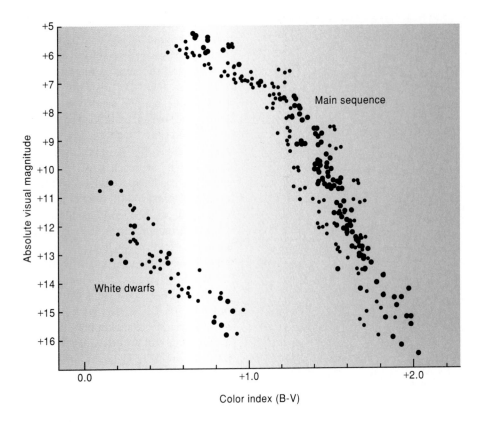

**figure 16.3**
White dwarfs are low-luminosity stars that occupy the region in the H-R diagram below the main-sequence stars of similar temperature.

stars, most of the elements are ionized—stripped of their electrons, which are free to move at random. In such plasma, the volumes occupied by the electrons are small compared to that of an atom with an electron in orbit. Indeed, in the average star there is more empty space than there are protons, alpha particles, and electrons. The stars behave as an ideal gas: if the pressure is increased but the temperature and mass remain constant, the star will decrease in volume; if the temperature is increased but the volume and mass remain constant, the pressure will increase.

This behavior does not apply to our model white dwarf star. In the white dwarf, matter is greatly compressed and completely ionized. The carbon-oxygen nuclei and free electrons are now much closer together, and the number of electrons moving at random is greatly reduced. Divergence from the ideal-gas laws occurs because of the confinement and electrostatic repulsions and attractions of the particles.

In 1926, Sir Ralph Fowler showed that further collapse of the star is limited by the interaction of matter and energy. The effect is the result of the **Pauli exclusion principle,** developed by the physicist Wolfgang Pauli. It states that no two free electrons can simultaneously occupy the same energy state. As density increases, electrons and nuclei are crowded together until only a few energy states are available to each electron. Ultimately, no electron may change its energy state until another is vacated. At this point the interior of the star has been crushed into a crystalline lattice of carbon and oxygen nuclei permeated by a **degenerate electron gas.**

In the 1930s, Subrahmanyan Chandrasekhar developed an elegant description of the limitations imposed upon a star approaching the degenerate state. What is beyond our experience is the unique mass-radius relationship that requires more massive stars to collapse into increasingly smaller white dwarfs. This leads to a theoretical upper limit to the mass at which a star will shrink down to zero radius. A star with only a perceptible amount of hydrogen left cannot exceed 1.44 solar masses and still become

a white dwarf. Larger stars must eject enough mass to bring them below this so-called **Chandrasekhar limit.** Stars below the mass limit make a less spectacular transition to the degenerate state. When their shell-burning fuel is exhausted, they slowly shrink down and become dense white dwarf stars.

As we have indicated, carbon and oxygen nuclei form a matrix that is analogous to the crystalline structure of matter at ordinary pressure and temperature. Degenerate matter is highly conductive, so most of the interior reaches a uniform temperature ranging from 10 to 15 million K.

The large mass and small size of a white dwarf creates an extreme gravitational field at least 100,000 times stronger than the Earth's. Evry Schatzman found that the strong gravitation causes heavy nuclei to sink to the core while lighter particles of residual hydrogen and helium float to the surface. By this process of differentiation, the white dwarf is divided into a degenerate interior overlaid by a thin, nondegenerate shell. In the shell, pressures and temperatures are sufficiently reduced to allow the particles to behave as ordinary matter (fig. 16.4). This outer layer contains a small fraction of the total mass of the star. Only about 50 km thick, the shell transports energy by convection from the interior to the surface. The temperature at the interface between the degenerate interior and the surface layer reaches 10 million K; at the surface the temperature is about 10,000 K.

Above the surface is an atmosphere about 200 m deep. If hydrogen still remains, it will be in the atmosphere of the star. Spectroscopic studies show that most white dwarf stars have atmospheres of virtually pure hydrogen. About 20% of the stars have lost the hydrogen; lines in their spectra indicate a pure helium atmosphere.

A white dwarf star may continue to radiate energy into space for over a billion years. But the star is doomed; the degenerate core prevents any further shrinking that might sustain the energy flow. Cooling becomes a relentless process that carries the one-time bright star to its ultimate end as a black dwarf, a dark cinder destined to follow an endless path about the center of the Galaxy.

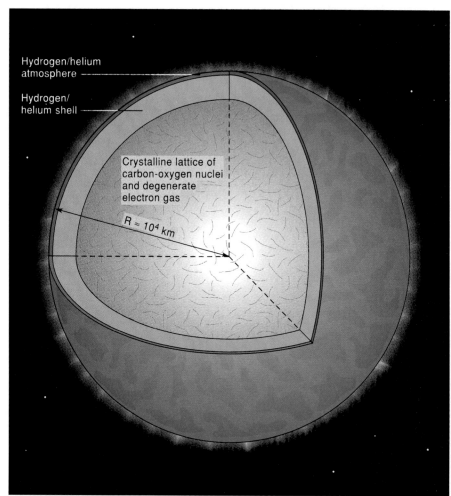

Hydrogen/helium
atmosphere

Hydrogen/
helium shell

Crystalline lattice of
carbon-oxygen nuclei
and degenerate
electron gas

$R \approx 10^4$ km

**figure 16.4**

Interior structure of a white dwarf star. The surface is covered by a tenuous atmosphere of hydrogen and/or helium about 200 m deep. Below the surface is a hydrogen/helium layer about 50 km thick. Most of the interior consists of a crystalline matrix of carbon-oxygen nuclei permeated with a degenerate electron gas.

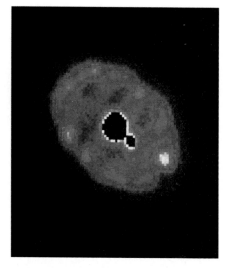

**figure 16.5**

Optical image of Nova Herculis taken in 1984 at Calar Alto Observatory, Spain.

## Novae

There are several types of erupting variable stars that suddenly increase in brightness. The so-called *cataclysmic variables,* the **novae** and more powerful **supernovae,** are explosive events associated with the final stages in the evolution of stars.

When an eruption takes place, a dim telescopic star may brighten into the most conspicuous star in the sky. Picture an ordinary 11th-magnitude star, one of many faint objects recorded on photographic plates. The star brightens unexpectedly and in a few days is thousands or even millions of times brighter than before the outburst. Such a spectacular outburst occurred in 1975 when a second-magnitude nova appeared in the constellation Cygnus. At maximum brightness,

Nova Cygni 1975 was 16 million times brighter than it was at minimum light.

After a nova subsides, a gas shell emerges from the central star at speeds approaching 2000 km/sec. Sometimes the expanding shell has the appearance of a small planetary nebula (fig. 16.5). However, the outburst does not destroy the star; the tenuous nebula represents only a fraction of the star's mass. There are less energetic novae that repeat the performance: *recurrent novae* flare up every 20 or 30 years; *dwarf novae* have outbursts at intervals ranging from a few weeks to more than a year.

A nova represents a violent explosion by a white dwarf star in an interacting binary system. The primary star is a larger and cooler nondegenerate star. On a line connecting the centers of the stars,

there is an equilibrium position called the inner **Lagrangian point** (fig. 16.6). Consider a fragment or a small gas cloud placed at the Lagrangian point, where the gravitational fields of both stars are in balance. Such an object would maintain a circular orbit at a fixed position along the line connecting the stars. Now picture a cavity defined as a **Roche lobe** that encloses a volume about each star. The size of the Roche lobe depends upon the mass of the star; the more massive star has a larger lobe. Both lobes are in contact at the Lagrangian point. All particles contained within each Roche lobe are influenced by the gravitational force of the central star. Particles outside of the lobes are subject to the gravitational effect of both stars. Thus, in a close binary system, an expanding star cannot exceed its Roche lobe without mass transfer through the Lagrangian point to its companion star.

As shown in figure 16.6, one or both stars may fill its Roche lobe. In a detached system neither star fills its lobe. In a semi-detached system, one component fills its lobe. In a contact system, both stars fill the Roche lobes.

Nova outbursts occur in semi-detached systems where a nondegenerate star has exceeded its Roche lobe. Hydrogen from the star's outer envelope overflows and falls toward the surface of the white dwarf companion. An accretion disk builds up

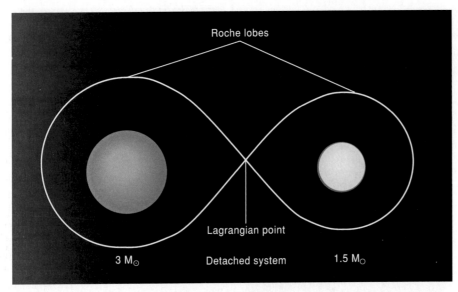

Roche lobes

Lagrangian point

3 M$_\odot$    Detached system    1.5 M$_\odot$

a.

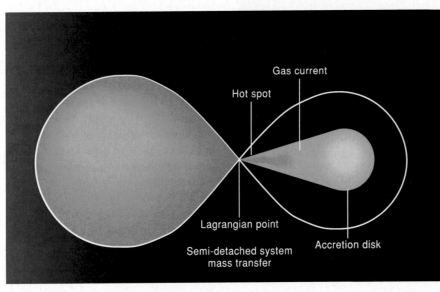

Gas current

Hot spot

Lagrangian point

Accretion disk

Semi-detached system
mass transfer

b.

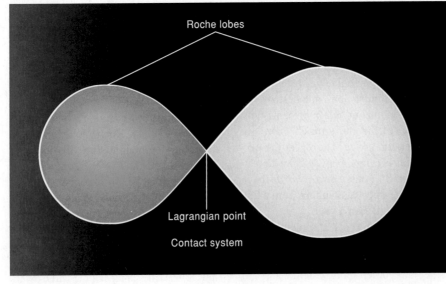

Roche lobes

Lagrangian point

Contact system

c.

around the degenerate star; a hot spot occurs where the overflowing stream of particles strikes the accretion disk. The nova outbursts are believed to originate from the unstable thermonuclear burning of hydrogen accreted on the disk and on the surface of the degenerate white dwarf star.

## Supernovae

Extremely luminous novae, or supernovae, are erupting stars that may attain absolute magnitude -17 or more at maximum. Most belong to two distinctive groups, *Type I* and *Type II supernovae*. Type I eruptions occur among older stars in the later stages of their evolution. Ejecta from the explosion show a lack of hydrogen; the progenitor star had already lost its hydrogen envelope through the action of stellar winds and/or a planetary nebula. Type II supernovae are derived from objects found among more recently evolved stars in the spiral arms of the Galaxy. Type II outbursts contain hydrogen ejecta and are believed to originate from supergiant progenitors. Prior to detonation, these red supergiants and horizontal-branch stars possess an extensive atmosphere of hydrogen that encloses an interior of successive shells of heavier elements.

Observations and data obtained through spectroscopic analysis point to a faint white dwarf as the progenitor of a Type I supernova outburst. Consider a binary system in which a carbon-oxygen white dwarf is the recipient of a stream of hydrogen from a larger nondegenerate companion. In this model, the hydrogen plasma builds up a layer on the surface of the white dwarf until the mass of the star approaches the Chandrasekhar limit. Carbon burning begins, heavier elements are produced, and finally the white dwarf is destroyed in a supernova outburst. The

◀ **figure 16.6**
Types of binary systems. *a.* Detached binary system in which neither star fills its Roche lobe. *b.* Semi-detached binary system in which one star exceeds its Roche lobe. Hydrogen from the expanded star's envelope overflows and falls toward the companion star. *c.* Contact system in which both stars fill their Roche lobes.

stars greater than 15 $M_\odot$. After about 12 million years as a hydrogen-burning object, a massive star reaches 100 million K, the minimum temperature required for helium nuclei to fuse and form a carbon-oxygen core. Energy production continues in helium- and hydrogen-burning shells surrounding the core.

When core contraction and shell burning increase the temperature to 600 million K and above, carbon and oxygen nuclei fuse into heavier elements. In each succeeding phase, the residue of the preceding reaction serves as the fuel for the synthesis of increasingly heavier nuclei. In one nuclear reaction, carbon burning produces neon, sodium, and magnesium. Oxygen fuses into silicon, phosphorus, and sulphur at temperatures of one billion K. Each time a new element ignites, nuclei having less atomic mass continue fusion reactions in concentric shells above the core.

**figure 16.7**

Supernova 1987A. In the top photograph, the arrow points to the progenitor star taken before detonation. The bottom photograph shows the supernova shortly after the explosion.

residue of such an awesome event may be the formation of a more exotic, degenerate neutron star.

## The Death of Massive Stars

What will be the ultimate fate of massive stars after they use up all accessible nuclear fuel? Unlike stars of low and moderate mass that contract into white dwarfs, high-mass stars are unable to shed enough matter to reach the Chandrasekhar limit. In the 1950s, Fred Hoyle and William A. Fowler explained how energy production through nuclear synthesis of heavy elements inside massive stars leads to the extraordinary bursts of matter and energy we defined as supernovae (see fig. 16.7).

## Type II Supernovae

Computer simulations by Arnett, Weaver, and Woosley depict the later stages of

The contraction of the star's central region raises the temperature to several billion K. At such high temperatures, silicon and sulphur pass through a series of reactions that eventually end with the formation of heavier nuclei in the iron group—manganese, iron, cobalt, and nickel. Iron is the most abundant element produced.

No further nuclear synthesis occurs at the center of the star after the formation of an iron-nickel core. The inner part of the star has an onion-like structure of concentric shells of different elements (fig. 16.8). The heavier constituents are in the innermost layers toward

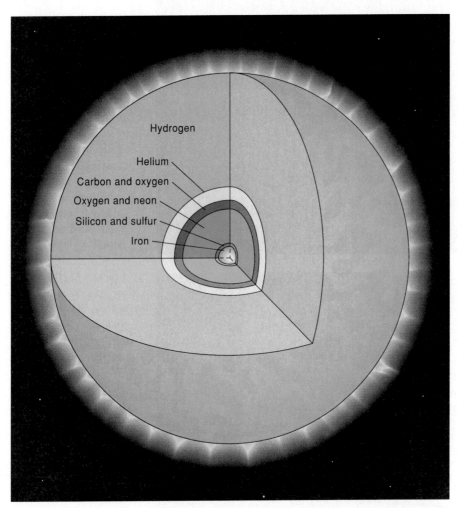

**figure 16.8**

The inner region of a massive star has an onionlike structure of concentric shells of progressively heavier elements.

the center: the iron-nickel core is surrounded by a thin layer of silicon and sulphur; above this are layers of neon and magnesium, oxygen and neon, carbon and oxygen, helium, and an outer envelope of hydrogen enclosing the star. Nuclear burning takes place at the interface between each shell.

As available nuclear fuel is depleted in the shells and thermal pressure is reduced, the inner core slowly shrinks owing to the immense bulk of the overlying layers. Since iron nuclei cannot be fused in the manner of the lighter elements, further contraction will not initiate new core-burning reactions.

Thus, no matter how massive a star might be, at some future time it must surrender to the force of gravity. The dormant central core is relentlessly crushed into a smaller volume by the enormous weight of the star. At this point

the iron core is very much like a white dwarf and supports the bulk of the star by the pressure of a degenerate electron gas. But the star is doomed. In less than one day, silicon burning adds enough mass to bring the iron core above the Chandrasekhar limit. When the mass reaches $1.4\,M_\odot$, gravity is strong enough to collapse the core.

Let us follow the progress of a massive star beginning at the time the core is about to surpass $1.4\,M_\odot$. At this point the iron core contains slightly more than $1.0\,M_\odot$ in a sphere no larger than the Earth. The core continues to contract and increase in temperature as more iron nuclei pour down from the silicon-burning shell. But iron nuclei are stable and do not respond to the increase in temperature and pressure by fusing into heavier elements.

Another process drives the core to its ultimate collapse. In a **photodisintegration** process, high-energy photons of gamma radiation break down the iron-group nuclei into alpha particles and neutrons. The procedure removes energy from the core, which in turn increases the contraction. Temperatures rise and the alpha particles are broken down into protons and neutrons. The mass of the core now exceeds $1.4\,M_\odot$. The pressure is high enough to force electrons to unite with protons and form neutrons. In the process, a neutrino is released (see Methods and Understandings 12.2, The Elusive Neutrino).

$$e + p \rightarrow n + \nu$$

Now the electron pressure is lost and, for all practical purposes, resistance to contraction has disappeared. The resulting collapse is an implosion that accelerates to 30,000 km/sec—one-tenth the velocity of light—in less than one second. In a matter of milliseconds the core is compressed to a density equal to $3 \times 10^{14}\,gm/cm^3$, or about three million times greater than the degenerate matter contained in a white dwarf star. The neutrons resist any further compaction; the iron core has been transformed into a neutron star with a density equal to that found in atomic nuclei. Indeed, the neutron star can be considered to be a giant atomic nucleus consisting of a **degenerate neutron gas** contained in a ball 10 to 30 km in diameter.

The rapid collapse of the core causes overlying lighter elements to free-fall toward the center. These nuclear-burning shells are subjected to extreme temperatures and pressures as they rush inward at high speed. Their progress is abruptly halted when they strike the unyielding neutron core, rebound at supersonic speed, and send a shock wave moving outward at speeds up to 45,000 km/sec.

The neutrinos released during photodisintegration transfer about 1% of their energy to particles in the outer layers of the star. This process, called *neutrino reheating,* supplies additional energy needed to eject the stellar envelope into space.

The initial explosion and expansion of the star provide the brightness we identify with a supernova. As the envelope

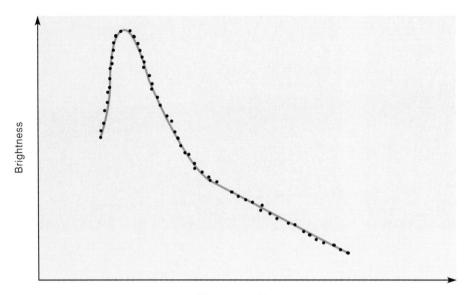

figure 16.9

A characteristic light curve of a type II supernova.

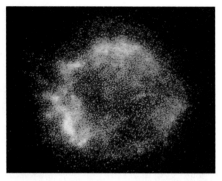

a.

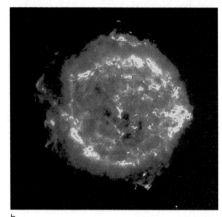

b.

figure 16.10

*a.* An X-ray image, and *b.* a radio image of the supernova remnant Cassiopeia A.

speeds outward at thousands of kilometers per second, the star continues to increase in size and luminosity. In less than one day, the supernova expands to about five times the diameter of the Earth's orbit. Figure 16.9 shows the light curve of a bright supernova. There is a sharp rise in luminosity as radiation continues to counteract the cooling effect of the star's rapid expansion. The star reaches a broad maximum brightness when its absolute magnitude is between −18 and −20. As expansion continues, the supernova gradually fades.

## Observations of Supernovae

Stellar eruptions have been observed since antiquity. When the Greek astronomer Hipparchus discovered a "new star," he realized that the stars are not immutable but can undergo rapid changes in brightness. A possible supernova recorded by Chinese chronologists in 135 B.C. may have been Hipparchus's star. Benedictine monks described a brilliant "stella nova" in A.D. 1006 that was confirmed by Chinese astronomers. The object, one of the brightest on record, is an example of a rare catastrophic outburst of a supernova.

In 1054, Chinese and Japanese observers reported seeing a "guest star" near the star Zeta Tauri, the tip of the southern horn of Taurus. At maximum, the supernova was as bright as the planet Jupiter. The star was seen during daylight hours for three weeks and remained visible at night for almost two years.

Stellar outbursts were seen again in 1572 and 1604. The first was *Tycho's star,* a supernova that appeared in the constellation Cassiopeia. Tycho carefully noted the position and changes in the star's brightness by comparing it to surrounding field stars. At maximum, the object was as bright as the planet Venus. Four centuries later, Walter Baade used Tycho's records to plot a light curve that identified the star as a supernova. Tycho's precise observations enabled astronomers to locate the supernova remnant and take X-ray images with the Einstein X-ray satellite. Radio images of the remnant also have been obtained (fig. 16.10).

Kepler's nova of 1604 was seen in the constellation Ophiuchus for more than 18 months. Both Tycho's and Kepler's novae were of particular importance because they occurred when changes were taking place in philosophical and scientific thinking. Their appearance challenged the views of Aristotle and helped bring about the Copernican revolution.

## The Crab Nebula

In 1781, Charles Messier published his now-famous catalogue of deep-sky wonders. The first entry, M1, was the remnant of the 1054 supernova in Taurus. William Parsons, the Earl of Rosse, named the object the *Crab nebula* after observing its filamentary structure (see photo at beginning of chapter). Modern astronomers recognize the Crab nebula as most important in the study of neutron stars. In 1932, soon after the discovery of the neutron, a hypothetical state of matter was proposed in which electrons are squeezed into nuclei and join with protons to form a neutron gas. The idea was applied to astronomy by Walter Baade and Fritz Zwicky, who suggested that the high density required to create a neutron star might occur at the center of a supernova explosion. In 1949, radio astronomers identified the Crab nebula as the first galactic radio source and, in

 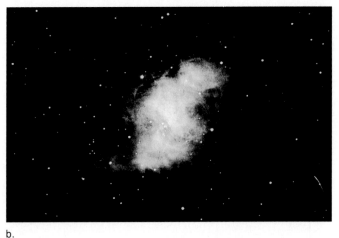

a.   b.

**figure 16.11**

The Crab nebula photographed to show *a.* its filamentary structure, and *b.* the continuous-spectrum emission caused by synchrotron radiation.

1953, proposed that **synchrotron radiation** rather than thermal radiation was the cause of radio and optical emissions from stars and nebulae. X-rays discovered in 1963 were explained as emissions from a dense source at the center of the Crab nebula.

### Structure of the Crab nebula

Photographs by Baade taken with different filters showed that the Crab nebula consists of two components (fig. 16.11). A narrow-band hydrogen-alpha filter revealed an intricate network of filaments extending to the visual boundary of the nebula. The filaments form an ellipsoidal mesh that encloses a diffuse central region. The emission lines in the spectrum are doubled owing to the Doppler effect caused by expansion; the nearside of the Crab is approaching the Earth while the farside is receding. The rate of expansion is equal to about 1000 km/sec.

The Crab appears entirely different when photographed through a wide-band filter transmitting the continuum radiation (no isolated spectral lines such as the hydrogen-alpha line). The filamentary structure disappears and in its place a bright, amorphous cloud is seen to extend over most of the nebula.

The photographs reveal the unique characteristics of the Crab. An emission spectrum originating in the filamentary network is composed of hydrogen-alpha and adjacent lines of ionized nitrogen.

The amorphous central region shows no emission lines but, instead, radiates a continuous spectrum. However, there is structural detail in the form of fibrous tufts that are aligned in the direction of the nebula's magnetic field.

The radiation emitted in the radio and visual range by the amorphous component in the Crab nebula differs from the thermal (blackbody) emission of ordinary interstellar nebulae. The radio and optical radiation are interpreted as synchrotron radiation, which occurs when high-energy electrons interact with magnetic fields and speed up as they spiral about magnetic field lines (fig. 16.12). As a result, the electrons emit radiation in an unbroken range of wavelengths.

The radiating electrons will lose their energy in a much shorter period than the lifetime of the Crab nebula. If the process has continued for over 900 years, there must be an energy source within the nebula that generates the magnetic field and supplies a continuous flow of electrons.

Near the center of the nebula there is a double star consisting of two 16th-magnitude components. The southernmost member is a most unusual star; its spectrum lacks the absorption and emission lines found in the spectra of ordinary stars. This object is the *Crab pulsar,* a rapidly spinning neutron star that provides the energy that drives the Crab nebula.

### SN 1987A

About 170,000 years ago in the Large Magellanic Cloud, one of the nearby satellite galaxies of the Milky Way system, a massive star reached its terminal stage, collapsed, and became a supernova. The event produced an expanding bubble of neutrinos and radiation greater than the total energy of a galaxy composed of billions of stars. The neutrino pulse reached the solar system in February 1987 and entered the Earth's southern hemisphere. The particles passed unimpeded through the Earth to the northern hemisphere, where neutrino detectors located in the United States and Japan recorded the passage. About three hours later, while photographing the southern sky at Las Campañas Observatory in Chile, astronomer Ian Shelton discovered a new star shining conspicuously among the faint stars in the Large Magellanic Cloud (fig. 16.13).

The discovery proved to be of great significance to astronomy. It was the first supernova to be examined at close range since Kepler's star of 1604; no previous supernova had been observed from its beginning. Indeed, the supernova provided astronomers the opportunity to confirm theoretical models by observing the events taking place during the formation of a neutron star.

The supernova received the designation *SN 1987A* indicating the year and order of discovery. In the first 24 hours,

308

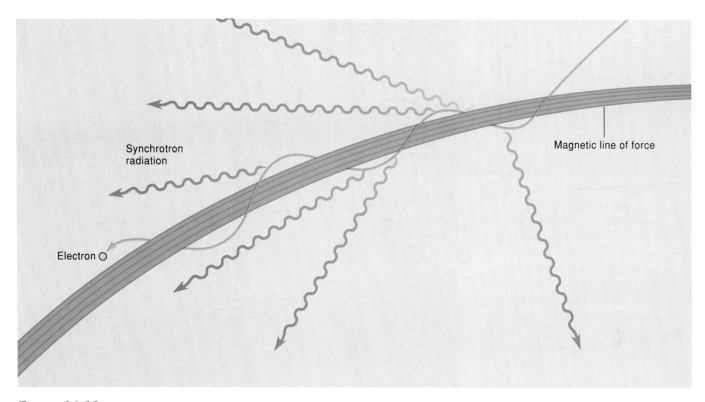

**figure 16.12**
Synchrotron radiation is emitted by electrons that spiral around lines of force in a magnetic field at velocities approaching the speed of light. The radiation is emitted in a narrow cone in the direction the electrons are traveling.

SN 1987A reached +4.5 magnitude. At maximum, the new star attained magnitude +2.9. Pre-discovery photographs of the field contain no stars brighter than 12th-magnitude, so the supernova must have increased nearly 4000 times in brightness. Among these faint stars, a 12th-magnitude blue giant star known as Sanduleak −69°202 was identified as the progenitor. The discovery came as a surprise to theorists, because a blue B3 supergiant is not a typical pre-nova star.

SN 1987A had some of the properties of a Type II supernova. Observations of its spectrum confirmed the expanding shell containing an abundance of hydrogen. The Doppler shift indicated an expansion velocity of 17,000 km/sec, which is equal to about one AU every 2.5 hours.

**figure 16.13**
Supernova 1987A is seen right of center. The bright emission cloud is the Tarantula nebula. Visually the supernova reached second magnitude. Its luminosity was equal to 200 million sunlike stars.

309

The detection of neutrinos was significant in a number of ways: it was the first time neutrinos were identified with a stellar source; according to theory, neutrinos are released during the formation of a neutron star; and the neutrinos released correspond to the number expected during a Type II supernova explosion.

The expansion of SN 1987A triggered thermonuclear reactions at the base of the region above the core. Radioactive nickel-56, with a half-life of six days, decayed into cobalt-56, which has a half-life of 77 days. After maximum brightness in May 1987, the supernova declined in brightness by one-half every 77 days as cobalt-56 decayed to iron-56. The supernova was driven by the energy from gamma rays emitted during the reactions.

A year after the first sighting of SN 1987A, astronomers obtained images of the light echo from the supernova (fig. 16.14). These emissions come from circumstellar material illuminated by the ultraviolet flash generated by the explosion of the progenitor star. The nebula extends in a hat-shaped double cone beyond the concentric ring structure of the light echo. The complex formation predates the supernova explosion. Astronomers explain the circumstellar nebula as material ejected from the envelopes of stars in a multiple system consisting of the progenitor as the primary and one or more companion stars.

## The Discovery of Pulsars

In 1967, while investigating extragalactic objects, Antony Hewish and Jocelyn Bell detected regular radio pulses that seemed to come from an unknown source. At first the signals were dismissed as some form of terrestrial interference. On closer inspection, they were found to originate from a point in the sky. Hewish correctly identified the source as an interstellar object by the annual changes in its periodicity due to the Earth's revolution. The regular pulses arriving every 1.337 seconds were interpreted as emissions from a rapidly spinning star. At the time, the most plausible explanation was

**figure 16.14**

Light echoes from Supernova 1987A. The light from the explosion has been scattered by fine dust particles and thus arrives after the light that traveled on a more direct path to Earth. The light echoes form two rings of dust in clouds located about 470 light years (*inner ring*) and 1300 light years (*outer ring*) from the supernova.

that the strange signals came from a white dwarf.

It was the first *pulsating radio source* or **pulsar** to be discovered. The object, catalogued as CP 1919 (Cambridge pulsar at R.A. = 19h 19m), is located in the constellation Vulpecula. Its period was the shortest of any known celestial body, but soon more radio pulsars were detected with periods ranging from 0.0015 to 4.0 seconds. The discovery was significant because the linear diameter of the object responsible for the emission must be smaller than a white dwarf. Only a neutron star could complete one rotation in such a brief interval of time.

The detection and analysis of CP 1919 by Hewish and Bell was a major event in astronomy. Bell has the distinction of making the discovery; Hewish was

## Angular Momentum and Neutron Stars

How do astronomers know that short-period pulsars are rapidly spinning neutron stars? To find the answer, we must find out how stars pulsate and then investigate a quantity known as angular momentum.

Periodic behavior in stars may be caused by several different mechanisms: oscillation, revolution, and rotation. For example, a cepheid variable star will vary in brightness as its surface and atmosphere move up and down and periodically change temperature. As eclipsing binaries revolve, one star passes in front of the other and causes periodic changes in brightness. A neutron star is surrounded by an enormous number of charged particles that are trapped in the star's magnetic field. The magnetic field and the star rotate with the same angular velocity. Therefore, radiation from the charged particles is emitted in pulses of the same period as the period of rotation.

The rapid rotation of a collapsed star is an example of the **conservation of angular momentum,** a physical law with many scientific applications. The momentum of a moving body is an important quantity because its value remains the same as long as no external force acts upon the body. Think of momentum in terms of inertia, which is the resistance that a body has to a change in motion. *Linear momentum* refers to the motion of a body in a straight line and is equal to the product of the mass and velocity. Velocity is a quantity having direction as well as magnitude.

$$\text{linear momentum} = \text{mass of the body} \times \text{the velocity}$$

*Angular momentum* refers to the motion of a rotating body about an axis, or a planet revolving around the Sun. Angular momentum ($L$) is defined by the product of the mass ($m$), tangential velocity ($v$), and the distance of the object from the center of motion ($r$).

$$L = mvr$$

One of the fundamental physical laws, the conservation of angular momentum states that the angular momentum of a body is constant if no external force or any change *within* a system alters its total angular momentum. For example, as a planet approaches perihelion and its distance from the Sun decreases, the planet must increase its orbital velocity to conserve its angular momentum. A spinning ice skater is another example of the conservation of angular momentum. The skater begins to spin with arms outstretched. When the skater's arms are brought in closer to the body, or closer to the axis of rotation, the spin (tangential velocity) increases to compensate for the decrease in distance from the center of motion.

The principle of conservation of angular momentum applies to a star whose core is about to collapse into a neutron star. In order to conserve angular momentum, as the radius of the progenitor star decreases, its angular velocity increases. The final result is a rapidly rotating neutron star.

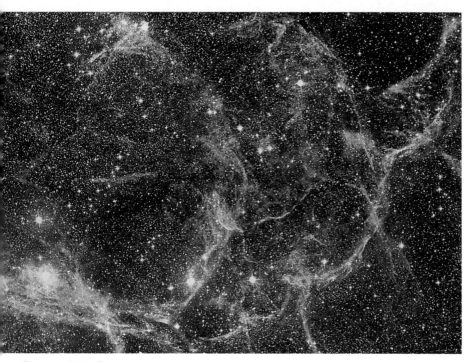

**figure 16.15**

The Vela supernova remnant, the Gum nebula, contains the Vela pulsar, which formed 11,000 to 12,000 years ago. Astronomers estimate that the explosion of the progenitor star appeared as bright on Earth as the full Moon.

awarded the Nobel Prize in physics for identifying the pulsar as a neutron star.

## Confirmation of Pulsars as Neutron Stars

Pulsars were identified as neutron stars when short-period radio pulses were detected in two supernova remnants: the Vela pulsar in the Gum nebula, and the Crab pulsar in the Crab nebula. The first to be discovered was the Vela pulsar, which has a period of only 0.089 seconds.

The Gum nebula stretches across an area of about 30 by 60 degrees centered in the region of the constellation Vela (fig. 16.15). By far the largest of its kind, the nebula is estimated to be 360 parsecs in radius and located about 460 parsecs from the Earth. Near its center, a filamentary structure and radio emissions identify a supernova explosion designated Vela X. The radio emission is caused by synchrotron radiation from the magnetic field surrounding the Vela X remnant. In 1968, the Vela pulsar was discovered in the center of the Vela X region. The age of the supernova, estimated at 11,000 years, is based upon the expansion rate of the remnant and the rate at which the pulsar is slowing down.

The 900-year-old Crab pulsar was discovered several months later and was found to have an even shorter period—only 0.033 seconds. The detection was very significant because only a neutron star can rotate at 30 cycles per second without flying apart. The discovery of pulsars in supernova remnants represents observational proof that neutron stars do exist. The investigations also showed that the youngest pulsars have the shortest periods, and only young pulsars are associated with supernova remnants. Old pulsars are singular objects that have dispersed their outer gaseous layers and dust into space.

The Crab pulsar emits part of its energy at optical wavelengths. In 1969, Wampler and Miller recorded the pulsar flashes visually by means of a rotating shutter and TV camera attached to the 120-inch reflecting telescope at Lick Observatory. The period of the rotating shutter was nearly the same as the pulsar. When the pulsar flashed in and out of phase with the rotating shutter, the stroboscopic effect produced a flashing image that identified the pulsar as an object known as Baade's star near the center of the expanding Crab nebula (fig. 16.16).

## Structure of a Neutron Star

Signals from pulsars show slow increases in their periods of rotation. For most, the rate of change is remarkably smooth although irregularities do exist. The irregularities in the rotational rate, called "glitches," are attributed to starquakes in the solid outer crust. A rapidly spinning neutron star is believed to be a spheroid with an equatorial bulge. As the star gradually slows down and becomes less oblate, there is an interruption in its steady decrease in rotational velocity.

The discontinuous changes provide clues to the interior structure of a neutron star. The outer layer consists of a thin photosphere covering an outer crust about 1 km thick (fig. 16.17). The sur-

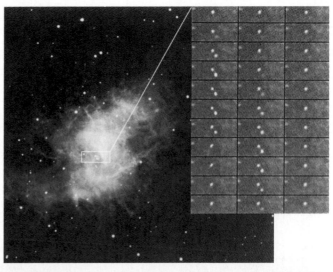

**figure 16.16**
The Crab pulsar, NP 0532. One complete cycle of light flashes represents one rotation of the pulsar.

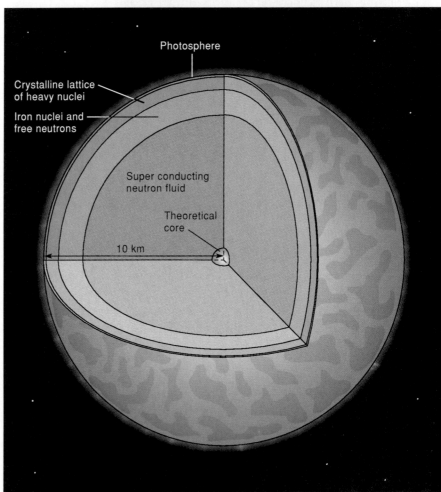

**figure 16.17**
A theoretical model of the structure of a neutron star. The radius is 10 km.

face is composed of a crystalline lattice of heavy nuclei, primarily iron, surrounded by a degenerate electron gas. At the inner crust, where the density is about $4 \times 10^{11}$ gm/cm³, iron nuclei begin to break down and shed neutrons.

The inner region consists of a highly compressed neutron fluid ranging in density from $10^{14}$ gm/cm³ to about $10^{15}$ gm/cm³. The majority of the protons and electrons have combined. The very strong magnetic field found in neutron stars

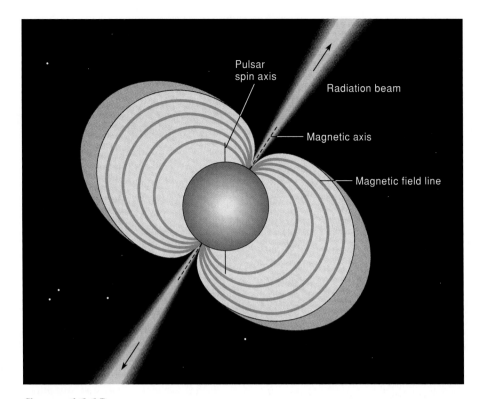

**figure 16.18**

A model of a pulsar as a rapidly rotating neutron star. If the magnetic axis is tilted in relation to the spin axis, an electron beam will sweep across the sky.

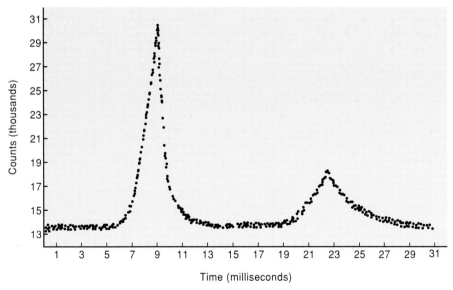

**figure 16.19**

The light curve of the Crab pulsar. There are two pulses in each period, one from each magnetic pole.

Source: Data from C. D. Papaliolios, N. P. Carleton, and P. Horowitz, Smithsonian Astrophysical Observatory.

originates in the superconducting neutron fluid region.

How do the pulses originate? The question is answered by astronomers in the following way. A pulsar is a dense neutron star emitting a beam of radiation coupled to the rotation of the star. The beam is detected as a pulse of energy just as a rotating beacon at an airport will produce a flash of light each time it points toward the observer. Let's investigate this mechanism in more detail.

All stars have axial spin. Ordinary stars like the Sun rotate in a period of about one month. Giant stars spin at an even slower pace. When a star shrinks to the size of a neutron star, it conserves angular momentum by spinning faster.

Ordinary stars have weak magnetic fields. The strength of the field is proportional to the number of field lines per unit area of the star's surface; the greater the number of lines, the stronger the magnetic field. If a star shrinks to the size of a neutron star, its surface area is reduced and the magnetic field lines are squeezed into a smaller area. The result is a magnetic field $10^{12}$ times greater than the Sun's.

A magnetosphere made up of ions and electrons from the surface is produced in the space above the star (fig. 16.18). These particles interact with the magnetic field and spiral outward along the magnetic field lines. In the process, electrons accelerated to speeds approaching the velocity of light escape along the magnetic field lines, emitting energy as synchrotron radiation. The emission is explained by a beam pattern associated with the magnetic poles of the star.

When the magnetic axis and spin axis are not aligned, the beam of radiation caught up in the magnetic field lines will sweep around the entire sky in one rotation. If the magnetic axis happens to be directed toward the Earth, we may detect two pulses, one from each magnetic pole (fig. 16.19).

## X-ray Binary Systems

X-ray astronomy began with rocket observations in the 1940s. These pioneering investigations were followed by X-ray satellites launched in the 1970s. The first, Uhuru, produced a catalogue of 161 sources, a number of which were identified as interacting binary systems. Later, High Energy Astrophysical Observatories (HEAO-2 was named the Einstein Observatory) and the EXOSAT Observatory revealed more intriguing objects in the X-ray sky.

In chapter 12, we learned how X-radiation is observed in disturbed regions of the solar corona. The first condensed interstellar source of X-rays was identified as the synchrotron mechanism found in the Crab nebula. Many celestial X-ray sources show cyclic changes in intensity that are attributed to the revolution of stars in an eclipsing binary system. Added to this are X-ray pulses having periods of a few seconds or less, indicating that one of the binary components is a rapidly rotating neutron star. Moreover, some binary systems exhibit recurrent outbursts believed to be thermonuclear explosions on the surface of the neutron star.

The bright X-ray sources found in binary systems may be grouped in two general categories. Group A contains systems where an optical component is a hot O or B supergiant star. Group B consists of a cooler, less luminous subgiant companion that has filled its Roche lobe. The X-ray binaries in group A are distributed in the galactic plane; those in group B are located above and below the galactic plane. *Centaurus X-3* is an X-ray pulsar in group A; its companion is a spectral type 06III giant star. Group B includes the X-ray pulsar known as *Hercules X-1;* its optical companion is a type A star designated HZ Herculis. These and other X-ray binaries derive their energy by the transfer of mass supplied by the optical star onto a compact neutron star.

The Centaurus X-3 system has a binary period of 2.1 days. When the visual star passes in front of the X-ray component, the X-rays from the source drop to minimum intensity during primary eclipse. At the end of the eclipse, the strong X-ray emission of the system is restored. Superimposed on the 2.1-day revolutionary period is a pulsation with a period of 4.8 seconds. These shorter pulses are attributed to the spinning neutron star. Analysis of the changes in pulsation revealed the physical and orbital properties of the system.

The visual star is a luminous object having an extensive atmosphere and a mass equal to about 15 $M_\odot$; its radius is $5 \times 10^6$ km, which is about 13 times the distance between the Earth and the Moon. The X-ray component is a neutron star slightly more massive than the Sun and located no more than about $10^6$

km from the outer envelope of the blue giant star.

Recall how the position of the Lagrangian point between two stars is determined by the mass ratio of the binary members. In the Centaurus X-3 system, the blue giant star has reached its Roche surface; the compact neutron star draws ionized matter from the visual star into an accretion disk. From here, the plasma spirals to the surface of the neutron star at relativistic speeds. Part of the incoming matter is converted to energy in the form of X-rays that are emitted into space.

The optical companion in Hercules X-1, HZ Herculi, varies in brightness between 13.1 and 13.7 magnitudes in a period of 1.7 days. The X-ray component pulsates in a period of 1.2 seconds, which varies in frequency over the 1.7-day orbital period of the binary system. The smooth sinusoidal change in the period is explained as a Doppler effect caused by the revolution of the X-ray star in its orbit. From this, the orbital velocity was determined. Plasma from the visual companion is drawn into an accretion disk and deposited onto the neutron star.

Other interacting binary systems known as *X-ray bursters* contain a neutron star and a low-mass companion. Plasma from the companion star is drawn into an accretion disk and from there spirals onto the surface of the neutron star. The accreted material on the neutron star reaches a critical mass; a thermonuclear reaction takes place that converts some of the excess matter into energy as X-rays. After a burst, the neutron star draws more matter from its companion to start the cycle again.

## Black Holes

The third possible final stage of a star is the most exotic of all, the mysterious object named a *black hole*. If a star ends up with more mass than the maximum allowed for the formation of a neutron star, it will contract into an object of such enormous gravitational force that nothing, not even energy, can escape, and all energy falling upon it will be absorbed. A black hole cannot be called

invisible, which implies that we could see through it, but is opaquely black. Particles and energy may surround the black hole at certain distances, revealing its existence. But inside its enigmatic boundary, our concepts of time and space no longer apply (fig. 16.20).

Are black holes real? So far, astronomers have no direct proof of their existence, but indirect evidence indicates that a black hole is more than a theoretical curiosity. If neutron stars are limited to no more than about 3 $M_\odot$, it seems reasonable to picture stars of greater mass that might collapse into smaller and denser bodies. Such a bizarre object is predicted in Einstein's general theory of relativity. A star greater than 3 $M_\odot$ will continue to contract unabated to a theoretically dimensionless point. No force known to exist is great enough to oppose the relentless gravitational field squeezing the star together.

Refer to the geometry of spacetime formulated by Einstein. According to the general theory, space is not just an empty void between the stars. Space has geometric properties that are dependent upon the mass it contains. Gravitation is treated as an effect of the curvature of space around a spherical body such as a star. Moreover, the general theory considers the spacetime properties of a massive object of no dimension—the inscrutable entity known as a black hole. The general theory of relativity is confirmed by three predicted effects: the advance of the perihelion of Mercury, the deflection of light by a gravitational field, and the displacement of spectral lines in the presence of a strong gravitational field. All three effects apply to black holes.

Soon after the publication of the general theory of relativity, Karl Schwarzschild computed a model for a sunlike star compressed to a density greater than a neutron star. Suppose the necessary forces were available to compact the Sun into an object smaller than a neutron star. (Of course we already know that the Sun's final configuration will be a white dwarf star.) According to relativity theory, when a sunlike star reaches a critical radius of about 3 km, there will be no way to halt a runaway collapse until the star has been reduced

**figure 16.20**
A model of a black hole by astronomy artist Helmut K. Wimmer. A star that ends up with more than the maximum mass required to form a neutron star will contract into a black hole. The enclosed region of space has such an enormous gravitational field that nothing can escape it.

to a point mass. Astrophysicists refer to a point mass as a **singularity.** Here is where all the mass of a black hole is found. Not all scientists find such a model acceptable. They argue that phenomena dealing with quantum theory come into play and prevent the formation of a true singularity.

The black hole extends a distance equal to a critical radius called the **Schwarzschild radius,** which marks the **event horizon** or spherical boundary separating the black hole from the universe at large. Stephen W. Hawking describes the event horizon as a one-way membrane through which particles, light signals, and even astronauts may enter but can never return.

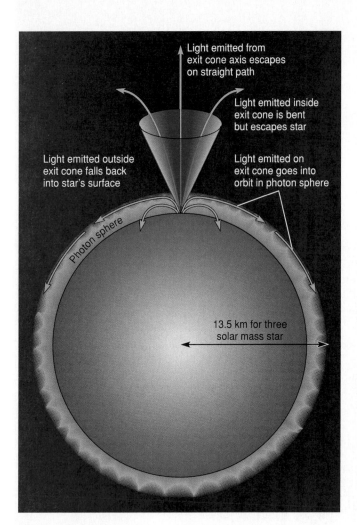

Light emitted from exit cone axis escapes on straight path

Light emitted inside exit cone is bent but escapes star

Light emitted outside exit cone falls back into star's surface

Light emitted on exit cone goes into orbit in photon sphere

Photon sphere

13.5 km for three solar mass star

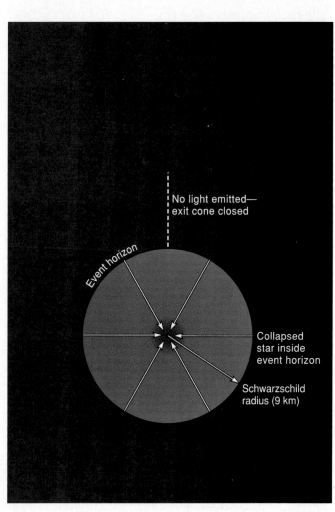

No light emitted— exit cone closed

Event horizon

Collapsed star inside event horizon

Schwarzschild radius (9 km)

**figure 16.21**

A model of black-hole formation showing the deflection of light that takes place as a massive star collapses into a black hole.

We have discussed only the simplest black hole, the Schwarzschild model, in which only one physical quantity, mass, has been introduced. There are three other parameters of black holes: spin, angular momentum, and electric charge. A *Kerr model* has spin and angular momentum; it is not spherical but bulges outward in its rotational plane. A *Reissner-Nordstrom model* has electric charge, and a *Kerr-Newman model* has all these features. Moreover, Hawking has shown that quantum mechanics requires a rotating black hole to be a source of radiation.

The properties of black holes can be visualized by means of "thought experiments" in the manner by which Einstein explained general relativity. Consider the

simplest model, a Schwarzschild black hole, which describes the collapse of a theoretical nonrotating spherical star (fig. 16.21). There are two observers taking part in the experiment: observer A is imagined to be located on the surface of the progenitor star, while observer B is in space at a distance from this hypothetical star. During the star's rapid implosion, the observers will examine the spacetime properties of the developing black hole from their respective stations, using synchronized clocks and other measuring devices.

During initial contraction, observer A on the surface of the star begins the experiment by shining a laser beam into space, which is detected by observer B. As collapse continues, the beam is de-

flected and follows the curvature of spacetime caused by the intensity of the star's gravitational field. Eventually, the light from the laser can escape only through an **exit cone** centered on an axis extending from observer A to the zenith. (Note: every radiating point on the star's surface has a similar exit cone.) Light emitted from a direction outside the exit cone will be deflected back to the surface by the enormous gravitational field produced by the shrinking star. If observer A shines the laser along the surface of the exit cone, the light will be deflected into a circular orbit about the star. Light from the laser and all radiating points on the surface contribute to a shell of radiation called the **photon sphere.** (Incident starlight that arrives

## observing nova and supernova remnants

Throughout the year, Sky Watchers can observe some of the deep-sky objects discussed in the present chapter. These are nova and supernova remnants that can be seen with moderate-sized telescopes. When seaching for faint deep-sky objects, use the "star hopping" procedure introduced in earlier Sky Watchers' projects.

The most famous supernova remnant, the Crab nebula, is situated 1.05° northwest of the star Zeta Tauri in the constellation Taurus (fig.16.22a). At a visual magnitude of +8.4, the Crab can be resolved in the telescope as a faint, green oval cloud among the background field stars. The pulsar at the center of the remnant has a magnitude of about +16.0 and requires a large-aperture telescope.

The constellation Cygnus contains a large but very faint supernova remnant named the Cygnus loop (fig. 16.23). Our goal is to locate the bright portion of the expanding shell called the Veil nebula. A moderate-sized telescope is required to resolve its fine details. Be sure that seeing is good and moonlight or artificial illumination of the sky does not degrade the condition of the atmosphere. To find the Veil, locate Epsilon Cygni, the eastern star in the Northern Cross (fig. 16.22b). Find Zeta Cygni about 6° southeast of Epsilon; then 52 Cygni, which is 3° south of Epsilon. The three stars form a distinctive right triangle. The brightest portion of the nebula lies in the direction of 52 Cygni.

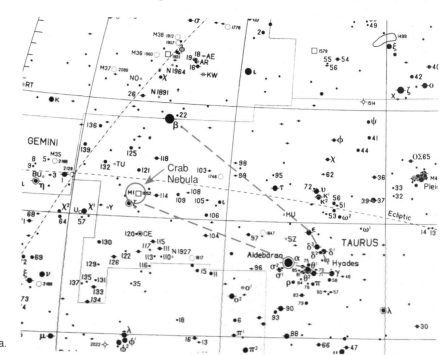

a.

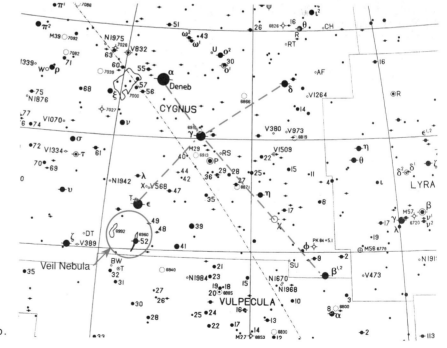

b.

▲ **figure 16.22**

Location of *a.* the Crab nebula in Taurus, and *b.* the Veil nebula in Cygnus.
From *Norton's 2000.0 Star Atlas and Reference Handbook*, 18th ed. Copyright © 1991 Longman Group UK, Ltd. Reprinted by permission.

◀ **figure 16.23**

The Cygnus loop. The supernova remnant contains the Veil nebula (***upper left***), and the Filamentary nebula (***right center***). The Cygnus loop is a strong source of radio and X-ray radiation.

how stars perish

tangentially to the photon sphere also contributes radiation.) Contraction continues, the exit cone narrows until no light can escape, and the surface of the star carries observer A across the critical event horizon into the black hole.

To observer B, there appears to be a continuous decrease in the rate of stellar collapse that approaches zero as the star reaches the event horizon. Signals from observer A are detected at increasingly longer wavelengths as predicted by Einstein's theory. To observer B, the star and observer A seem frozen in time at the event horizon. No unusual event is recorded by the observer B's instruments as observer A crosses into the black hole. Once inside the event horizon, there is no escape; the star and observer A will be crushed into a singularity at the center of the black hole.

## X-ray Binaries as Black Hole Candidates

If the event horizon acts as a one-way barrier to the internal investigation of black holes, how do astrophysicists find evidence for their existence? A black hole has mass and must have a gravitational field that exerts an influence beyond the event horizon. Suppose matter from a star is attracted by the gravitational field of a black hole. The gas will spiral into a plasma stream and form an accretion disk before crossing the event horizon. The rapidly spinning plasma will produce X-ray emissions in a strong magnetic field, which link black holes to the exterior space environment.

For example, a black hole might be a massive component in a close binary system. The gravitational effect of a body greater than 3 $M_\odot$ should be revealed in the motion of the companion star. Another feature of a suspected black hole are rapid fluctuations in X-ray emissions. Such high-energy waves are believed to originate in the inner region of an accretion disk surrounding a pulsating binary X-ray source. A black hole might be found by the detection of gravitational waves that, according to the general theory of relativity, should be released

during the collapse of a massive star. Thus far, gravitational waves have not been confirmed, so the most promising evidence for the existence of black holes is found in the distinctive features of pulsating X-ray binaries.

## Cygnus X-1

The first X-ray source to meet the above criteria is a binary system named *Cygnus X-1*. It was first observed by X-ray detectors aboard balloons and rockets in the 1960s, and by the Uhuru X-ray satellite in 1971. Cygnus X-1 was found to be a strong source of radiation. The discovery marked the first X-rays suspected to come from a black hole component in a binary system. The visual companion is a normal spectral class O9 blue supergiant star. Investigations of the star's spectral lines have provided mass estimates for both the binary components, and the orbital period of the system. As the star alternately approaches and recedes in our line of sight, its spectral lines are shifted respectively toward the blue and red regions of the spectrum. The radial velocity curve indicates a mass between 10 and 20 $M_\odot$ for the visible companion, and a 5.6-day period of revolution for the system.

The mass of the X-ray source is uncertain because the inclination and other orbital elements of the binary system are not known. However, astronomers have placed a minimum value of 6 $M_\odot$ for the X-ray source. An ordinary star of this mass will be bright enough to be visible from the Earth. Since a neutron star cannot exceed 2.5 $M_\odot$, the underluminous object can be ruled a suspected black hole candidate.

Superimposed on the spectrum of Cygnus X-1 are emission lines of helium that vary the same as the orbital period. Theorists believe that the visible companion has filled its Roche lobe and gas cascades from the star to the black hole (fig. 16.24). The helium emission lines may originate either in the plasma stream drawn to the center by the enormous gravitational field, or in the accretion disk surrounding the black hole.

## LMC X-3

The second black hole candidate, *LMC X-3*, was discovered in the Large Magellanic Cloud. After the location of the X-ray source was confirmed, the optical component was identified as a 17th-magnitude spectral class B3V star. The spectrum of the blue giant showed a familiar Doppler shift indicating that the star revolves about an unseen companion in a period of 1.7 days. The amplitude of the radial velocity curve confirmed that the mass of the compact X-ray source is at least 9 $M_\odot$ and the optical star's mass is about 6 $M_\odot$. If the X-ray component were a normal 9 $M_\odot$ star, it would appear more luminous than its optical companion. These observations provide indirect evidence that LMC X-3 is a black hole.

## A0620-00

Another strong black hole candidate is a variable star designated *V616 Monocerotis*. In 1917, the 18th-magnitude star in the constellation Monoceros rapidly increased in brightness by about seven magnitudes before it declined to its original luminosity. During a second eruption in 1975, the X-ray satellite Ariel V recorded powerful X-ray emissions for a period of two months. The X-ray source, called *A0620-00*, is associated with an optical star of spectral class K5V. This visible orange star is revolving about a compact X-ray source in only 0.32 days, or in a period of less than eight hours. Its radial velocity amplitude is about 460 km/sec. The orange main-sequence star has a mass of 0.7 $M_\odot$, which means that the mass of the X-ray source must be more than 3.2 $M_\odot$. Thus A0620-00 represents another X-ray binary system containing a degenerate component of a mass that exceeds the theoretical limit placed on neutron stars.

## V404 Cygni

Another object in Cygnus represents the fourth black hole candidate discovered by astronomers. The variable star designated V404 Cygni was found to be a

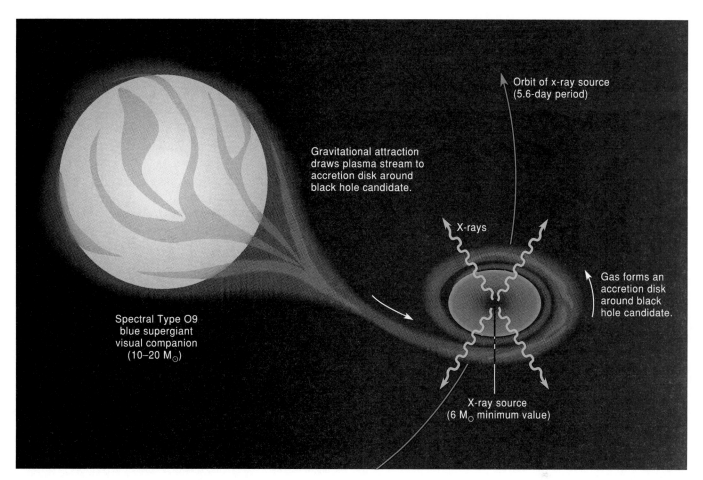

**figure 16.24**

A model of Cygnus X-1, an X-ray binary star and black hole candidate.

source of X-ray emissions. The star is classified as late G or K, cooler and less massive than the Sun. V404 Cygni varies in radial velocity more than 400 km/s in a period of 6.47 days. Measurements show the star to be revolving around a massive dark primary component whose mass is estimated to be at least 6 $M_\odot$. The high mass revealed in the orbital motion of V404 accompanied by X-ray emissions make the primary component a black hole candidate.

## SUMMARY

After ejecting mass as a planetary nebula, a star must be reduced to 1.4 solar masses or less in order to become a white dwarf. The substance of a white dwarf is compressed and completely ionized into a degenerate state, packed closer together than electrons and protons in ordinary matter. The extreme gravitational field of a white dwarf causes heavy elements to form a central core overlaid by a surface of lighter particles of hydrogen and helium. The degenerate core prevents further shrinking and energy production by nuclear synthesis.

A nova represents a violent explosion of the gas envelope of a white dwarf component in an interacting binary system. The nondegenerate companion has exceeded its Roche surface; matter overflows to the white dwarf and builds up an accretion disk. Nova outbursts originate from unstable nuclear burning of hydrogen in the accretion disk and on the surface of the white dwarf.

Supernovae belong to two groups, Type I and Type II. Type I supernovae occur in close binary systems where a white dwarf accumulates hydrogen from a nondegenerate companion. Hydrogen builds up on the surface of the white dwarf until the total mass exceeds the Chandrasekhar limit and the white dwarf explodes in a supernova outburst. Type II supernovae originate in high-mass stars that are unable to shed the mass required to reach the Chandrasekhar limit. In massive stars, contraction and nuclear burning continue in shells of heavy elements. No further synthesis takes place in the core after the formation of iron and nickel. More mass is added to the core as silicon synthesis continues above the dormant core. The core collapses and, under extreme pressure and temperature, alpha particles break down into protons and neutrons, and electrons are forced to unite with protons to form additional neutrons. The core is transformed into a degenerate sphere of neutrons having a density equal to that in atomic nuclei. Infalling matter strikes the neutron core, then rebounds at supersonic speeds in a supernova explosion.

The existence of neutron stars at the center of supernova remnants was confirmed by rapid radio signals called pulsars. The most famous pulsar is located in the Crab nebula in Taurus. The signals are emitted by a rapidly rotating neutron star. Above the neutron star, there are particles trapped in the strong magnetic field; they spiral along magnetic field lines and emit energy as synchrotron radiation. The result is a beam of radiation coupled to the star's rotation, which is observed as a flashing pulsar.

X-ray binary systems derive their energy from the transfer of mass supplied by an optical component onto a compact neutron star. The mass of the neutron star can be found in eclipsing binary systems. The pulsation due to the rapid rotation of the neutron star reveals the orbital and physical properties of the system.

Evidence for the existence of black holes is found in pulsating X-ray binary systems. The presence of a black hole is revealed by its gravitational effect upon the optical companion. If the mass of the X-ray component is found to be greater than three or more solar masses, the object may be a black hole candidate. There are several sources that meet the criteria: Cygnus X-1, LMC X-3, A0620-00, and V404 Cygni.

# KEY TERMS

black hole

Chandrasekhar limit

conservation of angular
    momentum

degenerate electron gas

degenerate neutron gas

event horizon

exit cone

general theory of relativity

Lagrangian point

neutron star

novae

Pauli exclusion principle

photodisintegration

photon sphere

principle of equivalence

pulsar

Roche lobe

Schwarzschild radius

singularity

spacetime

supernovae

synchrotron radiation

white dwarf star

# PROBLEMS

1. What internal pressure prevents a white dwarf from further collapse?

2. Explain how a white dwarf may become a neutron star.

3. Describe briefly the differences between novae and supernovae.

4. What important process breaks down the iron core and drives a massive star to its ultimate end?

5. Describe how the discovery of pulsars confirmed the existence of neutron stars.

6. Why was the detection of neutrinos from SN 1987A important to astrophysicists?

7. Explain why there is only indirect evidence for the existence of black holes.

8. The shock wave produced during a supernova collapse does not supply sufficient energy to eject the stellar envelope into space. What additional process provides the energy necessary for expansion?

9. What effects predicted by the general theory of relativity apply to black hole candidates?

10. Explain the importance of orbiting observatories in the investigation of X-ray binary systems.

11. Compare the physical characteristics of white dwarfs, neutron stars, and black holes.

12. Why can matter and energy pass into a black hole but are unable to escape?

13. How do the magnetic fields of ordinary stars and neutron stars differ?

14. Why does the structure of the Crab nebula consist of two parts? Why is the central region an amorphous cloud?

15. Describe in detail how pulsar signals originate.

16. SN 1987A declined in brightness by one-half every 77 days. Why?

17. What procedure would you follow to search for black holes?

18. Pulsars A, B, and C have periods of 1.33 seconds, 0.09 seconds, and 0.04 seconds respectively. Which pulsar is most recent? The oldest? Explain your answer.

19. A supernova remnant with an angular diameter of 6 arc minutes is located at a distance of 2000 parsecs. Find its linear diameter in kilometers.

20. If the supernova in problem 19 is expanding at a constant rate of 1900 km/sec, when did the explosion take place? Name the supernova remnant.

# REFERENCES

Balick, Bruce. 1987. The Shaping of Planetary Nebulae. *Sky and Telescope* 73, no. 2 (February).

Bethe, Hans A., and Gerald Brown. 1985. How a Supernova Explodes. *Scientific American* 253, no. 5 (May).

Chandrasekhar, Subrahmanyan. 1951. The Structure, the Composition, and the Source of Energy of the Stars. In *Astrophysics,* edited by J. A. Hynek. New York: McGraw-Hill Book Company, Inc.

Green, Louis C. 1977. "Ordinary Stars, White Dwarfs, and Neutron Stars." In *The New Astronomy and Space Science Reader,* edited by John C. Brandt and Stephen P. Maran. San Francisco: W. H. Freeman and Company.

Hawking, Stephen W. 1988. *A Brief History of Time.* Bantam Books.

Hewish, Antony. 1970. "Pulsars." In *New Frontiers in Astronomy: Readings from Scientific American.* San Francisco: W. H. Freeman and Company.

Hutchings, John B., and David Crampton. 1984. LMC X-3: A Black Hole in a Neighbor Galaxy. *Mercury* (Astronomical Society of the Pacific) 13, no. 4 (July/August).

Kawaler, Steven D., and Donald E. Winget. 1987. White Dwarfs: Fossil Stars. *Sky and Telescope* 74, no. 2 (August).

Maran, Stephen P. 1971. The Gum Nebula. *Scientific American* 225, no. 6 (December).

Marschall, Laurence A. 1988. *The Supernova Story.* New York: Plenum Press.

McClintock, Jeffrey E. 1988. "Stellar Black Holes." In *Supermassive Black Holes,* edited by Minas Kafatos. Cambridge: Cambridge University Press.

———. 1988. Do Black Holes Exist? *Sky and Telescope* 75, no.1 (January).

———. 1987. Stalking the Black Hole in the Star Garden of the Unicorn. *Mercury* 16, no. 4 (July/August).

Malin, David, and David Allen. 1990. Echoes of the Supernova. *Sky and Telescope* 79, no. 1 (January).

Mestel, L. 1965. "The Theory of White Dwarfs." In *Stellar Structure,* vol. 8 of *Stars and Stellar Systems,* edited by Lawrence H. Aller and Dean B. McLaughlin. Chicago: The University of Chicago Press.

Murdin, Paul, and Lesley Murdin. 1985. *Supernovae.* Cambridge: Cambridge University Press.

Ostriker, Jeremiah P. 1970. "The Nature of Pulsars." In *New Frontiers in Astronomy: Readings from Scientific American.* San Francisco: W. H. Freeman and Company.

Parker, Barry. 1986. In and Around Black Holes. *Astronomy* 14, no. 10 (October).

Podsiadlowski, Philipp. 1992. *The Progenitor of SN 1987A.* Publications of the Astronomical Society of the Pacific 104, no. 679 (September).

Schorn, Ronald A. 1987. A Supernova in Our Backyard. *Sky and Telescope* 73, no. 4 (April).

————. 1988. Happy Birthday, Supernova! *Sky and Telescope* 75, no. 2 (February).

————. 1988. Supernova 1987A's Changing Face. *Sky and Telescope* 76, no. 1 (July).

Schur, Chris. 1990. Finding a Supernova Remnant. *Astronomy* 18, no. 2 (February).

Shklovskii, Iosif S. 1975. *Stars: Their Birth, Life, and Death.* Translated by Richard B. Rodman. San Francisco: W. H. Freeman and Company.

Smith, F. G. 1977. *Pulsars.* Cambridge: Cambridge University Press.

Trimble, Virginia. 1986. White Dwarfs: The Once and Future Suns. *Sky and Telescope* 72, no. 4 (October).

Verschuur, Gerrit L. 1989. The Peculiar Pulsar in Supernova 1987A. *Astronomy* 17, no. 9 (September).

Woosley, Stan, and Tom Weaver. 1989. The Great Supernova of 1987. *Scientific American* 261, no. 2 (August).

An artist's conception of our Milky Way Galaxy.

We will begin our study of our home galaxy from a point many thousands of light years beyond the stars that fill the sky above the Earth. The darkness of space is broken by countless foggy patches of distant light like many islands in an endless sea. One of these glowing masses is near enough to be resolved into a whirlpool of stars, dust, and gas. It is the **Galaxy,** our star system, one of countless other galaxies that populate the universe.

The size of this stellar wheel is difficult to visualize. There is a condensation of stars and interstellar matter called the **central bulge.** A flat disk formation, only 600 parsecs thick, extends 15,000 parsecs from the center, and two or more **spiral arms** wind through this disk. A spherical **halo** of old stars and globular clusters surrounds the entire visible structure. Beyond the halo, there may be a massive, dark **galactic corona** that extends into intergalactic space as far as the nearest galaxies beyond our stellar system. This dark corona of unseen matter is believed to contain most of the mass of our galaxy. (See table 17.1 for more information on the Milky Way Galaxy.)

The Galaxy contains a detectable mass of stars, dust, and gas equivalent to about 200 billion solar masses moving in orbits around the central bulge. Our Sun occupies one of the spiral arms at a distance of about 9000 parsecs from the center. From Earth, we see a sky filled with stars that represent only a tiny fraction of the total number of stars in the Galaxy. The glowing Milky Way arching across the sky is made up of segments of several spiral arms (see fig. 17.1).

## A Tour of the Milky Way

On our return from intergalactic space, we plunge into the spiral arm that contains the Sun and planets. Once again the stars are seen in the familiar patterns we know as constellations. From Earth, the overall structure of our stellar system can be visualized by tracing the band of the Milky Way along its entire length.

**figure 17.1**

NGC 2997, a normal spiral galaxy in the southern constellation Antlia. It is generally believed the Milky Way system is similar in structure.

The word galaxy is derived from the Greek *galaktikos,* which means "milky in color," and was once applied to The Milky Way's diffuse light (in Latin, *Via Lactea*). Today, the term galaxy is restricted to the huge stellar systems found throughout the universe. The Galaxy, or **Milky Way system,** is the name of the

## data for the milky way galaxy

| | |
|---|---|
| Radius of the disk | 15,000 parsecs |
| Thickness of the disk | 600 parsecs |
| Radius of the central bulge | 4000 parsecs |
| Radius of the halo | 20,000 parsecs |
| Distance of the Sun from the center | 9000 parsecs |
| Rotation near the Sun | |
|     Velocity | 220 km/sec |
|     Period | $225 \times 10^6$ yrs |
| Number of globular clusters (estimated) | 200 |
| Number of galactic clusters (estimated) | 15,000 |
| Total detectable mass (estimated) | $2 \times 10^{11}$ solar masses |

**figure 17.3**
A wide-angle view of the southern Milky Way from Sagittarius to Centaurus.

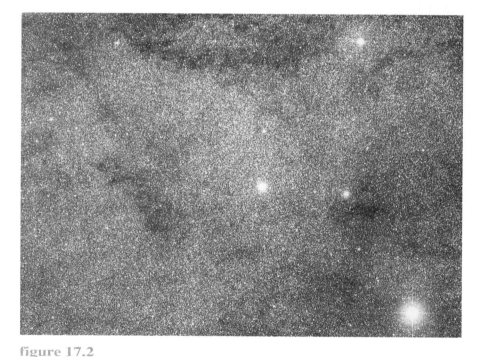

**figure 17.2**
Star clouds and globular clusters in the direction of the Galaxy's center.

stellar aggregation of which the Sun is a member.

We begin our tour of the Milky Way in the constellation Sagittarius which lies in the direction of the galactic center. From Scorpius through Sagittarius, Ophiuchus to Scutum, we can see the huge central bulge of The Milky Way, about 40° wide. There are extensive bright regions called *star clouds;* the more conspicuous formations include the Great Star Cloud in Sagittarius and the Scutum Cloud (fig. 17.2).

Continuing in a northeast direction from Sagittarius to Cygnus, the Milky Way is separated into two bands by a dark bay named the *Great Rift*. Here the Milky Way is striated with a dark, sinuous nebulosity that follows the galactic plane. The brighter branch of the Milky Way passes through Aquila and Vulpecula and rejoins the less prominent branch to form a single diffuse band in the constellation Cepheus. The Milky Way gradually diminishes in brightness through Cassiopeia, Perseus, and Auriga (the direction of the anticenter 180° from Sagittarius). In the Taurus region, the Milky Way is only about 5° wide. The most brilliant section lies between Carina, Crux, Circinus, Ara, and

the Scorpius-Sagittarius region (fig. 17.3). In the Northern Hemisphere, this part of the Milky Way is seen best during summer and autumn months.

Thus we find the Milky Way to be a diffuse, glowing band of light spanning the sky as a great circle. Its central line is the galactic equator, which is inclined 62° to the celestial equator. Light intensity varies from brightest in the direction of the Galaxy's center to faintest in the Auriga-Taurus region. Parts of the Milky Way are separated into dark rifts and bright star clouds.

## Size and Structure of the Galaxy

The first systematic investigation of the Milky Way was carried out by William Herschel in the late eighteenth century. He counted the number of stars visible in a selected region by means of a method he called "star gauging." He divided the sky into fields and measured the average stellar distribution by recording the number of stars in each direction. Herschel counted the stars in 683 fields and found that a greater number lie in the plane of the Milky Way than in the direction of the galactic poles. From this, he concluded that our galaxy is a disk of stars with the Sun located near the center.

Herschel's model was based upon two assumptions: (1) the spatial density of the stars is uniform throughout the stellar system, and (2) his telescope could resolve all the stars down to the faintest magnitude recognized at that time.

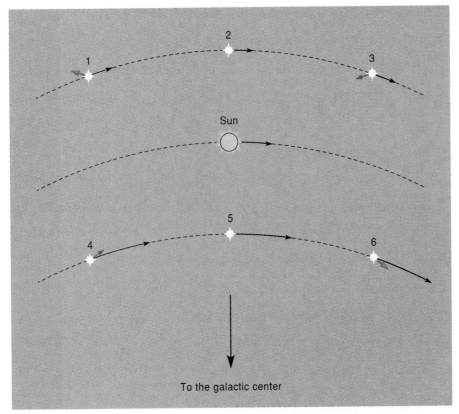

**figure 17.4**

Differential rotation of the Galaxy. Stars closer to the galactic center revolve at greater velocities than stars farther out relative to the Sun. The red and blue arrows indicate the Doppler shifts of the spectra.

Interstellar absorption was unknown in the eighteenth century; thus Herschel was unaware of the billions of stars hidden from view by intervening clouds of dust and did not realize the stellar density is greater toward the center of the Galaxy. In his model, the dark rift in Cygnus was shown as a void separating the stars into two branches. Moreover, in those days, astronomers believed the stars were wandering aimlessly without order or definite direction.

Herschel's scheme of the Milky Way persisted through the nineteenth century. But in the beginning of the twentieth century, the measurement of proper motions and radial velocities revealed the dynamics of the stellar system. Studies of radial velocities by Jan H. Oort provided evidence of galactic rotation. Figure 17.4 represents a view of the Galaxy within 3000 parsecs of the Sun. The motions of the stars show the effect of differential galactic rotation: stars inside the Sun have greater circular velocities, while stars beyond the Sun travel at a slower rate. When viewed from a point above the galactic plane, the Sun and stars travel their courses in a clockwise direction. Stars 1, 2, and 3 are traveling more slowly and will lag behind the Sun; stars 4, 5, and 6 will overtake and pass the Sun. Proof of differential rotation is found in the spectra of the stars. The radial velocity components of stars 1 and 6 have positive values indicating that the distances between the Sun and the stars are increasing. The radial velocities of stars 3 and 4 have negative values because the distances between the Sun and the stars are decreasing. According to these radial-velocity measurements, the Sun is moving in a slightly elliptical orbit about a center located in the direction of Sagittarius.

Harlow Shapley demonstrated in 1918 that the Sun is at a considerable distance from the galactic center. His model of our galaxy was based upon the distribution of globular clusters and their distances from the Sun. Shapley plotted the clusters and found most of them dispersed around the constellation Sagittarius, and in greater numbers toward the galactic plane. He argued that globular clusters represent a spherical formation distributed about the center of a lens-shaped disk of moving stars (fig. 17.5).

The distance between the Sun and the galactic center was determined from observations of cepheid variable and RR Lyrae stars found in the globular clusters. In 1912, Shapley's colleague at Harvard Observatory, Henrietta S. Leavitt, had discovered the period-luminosity relation while studying variable stars found in the Large Magellanic Cloud (see chapter 13). Shapley applied the relation to estimate the absolute magnitudes of selected variable stars in the globular clusters. A comparison between the derived absolute and observed apparent magnitudes gave the distances to the clusters. In computing the distances, Shapley assumed that interstellar space is free from absorption. But within the Milky Way, absorption is greatest in the direction of the galactic plane where intervening clouds of dust decrease the intensity of light emitted by distant sources. The stars appear to be farther away than they actually are and a correction must be applied to the apparent magnitude whenever distances are computed.

Moreover, Shapley was unaware that cluster-type variables belong to an entirely different population of stars than the classical cepheids studied by Leavitt. His model was correct, but Shapley overestimated the size of the Galaxy to a radius of 45,000 parsecs. Presently, the outer rim of the Galaxy is known to be about 15,000 parsecs from the center.

While Oort and Shapley were defining the dynamics and structure of the Milky Way, other astronomers were studying spiral nebulae that were suspected of being other galaxies. Until their distances were known, these spiral nebulae were thought to be clouds of interstellar gas. Nevertheless, as early as the 1890s, William Huggins had examined the spectra of spiral nebulae such as the Great Nebula in Andromeda and identified absorption lines associated with spectra of the Sun and other stars. By 1914, Arthur S. Eddington and other astronomers were convinced that spirals represented stellar systems similar to our own.

The problem of the structure and composition of the Milky Way as well as external galaxies continued to attract the attention of astronomers. In 1923, Edwin Hubble discovered cepheid variable stars in the Andromeda galaxy and was able to measure its distance by the period-luminosity relation. His investigations proved the spiral to be a distant stellar system and also confirmed the structural features of Shapley's model of the Galaxy.

## Rotation of the Galaxy

The rotation of the Galaxy has been investigated by studying the motions of stars, star clusters, and gas clouds at different distances from the galactic center (see Methods and Understandings 17.1). As we might expect in a huge, complex organization, these bodies move about the Galaxy at different velocities. The galactic rotation near the Sun, at 9000 parsecs from the center, is about 220 km/sec. The Sun requires approximately 225 million years to complete one revolution around the galactic center.

As described earlier, in the Sun's vicinity the motions of stars indicate that the galactic disk shows differential rotation. Stars nearer to the galactic center have greater circular velocities and those located farther from the center travel more slowly than the Sun. This motion of the stars in the galactic disk is similar to the revolution of the planets around the Sun.

A *rotation curve* of the Galaxy shows how the velocities of stars and gas clouds in the galactic disk vary with respect to their distances from the center (fig. 17.6). The central bulge turns like a rigid wheel that increases in velocity as the distance increases from the center (just as the rim of a wheel spins faster than the hub). There is a dip in velocity to about 200 km/sec at 2500 parsecs from the center, then the velocity increases to 220 km/sec at the Sun's distance. Beyond the Sun, the disk velocity remains almost constant as far as the rim, about 15,000 parsecs from the center.

What does the rotation curve of the Galaxy reveal? Why do stars in the outer parts of our stellar system revolve at about the same rate as stars in the inner region of the disk? Recall how Newton's

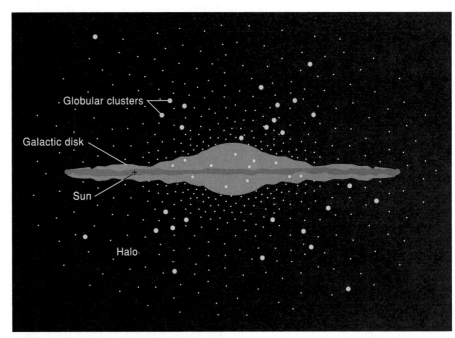

**figure 17.5**
The structure of the Milky Way Galaxy.

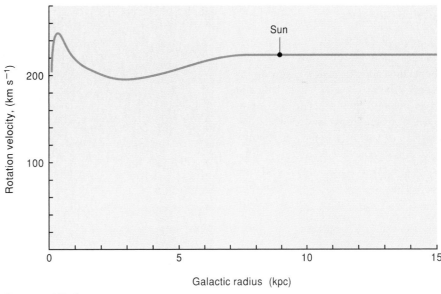

**figure 17.6**
The rotation curve for the Milky Way Galaxy.

derivation of Kepler's third law of planetary motion provided a way to compute the mass of Jupiter by the distance and period of its satellite, Io (Methods and Understandings 9.1). The gravitational attraction provided by Jupiter's mass determines the orbital velocity of Io. If Jupiter were more massive and possessed a stronger gravitational field, Io would be forced to revolve faster to keep its present distance from the planet. In a similar way, the motions of stars and gas clouds are dependent upon the mass of the Galaxy at any given distance from the center. The mass distribution of all the stars and interstellar matter determines the orbital velocity of a body at any location in the system. Therefore, the greater velocity at the external boundary of the disk is interpreted as a gravitational effect produced by unseen matter surrounding our galaxy beyond the visible halo.

In 1978, J. Einasto proposed that a massive, dark galactic corona extends no less than 60,000 parsecs into intergalactic space. If this hypothetical dark component exists, it is large enough to include several nearby galaxies—the Magellanic Clouds and a number of dwarf elliptical galaxies (see chapter 18).

Evidence for a massive dark corona is also found in distant external galaxies. Studies show that matter in the outer regions of these stellar systems rotates in the same way as the outer parts of the Galaxy's disk. A computer model of our galaxy based upon observational data from six galaxies and the Milky Way system was constructed by U. Haud, M. Joeveer, and J. Einasto. In the model, the estimated mass of the corona is nearly 20 times the combined mass of all the stars in the visible Galaxy.

## The Interstellar Medium

Photographs of the Milky Way, in particular the regions of Scorpius, Ophiuchus, and Sagittarius, show an intricate structure of stars, and dark and bright nebulous clouds. Here stars seem to be more numerous and crowded together than stars near to the Sun. But the picture is an illusion caused by our difficulty in perceiving the enormous expanse separating the stars. When stellar distances are measured and spatial density determined, the results show that the average distance between stars is about two parsecs.

The vast domain of space is permeated by an **interstellar medium** that dims the light from background stars. Most of the interstellar material is gaseous, about one atom per cubic centimeter. Atoms of interstellar gas may be ionized by radiation from nearby luminous stars to form glowing nebulae. Solid grains are scarce and make up only a fraction of the total mass, no more than 100 microscopic particles per cubic kilometer. These tiny grains scatter, reflect, and polarize starlight. The nature of the grains is not certain: they may be particles of carbon embedded in ice, dusty specks of iron, or perhaps tiny crystals of rock.

In 1930, while investigating open clusters, Robert Trumpler found a gen-

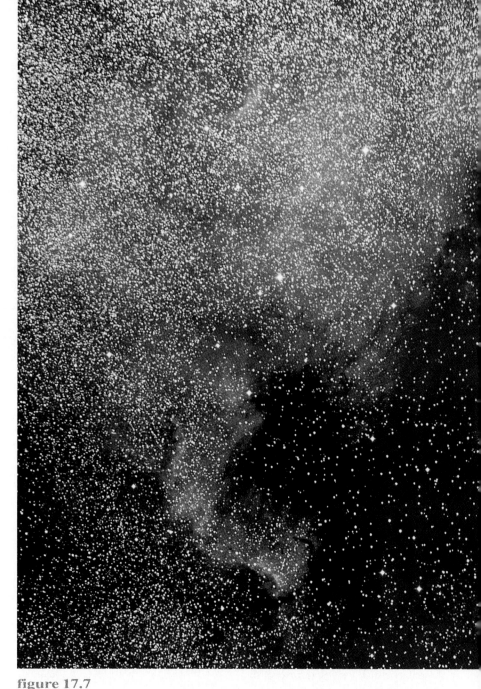

**figure 17.7**

The North American nebula, NGC 7000, in Cygnus. Clouds of tiny solid dust grains in the foreground obscure the light from distant stars to form an outline that resembles the North American continent.

eral dimming of starlight caused by the uniform distribution of dust. He classified star clusters according to three criteria: (1) the central concentration of the stars, (2) magnitude, and (3) the number of stars in each cluster. Trumpler was able to measure distances to the stars by comparing the angular diameters of clusters having similar characteristics. However, measurements determined by absolute magnitude derived from spectral classification and apparent magnitude

indicated the stars must be at even greater distances. Trumpler reasoned that the inconsistency proved the existence of intervening dust between the nearer and more distant objects (fig. 17.7).

Not only is starlight dimmed, it is also reddened by these interstellar grains. Short violet and blue wavelengths are scattered more than orange and red. Thus longer-wavelength light is able to pass through the medium more effectively and a star will appear redder than normal for its spec-

incident light from these distant stars enters the cloud and is absorbed and scattered in all directions. Thus, if the dust cloud and stars are in our line of sight, the region of the sky will appear dark and only the stars between us and the nebula can be seen.

An example of an extended complex of stars and dark and bright nebulosities is seen in the constellation Orion (fig. 17.8). Beginning at the star Alnitak (Zeta Orionis in the belt of Orion), a dark bay resembling a violent storm cloud extends southward more than 2°, or four times the angular diameter of the Moon. It is fringed by a narrow emission nebula, IC 434, which is composed of hydrogen excited by ultraviolet radiation from the star Sigma Orionis. From the rim of IC 434, fine strands of bright nebulosity extend westward and gradually fade in the direction of the star. The nebula is very tenuous; there are ten times as many stars between IC 434 and Sigma as there are in front of the dark nebular complex.

A spectacular obscuration resembling a horsehead projects from the dark bay into the bright region of IC 434. The famous Horsehead nebula contains dust particles that reflect starlight, producing a blue-white glow around the figure. Where the nebula is opaque, the horsehead casts a shadow into the dark complex in the foreground. Northeast of the Horsehead nebula, a blue-white nebula, NGC 2023, is made bright by the reflected light from a nearby star (fig. 17.9). To the east of Zeta Orionis, another strange reflection nebula, NGC 2024, is marked by sinuous dust lanes associated with the dark complex.

## Bright Nebulae

Extensive bright clouds of dust and gas are classified in two ways. **Reflection nebulae** consist of dust clouds that reflect light from nearby stars. **Emission nebulae** are principally hydrogen clouds ionized by neighboring stars.

Whether a dust cloud remains dark or shines with a suffuse glow depends upon the direction of the source of starlight scattered in the cloud. In reflection nebulae, incident light from a star is reflected by the dust grains within the cloud to the

**figure 17.8**

The dark, obscuring cloud containing the Horsehead nebula in Orion. The second-magnitude star Zeta Orionis, at the top of the photo, is the easternmost star in Orion's belt. NGC 2024, east of Zeta Orionis, is a reflection nebula.

tral class. (The Sun looks red at dawn and dusk when its light is scattered through a greater thickness of atmosphere.)

## Dark Nebulae

Extensive clouds of fine-grained dust are found in the spiral arms of the Milky Way. They appear as dark patches silhouetted against the background of rich star fields. Sometimes these **dark nebulae** are entangled in or appear in the foreground of bright nebulosities. Although few in number, dust grains occupy a volume of space great enough to obscure the stars that lie beyond the clouds. The

**figure 17.9**
The Horsehead nebula projects against the bright transparent emission nebula IC 434. To the northeast of the Horsehead is the bright white reflection nebula NGC 2023.

NGC 2023

observer. If a star is behind the dust cloud, the light from the star is dimmed and the result is a dark nebula. If a star is adjacent to the cloud, its light will be scattered as before, but a portion of the light reflected from the dust grains is observed as a bright nebula. The reflection nebula looks blue because shorter wavelengths of light are scattered more effectively than longer wavelengths (fig. 17.10).

The general interstellar gas consists mainly of neutral atomic hydrogen in the lowest energy state (refer to chapter 4). The cold gas cannot absorb photons of light and does not obscure the light from distant stars. However, neutral hydrogen is ionized by the intense ultraviolet radiation from high-temperature O- and B-type stars. When ultraviolet radiation is absorbed, hydrogen atoms change to an excited state and electrons jump to a higher orbit. If the electrons fall to a final energy level within the Balmer series, the transition will pro-

duce photons of visible light. The fluorescence is observed as a bright emission nebula which is also referred to as an H II region. The nebula appears red when photographed owing to the prominence of the Hα line in the Balmer series (figs. 17.9 and 17.10). In addition to hydrogen, the spectra of emission nebulae contain lines of ionized oxygen and nitrogen. These spectral lines are normally produced only in the rarified gases of emission nebulae.

## Stellar Populations

In 1944, Walter Baade introduced a classification that divides the stars into two

**figure 17.10**

The Trifid nebula, M20 (NGC 6514), in Sagittarius. The blue region is a reflection nebula in which shorter wavelengths of light are scattered by dust grains. The red region is an emission nebula where neutral hydrogen is ionized by ultraviolet radiation from high-temperature stars. The prominent Hα line in the Balmer series makes the nebula appear red.

categories, **population I** and **population II**. While photographing the Andromeda galaxy using red and blue filters, he discovered that stars in the spiral arms are hot, blue stars similar to those found in OB associations and young galactic clusters in our Milky Way. Stars in the central region of the Andromeda galaxy are predominantly red giant stars such as those found in the globular clusters of our own galaxy. Baade identified the stars in the central region of the Andromeda galaxy as population II and the stars in the spiral arms as population I. In our galaxy, population II stars are found in the halo, disk, and central bulge.

In addition to galactic distribution, there are fundamental differences between the stellar populations. Population I stars are relatively young, as stars go; their ages are measured from a few million years to about five billion years. Some stars are still associated with the nebulae from which they evolved. Also,

population I stars are distinguished by a greater abundance of heavier elements. Astronomers refer to chemical elements (with the exception of hydrogen and helium) as "metals." Thus population I stars are considered to be metal-rich and represent second-and third-generation stars. In chapter 15, we learned that the source of newly-emerged stars, the interstellar medium, was enriched with metals released during supernovae explosions of first-generation stars.

Thus population I members include stars associated with the spiral structure of the Galaxy and other spiral systems. The greatest number are the hydrogen-burning main-sequence stars; others include the luminous red supergiants and type I cepheid variables.

In contrast, the population II category contains the oldest known stars. They are metal-poor stars that evolved early in the history of the Galaxy. Supernovae of the earlier stellar generation supplied the heavy elements for the more recent metal-rich stars. Examples include stars in advanced stages of evolution: the red giants, RR Lyrae variables, type II cepheid variables, planetary nebulae, and white dwarf stars.

Geoffrey and Margaret Burbridge describe a more detailed classification of stars into five populations:

*Extreme population II*. This category represents the oldest group of stars. It contains the stars in globular clusters and the stars found between clusters in the galactic halo.

*Intermediate population II*. These are supernovae and planetary nebulae distributed spherically about the center of the Galaxy.

*Disk population*. The greatest number of stars belong to the disk population. These stars may be considerably older than five billion years.

*Intermediate population I*. Stars in this group range in age from the youngest main-sequence stars to about three billion years. They are found near the galactic plane, in and outside the spiral structure.

*Extreme population I*. These are the youngest stars, including pre-main-sequence T Tauri stars and O associations enmeshed in dust and gas nebulae found in the spiral arms.

# The Spiral Structure

Studies of other galaxies and the Milky Way have revealed the interaction between the dust and gas lanes and bright population I stars that define the spiral arms. Large nearby galaxies show a series of O associations and emission nebulae that trace the spiral structure like a sweeping string of pearls, while dark dust lanes follow the inner edges of the spiral arms. No dust and only a fraction of interstellar gas are found between the spiral arms in the region occupied by disk population stars.

The spiral structure of the Milky Way can be traced optically by pinpointing the directions and determining the distances of population I objects that make up the spiral arms. In addition to O- and B-type stars and nebulae, there are luminous cepheid variable stars, T Tauri stars, and red supergiant stars. Cepheids are especially useful since their changing brightness can be observed to greater distances than OB stars. Astronomers call these objects and stars **spiral tracers.**

## Optical Tracers

W. W. Morgan and his associates, S. L. Sharpless and D. E. Osterbrock, by 1951 had determined the distances to over 900 OB stars and luminous emission nebulae. From these studies, they constructed a provisional model representing the spiral structure within 3000 parsecs of the Sun. In the model, the Milky Way is resolved into segments of three separate spiral arms. A spiral arm from the Orion region stretches to the Sun and continues to the stars and cosmic clouds in Cygnus. Later, the arm was extended to include the southern constellation Carina.

The **Sagittarius arm** lies between the Sun and the central bulge. The Sun is located in the spiral designated the **Orion arm;** beyond the Sun lies the **Perseus arm** where the features of the Milky Way are less pronounced (fig. 17.11). In addition to its orbital velocity of about 220 km/sec, the Sun travels in a sinuous curve above and below the central plane several times during its 225-million-year trek around the Galaxy.

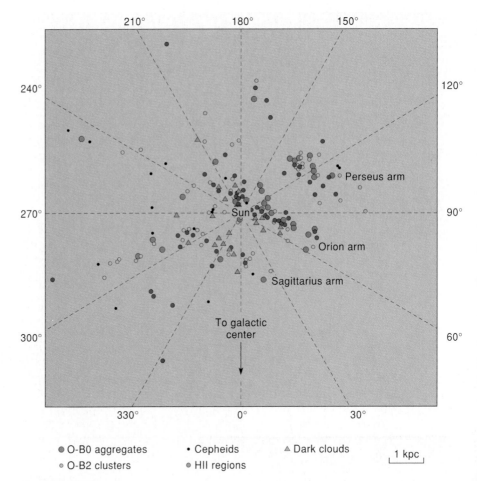

**figure 17.11**

Optical tracers of spiral arms. The Milky Way is resolved into segments of three spiral arms. The Sun is located in the Orion arm at the center of the diagram. Directions in the galactic plane are measured in degrees of galactic longitude.

## The 21-cm Spectral Line of Neutral Hydrogen

The pronounced spiral structure in the Galaxy can be traced through investigation of the radio spectrum of neutral atomic hydrogen (H I) regions. As we have seen, in the cold, dark interstellar medium, hydrogen atoms exist in the ground state. Recall the Bohr model of hydrogen in which the proton and electron are depicted as tiny spheres; the electron revolves in an orbit within the electric field of the proton. In addition, the particles possess angular momentum so that both proton and electron spin about their respective axes. The rotating particles may assume two possible ground-state positions: (1) the proton and electron can spin parallel in the same direction, or (2) they can spin antiparal-lel in opposite directions. In either case, the atom is in the ground state, but at a slightly lower energy level if the spin is antiparallel, and in a higher energy state if the particles spin in the same direction.

Collisions between any two hydrogen atoms in the tenuous H I regions may occur only a few times in a thousand years. When such rare events do take place, electrons are exchanged between the atoms, which may result in a conversion to a higher or lower energy level. If the transfer causes an antiparallel configuration, there will be a transition to a lower state and the emission of a photon of electromagnetic energy detected as the 21-cm line in the radio spectrum. In some transitions the atom is in a higher energy state. Eventually, after an interval lasting many millions of years, the electron will "spin-flip" into

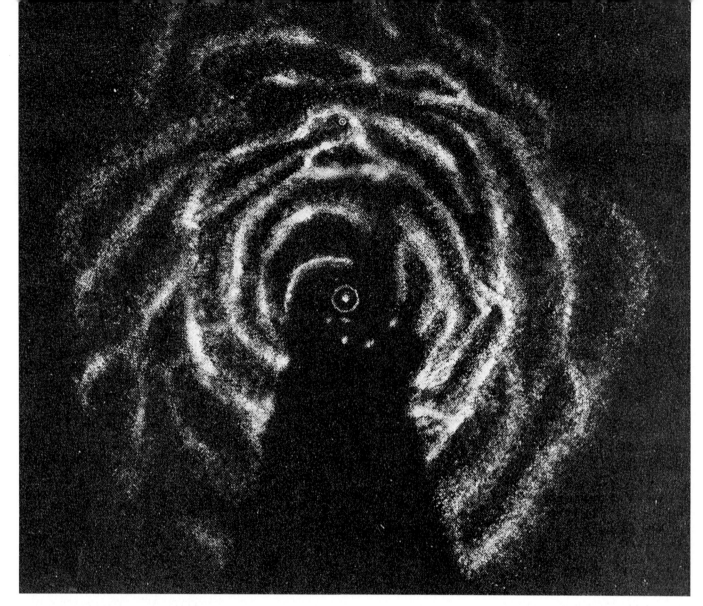

**figure 17.12**

Radio tracer of spiral arms. This chart of the spiral structure of the galaxy is based on the 21-cm signal emitted by interstellar hydrogen atoms. The galactic center is represented by a large circle. The position of the Sun is indicated by the small circle in a spiral arm above center.

the antiparallel configuration and release a photon of 21-cm wavelength. Collection and analysis of 21-cm data has allowed astronomers to trace the radio spiral structure of the Galaxy.

## Radio Tracers

As early as 1944, H. C. van de Hulst predicted the existence of the neutral hydrogen transitions, but, in those days, radio astronomy was in its infancy and telescopes were unable to detect the 21-cm signal. By 1951, these theoretical studies were confirmed, and a map of the spiral structure was made from radial-velocity measurements based upon Jan H. Oort's analysis of differential galactic rotation.

Figure 17.12 is a schematic representation of the spiral structure of the Galaxy observed at 21-cm wavelength. In the direction of the galactic center and anticenter, where neutral hydrogen arms are moving across the line of sight, radial velocities are zero and the radio structure cannot be mapped. In other directions, the radial velocities are measured by the Doppler effect. At each position observed, the frequency of the radiation is slightly shifted owing to the cloud's radial velocity toward or away from the Sun.

Consider neutral hydrogen clouds in different spiral arms measured along line-of-sight positions in a given direction. A cloud with maximum radial velocity for its distance from the galactic center will

be located at a point tangent to the line of sight (see Methods and Understandings 17.1). Some clouds have positive radial velocities indicating that they are receding from the Sun. Other clouds have negative radial velocities and are approaching the Sun. The motions of the clouds show the effect of differential galactic rotation. The spiral structure is traced by combining data from many hydrogen clouds observed at different intervals in galactic longitude.

## Molecular Tracers

In the spiral arms, molecular hydrogen is as abundant as the neutral atomic hydrogen that is observed at the 21-cm

333

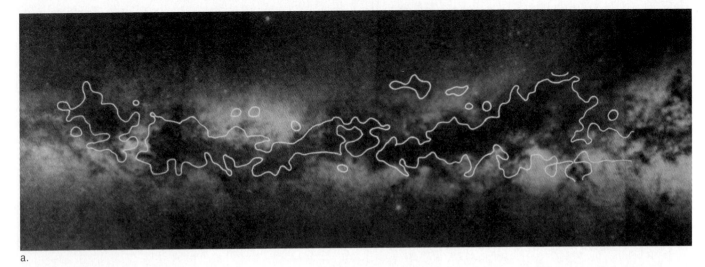

a.

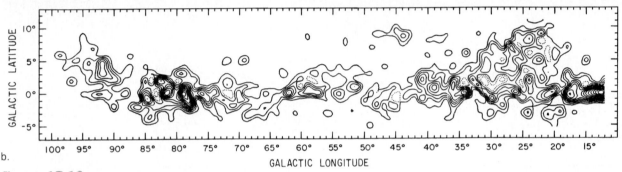

b.

**figure 17.13**

Molecular tracers of spiral arms. *a.* Carbon monoxide clouds are found in the obscuring dust clouds in the disk of the Galaxy. *b.* Radio brightness of the clouds at intervals of galactic longitude.

wavelength. In chapter 15, we described how **giant molecular clouds** represent the breeding grounds for new stars. They are enormous cloud formations, composed mainly of molecular hydrogen and carbon monoxide, that occupy the same region as the dark rifts along the Milky Way.

In a cold giant cloud, an isolated molecule will remain at the ground state. When a collision occurs between hydrogen and carbon monoxide molecules, the CO molecule absorbs energy and assumes a higher energy state. In the transition, the CO molecule releases a photon of electromagnetic energy of 2.6-mm wavelength in the radio spectrum.

Radio astronomers plot the brightness of the CO clouds in a given direction at intervals of galactic longitude (fig. 17.13). As in the case of 21-cm neutral hydrogen studies, a cloud showing the highest radial velocity is located in a spiral arm tangent to the line of sight; the velocity data from the clouds corresponds to positions nearer to or more

distant from the Galaxy's center than the Sun.

## The Density Wave Theory

Having traced the spiral structure of the Galaxy, we now turn to the perplexing problem of the processes that sustain the spiral pattern. One fact is certain: in nature, a spiral formation is indicative of growth and motion. Consider, for instance, the spiral chambers of a nautilus shell, the cloudy coils surrounding the eye of a hurricane, or the circular motion of water in a whirlpool.

A preliminary step in finding the mechanism that drives the complex galactic structure is to investigate the effect of galactic rotation. Let us begin with the myriads of stars distributed throughout the galactic disk. As they revolve about the Galaxy, the stars nearer to the center will have greater angular velocity than those located further away. Eventually, the stars will form two or more trailing spiral arms. If the process

continues for a long interval of time, there will be no less than 50 windings in the spiral pattern. Yet the spiral structure found in the Milky Way, as well as other galaxies, has fewer turns than would be the case if differential galactic rotation were solely responsible for their formation. How is the spiral structure preserved? Some other process must segregate young stars and dense interstellar clouds into spiral arms.

An elegant explanation proposed by B. Lindblad was developed into a **density wave theory** by C. C. Lin and F. H. Shu in the 1960s. Rather than a material component, the spiral arms of the Galaxy are regarded as ripples or waves caused by uneven distribution of matter in the galactic disk. In the model, the spiral arms are denser concentrations of stars and interstellar gas and dust.

As numerous photographs indicate, various types of galactic spiral structures exist. To name a few, there are *grand design* galaxies where two symmetric arms wind outward from the center;

## The Spiral Structure and Rotation Velocity of the Galaxy

The spiral arms of the Galaxy can be mapped by observing neutral hydrogen clouds at 21-cm wavelength and giant carbon monoxide clouds at 2.6-mm wavelength in the radio spectrum. Figure 17.14 is a representation of the spiral structure made from radio telescope observations. Neutral hydrogen clouds outline the spiral arms. Giant molecular clouds are shown along line-of-sight positions at 20° and 327° galactic longitude. (Galactic longitude is measured eastward from the galactic center, 00°, through 360° along the galactic equator.)

Clouds 1 and 3 will have about the same radial velocity and are located in the same spiral arm. How do astronomers know which cloud is nearer to the Sun? Cloud 3 will have a weaker signal owing to its greater distance on the far side of the spiral arm. Cloud 2 lies in the same line-of-sight but has a different radial velocity. Its velocity corresponds to an orbit nearer to the galactic center.

Clouds 4, 5, and 6 have varied radial velocities. Cloud 5 is at about the same distance from the center as clouds 1 and 3. Cloud 6 revolves at a greater distance from the galactic center than the Sun.

The radius of a cloud's orbit is determined from observations of radial velocity. As described in Methods and Understandings 13.1 and fig. 13.6, radial velocity is the component of a body's motion along the observer's line of sight. Tangential velocity is the velocity component at 90° to the line of sight. If a body is approaching or receding from the observer in the line of sight, the tangential velocity is reduced to zero and radial velocity reaches its maximum value (see fig. 14.8). Picture cloud 4 where the line-of-sight is tangent and perpendicular to the radius of the orbit. The radial velocity of the cloud is 225 km/sec. The radius of the orbit may be computed by the same method used in chapter 3 to find the distance between Venus and the Sun.

Let the distance, $R_\odot$, between the Sun and the galactic center be equal to unity ($R_\odot = 1$); and let it represent the hypotenuse of a right triangle formed by the Sun, the galactic center, and the hydrogen cloud. The sine of the angle (A) at the Sun is

$$\sin A = \frac{\text{radius of the cloud's orbit } (R_1)}{\text{radius of the Sun's orbit } (R_\odot)}.$$

The radius of the cloud's orbit ($R_1$) is expressed

$$R_1 = R_\odot \sin A$$

where angle $A$ represents the co-longitude of the cloud, $360° - 327°$, or $33°$. The sine of $33°$ is equal to 0.544.

$$R_1 = 9000 \text{ parsecs} \times 0.544$$
$$R_1 = 4900 \text{ parsecs}$$

The quantities 4900 parsecs and 225 km/sec are one set of coordinates on the graph representing the rotation curve for the Galaxy (fig. 17.6).

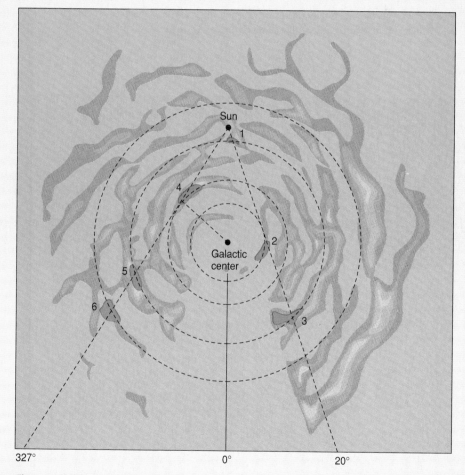

327°        0°        20°

**figure 17.14**

The spiral structure and rotation velocity of the Galaxy can be determined using radio telescope data.

**figure 17.15**

Stars, dust, and gas moving in elliptical orbits around the galactic center create density waves, which combine into patterns that produce the spiral structure of a galaxy.

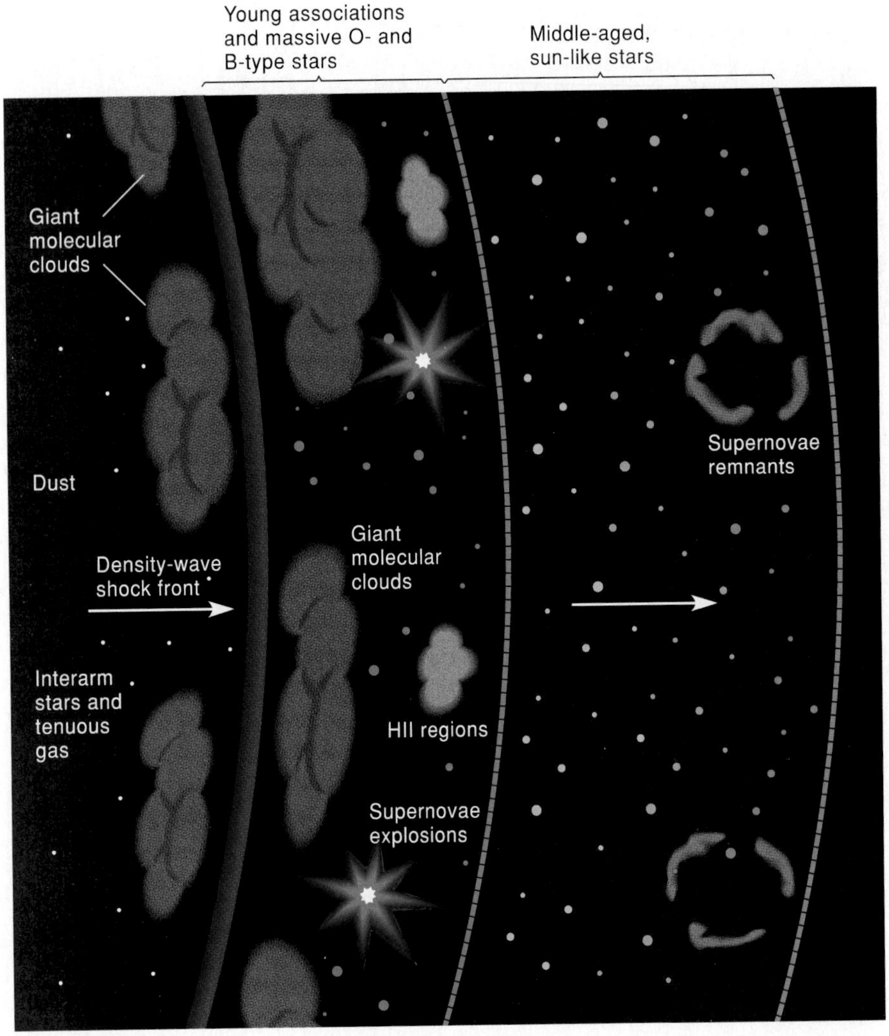

Young associations and massive O- and B-type stars

Middle-aged, sun-like stars

Giant molecular clouds

Dust

Density-wave shock front

Interarm stars and tenuous gas

Giant molecular clouds

HII regions

Supernovae explosions

Supernovae remnants

**figure 17.16**

Formation of stars in association with density waves.

*multiple arm* galaxies that contain many spiral arms in their outer regions; and *flocculent* spiral galaxies, with small segments that appear as cloudlike patches following a spiral structure.

These differences between galaxies indicate that no single density wave model can adequately explain the formation and maintenance of the spiral structure. Therefore our purpose will be simply to discuss the dynamic forces responsible for the spiral pattern.

Consider billions of stars in the galactic disk moving under their mutual gravitational forces. In an intricate gravitational field, stars and interstellar particles will deviate from simple circular paths. Complex motions of the stars cause a compression (higher stellar density) in some regions and rarefaction (lower stellar density) in other regions of the disk. (Compare this to the longitudinal wave introduced in chapter 4.)

Figure 17.15 shows the formation of density patterns proposed by A. J. Kalnajs in 1973. In his model, disk stars travel in nested elliptical paths rather than in random orbits about the galactic center. The major axis of each orbit is turned so that the apsis of an inner orbit moves in advance of the next outer orbit. The configuration creates a point of maximum star density where the distance between two orbits is at a minimum. The points of maximum star density form double-arm spiral density waves that swirl outward between 6000 and 16,000 parsecs from the galactic center. At the Sun's distance, this wavelike structure rotates at about one-half the speed of the stars and interstellar matter found in the interarm region of the disk. Moreover, the density waves represent stable regions rotating at virtually constant angular velocity so that the spiral structure remains intact over a long period in the life of the Galaxy.

The density of the wave will increase as interarm stars and tenuous gas catch up with and pass through the wave pattern. As depicted in fig. 17.16, stars and gas enter the inner edge of the density wave and produce a strong shock front when they collide with slower-moving particles. The compression causes molecular clouds and dust lanes to form ahead of the shock front. Deeper inside

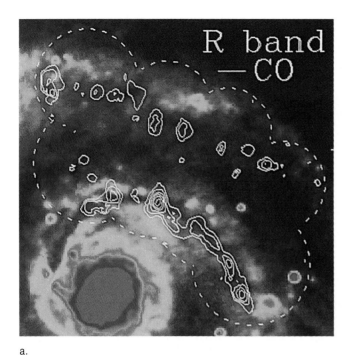

R band
— CO

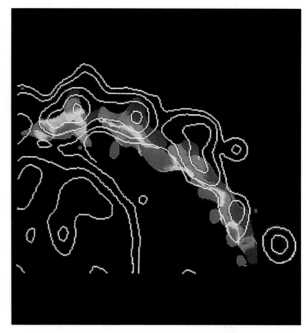

a.                                                                    b.

**figure 17.17**

Molecular clouds in M51, the Whirlpool galaxy, support the connection between density waves and stellar evolution. *a.* Carbon monoxide clouds are identified along the inner edge of a spiral arm. *b.* Contour lines show the formation of new stars inside the spiral structure.

the inner edge, gases and dust condense into massive O- and B-type stars; and there are young associations and H II regions where star formation occurred several million years earlier. Beyond the crest of the wave, at the leading edge of the spiral arm, there are old stellar associations, supernovae remnants, middle-aged sunlike stars, and other population I members.

After a long period of time, the stars and gases that were in the density wave will pass through and enter the interarm region where older population II stars are found. New matter overtakes the density wave and replenishes the spiral arms with dust and gas to sustain the formation of future stellar generations.

Support for the density wave theory is found in studies of star formation in other galaxies. The 2.6-mm emission from carbon monoxide was used to trace the molecular clouds in the spiral arms of M51, the Whirlpool galaxy (fig. 17.17). As predicted by the theory, new stars were found in the region beyond the material passing through the shock front of the density wave.

## The Active Center of the Galaxy

In view of what we already know about the absorbing matter in the spiral arms, it is not surprising to learn that the galactic bulge seen from the Earth is merely the external boundary of a very complex region extending about 4000 parsecs from the center. The nature of the core was a mystery to astronomers when only optical telescopes were in use, because visible radiation cannot penetrate the profusion of stars and dust that make up the central bulge.

Fortunately, radiation at longer as well as shorter wavelengths than light does pass through the absorbing matter in the galactic center. The emissions represent other familiar forms of electromagnetic radiation. Radio, microwave, and infrared waves are collected and studied using ground-based telescopes. X-rays, gamma rays, and infrared radiation are detected by orbiting telescopes (fig. 17.18). Long radio waves are emitted by cold interstellar dust and neutral gas. Infrared radiation identifies huge dust clouds and red supergiant stars. Ultraviolet radiation and the shorter X-rays and gamma rays from deep sources re-

veal H II regions, O and B stars, supernova remnants, neutron stars, and possibly black holes.

Thus the galactic core contains more than the population II objects discovered by Baade; there are vast clouds of gas rushing from the center as though a violent explosion had occurred millions of years ago. Other galaxies show evidence of similar eruptions. At the heart of our galaxy, the **galactic nucleus** may contain one of the strangest of all objects— a supermassive black hole believed to be the driving mechanism of the Galaxy.

### Observations in Many Wavelengths

In the early 1960s, J. H. Oort and G. W. Rougoor were the first astronomers to discover 21-cm radiation from neutral hydrogen clouds within the galactic bulge. Doppler shifts of the spectral lines indicated that the signals came from two huge rotating arcs of hydrogen located at distances of three kiloparsecs (3000 parsecs) and 2.5 kiloparsecs from the center. The 3-kpc arm lies between us and the galactic center and is approaching at a radial velocity of 53 km/sec. The 2.5-kpc hydrogen arc, called the expanding arm, is on the opposite side of the center and is receding at about 135 km/sec (fig. 17.19).

Moreover, carbon monoxide emissions from the 3-kpc arm have been detected from radio observations at 2.6-mm wavelength. The carbon monoxide traces strings of molecular hydrogen clouds throughout the region.

Radio astronomers have detected another structure nearer to the galactic center. A rotating disk of neutral hydrogen occupies the region between 300 and 500 parsecs from the nucleus. At the inner boundary of the nuclear disk, there is a partial ring of molecular clouds rushing outward at about 100 km/sec.

What is the significance of expanding molecular cloud structures in the innermost regions of the Galaxy? Astronomers believe that at one time the elements in the clouds were synthesized in the interiors of massive stars. Later, supernovae explosions ejected material and seeded the clouds with dust and heavy elements.

Moreover, radio astronomers have identified emissions from H II regions. The radiation in the emission nebulae is caused by electrons in near-collision with protons in the ionized gas. The H II regions found within a few hundred parsecs of the nucleus are believed to be connected with nearby molecular clouds. From observations of similar structures in the spiral arms, we can expect that new stars are evolving near the galactic center. These new stars are not only OB-type stars but also the less massive and cooler main-sequence stars.

Further evidence of star birth is also found at infrared wavelengths. Astronomers have identified bright infrared sources within three parsecs of the nucleus. These emissions are believed to be caused by clouds of dust particles heated by luminous stars as massive as 50 suns. The intensity of radiation shows that the galactic center has a higher density of stars than found elsewhere in our galaxy.

The dust clouds emit radiation at longer IR wavelengths. Astronomers detect red giant stars at shorter IR wavelengths, 2.2 micrometers (1 micrometer = $10^{-4}$ cm), or about three times longer than the wavelength of red light. The red giant stars are used to estimate the distribution of all stars in the region.

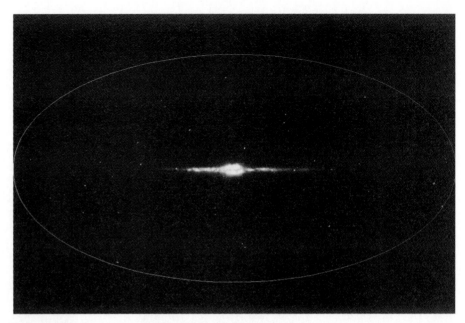

**figure 17.18**

Near-infrared image of the center of the Galaxy taken by the Diffused Infrared Background Experiment aboard the Cosmic Background Explorer (COBE) satellite.

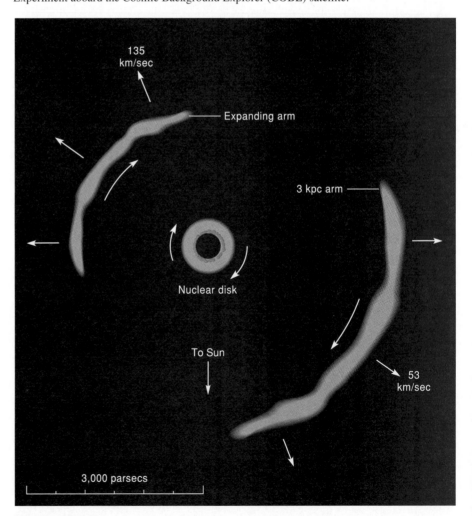

**figure 17.19**

The center of the Galaxy contains an expanding arc of molecular clouds inside a rotating disk of neutral hydrogen gas. Two expanding and rotating gaseous arms are situated beyond the disk.

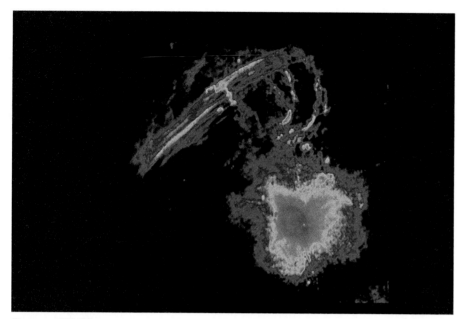

**figure 17.20**

A false-color image of the galactic center at 20-cm wavelength, mapped by the Very Large Array (VLA) radio antennas. The narrow blue arcs at the upper right are nearly 200 light-years in length and are emitting synchrotron radiation. The red oval structure may be gas ionized by UV radiation by a source near the galactic center.

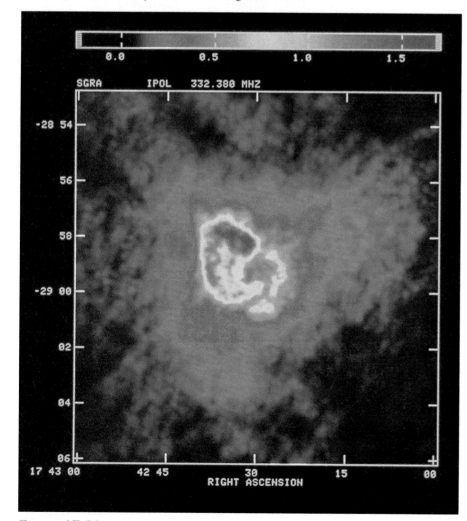

**figure 17.21**

A pseudocolor representation of Sagittarius A* and its halo at 90-cm wavelength made at the NRAO Very Large Array telescope at Socorro, New Mexico.

The number of stars within the galactic core is enormous. For comparison, consider a sphere with a diameter of one parsec centered on the Sun. The region is completely void of stars; the nearest stars to the Sun are located at more than twice this distance. If the solar neighborhood had the same stellar density as the galactic core, there would be no less than two million stars surrounding the Sun. The mean distance between the stars would be only about 1000 AU.

## The Galactic Nucleus

Among the many stars and gas clouds within the central parsec is an intense radio source called **Sagittarius A\*** that is believed to coincide with the nucleus of the Galaxy. Observations indicate that Sgr A* is very small, no larger than about 10 AU. Moreover, it is virtually motionless compared to other objects in the area, which may indicate that Sgr A* is an extremely dense body representing the central mass.

Radio emissions reveal Sgr A* to be a strong source of synchrotron radiation (fig. 17.20). In fact the steady radio "noise" discovered by Jansky in the 1930s is attributed to high-energy electrons spiraling along magnetic field lines. As described earlier, synchrotron radiation is associated with neutron stars and massive black holes, which may explain why Sgr A* is an extremely massive body emitting copious amounts of energy.

Radio and infrared studies show that the stars and gas less than a parsec from the center are affected by a strong gravitational field produced by an unknown mass equal to that of three million suns. At present, the best explanation astronomers can give for such a massive yet undetected object is a giant black hole. Nearby stars and gas clouds will be reduced to plasma streams inexorably drawn into the accretion disk surrounding the giant black hole, which can account for the strong radio source identified as Sgr A* (see fig. 17.21).

Although Sgr A* seems to be the best candidate, the identity of a single object representing the nucleus of the Galaxy remains an enigma. Studies in infrared and radio wavelengths have revealed compact as well as extended sources near

# SKY WATCHERS 17.1

## finding the local structure of the galaxy

What can we learn about the structure of the spiral arm in which the Sun is located? Do OB stars and emission nebulae near the Sun lie in the galactic plane? As we have seen, optical astronomers use OB stars to trace the spiral arms. Let us follow their procedure and identify the bright blue giant stars that mark the galactic structure nearest to the Sun.

How do we distinguish between the nearest and more distant blue giant stars? Identifying the stars is not as difficult as it might seem. Remember how the distance to a star may be found by the difference between its apparent and absolute magnitudes. In our present assignment, all the stars have about the same absolute magnitude; therefore the brightest OB stars are also the nearest to the Sun. They represent the brilliant blue stars found in the prominent constellations introduced in earlier exercises. These include Scorpius, Lyra, Cassiopeia, Orion, and others. Table 17.2 represents a partial list of bright blue stars down to third magnitude that are visible in the northern middle latitudes.

Identify as many of the selected stars as your sky conditions permit. Keep in mind that not all the stars in table 17.2 can be viewed in one night. The stars you can see will depend upon the season of the year. When you locate the stars, measure their angular distances from the Milky Way on your star map.

The stars may seem to be scattered at random on both sides of the Milky Way. But careful examination will show the stars to be concentrated in a belt inclined about 16° to the galactic equator. Altogether, the bright stars make up *Gould's belt,* which is our "local system" of O associations and H II regions. The nineteenth-century astronomer Benjamin A. Gould was first to call atten-

tion to the distribution of the nearest O and B stars. They make up a nonconforming system within the local spiral arm.

Why are the stars in Gould's belt out of their expected positions? Some astronomers think that Gould's belt marks the passage of a density wave at our location in the spiral arm. If so, the mechanism that triggers star birth in the spiral arms may be revealed by the distribution of the brightest stars.

## Table 17.2

### OB stars brighter than M. = 5.0

| Star Name | | Constellation | Visual Magnitude |
|---|---|---|---|
| α | And | Andromeda | 2.1 |
| γ | Peg | Pegasus | 2.8 |
| γ | Cas | Cassiopeia | 2.5 |
| β | Per | Perseus | 2.1 var. |
| ε | Tau | Taurus | 2.9 |
| ζ | Per A | Perseus | 2.8 |
| ε | Per A | Perseus | 2.9 |
| β | Ori | Orion | 0.1 |
| γ | Ori | Orion | 1.6 |
| β | Tau | Taurus | 1.7 |
| ε | Ori | Orion | 1.7 |
| ζ | Ori | Orion | 2.1 |
| κ | Ori | Orion | 2.1 |
| β | C Ma | Canis Major | 2.0 |
| ε | C Ma | Canis Major | 1.5 |
| η | C Ma | Canis Major | 2.5 |
| β | C Mi | Canis Minor | 2.9 |
| α | Leo | Leo | 1.4 |
| α | Vir | Virgo | 1.0 |
| η | U Ma | Ursa Major | 1.9 |
| β | Lib | Libra | 2.6 |
| δ | Sco A-B | Scorpius | 2.3 |
| β | Sco A-B | Scorpius | 2.6 |
| λ | Sco | Scorpius | 1.6 |
| σ | Sgr | Sagittarius | 2.0 |
| γ | Lyr | Lyra | 3.2 |
| β | Cep | Cepheus | 3.2 |

the center that may be physically associated with Sgr A*.

Moreover, astronomers have detected a source of erratic gamma-ray emissions about one degree from the galactic center. The radiation is emitted by a source that has a spectrum similar to the black-hole candidate Cygnus X-1. The gamma rays are believed to come from an accretion disk surrounding a black hole with a maximum mass of only 15 $M_\odot$. The nature of the nucleus remains one of the unsolved mysteries of the Galaxy (see fig. 17.22).

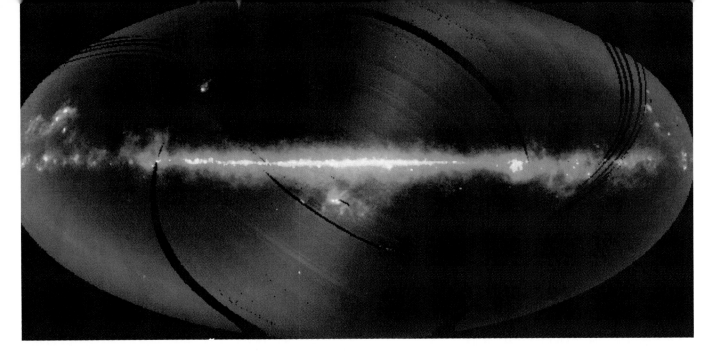

**figure 17.22**

An image made by the Infrared Astronomy Satellite (IRAS) of the entire Milky Way Galaxy. The bright central band is the emission from interstellar matter in the galactic disk.

## SUMMARY

The Galaxy is a huge spiral formation containing a mass equivalent to billions of sunlike stars. Its structure includes a central condensation of stars and interstellar matter with a flat disk formation extending 15,000 parsecs in radius. The halo, a spheroidal cloud of variable stars and globular clusters, surrounds the central bulge and disk.

The most prominent feature of the Galaxy are the spiral arms that contain young population I stars, and neutral and ionized hydrogen clouds. Two or more spiral arms extend outward from the center along the galactic plane. Astronomers map the spiral structure in several ways. O associations and H II regions serve as optical tracers. The arms are identified by the distribution of neutral hydrogen observed at the 21-cm line of the radio spectrum. Molecular clouds reveal the location of the spiral arms by carbon monoxide emissions at 2.6-mm wavelength.

The spiral structure is explained by density wave theories. The spiral arms are regarded as concentrations of stars, gas, and dust caused by uneven distribution of matter rotating in the galactic disk.

Radiation from the galactic center represents emissions from different objects. Radio waves are emitted by neutral hydrogen gas. Infrared radiation identifies dust clouds and huge supergiant stars. Ultraviolet, X-ray, and gamma radiation reveal H II regions, OB stars, supernova remnants, neutron stars, and possible black holes. At the nucleus, Sagittarius A* may represent a massive black hole believed to be the driving mechanism of the Galaxy.

## KEY TERMS

central bulge

dark nebulae

density wave theory

emission nebulae

galactic corona

galactic nucleus

Galaxy

giant molecular clouds

halo

interstellar medium

Milky Way system

Orion arm

Perseus arm

population I stars

population II stars

reflection nebulae

Sagittarius A*

Sagittarius arm

spiral arms

spiral tracers

## PROBLEMS

1. Which constellations contain the brightest regions of the Milky Way? At your home latitude, when are these constellations visible in the early evening?

2. In the northern hemisphere, the Milky Way is sometimes seen high overhead and at other times low on the horizon. Why?

3. Describe the method used by William Herschel in his survey of the Milky Way.

4. Why is it necessary to apply a correction to the apparent magnitude when determining the distances to stars in the direction of the galactic plane?

5. What proof do we have that our galaxy is rotating?

6. Describe the methods used by optical and radio astronomers to define the spiral arms in the Galaxy.

7. What observational evidence have astronomers found to indicate that a massive corona surrounds the Galaxy?

8. Explain how the interstellar medium affects light from distant stars.

9. Explain why an interstellar dust cloud can appear as either a dark nebula or a reflection nebula.

10. Why does a reflection nebula appear blue? An emission nebula red?

11. Describe the different populations of stars and their locations in the Galaxy.

12. What are spiral tracers? Describe how tracers are used to study the spiral structure at different wavelengths.

13. Explain why a neutral hydrogen atom emits a photon of energy detected as the 21-cm line in the radio spectrum.

14. How do astronomers detect molecular clouds? Explain.

15. How does the density wave theory explain the formation of spiral arms?

16. Why are the youngest stars found along the inner edge of a spiral arm? Where are middle-aged stars and supernovae remnants located? Why?

17. Explain why very little was known about the galactic center when only optical telescopes were in use.

18. Make a drawing of the different components of the galactic center. Include the 3-kpc and expanding arms, rotating neutral hydrogen disk, expanding molecular hydrogen clouds, and galactic nucleus.

19. What evidence is there that a black hole might occupy the center of the Galaxy?

20. If the Sun is located 9000 parsecs from the galactic center and has an orbital velocity of 250 km/sec, how many years will the Sun require to complete one circuit?

## REFERENCES

Bok, Bart J. and Priscilla F. Bok. 1981. *The Milky Way.* Cambridge, Mass.: Harvard University Press.

Burbridge, Geoffrey, and Margaret Burbridge. 1970. "Stellar Populations." In *New Frontiers in Astronomy: Readings from Scientific American.* San Francisco: W. H. Freeman and Company.

Burton, W. Butler, ed. 1979. *The Large-Scale Characteristics of the Galaxy.* Proceedings of the 84th Symposium of the International Astronomical Union. Dordrecht, Neth.: D. Reidel Publishing Company.

Catchpole, Robin M. 1988. A Window on Our Galaxy's Core. *Sky and Telescope* 75, no. 2 (February).

Chaisson, Eric J. 1978. Gaseous Nebulae. *Scientific American* 239, no. 6 (December).

Geballe, Thomas R. 1979. The Central Parsec of the Galaxy. *Scientific American* 241, no. 1 (July).

Heiles, Carl. 1978. The Structure of the Interstellar Medium. *Scientific American* 238, no. 1 (January).

Kuhn, Ludwig. 1982. *The Milky Way.* New York: John Wiley & Sons.

Malin, David. 1987. In the Shadow of the Horsehead. *Sky and Telescope* 74, no. 3 (September).

Palmer, E. Samuel. 1989. Unveiling the Hidden Milky Way. *Astronomy* 17, no. 11 (November).

Sanders, R. H., and G. T. Wrixon. 1970. "The Center of the Galaxy." In *New Frontiers in Astronomy: Readings from Scientific American.* San Francisco: W. H. Freeman and Company.

Smith, David H. 1986. A Sideways Look at Galactic History. *Sky and Telescope* 72, no. 2 (August).

Taubes, Gary. 1990. The Great Annihilator. *Discover* 11, no. 6 (June).

Townes, Charles H., and Reinhard Genzel. 1990. What is Happening at the Center of Our Galaxy? *Scientific American* 262, no. 4 (April).

Tucker, Wallace, and Karen Tucker. 1989. Dark Matter in Our Galaxy. *Mercury* (Astronomical Society of the Pacific) 18, no. 1 (January/February).

Van Woerden, Hugo, Ronald J. Allen, and W. Butler Burton, eds. 1985. *The Milky Way Galaxy.* Proceedings of the 106th Symposium of the International Astronomical Union. Dordrecht, Neth.: D. Reidel Publishing Company.

Verschuur, Gerrit L. 1987. Molecules Between the Stars. *Mercury* 16, no. 3 (May/June).

chapter

18

g a l a x i e s :    i s l a n d s    o f    s t a r s

A part of the Virgo cluster of galaxies. This
irregular cluster contains more than 2000 spiral
and giant elliptical galaxies. Recent estimates
place the Virgo cluster at a distance of 48 ± 3
million light-years.

Thus far, our investigation of galaxies has been limited to our own system of stars, clusters, and interstellar matter. The Galaxy is a closed spiral system in which stars, such as our Sun, serve as the basic elements or parts. There are perhaps 200 billion stars of various types and ages in our galaxy, and a number more than 10 times as large is not out of the question. The spiral arms contain concentrations of dust and gas out of which several generations of stars have formed.

Until the present century, astronomers believed that our galaxy contained all the substance in the universe; that it was like an island of stars in an endless sea of empty space. But advances in astronomy revolutionized our understanding of the cosmos. Now we know that our galaxy is merely one of many stellar systems reaching millions and billions of light-years into space. How many galaxies are there in the universe? They are more numerous than stars in the Milky Way.

Fortunately, we don't need a powerful telescope to view a spectacular neighbor galaxy. Look in the direction of the stars of Andromeda. The constellation is conveniently observed in the middle northern latitudes during autumn and winter. Here you will find the only large spiral galaxy visible without the aid of a telescope. The **Andromeda galaxy** appears as a diffuse oval patch of light about 7° northwest of the second magnitude star Mirach. By far, it is the most distant object that can be viewed by the unaided eye—the light you see took over two million years to reach the Earth.

In the southern hemisphere, there are two naked-eye galaxies called the *Magellanic Clouds*. They are nearer to us than the Andromeda galaxy and are within the dark corona surrounding the Milky Way system.

On the cosmic scale, the Andromeda galaxy, Magellanic Clouds, and our galaxy are close neighbors. Together with about 30 smaller systems, they form the so-called **Local Group** of galaxies. As

## Table 18.1

### brightest galaxies in the Messier Catalogue

| M | Constellation | Type* | Distance (10⁶ LY) | m_v |
|---|---------------|-------|-------------------|-----|
| 31 | Andromeda | S | 2.3 | 4 |
| 32 | Andromeda | E | 2.3 | 9 |
| 33 | Triangulum | S | 2.2 | 6 |
| 49 | Virgo | E | 71.7 | 9 |
| 51 | Canes Venatici | S | 35.9 | 9 |
| 60 | Virgo | E | 71.7 | 10 |
| 63 | Canes Venatici | S | 35.9 | 9 |
| 64 | Coma Berenices | S | 22.8 | 8 |
| 66 | Leo | S | 39.1 | 9 |
| 74 | Pisces | S | 55.4 | 10 |
| 77 | Cetus | S | 81.5 | 10 |
| 81 | Ursa Major | S | 11.7 | 7 |
| 82 | Ursa Major | Irr. | 11.7 | 9 |
| 83 | Hydra | S | 22.5 | 8 |
| 87 | Virgo | E | 71.7 | 10 |
| 94 | Canes Venatici | S | 22.5 | 9 |
| 101 | Ursa Major | S | 24.8 | 8 |
| 104 | Virgo | S | 55.4 | 8 |
| 106 | Canes Venatici | S | 32.6 | 9 |

*S = spiral; E = elliptical; Irr. = irregular.

we shall see, there are also **galaxy clusters** at much greater distances that contain many thousands of members, each composed of billions of stars.

## A History of Galaxies

The idea that some hazy patches of light might be other galaxies came from discoveries made in the eighteenth century. Astronomers of that time grouped celestial objects in two classes: stellar and nonstellar light sources. The second category was a collection of diverse objects such as gaseous nebulae, planetary nebulae, hazy star clusters, and faint lens-shaped formations. These structures were listed in catalogues according to their appearance and distribution in the sky. William Herschel was one of the first observers to systematically study star clusters and nebulous nonstellar objects. Noting similarities in structure between oval-shaped nebulae and his model of our galaxy, Herschel wondered if such faint objects might be distant stellar systems.

## Catalogues of Clusters and Nebulae

The need for catalogues became necessary as more clusters and nebulae were discovered. By 1784, a catalogue was compiled by Charles Messier, a successful comet hunter who listed the coordinates of 103 objects. His purpose was to help other observers distinguish between fixed deep-sky objects and approaching comets. In a telescope, faint nebulae, unresolved star clusters, and tail-less comets are similar in appearance. The entries in the *Messier Catalogue* are listed by number: Messier 1, M1, is the famous Crab Nebula; the Andromeda galaxy is designated M31. Over 40 objects out of 103 entries were later identified as galaxies. Table 18.1 is a partial list of the brightest galaxies in the catalogue.

The Messier Catalogue and William Herschel's catalogue of clusters and nebulae have been revised and are still in use. Herschel discovered and listed over 2500 deep-sky objects such as star

**figure 18.1**

The Whirlpool galaxy M51 and its companion NGC 5195 are examples of interacting galaxies.

clusters, planetary nebulae, and emission nebulae, as well as the oval formations he suspected of being stellar systems. John Herschel added to the original list and compiled over 5000 objects in both the northern and southern hemispheres. At the Cape of Good Hope during the 1830s, he characterized the Magellanic Clouds as members of a unique class of celestial objects unknown in the northern skies.

John Herschel's *General Catalogue* was expanded by J. L. E. Dreyer in 1888 into the ***New General Catalogue of Nebulae and Clusters of Stars (NGC)***, which contains about 8000 entries. In 1973, the catalogue was updated by Jack Sulentic and William Tifft as *The Revised New General Catalogue (RNGC)*. The Crab Nebula is listed as NGC 1952; the Andromeda galaxy as NGC 224. One-half of the brightest objects in the catalogue are galaxies.

### Discovery of the Galaxies

The nature of the symmetrical nebulae catalogued by early observers remained a mystery until more powerful telescopes were constructed and technological advances were applied to astronomy. William Herschel's 24-inch reflector was the largest telescope in use until the middle of the nineteenth century. In 1845, William Parsons, the Earl of Rosse, constructed a reflector with a 72-inch aperture. With this larger telescope, Lord Rosse was able to resolve the spiral structure of several circular and elliptical objects. His sketches of M51, later named the Whirlpool galaxy, revealed spiral arms swirling outward from a bright central bulge (fig. 18.1). Moreover, Lord Rosse reported seeing individual stars in the spiral structure.

Spectral analysis was used to study the physical and chemical properties of the nebulae. In 1864, William Huggins detected the bright-line spectrum of the Orion nebula (M42, NGC 1976). The discovery proved that amorphous nebulae are composed of ionized gases. In contrast, Huggins found that symmetrical nebulae have the same spectra as concentrations of stars.

By the end of the century, astrophotography was essential to the study of nebulae and stellar systems. The effect of light on photographic emulsion is additive, and fine structure that is invisible to the eye can be recorded by increasing the exposure.

In the early 1920s, Edwin Hubble photographed M31 through the 100-inch reflecting telescope at Mount Wilson. The photographs revealed individual stars, dark and bright nebulae, and open and globular clusters. Of even greater significance, Hubble discovered variable stars and supernovae in the spiral arms. He proved conclusively that M31 and other structures like it are not nebulae but galaxies that lie beyond the Milky Way system.

### Classification of Galaxies

After M31 was identified as a spiral galaxy, Edwin Hubble and other observers photographed hundreds of bright and thousands of fainter galaxies. Out of this vast amount of data, Hubble grouped

345

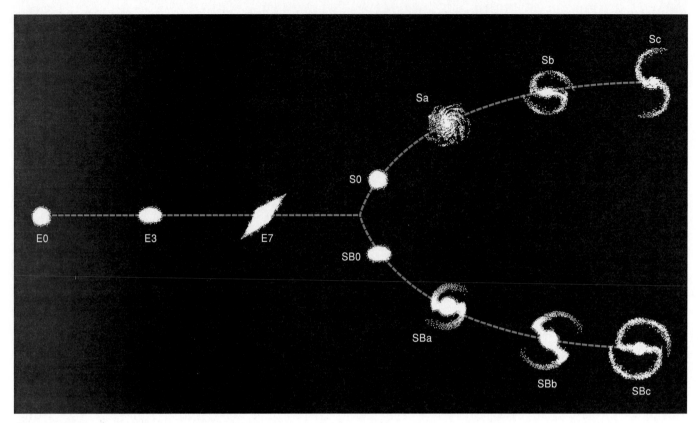

**figure 18.2**
Edwin Hubble's scheme for classification of galaxies.

stellar systems into three categories: **elliptical galaxies, spiral galaxies (normal** and **barred**), and **irregular galaxies.** Hubble's classification is still in use although the system is too simple to include all known types of galaxies (fig. 18.2).

## Elliptical Galaxies

Elliptical galaxies are star systems without spiral arms. In the telescope, they appear brightest at the center and gradually fade toward the edge. Ellipticals vary in shape from almost spherical to flat, lens-shaped formations.

Hubble grouped the galaxies according to their increasingly elliptical shape by the letter E and a series of numbers from zero to seven. Round, almost spherical galaxies are designated E0, slightly elliptical galaxies are classified E1 and E2, and galaxies with maximum elongation are typed E7 (fig. 18.2).

It should not be assumed that the differences from E0 to E7 ellipticals correspond to the actual flattening or the true shape of the galaxies. The space orienta-

tion of the ellipticals can be at any inclination to the plane of the sky. Thus an E7 elliptical galaxy may appear as an E0 if its central plane is perpendicular to our line of sight. However, the images of spherical galaxies will always project as E0 objects regardless of their orientation. Therefore, the apparent elongation of an elliptical galaxy is related to its actual shape and inclination with respect to the observer.

The spherical E0 galaxies are further classified as **dwarf** and **giant** elliptical galaxies. Dwarf ellipticals are represented by NGC 205 and M32, two satellites of M31 (fig. 18.6); M87 is an example of a giant elliptical galaxy (fig. 18.10). Giant ellipticals are the dominate members in a number of distant clusters. They are many times as massive as our spiral Milky Way Galaxy.

The featureless exterior of dwarf elliptical galaxies conceals a dynamic central region composed of stars and interstellar matter. The core of an elliptical may rotate on a different spin axis than the rest of the galaxy. The interstellar gas in some ellipticals is found in a ro-

tating disk, or ring, around the nucleus. Moreover, astronomers believe that the majority of known ellipticals may have been formed by the near collision or merger of two interacting galaxies (see section later in this chapter).

## Spiral Galaxies

The two general types of spiral galaxies are designated as *normal spirals* (*S*) and *barred spirals* (*SB*). Several examples are shown in figures 18.2 and 18.3. M33 and M31 are examples of nearby normal spiral galaxies. A few galaxies have an S classification although they differ from galaxies with pronounced spiral arms. These so-called S0 and SB0 galaxies contain a flattened central bulge but lack spiral arms, interstellar dust and gas, and young population I stars. In normal spirals, the arms emerge from the central bulge and wind around the galaxy. Barred spirals are distinguished by spiral arms that originate at the end points of a bar of matter extending from opposite sides of the galactic nucleus.

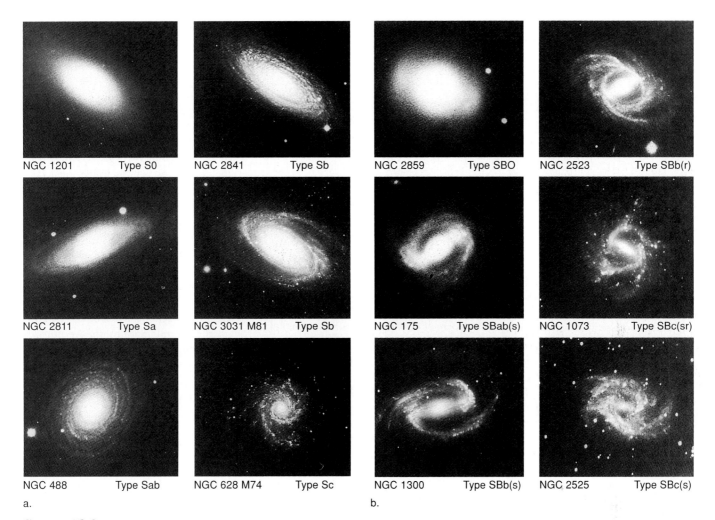

| NGC 1201 | Type S0 | NGC 2841 | Type Sb | NGC 2859 | Type SB0 | NGC 2523 | Type SBb(r) |
| NGC 2811 | Type Sa | NGC 3031 M81 | Type Sb | NGC 175 | Type SBab(s) | NGC 1073 | Type SBc(sr) |
| NGC 488 | Type Sab | NGC 628 M74 | Type Sc | NGC 1300 | Type SBb(s) | NGC 2525 | Type SBc(s) |

a.

b.

**figure 18.3**

The two general types of spiral galaxies: *a.* normal (S), and *b.* barred (SB).

Normal spiral galaxies are subdivided into groups designated by the letters Sa, Sb, and Sc, according to the relative size of the central bulge and the development of the spiral arms. Sa galaxies have large nuclei and tightly wound spiral arms that show little or no structure. Sb galaxies have relatively smaller centers and more open spiral arms. Concentrations of emission nebulae and stellar associations appear in the spiral arms. Sc galaxies have small nuclei and open spiral arms; in nearby systems, stellar clouds and H II regions are resolved. The arms of some Sc galaxies are narrow, and clumps and knots of matter are clearly defined. Other Sc galaxies have arms that are broad, with more intricate structure.

The barred spirals follow the same classification scheme as the normal spirals. SBa galaxies have a large central bulge and tightly wound arms extending from the ends of a relatively short bar.

Some SBa spirals wind into an elliptical formation and give the galaxies the appearance of the Greek letter theta (θ), a ringlike structure crossed with a bar. In SBb galaxies, the arms extend perpendicular from the bar and spiral independently around the center. The SBc spirals have a small center and arms spread out in an elongated cursive letter *S*. (See table 18.2 for more information on the physical properties of galaxies.)

## Irregular Galaxies

Irregular galaxies are small, asymmetric stellar systems that lack spiral arms and a central bulge. However, there are exceptions. Some are brighter at the center than at the edges. Others, like the Large Magellanic Cloud, have a bar-shaped structure. There are irregular galaxies that resemble huge clusters of stars. In gen-

eral, irregular galaxies look like dismembered pieces of spiral arms. Most of them contain an abundance of young population I stars and interstellar dust and gas.

## Measurement of Extragalactic Distances

In 1924, Edwin Hubble announced that the variable stars he observed in M31 were cepheids. As described in chapter 13, the longer a cepheid's period, the greater its luminosity (the period-luminosity relation). Knowing the luminosity, the distance to M31 is expressed by the difference between the apparent and absolute magnitudes (*m-M*) of the observed cepheids. Hubble estimated that the galaxy is almost one million light-years away, an astounding distance in those days. At the time, astronomers were unaware of the difference between

## Table 18.2

### physical properties of galaxies

| Galaxy | Dwarf Elliptical | Giant Elliptical | Spiral | Irregular |
|---|---|---|---|---|
| Stars | Old pop. I Pop. II | Old pop. I Pop. II | Pop. I Pop. II | Pop. I |
| Mass $(M_\odot)^*$ | $10^8$ | $10^{13}$ | $10^{11}$ | $10^9$ |
| Luminosity $(L_\odot)^{**}$ | $10^8$ | $10^{11}$ | $10^{10}$ | $10^8$ |
| Diameter (kpc) | 3 | 50 | 30 | 6 |
| Dust and gas | Sparse | Sparse | Abundant | Abundant |

*Mass of the Sun = $2 \times 10^{33}$ grams

**Luminosity of the Sun = $3.83 \times 10^{33}$ ergs/sec

population I classical cepheids and population II variables found in globular clusters. By the 1950s, astronomers had distinguished between the two types of cepheids and corrected the distance of M31 to twice Hubble's original estimate. The present value is set at 2.3 million light-years.

Finding the distances to celestial bodies is a fundamental problem faced by astronomers. The method used depends upon the distances to the objects under scrutiny. We have seen how distances within our own galaxy are determined by trigonometric parallax, luminosity criteria, and the period-luminosity relation. Estimating the distances to other galaxies requires more complex procedures. Cepheid variables and luminous supergiant stars are the most reliable yardsticks. They are the **standard distance indicators** to nearby galaxies in which stars can be observed. The period-luminosity law can give dependable distances to galaxies within a few million light-years. Supergiant stars are used at greater distances where variable stars are too faint to be seen.

The brightest globular clusters in nearby galaxies serve as distance indicators to globular clusters observed in galaxies as far as 100 million light-years away. The brightness ratios of the clusters are computed and distances are found by the inverse-square law (see chapter 13).

Novae and supernovae have been observed in other galaxies. These exploding stars are distinguished by their changes in brightness. Since the luminosities of all novae and the luminosities of all supernovae are about the same, these eruptive stars can be used as distance indicators to remote stellar systems. When a supernova explodes it may equal the brightness of an entire galaxy.

The largest nearby galaxies are the stepping stones to more remote stellar systems. When distance, size, and total luminosity are known, a galaxy can be used to estimate the distance to fainter galaxies more than 100 million light-years away. The brightest galaxy in a remote cluster is compared with a bright nearby galaxy of the same type. Distances are estimated by means of the inverse-square law.

## The Local Group of Galaxies

There is a tendency for matter to group into increasingly complex systems. Satellites are associated with planets; planets revolve about the Sun; stars are found in binary systems, clusters, and associations that travel their courses within a galaxy. Most galaxies are also found in pairs, small groups, and clusters of all sizes, *rich* and *poor*. Some rich clusters contain thousands of members and extend many millions of light-years in diameter. Poor clusters have only a few member galaxies and are generally called *groups*. Our galaxy and the spirals M31 and M33 are the largest components in a poor galaxy cluster known as the *Local Group*. The remaining members in the Local Group are much smaller and fainter dwarf elliptical and irregular galaxies (see table 18.3).

Our neighboring galaxies are not uniformly distributed in the Local Group. Most of the smaller members are clustered about our own galaxy and M31, the two largest spirals in the local family. There are at least seven dwarf elliptical galaxies and the two Magellanic Clouds within one million light-years of our spiral system. The Andromeda galaxy is surrounded by seven elliptical companions and a neighboring spiral, M33. Motion accompanies gravitation; in each subgroup, the smaller galaxies are influenced by the attraction of the massive spirals. In turn, the Andromeda galaxy and our Milky Way system are moving around a common center of mass located about 1.2 millon light-years from our galaxy and in the direction of M31.

## The Magellanic Clouds

The Magellanic Clouds are seen in the southern hemisphere as two faint patches of light. The **Large Magellanic Cloud (LMC)** is located at a distance of about 160,000 light-years; the **Small Magellanic Cloud (SMC)** is 200,000 light-years away (fig. 18.4). They are classified as irregular galaxies although both show structure and the effects of rotation. The LMC has a pronounced bar of stars through its center that gives the galaxy the appearance of a barred spiral. The SMC resembles a teardrop pendant with bright stars trailing from its center. The mass of the LMC is estimated to be 20 billion suns, or about one-tenth the mass of the Galaxy. The mass of the Small Cloud is about five billion suns.

In a telescope, both galaxies are resolved into young blue-white main-sequence stars, clusters, and nebulae that are similar to those found in the spiral arms of the Milky Way. In fact, the largest known H II region, 30 Doradus (Tarantula nebula), is located in the LMC (figs. 18.4 and 16.7). Unlike our home galaxy, the Magellanic Clouds contain two classes of globular clusters. There are young globulars containing blue giant stars as

## galaxies of the Local Group

| | R. A. (2000.0) h m | Dec. | Hubble type | Apparent blue mag. | Distance (10⁶ LY) | Diameter (10³ LY) |
|---|---|---|---|---|---|---|
| WLM | 0 02.0 | −15 28 | Irr. | 11.3 | 2.0 | 7 |
| IC 10 | 0 20.3 | +59 19 | Irr. | 11.7 | 4.0 | 6 |
| NGC 147 | 0 33.1 | +48 31 | E5 | 10.4 | 2.2 | 10 |
| Andromeda III | 0 35.3 | +36 31 | E5 | — | 2.2 | 3 |
| NGC 185 | 0 38.9 | +48 20 | E3 | 10.1 | 2.2 | 6 |
| NGC 205 | 0 40.3 | +41 41 | E5 | 8.6 | 2.2 | 10 |
| M32 | 0 42.7 | +40 52 | E2 | 9.0 | 2.2 | 5 |
| M31 | 0 42.7 | +41 16 | Sb | 4.4 | 2.2 | 200 |
| Andromeda I | 0 45.7 | +38 00 | E3 | 14.4 | 2.2 | 2 |
| SMC | 0 52.7 | −72 54 | Irr. | 2.8 | 0.3 | 15 |
| Sculptor | 0 59.9 | −33 42 | E3 | 9.1 | 0.2 | 1 |
| Pisces | 1 03.7 | +22 03 | Irr. | 15.5 | 3.0 | 0.5 |
| IC 1613 | 1 04.9 | +2 07 | Irr. | 10.0 | 2.5 | 12 |
| Andromeda II | 1 16.3 | +33 25 | E2 | — | 2.2 | 2 |
| M33 | 1 33.9 | +30 39 | Sc | 6.3 | 2.5 | 45 |
| Fornax | 2 39.6 | −34 31 | E3 | 8.5 | 0.5 | 3 |
| LMC | 5 23.6 | −69 47 | Irr. | 0.6 | 0.2 | 20 |
| Carina | 6 41.7 | −50 58 | E4 | — | 0.3 | 0.5 |
| Leo A | 9 59.4 | +30 45 | Irr. | 12.7 | 5.0 | 7 |
| Leo I | 10 08.5 | +12 18 | E3 | 11.8 | 0.6 | 1 |
| Sextans I | 10 12.8 | −1 41 | E | — | 0.3 | 3 |
| Leo II | 11 13.5 | +22 10 | E0 | 12.3 | 0.6 | 0.5 |
| GR8 | 12 59.2 | +14 09 | Irr. | 14.6 | 4.0 | 0.2 |
| Ursa Minor | 15 08.8 | +67 07 | E5 | — | 0.3 | 1 |
| Draco | 17 20.2 | +57 55 | E3 | — | 0.3 | 0.5 |
| Milky Way | 17 45.7 | −29 00 | Sbc | — | 0.03 | 130 |
| SagDIG | 19 30.0 | −17 41 | Irr. | 15.6 | 4.0 | 5 |
| NGC 6822 | 19 44.9 | −14 46 | Irr. | 9.3 | 1.7 | 8 |
| DDO 210 | 20 47.0 | −12 51 | Irr. | 15.3 | 3.0 | 4 |
| IC 5152 | 22 02.9 | −51 17 | Irr. | 11.7 | 2.0 | 5 |
| Tucana | 22 41.9 | −64 25 | — | — | — | — |
| Pegasus | 23 28.6 | +14 46 | Irr. | 12.4 | 5.0 | 8 |

a.

b.

well as old clusters dominated by red giant stars. Astronomers believe that the globular clusters in the Magellanic Clouds formed more recently than those found in the halo of the Galaxy.

In the 1980s, radio studies by Don Mathewson and Vincent Ford revealed that the Magellanic Clouds are enclosed in a huge envelope of hydrogen. A bridge of gas connecting the two bodies may extend to the Milky Way galaxy. The SMC is composed of two separate parts; a *Mini-Magellanic Cloud* is located 26,000 light-years behind the Small Cloud along our line of sight. The two galaxies were distinguished by the differences in their radial velocities detected by the Doppler effect of the 21-cm line of neutral hydrogen. In addition, radio observations of the 21-cm line were important in the discovery of the **Magellanic stream,** a trail of neutral hydrogen extending from the Large and Small Clouds to the vicinity of the Andromeda galaxy (fig. 18.5).

## M31, the Andromeda Galaxy

The Great Galaxy in Andromeda has inspired observers since the beginning of the seventeenth century as one of the brightest diffuse objects viewed with the unaided eye. The optical portion of the spiral measures one degree of arc, twice the angular size of the Moon.

In a telescope, the galaxy shines with a hazy glow. Long-exposure photographs are needed to resolve the bright stars and gas clouds in the spiral arms (fig. 18.6). The central bulge contains population II stars that give it a distinctive yellow color. Thin spiral arms are filled with blue giant stars strung out like clusters of beads, while dust lanes trace out the inner edges of the spiral arms.

◀ figure 18.4
The Large Magellanic Cloud (LMC) and Small Magellanic Cloud (SMC) are two irregular galaxies named after explorer Ferdinand Magellan. *a.* The LMC is 200,000 light-years away, and *b.* the SMC is 160,000 light-years away. The bright globular cluster to the right of the SMC is 47 Tucana, located in our Milky Way Galaxy about 16,000 light-years from the Sun.

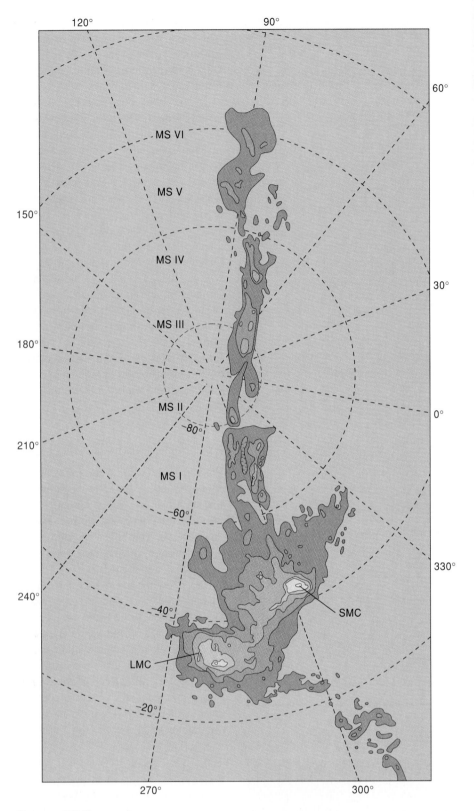

MS VI

MS V

MS IV

MS III

MS II

MS I

SMC

LMC

**figure 18.5**
Radio map of the Magellanic stream of neutral hydrogen.

**figure 18.6**
The Andromeda galaxy M31 and its elliptical satellite galaxies, M32 (*below*) and NGC 205 (*above, right*). M31 and our Milky Way dominate the Local Group of nearby galaxies.

neutral hydrogen in the Andromeda galaxy's central plane to a distance of nearly 100,000 light-years.

There is evidence that the nucleus of M31 contains remnants of collapsed stars. The center of the galaxy may contain a huge black hole millions of times more massive than the Sun and as large as the Earth's orbit.

The Andromeda galaxy has two prominent elliptical companions, M32 and NGC 205. M32 is about as luminous as the Small Magellanic Cloud. NGC 205 is distinguished by young blue giant stars and dust lanes in some of its globular clusters. The remaining clusters contain the familiar red stars found in globulars surrounding other elliptical galaxies.

## M33 in Triangulum

The third large galaxy in the Local Group is M33, an Sc-type spiral located in the direction of the Andromeda galaxy. Since the plane of M33 is almost perpendicular to our line of sight, the galaxy appears as a pinwheel of stars tracing indistinct spiral arms (fig. 18.7). Photographs reveal bright blue stars, clusters, and H II regions. The emission nebulae found in M33 are almost as large as 30 Doradus in the Large Magellanic Cloud.

In 1983, the Einstein high-energy orbiting observatory detected X-ray sources

Photographs reveal that the H II regions and stellar associations in the spiral arms extend as far as 50,000 light-years from the center. Thus the visible region of the spiral is about the same size as our own galaxy. But M31 is much larger and more massive than the Galaxy. Radio astronomers have detected

**figure 18.7**
M33 in Triangulum, the third largest galaxy in the Local Group.

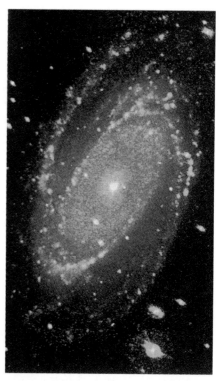

**figure 18.8**
A color-enhanced image of M81, an Sb spiral galaxy about 11 million light-years from our galaxy. The gaseous oxygen emissions shown in blue define the spiral arms and younger stars. The older stars in the disk are shown in orange.

in the nucleus of M33. The emissions are more powerful than those found in M31 and our own galaxy. Some astronomers believe that the source of radiation may be a collapsed object—a black hole—equal in luminosity to millions of sunlike stars.

## Large-Scale Structures

There are numerous aggregations of galaxies within a radius of 60 million light-years. Most of them are poor clusters with a few member galaxies; our Local Group is an example. Another relatively nearby group is made up of an Sb spiral, M81 (fig. 18.8), and its amorphous companion, M82 (fig. 18.9). They are located about 11 million light-years away.

Rich clusters are much larger in size and may have more than 1000 member galaxies. These larger clusters are found at greater distances in space. The nearest rich cluster to us, the **Virgo cluster,** lies between 50 and 72 million light-years beyond the stars in the constellation Virgo.

There is a hierarchy of clustering in the universe beginning with the smallest subatomic particles and continuing upward to the largest associations of galaxies. Near the summit of the hierarchy are the galaxy clusters, which are organized into even larger systems. These are the **superclusters** that extend hundreds of millions of light-years in space. In turn, superclusters are linked to other superclusters to form the largest aggregations of matter known to astronomers.

## The Nearest Rich Clusters

Rich clusters are classified according to their form and composition. In one category, the clusters have galaxies of all types including many bright spirals. These clusters are *irregular* in shape and lack a definitive central concentration of many galaxies. Another type, a *regular* cluster, is symmetrical in form and is dominated by elliptical and S0 galaxies in the central core. The galaxies are distributed in the cluster much like the member stars in sparsely populated dwarf el-

liptical galaxies. The centers of some clusters contain a diffuse supergiant elliptical galaxy surrounded by a swarm of spiral and elliptical components.

The irregular Virgo cluster contains more than 2000 galaxies. Long-exposure photographs reveal the supergiant elliptical galaxy, M87, surrounded by many spiral galaxies and other giant ellipticals (see photo at beginning of chapter and fig. 18.10). Hubble Space Telescope images reveal a possible black hole at the heart of NGC 4261 in the Virgo cluster (fig. 18.11).

Another rich cluster of all types of galaxies lies in the direction of the constellation Perseus at a distance of 250 million light-years. The Perseus cluster is an irregular cluster with a giant elliptical galaxy at its center.

The **Coma cluster,** in Coma Berenices, is a huge formation of thousands of galaxies about 325 million light-years from the Local Group. Coma is a regular cluster that shows spherical

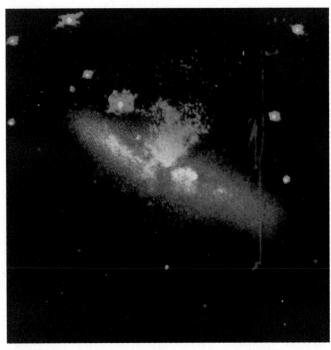

**figure 18.9**

The peculiar galaxy M82. Along with M81, it is part of a sparse galaxy cluster not far beyond the Local Group. Evidence of the explosive nature of M82 is seen in the asymmetric blue oxygen emissions and in the fragmented appearance of the redder stars.

**figure 18.10**

The giant elliptical galaxy M87 (NGC 4486) lies at the center of the Virgo cluster. The globular clusters associated with M87 appear as faint hazy objects around the galaxy. Several other galaxies in the cluster are visible.

symmetry and a central concentration of galaxies. Unlike the Virgo cluster, the central region of Coma is populated by elliptical and S0 galaxies. The average distance between member galaxies is less than one million light-years. Two diffuse supergiant elliptical galaxies dominate the core (fig. 18.12). The Coma cluster is located a few degrees from the north galactic pole, about 90° from the plane of the Milky Way.

## Superclusters

Studies indicate that rich clusters and neighboring galaxy groups are joined together in much larger assemblages called superclusters. Generally, a supercluster consists of five or more members. Most superclusters are spread out in clumps reaching distances of hundreds of millions of light-years. Some are concentrated about a dominant rich cluster.

Our own galaxy and other galaxies in the Local Group belong to the *local supercluster*, which is centered on the Virgo cluster. Surrounding the Virgo cluster are many galaxy groups linked together in long, clumpy filaments that

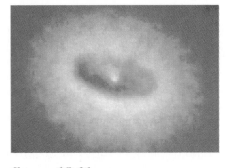

**figure 18.11**

The nucleus of the galaxy NGC 4261 in the Virgo cluster. This image from the Hubble Space Telescope shows an accretion disk of gas and dust that may indicate the presence of a massive black hole at the center of the galaxy.

form a disklike structure through the center of the supercluster. Our galaxy lies in the plane of the disk at the end of a long tendril of galaxies extending about 60 million light-years from the center.

A more representative supercluster is located at a distance of about 320 million light-years. From the Coma cluster, a continuous stream of galaxies extends to another large cluster designated A1367

**figure 18.12**

The center of the rich cluster of galaxies in Coma Berenices. The bright galaxy in the center is NGC 4889, one of two giant elliptical galaxies that dominate the core of the cluster.

(number 1367 in the *Abell Catalogue* of rich clusters). The supercluster is observed as a dense concentration dominated by the Coma cluster.

Surveys of the large-scale structure of the universe have been made in a narrow field of view in the direction of the north and south galactic poles. The surveys confirmed that superclusters are spaced about 400 million light-years

### plotting the Virgo cluster

Picture yourself at the eyepiece of a moderate-sized telescope on a dark, clear, moonless night. You point the instrument toward the constellations Coma Berenices and Virgo in the region Hubble called the "realm of the galaxies."

In general, there are more bright galaxies in the northern galactic hemisphere than elsewhere in the sky. The Coma-Virgo region is particularly rich in galaxies for two reasons: the nearest rich cluster is found in this direction in space, and the north galactic pole is located in Coma Berenices. Light from a distant galaxy is dimmed in its passage through interstellar dust in our own galaxy. There is less absorption toward the galactic poles than in the plane of the Milky Way.

The Virgo cluster could not be better placed in the sky for observation. For this reason, faint nonstellar sources in the Coma-Virgo region were recorded as early as the eighteenth century by William Herschel and Charles Messier. No less than 15 entries in the *Messier Catalogue* are members of the Virgo cluster.

Let us observe the galaxies. Find the Virgo cluster by the familiar star hopping method described in earlier Sky Watchers' exercises. Locate the third magnitude star Epsilon (ε) Virginis in the finder telescope. Move the telescope in right ascension due east to a point midway between Epsilon and the fourth-magnitude star Omicron (o) Virginis. Change the declination one degree north and the elliptical M87 should be centered in the field of view of the finder telescope. This supergiant galaxy is the most massive member of the cluster (fig. 18.10).

The telescope shows M87 as a diffuse, glowing ball. But the smooth appearance of the galaxy provides us with no clue as to its true nature. M87 is an active galaxy with a jet of material extending no less than 600 light-years from its center (see chapter 19).

If sky conditions permit, plot the relative positions of other galaxies that you can identify. M87 is flanked by two galaxies to the east, M84 and M86. There are three galaxies to the west, M58, M89, and M90. Compare your results with a sky map from a star atlas. Then identify the size, magnitude, and type of each galaxy you have observed by referring to the *Messier Catalogue*.

---

apart for distances of up to billions of light-years. Furthermore, superclusters are not scattered at random but are grouped into an interlocking network of filaments enclosing regions called **voids.** The average diameter of a void is about the same length as a supercluster filament. Think of voids as twisted, interconnected tunnels forming gaps between the superclusters. The largest known void is about 300 million light-years across. The discovery of these voids has surprising consequences—because such regions occupy a greater volume than the superclusters, it seems that most of the universe—perhaps more than 95%—does not contain visible matter (fig. 18.13).

Steve J. Maddox and his associates have constructed a map showing the distribution of about two million galaxies covering a large area around the south galactic pole. Superclusters appear as bright, curved filaments that extend for millions of light-years. The filaments are separated by voids where only a few, if any, galaxies are found.

## Dark Matter

Do the interconnecting bubbles of galaxies contain most of the mass in the

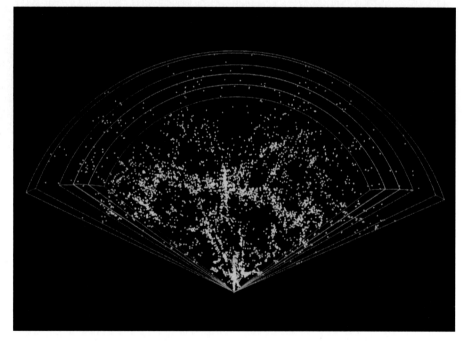

**figure 18.13**

A large-scale map of four wedges of the universe. The Milky Way galaxy is at the apex of the edges. Each wedge is a three-dimensional representation giving distance and direction from us. Galaxies and superclusters are grouped into interconnecting bubbles separated by voids up to 300 million light-years across. The extensive network of galaxies across the map is called the "Great Wall"; it represents the largest aggregation of galaxies known at the present time.

*galaxies: islands of stars*

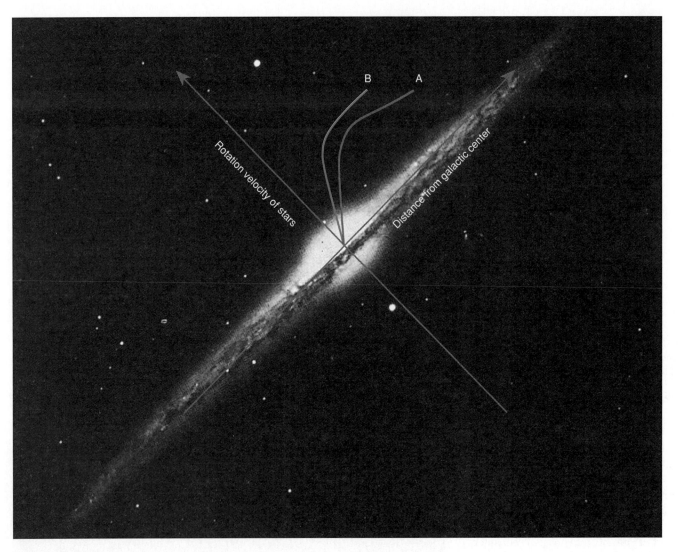

**figure 18.14**
Galaxies show evidence of dark matter by the way their stars and other material revolve.

universe? Until the 1930s, astronomers believed this to be true, since almost all knowledge about the physical and dynamic properties of matter and its distribution is obtained from objects that emit electromagnetic radiation.

We learned in chapter 17 that a massive corona, or *dark halo,* surrounds our galaxy. Other galaxies show the same evidence of dark matter by the way their stars and gas revolve. Figure 18.14 illustrates the galaxy NGC 4565 and two velocity curves, *A* and *B,* of the disk stars. If only stars and interstellar matter that are detected by their emissions are present, orbital velocities would decrease as distances from the center increase (velocity curve *A*). However, the rotational speed of the disk objects does not decrease, but remains fairly constant to the outer rim of the galaxy (velocity curve

*B*). Such a distribution of orbital velocity is indicative of a large mass of dark matter that produces a gravitational effect upon the visible components of the disk.

Studies indicate that the dark halo is not gaseous, nor is it composed of matter in the form of ordinary stars. Whatever its composition, invisible material makes up about 90% of the mass of some galaxies, especially younger ones, leaving only 10% for all detectable matter—stars, dust, and gas in the core, the disk, and the visible halo of a spiral galaxy.

In 1933, Fritz Zwicky discovered dark matter while studying the distribution and motions of galaxies in the Coma cluster. If a cluster is stable and has remained intact for the lifetime of its oldest stars, the cluster must contain a large amount of unseen mass to provide the gravita-

tional force needed to hold it together. Otherwise, clusters would be transient formations where member galaxies periodically disperse and go their separate ways. Zwicky found the Coma cluster to be stable and concluded that invisible matter between the galaxies provides the required mass.

As yet, astronomers do not agree upon the nature of the mysterious unseen mass. Some astronomers contend that dark matter might consist of exotic particles or perhaps elusive neutrinos that did not take part in the early processes that led to the evolution of stars. Other astronomers have a more conservative explanation for dark matter. They believe that the invisible mass is composed of ordinary matter that has formed familiar objects such as cool dwarf stars, dark rocky and metallic bodies, or black holes.

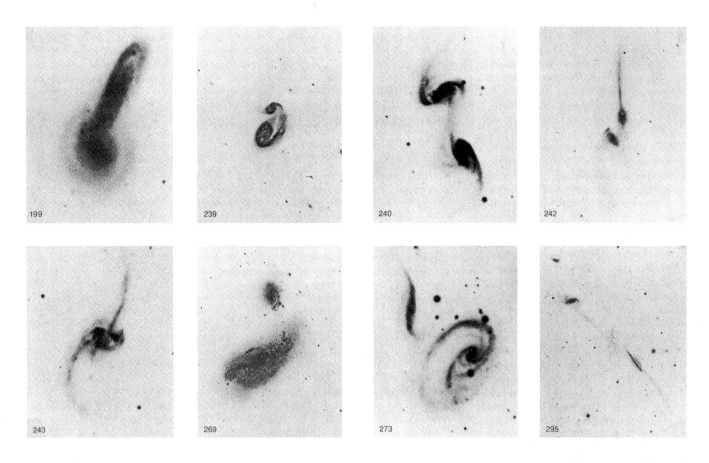

figure 18.15

Several examples of interacting galaxies, published in the *Atlas of Peculiar Galaxies* by Halton Arp.

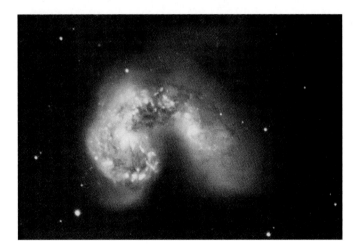

figure 18.16

The interacting galaxies NGC 4038 and 4039, named the Antennae.

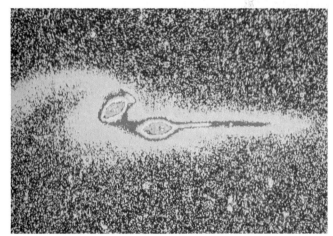

figure 18.17

A computer-enhanced image of the interacting galaxies NGC 4676A and 4676B, named the Mice.

## Interactions, Collisions, and Mergers Among Galaxies

Not all galaxies fit the Hubble classification scheme. A small percentage called **peculiar galaxies** have distorted shapes and other bizarre features. Many are pairs in close approach to or actual collision with each other. Such **interacting galaxies** are characterized by curved tails, streamers, and filaments extending into space. In some instances, the deformed stellar systems are connected by bridges of luminous matter (fig. 18.15).

The earliest known peculiar pair, NGC 4038 and 4039, were recognized in 1917. Photographs reveal two long filaments extending in opposite directions that give the system the appearance of an insect's head. It comes as no surprise that the object was dubbed the *Antennae* (fig. 18.16). Another interacting set, called the *Mice* (NGC 4676A and 4676B), have almost straight tails (fig. 18.17).

Why galaxies show long extensions is not entirely understood. Astronomers explain the distortion as a tidal effect produced by the close encounter of the two bodies. As the galaxies merge, there is little chance that stars will collide; the distances between stars are far too great. However, the same is not true for the interstellar medium. The tenuous gas between the stars responds to galactic tides in the same manner as the Earth's oceans react to lunar and solar tides.

By the 1970s, computer models had been designed to illustrate how tides caused by near collisions can lead to the strange formations found in peculiar galaxies. Computer simulations by Alar and Juri Toomre produced structures similar to actual systems such as the Antennae and the Mice (fig. 18.18). Their work showed that three conditions are essential for interacting spiral and S0 galaxies to produce bridges and tails: (1) the galaxies must revolve around a center of mass and approach each other in elliptical or parabolic orbits; (2) at closest approach, the galaxies may penetrate, but not through the center; and (3) the passing galaxy must travel in the same direction as the companion galaxy's rotation. If the mass of the passing galaxy is small, the tidal effect will produce a bridge connecting both galaxies. Long, narrow filaments and tails will form when the two merging galaxies are about equal in mass.

## Starburst Galaxies

Not all interstellar gas associated with interacting pairs is pulled into fanciful shapes. Some of it may be squeezed into denser clouds that trigger the birth of new stars. Some interacting galaxies are bluer in color than the average galaxy because they contain an excess of hot, young stars. These so-called **starburst galaxies** are experiencing a period of intense star formation that happens when they merge with another galaxy.

As described in chapters 15 and 17, stars are formed when interstellar dust and gas contract into dense globules. The stars evolve within molecular hydrogen clouds that absorb starlight and emit energy as infrared radiation.

Evidence of starbursts caused by galactic tides was obtained in 1983 by the

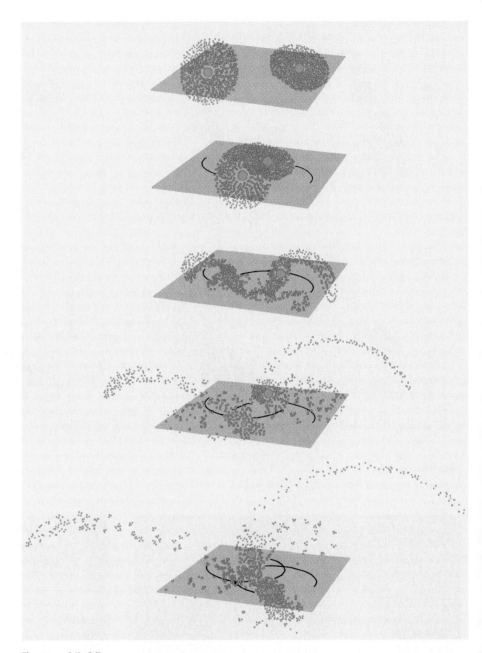

**figure 18.18**

A sequence of computer simulations depicting interacting galaxies, similar to actual systems in which stars respond to galactic tides. Long narrow tails will form when merging galaxies are about the same size.

Infrared Astronomical Satellite (IRAS). The IRAS observations led to the discovery of many galaxies that radiate more than 90% of their energy in the infrared region of the spectrum. Photographs of such galaxies revealed the familiar tails and bridges characteristic of interacting galaxies (fig. 18.19).

The enormous amounts of infrared radiation from these galaxies confirmed the presence of high concentrations of molecular clouds and young stars. New stars are being produced at a rate 100 times greater than in our own galaxy. Moreover, radio telescopes show that the molecular clouds and young stars are concentrated at the center of the interacting pairs. As the galaxies merge, the interstellar gas collides, loses angular momentum, and spirals toward the center. A shock front develops and the gas at the center is compressed into clouds where intense star formation takes place. The starburst activity lasts for about 10 million years.

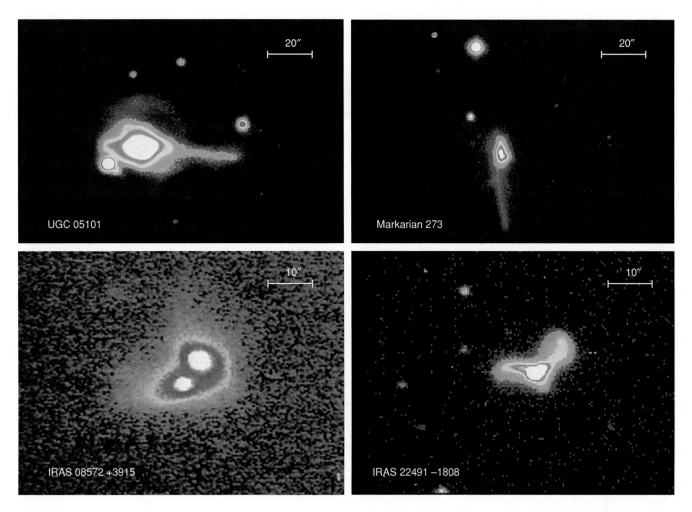

**figure 18.19**

Observations by the Infrared Astronomical Satellite (IRAS) led to the discovery of highly luminous galaxies that radiate most of their energy at infrared wavelengths. These charge-coupled-device (CCD) images reveal the tails and bridges found among interacting galaxies.

## The cD Galaxies

In the center of some rich clusters are diffuse supergiant spherical galaxies surrounded by a retinue of lesser spiral and elliptical galaxies. These objects, called *cD galaxies,* are believed to be huge merger remnants (fig. 18.20). Such galaxies are sustained by their enormous gravitational influence. Nearby companion galaxies are torn apart and their stars and interstellar matter are drawn into the dominant central body.

In some respects, a massive cD galaxy resembles an E-type elliptical. In fact, the large, luminous object has a central region similar to an elliptical and at one time it may have been a giant elliptical system. However, there is a basic difference between cD galaxies and ellipticals. Supergiant cD galaxies are distinguished by a luminous envelope of matter. They do not decrease in brightness from the center outward, which is a common feature of E-type galaxies.

There are a number of reasons why astronomers support the merger hypothesis as an explanation for cD galaxies. A diffuse supergiant is much larger and more luminous than other members of the cluster. These immense objects are found at the cluster's center of mass around which other galaxies revolve. During close approach, other galaxies may be tidally stripped of their halos, which eventually spiral into the central galaxy. As further evidence of merger, many cD galaxies show two or more nuclei within an extended envelope (fig. 18.20).

Such tidal stripping and eventual absorption of smaller galaxies by the gravitational attraction of a huge central mass is called **galactic cannibalism.** As more and more matter falls to the center, a large envelope accumulates about the one-time elliptical galaxy. The huge extended galaxies found at the centers of some clusters have increased in size at the expense of their neighbors.

## The Hubble Law and the Expansion of the Universe

Through the years, astronomers have studied the galaxies and their motions, distances, and distribution in order to

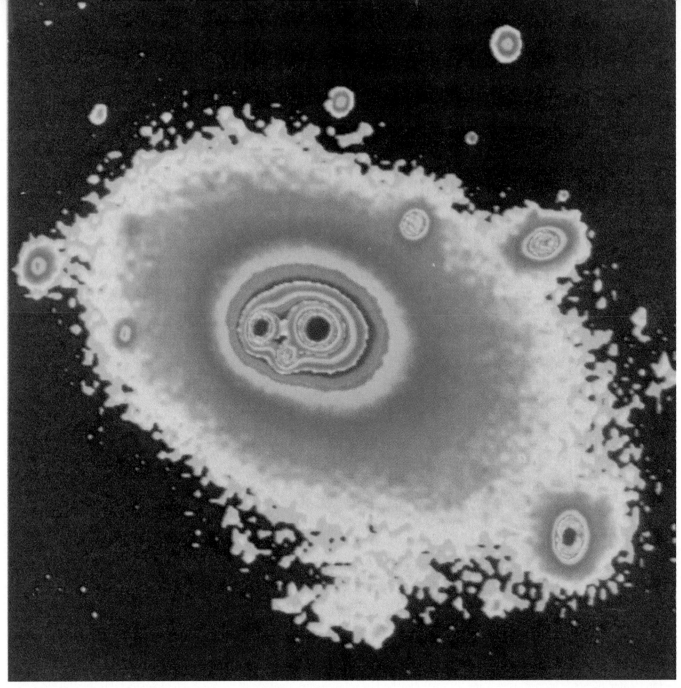

a.

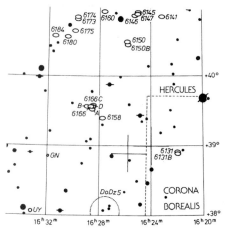

b.

**figure 18.20**

**a.** A false-color image of the cD galaxy NGC 6166, and **b.** location of the galaxy in Wil Tirion's *Uranometria 2000.0*.

obtain a better understanding of the structure of the universe. Perhaps the most interesting and significant discovery made during such investigations is that the universe is expanding in size.

The more distant galaxies are measured by their velocity of recession. In 1912, V. M. Slipher observed that most galaxies have spectral lines shifted toward the red. According to the Doppler principle, the displacement in wavelength of electromagnetic radiation is due to the motion of the source (galaxy) or receiver (observer) of the radiation. If a galaxy is approaching, its spectral lines will be shifted toward the blue; if a

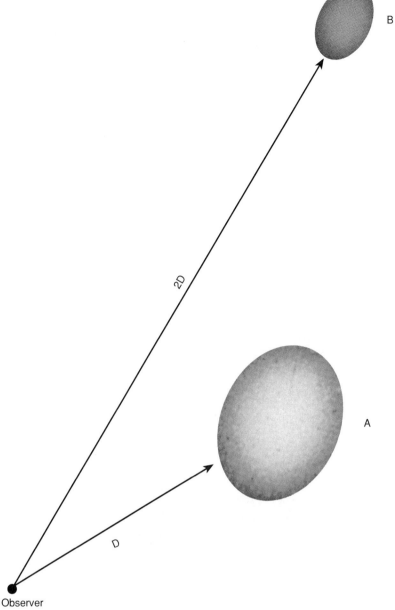

figure 18.21

The relative distance between two galaxies of similar type can be found by means of the inverse-square law.

galaxy is receding, its spectral lines will be redshifted. Most astronomers interpret the redshift in spectral lines as an indication that galaxy clusters are receding in every direction.

Edwin Hubble discovered that the distances to remote galaxies can be measured by their redshift. First he used the apparent brightness of galaxies to estimate their relative distances. For example, consider two galaxies, A and B, of similar type at different distances from the Earth (fig. 18.21). If the distance to the nearer galaxy A can be estimated, and the more distant galaxy B is only one-fourth as bright as galaxy A, then galaxy B must be twice as far away as galaxy A (the inverse-square law).

Hubble found that the recessional velocity determined from the amount of redshift of a galaxy increased in proportion to its distance (fig. 18.22). The relationship is known as the **Hubble law.** Remote galaxies show a greater redshift than nearby ones (fig. 18.23). Astronomers use Hubble's law to estimate distances to the farthest objects observed in the universe.

In chapter 20, we shall treat Hubble's law and the expansion of the universe in more detail. Studies of the recession of galaxies has led to various models describing the evolution of the universe. In one theoretical model, clusters of galaxies appear to be farther away from each other with increasing distances, which implies that at some earlier time space occupied a smaller volume and galaxies were closer together.

g a l a x i e s : i s l a n d s o f s t a r s

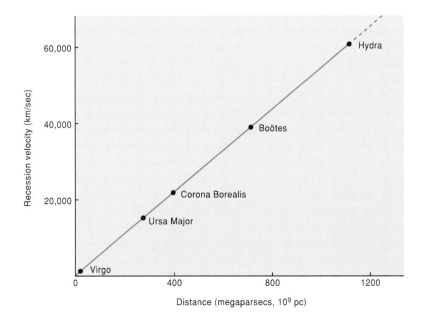

**figure 18.22**

The velocity-distance relation derived from the galaxy clusters shown in figure 18.23.

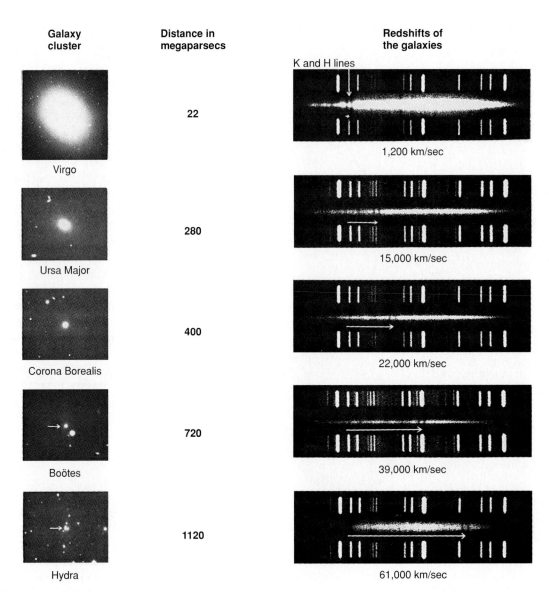

| Galaxy cluster | Distance in megaparsecs | Redshifts of the galaxies |
|---|---|---|
| Virgo | 22 | 1,200 km/sec |
| Ursa Major | 280 | 15,000 km/sec |
| Corona Borealis | 400 | 22,000 km/sec |
| Boötes | 720 | 39,000 km/sec |
| Hydra | 1120 | 61,000 km/sec |

K and H lines

**figure 18.23**

According to the Hubble law, the redshift of the spectral lines is proportional to the distance of a galaxy and the cluster containing it. The displacement of spectral lines to longer wavelengths is larger for galaxies and clusters that are fainter and are at greater distances.

# SUMMARY

The Galaxy, or Milky Way system, represents one of many galaxies that populate the universe. Most exterior stellar systems are too faint to be observed without a telescope. Only three are visible to the unaided eye—the Andromeda galaxy and the two Magellanic Clouds.

More than two centuries ago, nonstellar objects were catalogued according to their appearances and distribution in the sky. The first catalogues were compiled by Charles Messier and William Herschel. Later, Herschel's original catalogue of clusters and nebulae was updated and expanded into the *New General Catalogue (NGC)* in use today.

The nature of galaxies was unknown until larger telescopes and advanced methods of detection were applied. By the early 1920s, Edwin Hubble had discovered cepheid variable stars in M31 and later photographed hundreds of bright and thousands of faint galaxies.

Hubble grouped the galaxies into three categories: elliptical galaxies, normal and barred spiral galaxies, and irregular galaxies. Elliptical galaxies lack spiral arms. They vary in shape from almost spherical objects to flattened, lens-shaped formations. Spherical galaxies are further classified as dwarf and giant ellipticals. Normal spiral galaxies have arms that swirl outward from opposite sides of the nucleus; barred spirals have arms that originate at the ends of a bar extending from the nucleus. Irregular galaxies are small, asymmetrical stellar systems.

## Hubble's Law and the Receding Galaxies

As described in chapter 14, the relationship between radial velocity and change in wavelength due to the Doppler effect is expressed as

$$V = c \, \frac{\Delta\lambda}{\lambda_e}$$

where $\Delta\lambda$ is the difference between the rest wavelength (the wavelength emitted at the source), $\lambda_e$, and the observed wavelength, $\lambda_o$, which has been changed by the relative motion of the source and observer. $\Delta\lambda$ is considered negative if the source is approaching and positive if the source is receding (see fig. 14.8). Thus $\Delta\lambda = \lambda_o - \lambda_e$.

Let the ratio

$$\frac{\Delta\lambda}{\lambda_e} = z,$$

and

$$V = cz$$

where

   $z$ = the redshift of the observed spectral lines,

and

   $V$ = the velocity of recession.

What is the recession velocity of the Virgo cluster if its redshift is 0.004?

$$V = cz$$
$$= (3.0 \times 10^5 \text{ km/sec}) \, (4.0 \times 10^{-3})$$
$$V = 1200 \text{ km/sec}$$

This simple expression is correct only if the velocity of recession ($V$) is a small fraction of the velocity of light ($c$). At higher recessional speeds approaching the velocity of light, the equation must be modified for the effect of relativity, which is negligible for nearby clusters such as Virgo where the value for $z$ remains the same in both equations (see Methods and Understandings 19.1).

Figure 18.23 describes the linear relationship between the velocity of recession ($V$) and the distance ($r$) to a galaxy cluster. From this, the Hubble law can be stated as

$$V = H_0 r$$

where $H_0$ = the Hubble constant also known as the **Hubble parameter.** Consider the Hubble parameter as the slope of the graph in figure 18.23, which represents the rate of recession measured in kilometers per second per million parsecs (km/sec/Mpc). (See Methods and Understandings 20.1.)

Most of the data needed to establish the value of the Hubble parameter has been derived from the Virgo cluster. The distance to the cluster is estimated at 15 to 22 Mpc. Since its recessional velocity is approximately 1200–1300 km/sec, the value of $H_0$ will lie between 50 and 100 km/sec/Mpc. In 1992, Sidney van den Bergh placed the value of $H_0$ at 83 ± 6 km/sec/Mpc and the velocity ($V$) at 1311 km/sec. He determined the distance to the Virgo cluster to be 15.8 Mpc.

What is the value of $H$ based upon the estimated distance and recessional velocity of the Virgo cluster as shown in figures 18.23 and 18.24?

$$H_0 = \frac{V}{r}$$

$$H_0 = \frac{1200 \text{ km/sec}}{22 \text{ Mpc}}$$

$$H_0 = 54.5 \text{ km/sec/Mpc}$$

Once the value of $H_0$ is established, we can measure the distance to more remote galaxies. Find the distance ($r$) to the Hydra cluster if the redshift of one of its galaxies indicates a recessional velocity of 61,000 km/sec.

$$r = \frac{V}{H}$$

$$r = \frac{61,000 \text{ km/sec}}{54.5 \text{ km/sec/Mpc}}$$

$$r = 1119 \text{ Mpc}$$

---

Estimating distances to galaxies requires the use of standard distance indicators. Cepheid variables and luminous supergiant stars are the most reliable yardsticks to the nearby galaxies. The distances to more remote galaxies are estimated by means of the inverse-square law.

There is a relationship between the distance to a galaxy and its velocity of recession. According to Hubble's law, the radial velocity of a galaxy increases as its distance increases; remote galaxies show a greater velocity of recession than nearby galaxies. The radial velocity is determined from the redshift in the spectral lines of the galaxy.

Most galaxies are found in small groups and clusters. Our galaxy, M31, M33, and about two dozen elliptical and irregular galaxies make up the Local Group. The Virgo cluster is the nearest rich cluster. Our galaxy and its neighbors are joined into the local supercluster, which is centered on the Virgo cluster. The orbital velocities of the galaxies within a cluster indicate that a large amount of unseen mass provides the required gravitational attraction needed to hold the cluster together. The nature of the dark matter is unknown.

Superclusters are grouped into a network of filaments enclosing spherical regions called voids. The voids occupy a greater volume of space than the interconnecting bubbles of galaxies. Most of the universe is devoid of visible matter.

Interacting galaxies have distorted shapes caused by galactic tides. Starburst galaxies are interacting pairs that experience a period of intense star formation. Diffuse cD galaxies absorb nearby smaller galaxies by galactic cannibalism.

galaxies: islands of stars

# KEY TERMS

Andromeda galaxy

Coma cluster

elliptical galaxies (dwarf, giant)

galactic cannibalism

galaxy clusters

Hubble law

Hubble parameter

interacting galaxies

irregular galaxies

Large Magellanic Cloud (LMC)

Local Group

Magellanic stream

*Messier Catalogue*

*New General Catalogue of Nebulae and Clusters of Stars (NGC)*

peculiar galaxies

Small Magellanic Cloud (SMC)

spiral galaxies (normal, barred)

standard distance indicators

starburst galaxies

superclusters

Virgo cluster

voids

# PROBLEMS

1. Name the naked-eye galaxies. At which latitude must you be to observe these galaxies in the sky at the same time? When during the year can they be seen shortly after sunset?

2. Explain how Edwin Hubble measured the distance to the Andromeda galaxy and proved it to be another stellar system.

3. How do astronomers estimate the distance to a galaxy if its absolute magnitude is known?

4. Explain how the distance to a remote galaxy can be measured by its redshift.

5. What observational evidence is there to indicate that galaxy clusters are not randomly scattered through space?

6. Why do some interacting galaxies form tails while others produce bridges?

7. Why did astronomers once classify gaseous nebulae and galaxies in the same category?

8. Describe the types of galaxies included in Hubble's classification.

9. In a paragraph, describe the properties of the prominent members of the Local Group.

10. How do the globular clusters in the Magellanic Clouds differ from those found in our Milky Way galaxy?

11. Explain how nearby galaxies are used as stepping stones to more remote galaxies.

12. What does Hubble's law tell us about the evolution of the universe?

13. Describe the large-scale structure of superclusters and voids.

14. What evidence is there that starbursts are caused by galactic tides?

15. How was Messier able to distinguish between a comet entering the inner solar system and an object in his catalogue?

16. Which type of elliptical galaxy might be found at the center of a galaxy cluster? Why?

17. Explain how the distribution and motions of galaxies may indicate the presence of dark matter in a cluster.

18. What conditions are necessary for galactic cannibalism to take place?

19. Name three distance indicators and how they are used by astronomers to measure distances to the galaxies.

20. Find the redshift of a cluster if its recessional velocity is 2400 km/sec.

21. The redshift of a cluster is equal to 0.05. Find its distance. (Let $H = 55$ km/sec/Mpc.)

# REFERENCES

Binney, James. 1991. Inner Secrets of Ellipticals. *Nature* (London) 354, no. 6350 (November 21).

Burns, Jack O. 1986. Very Large Structures in the Universe. *Scientific American* 255, no. 1 (July).

de Vaucouleurs, Gerard. 1987. Discovering M31's Spiral Shape. *Sky and Telescope* 74, no. 6 (December).

Dressler, Alan. 1987. The Large-Scale Streaming of Galaxies. *Scientific American* 257, no. 3 (September).

Edmunds, M. G. 1989. Origin of the Hubble Sequence. *Nature* 337, no. 6208 (February 16).

Fienberg, Richard Tresch. 1990. A Universe of Bubbles and Voids. *Sky and Telescope* 80, no. 3 (September).

Geller, Margaret J. 1990. Mapping the Universe: Slices and Bubbles. *Mercury* (Astronomical Society of the Pacific) 19, no. 3 (May/June).

Geller, Margaret J., and John P. Huchra. 1991. Mapping the Universe. *Sky and Telescope* 82, no. 2 (August).

Gregory, Stephen A. 1988. The Structure of the Visible Universe. *Astronomy* 16, no. 4 (April).

Gregory, Stephen A., and Nancy D. Morrison. 1986. The Largest Supercluster Filament. *Mercury* 15, no. 2 (March/April).

———. 1987. New Observations of Three Nearby Galaxies. *Mercury* 14, no. 3 (May/June).

Gregory, Stephen A., and Laird A. Thompson. 1984. "Superclusters and Voids in the Distribution of Galaxies." In *The Universe of Galaxies, Readings from Scientific American,* compiled by Paul W. Hodge. New York: W. H. Freeman and Company.

Groth, Edward J., James E. Peebles, Michael Seldner, and Raymond M. Soneira. 1977. *The Clustering of Galaxies.* Scientific American Offprint, vol. 237, no. 5 (November). San Francisco: W. H. Freeman and Company.

Hodge, Paul W. 1982. M31: The Andromeda Galaxy. *Mercury* 11, no. 4 (July/August).

———. 1986. *Galaxies.* Cambridge, Mass.: Harvard University Press.

———. 1987. The Local Group: Our Galactic Neighborhood. *Mercury* 16, no. 1 (January/February).

Kaufman, Michele. 1987. Tracing M81's Spiral Arms. *Sky and Telescope* 73, no. 2 (February).

Kiernan, Vincent. 1989. How Far to the Galaxies? *Astronomy* 17, no. 6 (June).

Mathewson, Don. 1984. The Mini-Magellanic Cloud. *Mercury* 13, no. 2 (March/April).

Morrison, Nancy, and David Morrison. 1982. The Local Supercluster and the Large-Scale Structure of the Universe. *Mercury* 11, no. 5 (September/October).

Parker, Barry. 1986. Discovery of the Expanding Universe. *Sky and Telescope* 72, no. 3 (September).

Quinn, Peter J. 1991. When Galaxies Get Together. *Nature* 349, no. 6310 (February 14).

Robinson, Leif J. 1987. Giant Galactic Arcs. *Sky and Telescope* 73, no. 4 (April).

Smith, David H. 1987a. Secrets of Galaxy Clusters. *Sky and Telescope* 73, no. 4 (April).

———. 1987b. Six-Meter Views of M33. *Sky and Telescope* 74, no. 2 (August).

Struble, Mitchell F., and Herbert J. Rood. 1988. Diversity among Galaxy Clusters. *Sky and Telescope* 75, no. 1 (January).

Toomre, Alar, and Juri Toomre. 1984. "Violent Tides between Galaxies." In *The Universe of Galaxies, Readings from Scientific American,* compiled by Paul W. Hodge. New York: W. H. Freeman and Company.

Van den Bergh, Sidney. 1992. *The Hubble Parameter.* Publications of the Astronomical Society of the Pacific, 104, no. 680 (October).

active galaxies and quasars

A red giant star is torn apart by a supermassive
black hole at the heart of a quasar.

There are numberless galaxies in clusters and superclusters that extend for billions of light-years throughout the universe. Most of them are ordinary galaxies composed of hundreds of billions of stars, like our Milky Way system. Visible light from stars provides most of the radiation emitted by *normal galaxies*. Recall how radiation emitted by stars follows Planck's radiation law, which describes the relationship between the intensity of radiation and wavelength. Planck's law shows that the wavelength of maximum intensity of most stars falls within the visible spectrum. For this reason, normal galaxies radiate most of their energy as light.

But there are a few exceptions. About 10% of galaxies, called **active galaxies,** release vast amounts of radiation across the entire electromagnetic spectrum. Such a galaxy has an **active galactic nucleus (AGN)** that may generate up to one million times more energy than an ordinary galaxy. Some strange mechanism other than thermal radiation from stars must be responsible for the unusual distribution of energy observed among active galaxies.

There are several types of distant bodies that have active galactic nuclei. A **radio galaxy** represents a class of objects with radio luminosities ranging from ten to thousands of times greater than their optical luminosities. A **Seyfert galaxy** has a small, bright nucleus that contains high-temperature stars, dust, and gas. An intensely energetic compact mass is found at the center of the galaxy. A **BL Lacertae object** belongs to a class of AGNs that are among the most luminous sources of intense radio frequency and visible radiation.

A **quasar** is the most exotic object with an active center. On photographs, quasars look like faint blue stars, but their large redshifts indicate that they may be more distant than any known object. Many astronomers believe quasars to be the luminous centers of remote galaxies.

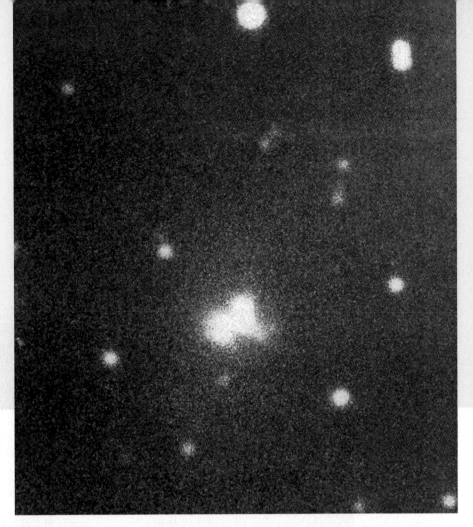

**figure 19.1**

The strongest radio source in the sky, Cygnus A, was the first radio source to be identified with an elliptical galaxy. It is the indistinct butterfly-shaped object just below the center of this photograph taken with the 200-inch Hale telescope at Mt. Palomar.

## Radio Galaxies

A radio galaxy belongs to a class of active galaxies that produce many times more radio emissions than a normal stellar system. However, normal and radio galaxies have about the same optical luminosity. Thus a distant galaxy may be detected as a strong radio source but remain too faint to be resolved at visible wavelengths.

Such unusual radiative properties were difficult to explain in the early days of radio astronomy. Some radio emissions detected in the late 1940s were believed to come from extragalactic objects, but astronomers were unable to connect them with a visible source. By 1954, the 200-inch (5-m) Hale reflector was used to identify faint visible objects where strong radio signals had been previously discovered. The strongest radio source in the sky, *Cygnus A,* was the

first radio galaxy to be recognized through optical and radio investigations (fig. 19.1). Its spectral redshift corresponds to a distance of 700 million light-years.

The first radio sources were identified by the constellations in which they are located, and by a letter—A, B, C, etc.—indicating the order of brightness. Cygnus A represents the brightest radio source in Cygnus; Cygnus B, the second brightest. Today, radio sources are catalogued according to numbers that identify their coordinates on the celestial sphere. For example, the brightest radio source in Virgo, Virgo A, is also designated 1228+126.

Radio astronomers cannot see the radio waves they detect. Instead, a particular source is scanned and signals of varying intensity are recorded. A map of the region is constructed and radio contours are drawn through points of equal

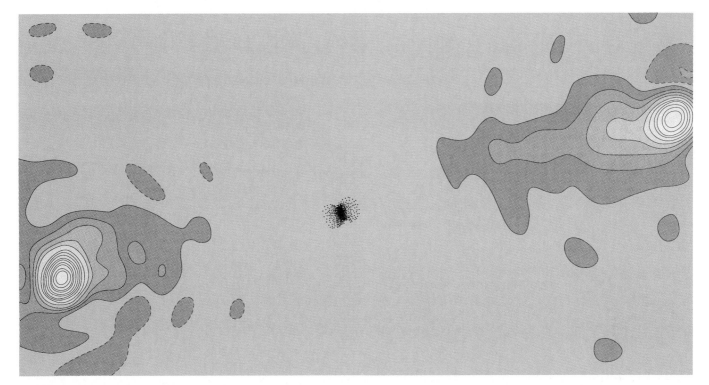

**figure 19.2**

A map of the radio emissions from Cygnus A.

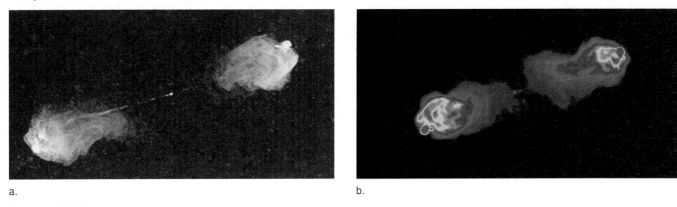

a.                                                                                          b.

**figure 19.3**

Visual representations of Cygnus A. *a.* Jets extending from the nucleus to the lobes. *b.* A false-color image showing the varying intensity of emissions from the radio structure. Regions of least intensity are blue; regions of greatest intensity along the rim of the lobes are shown in red.

radio intensity. The contours resemble the isobars of equal barometric pressure found on a weather map (fig. 19.2).

A radio map can be converted into a visual representation of a radio galaxy. Figure 19.3 shows a representation of Cygnus A. Astronomers were surprised to find a cloudlike structure called a **lobed radio source,** or *lobe,* on each side of a compact center only 20,000 AU across. Two elongated jets extend from the galactic nucleus to the complex lobe structure (fig. 19.3a). The radio structure reaches 400,000 light-years beyond the optical region of the galaxy.

A classical radio galaxy usually has a giant elliptical galaxy at its center. In the nucleus of the elliptical, there is a huge concentration of mass in a limited volume of space. Its nature is unknown at present, but many astronomers are convinced that such a small energetic body must be a black hole (see chapter 16). Surrounding the massive black hole is an accretion disk of hot plasma; X-rays are emitted as plasma spirals into the vortex. A constant supply of hot gas is necessary to feed the voracious "engine" in the core. Turbulent gas from nearby stars may be drawn into the accretion

disk, or perhaps stars from neighboring galaxies and intergalactic gas are subjected to the strong gravitational attraction of the central mass. Finally, streams of matter and radiation gush forth from the polar regions of the black hole. These emissions form the narrow jets that extend far beyond the visible stars and terminate as radio lobes thousands of light-years in intergalactic space.

**figure 19.4**

The peculiar elliptical galaxy NGC 5128 is the optical component of the active radio galaxy Centaurus A. A ring of dust encircles the equatorial region of the galaxy.

## Centaurus A

For years, the nearest active galaxy was referred to as the "enigmatic object" in Centaurus. Centaurus A is a radio galaxy located only 15 million light-years from our own Milky Way system. Its visible component is an elliptical galaxy about 31,000 light-years in diameter (fig. 19.4). In contrast, the radio structure includes two outermost lobes about three million light-years apart. If you could see the radio lobes, they would stretch 10° across the celestial sphere, or an angular distance equal to 20 full Moons placed side-by-side.

The so-called enigmatic object is the peculiar elliptical galaxy listed as NGC 5128. The system is located in the southern sky, below the horizon throughout most of the United States. Fortunately the strong radio source is available to the Very Large Array (VLA) in New Mexico. Centaurus A is also studied by means of ground-based optical and radio telescopes in South America and Australia. Investigations in X-ray frequen-

cies were made by the Einstein high-energy orbiting observatory (HEAO-2).

The peculiar galaxy NGC 5128 is one of the brighter extra-galactic objects observed in an optical telescope. It resembles a typical E1 elliptical except for a dark, irregular ring of dust circling the galaxy. NGC 5128 has the outward appearance of a spiral galaxy entangled in an elliptical system. The dark band has the features one would expect to find in the arms of normal spirals. In addition to dust, the dark lane contains populations of young stars that have recently emerged from condensations of interstellar matter. There are H II regions—clouds of hydrogen ionized by radiation from nearby O- and B-type stars.

As illustrated in figure 19.5, the radio structure of Centaurus A rises from the center almost perpendicular to the dust band that lies in the plane of the galaxy. Nearer to the core, there is a middle radio lobe located along the northern branch of the radio structure about 100,000 light-years from the nucleus (fig. 19.6). Clusters of young hot stars in the

middle lobe region indicate that stellar evolution is underway. Inside the middle lobe, some 30,000 light-years from the center, there are two opposing inner radio lobes (fig. 19.5). A jet carrying electrons that are spiraling around magnetic fields is located between the northern inner lobe and the nucleus of the galaxy.

## Virgo A

In the late 1940s, another strong radio source, Virgo A, was discovered in the Virgo cluster of galaxies. Further investigation revealed that M87, the most impressive galaxy in the local supercluster, was associated with the intense radio emission. Later, M87 was identified as a source of X-rays by HEAO-1 and HEAO-2.

M87 was known to be a strange galaxy 30 years before it was recognized as a nearby radio source. In 1918, observers discovered an unusual glowing stream of matter bulging from the center of the galaxy. This bright streak is resolved as a jet of material that has been ejected

figure 19.5
Radio contours of the inner lobes of Centaurus A spread across a photograph of the galaxy. The lobes extend from the center of the galaxy along its polar axis.

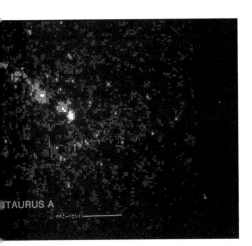

figure 19.6
A computer image of the inner jet of Centaurus A, showing a beam of high-energy electrons accelerated to relativistic speeds by the synchrotron process. The jet extends from the galaxy's nucleus at the center to the upper left. The jet conforms to X-ray emissions between the nucleus and one of the radio lobes.

figure 19.7
The giant elliptical galaxy M87 and its narrow blue-white jet. Radio and optical investigations have shown that the jet emits synchrotron radiation.

from the core of the galaxy (fig. 19.7). Short-exposure photographs reveal a series of bright clumps extending 6500 light-years from the nucleus of the galaxy along the length of the jet. The jet is recognized as a beam of high-energy electrons spiraling in magnetic fields emerging from the nucleus along the north polar axis of the galaxy.

The brightness and color of the jet are another clue pointing toward the nature of the mysterious energy source. M87 is classified as a type E1 giant elliptical galaxy. As such, the system contains an abundance of post-main-sequence stars that give the galaxy a pronounced yellow-amber hue. The protruding jet has a blue-white color, unlike the thermal emissions of aging stars.

Radio investigations provide additional information about the nature of the radiation emitted by the jet. Of particular importance are the high-resolution images achieved with the VLA. When all 27 radio antennae are combined, details down to 0.1 arc second—10 times the resolution of optical images—are detected. High-resolution radio images show the jet as a complex channel through which electrons flow from the nucleus. The bright knots may be emissions caused by the collisions of electrons in the jet with the surrounding interstellar medium (fig. 19.8).

active galaxies and quasars

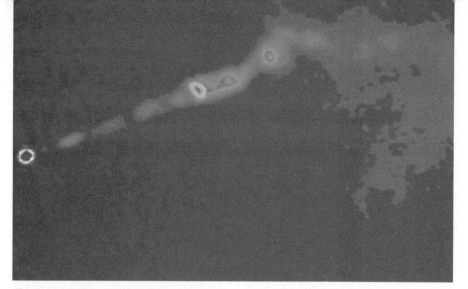

**figure 19.8**

Color-enhanced high-resolution images of the M87 jet. The jet is produced by an outflow of electrons in a magnetic field generated by a powerful energy source at the center of the galaxy.

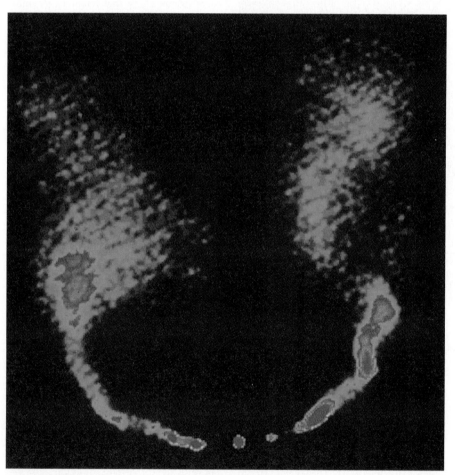

**figure 19.9**

The two jets from the center of NGC 1265 in Perseus may be warped by their encounter with the intergalactic medium.

Radio observations have identified twin jets of emissions spiraling outward from the galaxy's active center. But until 1991, only the conspicuous west jet was observed in visible light. Today, high-resolution images of M87 reveal the "counterjet" on the eastern side as a faint arc of emissions in the same location as the radio lobe.

## Nature of the Energy Source

What is the nature of the powerful energy source at the center of a radio galaxy? How is the radio structure sustained? Astronomers agree that high-velocity electrons in magnetic fields are ejected from a compact source at the nucleus of the galaxy. Investigations in a wide range of frequencies confirm that the energy from the nucleus is emitted as synchrotron radiation. The electrons are accelerated to relativistic speeds as they spiral about strong magnetic fields. Many investigators believe that an active galaxy is powered by a supermassive black hole with a mass equal to five billion solar masses.

Recall our introduction to black holes in chapter 16. The simple hypothetical model described at that time was a nonrotating black hole with one property—mass. But additional properties are preserved and found in the supermassive black holes contained in the nuclei of active galaxies. These properties are spin and electric charge. Such black holes act as gigantic dynamos and therefore possess strong magnetic fields.

According to this model, the enormous gravitational influence of a massive black hole will draw gas into the galaxy by cannibalizing nearby smaller galaxies or by stripping the gas found in intergalactic space. The inward flow of ionized gas reaches the nucleus and falls onto an accretion disk rotating around the black hole. Most of the plasma eventually feeds the black hole, but a portion will become entangled in the magnetic field lines that extend from the polar regions of the black hole. In this manner, particles, mostly electrons, are ejected from the center and spiral outward along the magnetic field lines. The particles emit synchronous radiation when the magnetic field accelerates the electrons to almost the speed of light. The outward beam of particles and energy creates the radio structure (fig. 19.9).

## Seyfert Galaxies

Galaxies with active nuclei were first detected by Carl K. Seyfert in 1943. A Seyfert galaxy is distinguished from an ordinary galaxy by its bright, starlike nucleus

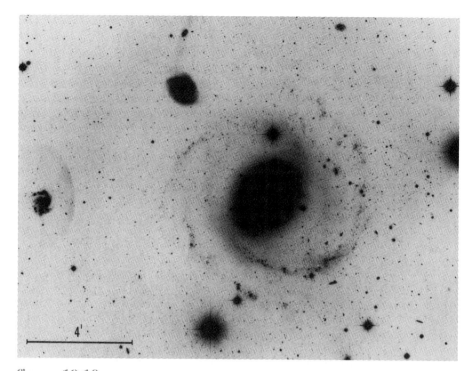

**figure 19.10**
Seyfert galaxy NGC 4151. Seyfert galaxies are distinguished by their active nuclei.

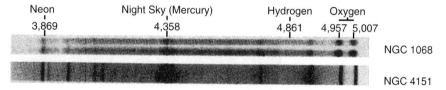

**figure 19.11**
The nuclei of Seyfert galaxies such as NGC 1068 and NGC 4151 have spectra containing prominent emission lines.

(fig. 19.10). The spectra of such objects show strong, broad emission lines, while the spectra of normal galaxies have absorption lines that are found in the spectra of ordinary stars (fig. 19.11). The energy output at the center of a Seyfert galaxy is enormous and must originate from a nonstellar source. The emission lines are from a dense gas composed of excited atoms and ions. The broad spectral lines indicate that the gas velocities are high, ranging up to 10,000 km/sec. In addition to these spectral differences, the nuclei of Seyfert galaxies are blue in color and emit more ultraviolet radiation than expected from ionized gas and blue giant stars. In contrast, the nuclei of normal galaxies are orange-red because of the abundance of population II stars.

Seyfert galaxies are different than normal galaxies in a number of ways. Some are variable and change magnitude in periods ranging from months down to several minutes. The rapidly pulsating nuclei must be small (their diameters are measured in light-hours, not light-years) to be able to complete one cycle in such short periods of time.

Another class of Seyfert galaxies emit radio energy and infrared radiation. The radio emissions are *core-dominated*—that is, Seyfert galaxies do not have the extended radio lobes characteristic of radio galaxies. The infrared radiation is believed to originate from dust clouds in the surrounding galaxy that are heated by the central energy source.

## Profile of a Seyfert Galaxy

Let us examine a bright, nearby Seyfert galaxy, NGC 4151. This magnitude-11 object can be observed in a moderate-sized, portable telescope. Visually, NGC

4151 looks like a blue star surrounded by a field of faint stars. Long-exposure photographs taken with large professional telescopes reveal the galaxy's spiral structure. Short-exposure photographs show a fuzzy, starlike object representing the intensely energetic core.

NGC 4151 is a member of the Virgo cluster and is near enough to be studied in detail. The mass of the nucleus is equal to about 700 million suns, but is only about 2200 AU in diameter. Such a compact mass with a surprisingly large energy output is believed to be powered by a supermassive black hole. The source of X-rays emitted by Seyfert galaxies may be an accretion disk surrounding a black hole. Stars and interstellar matter from the host galaxy provide the material for the accretion disk.

In summary, Seyfert galaxies have extremely bright centers and spiral arms similar to those of other galaxies. If a Seyfert galaxy were located billions of light-years in space, only its bright nucleus would be visible. Similarities exist between Seyfert galaxies and quasars, which are the most distant objects we can see.

## Quasars

The radio sources investigated thus far are grouped in two general categories—extended and compact sources. In many instances, radio waves are detected from two lobes on opposite sides of an active galactic nucleus. Such extended sources are common to the radio galaxies discussed earlier. A compact source is found at the center of a radio galaxy; for example, Centaurus A or a Seyfert galaxy.

Improvement in radio techniques and telescope design made possible the discovery of a point source that turned out to be one of the strangest objects in the universe—a *quasar*. In the 1960s, radio sources were identified with optical images, some of which were point sources resembling distant stars. Astronomers were puzzled when a blue starlike object was found in the same direction of the sky as the radio source 3C 48 (number 48 in the *Third Cambridge Catalogue*). The optical observations revealed that the spectrum of 3C 48 contained bright emission lines at all wavelengths. The familiar absorption lines found in the spectra of ordinary stars were missing. Moreover, the emission lines could not be identified with any known substance.

At the time, astronomers wondered if the point sources represented an entirely new class of radio "stars" within our galaxy. Obviously, a strong radio source such as 3C 48 cannot be a star. Ordinary stars like our Sun radiate most of their energy in the visible range and therefore are weak radio sources. We detect the Sun's radio emission only because it is near to the Earth.

In 1962, another radio source, listed in the same catalogue as 3C 273, was found to coincide with a bright starlike image (fig. 19.12). Fortunately, the radio source is located in the direction of the Moon's orbit, which allowed its precise position to be determined. During lunar occultation, the Moon's limb cuts off the radiation from 3C 273. Since the Moon's coordinates are known, the radio source and optical image can be correlated.

In 1962, Maarten Schmidt used the prime focus spectrograph at the Hale Telescope to photograph the spectra of radio galaxies. A comparison spectrum was produced on each photographic plate before observing the sky. A comparison spectrum has emission lines in their rest position and therefore can be used to measure the shift in the spectral lines of the object under investigation (see chapter 5).

Among the objects selected was the point source in Virgo called 3C 273. Schmidt matched the Balmer lines in the comparison spectrum with the corresponding Balmer lines in the spectrum of 3C 273. The spectral lines were redshifted by 15%, which places the object at a distance of about two billion light-years (fig. 19.13). The spectra of 3C 48 and 3C 273 look unusual because the features that are normally observed in the ultraviolet region are shifted into the optical range. 3C 48 has a redshift of 37%, which represents a distance of five billion light-years.

At first, astronomers called the distant radio sources *quasi-stellar radio sources*—i.e., starlike objects with nonstellar properties. Later the name was replaced with the term *quasar,* from the acronym QSRS. For the present, consider a quasar as a starlike object that has an emission spectrum with lines

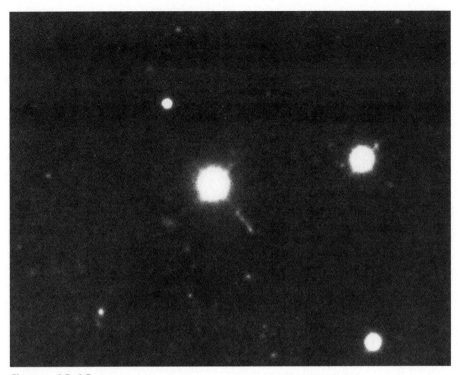

**figure 19.12**

Quasar 3C 273 in the constellation Virgo was the first radio source discovered to have a large redshift in its spectrum. Note the jet extending from the nucleus of the quasar.

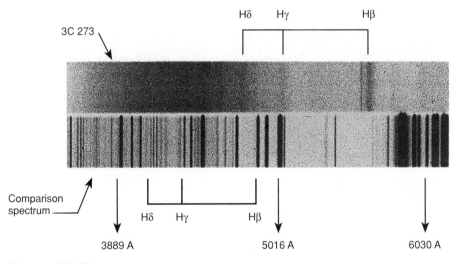

**figure 19.13**

The spectrum of 3C 273 (*top*) and a comparison spectrum (*bottom*). The Balmer lines of hydrogen are redshifted 16%.

greatly displaced to longer wavelengths than their rest position.

Soon other radio sources were identified and matched with corresponding optical images that showed a large redshift. In addition, the cosmologist Allan Sandage discovered quasars that are radio quiet. Radio-quiet quasars are identified optically among the many field stars by their emission spectra.

The *objective prism* method is used to distinguish radio-quiet quasars from ordinary foreground stars. The spectra of many objects are produced on one photographic plate by a prism attached to the front of the telescope objective. On the photograph, star images appear as small spectra rather than points of light. Spectra of all starlike sources in a given area can be photographed in one

### Recession Velocities Approaching the Speed of Light

In Methods and Understandings 18.1, we discussed how recession velocities of relatively nearby galaxies can be calculated by the expression

$$V = c \, \frac{\lambda_o - \lambda_e}{\lambda_e}$$

where $\lambda_o$ is the observed wavelength and $\lambda_e$ the wavelength emitted by the source. Let $z$ represent the redshift so that

$$\frac{V}{c} = z.$$

The term $V/c$ is also used to describe the **relativistic redshift** of distant galaxies and quasars. But, as we learned in chapter 18, the equations shown above must be modified when recessional velocities approach the speed of light. According to the special theory of relativity, measurements of time and distance are relative, and their values depend upon the motions of the observer and the object (in this case, a quasar) that emits the radiation. Moreover, the speed of light is a constant that is independent of the motions of the observer and the object emitting the radiation. The recession velocity is the *relative* speed of the observer and object and cannot attain or exceed the value of $c$.

At relativistic speeds, the ratio of the observed wavelength to the wavelength of the source is

$$\frac{\lambda_o}{\lambda_e} = \sqrt{(c + V)/(c - V)}.$$

Since

$$z = \frac{\lambda_o - \lambda_e}{\lambda_e} = \frac{\lambda_o}{\lambda_e} - \frac{\lambda_e}{\lambda_e} = \frac{\lambda_o}{\lambda_e} - 1,$$

we find that

$$z + 1 = \sqrt{(c + V)/(c - V)}$$

and

$$(z + 1)^2 = (c + V)/(c - V),$$

or

$$(z + 1)^2 = \left(1 + \frac{V}{c}\right) \Big/ \left(1 - \frac{V}{c}\right)$$

In the following operation, we shall solve for the ratio $V/c$ that describes the relativistic recession velocity. To simplify our work, let $A = (z + 1)$ and $B = (V/c)$. Then

$$A^2 = \frac{(1 + B)}{(1 - B)}.$$

To solve for $B$, rearrange the terms

$$A^2 - A^2 B - B = 1$$

and

$$B(A^2 + 1) = (A^2 - 1)$$

to obtain

$$B = \frac{A^2 - 1}{A^2 + 1}.$$

Substitute the original values for $A$ and $B$.

$$\frac{V}{c} = \frac{(z + 1)^2 - 1}{(z + 1)^2 + 1}$$

*Example:* Find the recessional velocity of 3C 273 if the observed wavelength of the Balmer series Hβ spectral line is redshifted to 5629 angstroms. The emitted wavelength is 4861 angstroms.

$$z = \frac{5629 - 4861}{4861}$$

$$z = 0.158$$

$$\frac{V}{c} = \frac{0.341}{2.341} = 0.146$$

$$V = 0.146 \, c$$

Astronomers have discovered quasars with redshifts equal to 4 and 5. These quasars were formed during an early period in the history of the universe. Using the above equations, find the recessional velocity of a quasar with a redshift of 5. (Ans. $V = 0.946 \, c$).

active galaxies and quasars

exposure. Thus the spectra of quasars can be identified by their emission lines, and the spectra of field stars are distinguished by their absorption lines.

### Spectral Characteristics

Recall from our earlier discussions how the spectrum of an ordinary star or a normal galaxy can be identified by a con-

tinuous emission that peaks in intensity within the optical region. The continuum is filled with dark absorption lines and bands produced when radiation is absorbed in the upper layers of the stars. Quasars are definitely not stars and, as their brightnesses and distances indicate, some other excitation mechanism is at work. Quasars and active galaxies have strong continuous radiation of about

equal intensity across the entire spectrum from the infrared to the X-ray and possibly beyond into the gamma-ray region. Only about 10% of the quasars radiate in the radio range. Moreover, the spectra of quasars show regular emission lines that have been confirmed as ultraviolet wavelengths displaced to the visible region of the spectrum. We have seen how Maarten Schmidt identified the

Balmer lines Hβ through Hε redshifted by as much as $z = 0.158$.

## Quasars as Distant Objects

Many astronomers believe the large spectral shift of quasars indicates that they are receding from us according to the Hubble law. This so-called *cosmological interpretation* of the redshift means that the observed radial velocities are a result of the expansion of the universe. The quasars are distant objects that extend beyond the faintest galaxies we can resolve in the largest optical telescopes (see Methods and Understandings 18.1).

According to the Hubble law, the amount of redshift, and therefore the radial velocity, increases in proportion to the distance of the quasar. Consequently, a relatively nearby quasar, 3C 273, is receding from the Earth at about 15% of the speed of light, $0.146\ c$, which indicates that its distance from us is about two billion light-years. The radial velocity of 3C 48 was found to be about $0.37\ c$; thus its distance is about five billion light-years. Both quasars are relatively close by; remote quasars can be detected to distances beyond 12 billion light-years. In contrast, the more distant galaxies are in the range of about six billion light-years. Any galaxy beyond this limit will be extremely faint and difficult to resolve in the largest optical telescopes.

The redshifts observed in quasars indicates that they extend billions of light-years beyond the visible galaxies. Thus quasars must be more luminous than galaxies, otherwise they would be too faint to be photographed. At the distances given by the Hubble law, it is estimated that the luminosities of quasars such as 3C 273 must be about 1000 times that of a normal galaxy.

## Local Interpretation

Some astronomers maintain that the quasars are much nearer to us and the observed radial velocities can be explained by a *local interpretation* of the redshifts. Several models have been proposed. In one scenario, an explosion in the center of our galaxy may have ejected massive objects that are moving away at enormous speeds. If quasars are relatively nearby objects, they need not be the superluminous and powerful energy sources required by the cosmological interpretation.

Another explanation attributes the observed displacement of spectral lines to a *gravitational redshift* (see chapter 16). The light emitted from a massive luminous object will have its spectral lines redshifted by an amount directly proportional to its mass and inversely proportional to its radius. If quasars are nearby objects, they need not have enormous radial velocities; they might be small massive objects with strong gravitational fields. However, many astronomers argue that a close-by object with the required size and mass to cause the observed redshift cannot exist for a long period of time, but will collapse into a black hole. Moreover, a quasar has an emission spectrum that is associated with low-density gas clouds rather than a compact source required by the local hypothesis.

There are some galaxies and quasars that seem to be close to each other in space and appear to be members of the same galaxy cluster. Such alignments are puzzling because the redshifts of the quasars are far greater than the associated galaxies. If the quasars are adjacent to galaxies located in relatively nearby clusters, some phenomenon other than cosmological expansion must be responsible for their excessive redshifts. Many astronomers interpret these alignments as optical effects caused by distant quasars and foreground galaxies located in the same direction.

In summary, most astronomers favor the cosmological model—that a quasar's redshift is an effect caused by the expansion of the universe. Spectroscopic properties indicate that quasars are distant active galactic nuclei. They are similar to Seyfert galaxies, but, in most quasars, the host galaxy cannot be resolved. The intense radiation from the quasar overwhelms the feeble light emitted by the stars in the host galaxy.

Studies indicate that most quasars have redshifts ranging from about $z = 2$ to $z = 3$. At greater redshifts, quasars are dramatically reduced in number, although more than two dozen are known with redshifts of 4 to 5. The discovery of quasars with such large redshifts is evidence that quasar activity was present at an early epoch in the history of the universe.

## Evidence Linking Quasars to Galaxies

Most quasars photograph as points of light. However, a few relatively nearby quasars, such as 3C 273, do show physical structure. 3C 273 is surrounded by a glow that gives the quasar the appearance of a giant elliptical galaxy; a faint jet protrudes from its core. As described earlier, radio radiation from active galaxies such as M87 originates in a similar jetlike structure. Most interesting is that the ratio of quasars having radio properties to those emitting little or no radio radiation is about the same as the ratio of radio to normal galaxies.

Other properties support the argument that quasars might be the active centers of distant galaxies. Astronomers have discovered a number of quasars surrounded by a "fuzz" that gives them the appearance of a remote galaxy with a bright nucleus. Studies show that the light emitted by the fuzz is similar to the starlight from an ordinary galaxy. An object listed as Markarian 1014 is a galaxy with a luminous quasar at its center. The galaxy is near enough to the Earth ($z = 0.16$) to allow its features to be investigated (fig. 19.14). The spectrum of the nucleus shows the broad emission lines found in the spectra of quasars. In contrast, the spectra of the surrounding fuzz indicates the presence of a large number of population I stars. Markarian 1014 has the properties of a bright Seyfert galaxy as well as a quasar. Also, images of quasar 3C 275.1 show it to be located at the center of a cluster of galaxies at an estimated distance of seven billion light-years (fig. 19.15).

There are optical phenomena that establish the size of a quasar. Observations reveal that the light from many quasars varies in brightness. More surprising are small fluctuations taking place in less than a day; other light changes occur in a matter of weeks and months. A quasar may vary as much as one magnitude, more than double its brightness, in less than one month. Its bright nucleus must be small because the light variations set limits on its size.

Let the spherical object in figure 19.16 represent a hypothetical quasar. At a given instant, light leaves the quasar from

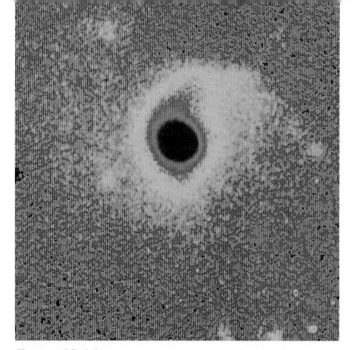

**figure 19.14**

A false-color image of the quasar Markarian 1014. The green region surrounding the bright nucleus may be the distorted arms of the host spiral galaxy.

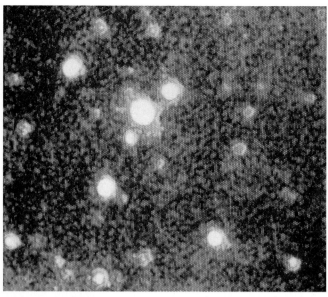

**figure 19.15**

Quasar 3C 275.1. Discovery of this object at the center of a cluster of galaxies provides evidence linking quasars to distant galaxies.

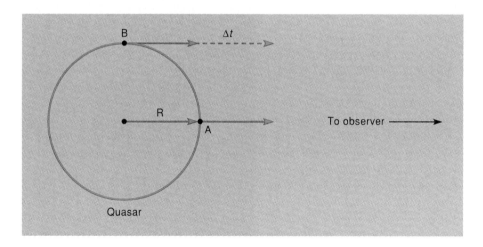

**figure 19.16**

This figure illustrates why an object cannot complete its variation in brightness in less time than it takes light to cross a distance equal to the radius R. Light from point B must travel an additional distance in the time interval $\Delta t$ for the light from all parts of the quasar to reach an observer.

point A at the center of the object and point B at the limb. Suppose the quasar suddenly increases in brightness. At some future time, the event is recorded by an observer on Earth. But the light from point B must travel an additional distance equal to the radius of the quasar and therefore reaches the observer later than the light from point A by a time interval represented by $\Delta t$.

The quasar cannot vary its brightness in less time than it takes light to travel a distance equal to its radius. If $\Delta t$ is equal to one day, the radius of the quasar cannot exceed a light-day. If $\Delta t$ is equal to one week, the radius must be less than one light-week.

What is the maximum radius of a quasar that varies in brightness over a period of one day? The maximum radius is

one light-day, which is equal to about 170 AU, or twice the size of Pluto's orbit.

## How Quasars Generate Energy

How can a compact quasar, no larger than the outer limit of the solar system, generate as much energy as hundreds of galaxies? When quasars were discovered to be distant luminous objects, a number of models were proposed, ranging from a dense concentration of stars to matter-antimatter annihilation.

According to physicist Edward R. Harrison, the energy radiated at the nucleus of a quasar comes from the release of gravitational energy. During the formation of a galaxy, primordial matter contracted into a nucleus of stars and gas. In a giant elliptical galaxy, the interstellar gas may represent about one-tenth of the total mass of the system. In time, the stars and gas contracted into a dense central mass that evolved into a quasar capable of radiating an immense amount of energy for billions of years. Many of the first-generation stars were blue giants that ended up as neutron stars and black holes.

Astronomer Martin Rees proposed that hundreds of thousands of pulsars may have combined to form intense beams of particles that are detected from radio galaxies and quasars. In another model, the central region of a protogalaxy contracts into a number of supermassive stars having strong magnetic fields. These so-called *spinars* are equal to millions of solar masses and have the properties of enormous pulsars, with intense bipolar jets radiating into intergalactic space.

Generally, scientists support the black-hole model as the driving mechanism for a quasar. In the beginning, there may have been many black holes representing the terminal stages of the most massive first-generation stars. In time, more matter in the form of stars and gas falls to the center and increases the mass of the black holes. Eventually, one huge black hole will increase in size at the expense of stars, gas, and other black holes and may reach a mass over one million times greater than the Sun.

A model proposed by Belinda J. Wilkes describes a quasar as a supermassive black hole surrounded by an accretion disk of dust and gas at the center of a host galaxy (fig. 19.17). Matter from stars and interstellar space beyond the black hole spirals into the accretion disk and adds to its mass. A fraction of the infalling mass is converted into energy equivalent to that produced by a galaxy of stars. How the energy is produced can be determined by studying the way in which a quasar emits energy across the electromagnetic spectrum.

As we have seen, only about 10% of the quasars are radio sources. The process responsible for the radio emission is synchrotron radiation. It is a primary source of radio emission that probably originates near the central black hole. The radiation is concentrated in a narrow cone and can be detected only if its direction of travel is toward the observer.

Radiation at infrared wavelengths indicates that dust clouds heated to different temperatures are scattered throughout the host galaxy. Dust particles absorb high-energy radiation from the central region and emit the energy as infrared radiation. In addition, huge amounts of dust and gas in a ringlike structure called a *torus* may be revolving around the nucleus.

Stars emit most of their energy as light, and a large portion of the optical

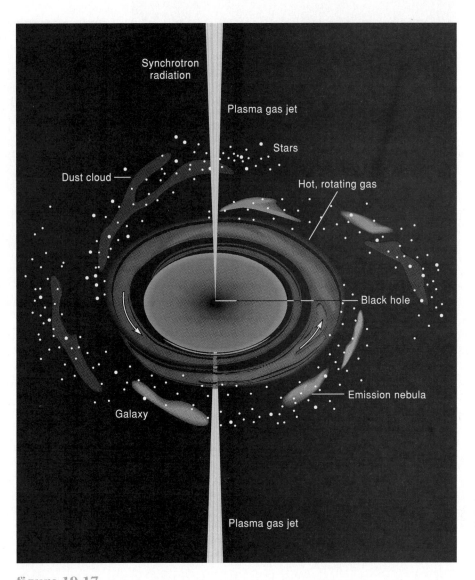

**figure 19.17**

Hypothetical structure of a quasar, showing various components that contribute to its overall emissions.

radiation emitted by a quasar stems from billions of ordinary stars found in the host galaxy. Most of the ultraviolet radiation comes from gas at different temperatures. X-rays from the central energy source are reflected by warm gas spiraling in the accretion disk. Energy absorbed by the heated gas is later emitted as ultraviolet radiation. The source of the X-rays might be synchrotron emission or the interaction between electrons and positrons.

## BL Lacertae Objects

Another class of energetic sources are called *BL Lacertae objects,* distinguished by their unusual radio and optical spectra. Visually, BL Lac objects appear star-

like or as a bright core surrounded by a nebulous fuzz (fig. 19.18). In fact, until the discovery of its spectral characteristics in the late 1960s, the prototype, BL Lacertae, had been listed as an irregular variable star. However, BL Lac cannot be a star or an ordinary galaxy because its spectrum does not have absorption lines. Neither are there broad emission lines that identify the spectra of quasars. The spectra of BL Lac objects show continuous emission and lack distinctive emission and absorption lines that might be used to determine their distances.

As shown in figure 19.19, there are unmistakable differences in the total energy emitted by a BL Lac object, a quasar, and an ordinary galaxy. The radio spectrum of a BL Lac is inverted and

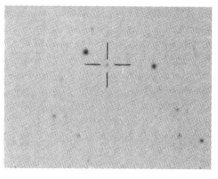
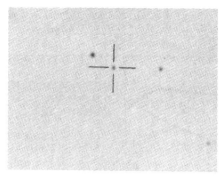
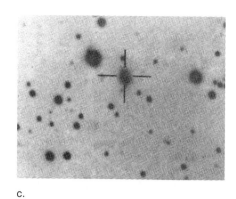

a.                              b.                              c.

▲ figure 19.18

Three exposures of BL Lacertae. Photographs **a.** and **b.** illustrate the variability in brightness of the object. In photo **b.**, taken about two months after **a.**, BL Lac has increased in brightness about 1.5 times. A long-exposure, photo **c.**, resolves the halo surrounding the nucleus.

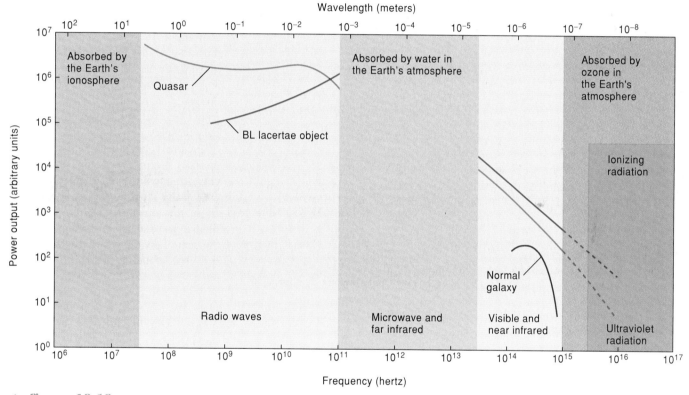

▲ figure 19.19

Comparison of energy emissions of a quasar, a BL Lacertae object, and a normal galaxy.
From "BL Lacertae Objects" by Michael J. Disney and Phillippe Verón. Copyright © 1977 by Scientific American, Inc. All rights reserved.

shows a distinctive rise in power output as wavelength decreases. In contrast, the power output of quasars is nearly horizontal—i.e., about the same at all radio wavelengths. Both BL Lacs and quasars are strong radio sources. In the near infrared and visible range, both show intense emission over a greater range of wavelengths than a normal galaxy. Nearly all the radiation emitted by a normal galaxy represents the combined light from billions of stars. Moreover, BL Lac

objects do not have extended radio lobes characteristic of radio galaxies. Instead, the strong radio signals come from an active source at the center.

Like their prototype, other BL Lacs are variable in radio, visible, and X-ray wavelengths. Large changes in luminosity occur in periods ranging from weeks to only a few hours (fig. 19.20). Variations in such short periods of time indicate that the central regions must be small, on the order of a few light-weeks. Varia-

tions in the prototype BL Lac indicate that the light comes from a region only a few light-days in diameter (fig. 19.20).

An interesting feature is the faint fuzz surrounding a few BL Lac objects. As seen in figure 19.18c, long-exposure photographs reveal a nebulous halo surrounding the bright core of the prototype. Moreover, the halo has the appearance of a distant giant elliptical galaxy. Another object, AP Librae, similar to BL Lac, has absorption lines in the

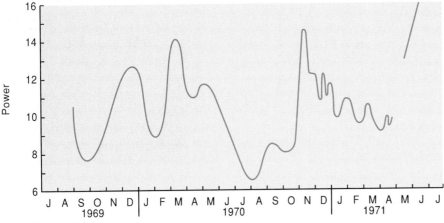

a. Radio intensity

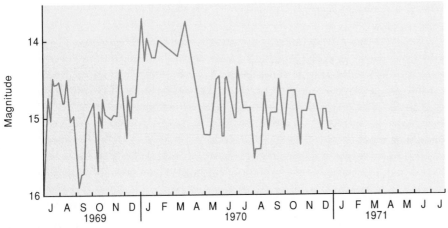

b. Optical brightness

**figure 19.20**

*a.* Variations in radio intensity and *b.* optical brightness of BL Lacertae. The pattern of changes in visual magnitude suggests that the light is coming from a region only a few light-days in diameter.

From "BL Lacertae Objects" by Michael J. Disney and Phillippe Verón. Copyright © 1977 by Scientific American, Inc. All rights reserved.

spectrum of its halo similar to those found in the spectra of galaxies (see fig. 19.21). Redshift measurements of the lines indicate that AP Librae is an extragalactic object located about one billion light-years away.

## A Unified Model for Active Galactic Nuclei

Despite their differences, radio galaxies, quasars, Seyfert galaxies, and BL Lac objects have one fundamental property in common—an active galactic nucleus (AGN). The energy produced by an AGN is intense across the entire spectrum, ranging in wavelength from radio to X-ray emissions. The nuclei of normal galaxies consist of stars and interstellar gas clouds. The bulk of the radiation from a normal galaxy is provided by the stars and emission nebulae at infrared, visual, and ultraviolet wavelengths.

Luminous AGNs must contain some mechanism other than stellar radiation to account for their enormous energy output. The nature of the central power source remains a mystery, so astronomers refer to it in general, or indefinite terms such as "monster," "beast," or "central engine." The most popular explanation is that the core of an AGN is a supermassive black hole several million to several billion times more massive than the Sun (fig. 19.17).

Assuming that a supermassive black hole is lodged at the center, why do AGNs appear as different kinds of objects? Many astronomers suspect that the diverse examples of active galactic nuclei are aspects of the same phenomenon. Theorists have proposed a *unified model* in which radio galaxies, quasars, Seyfert galaxies, and BL Lac objects are considered to be the same type of body, a black hole, seen from different angles of position.

Refer again to figure 19.17, which depicts a spinning black hole surrounded by an accretion disk of dust and gas. High-temperature clouds absorb and radiate energy from the central region. A thick torus of dust and gas lies in the central plane several light-years beyond the accretion disk. High-speed clouds revolve inside the torus. Cooler clouds drift at greater distances above and below the doughnut-shaped ring. Intense bipolar jets extend many light-years into intergalactic space.

Picture yourself observing the core emissions from a black hole at different angles: edge-on in the plane of the accretion disk and the opaque torus; end-on in the direction of an approaching bipolar jet; and at an oblique angle to the central plane, which provides a partial view of the bright core inside the dusty torus.

Radio and Seyfert galaxies are seen when the accretion disk is edge-on and oblique in our line of sight. The outward moving jets create radio lobes on opposite sides of the active nucleus. Seyfert galaxies and low-temperature clouds are revealed if the angle is sufficient to expose the core beyond the opaque torus. The end view of a high-energy particle beam streaming from the polar region represents the bright core of a quasar or a BL Lac object.

## Gravitational Lensing

A unique phenomenon predicted by Albert Einstein has provided astronomers with a method to make systematic studies of the most distant objects in the universe. Einstein calculated that starlight will be deflected while passing through the gravitational field of the Sun (see chapter 16). This so-called **gravitational**

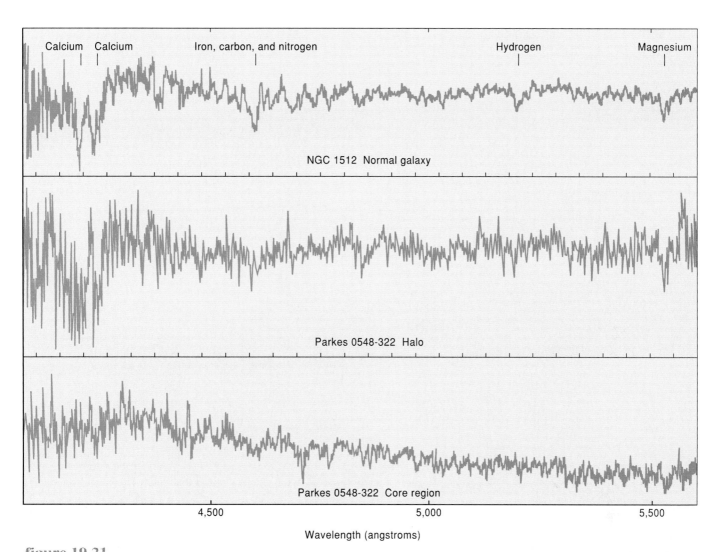

Absorption lines in the halo of the BL Lac object designated Parkes 0548-322 are similar to those found in a normal galaxy such as NGC 1512. The presence of absorption lines supports the view that BL Lac objects are distant galaxies.

lensing, or bending of light, was photographed by Arthur Eddington during the solar eclipse of May 29, 1919. Later, Einstein suggested that if two distant stars were situated in the line of sight to an observer on the Earth, light from the distant source would be deflected and form halos and rings about the foreground star.

Galaxies and quasars may function as gravitational lenses and produce strange multiple images. In the constellation Ursa Major there is a radio source consisting of two images of quasars designated 0957+561 A and B. In 1979, astronomers confirmed that the double quasars are two mirages of the same object. A distant quasar is in the line of sight of a foreground galaxy. As shown in figure 19.22, light from the quasar is bent by the strong gravitational field of the

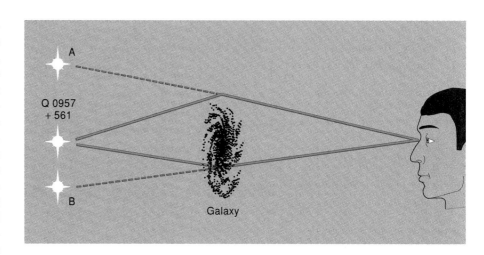

figure 19.22

Gravitational lensing. Light from the quasar Q 0957+561 is deflected by a foreground galaxy so it appears to be coming from points A and B. This quasar was the first lensing object to be identified.

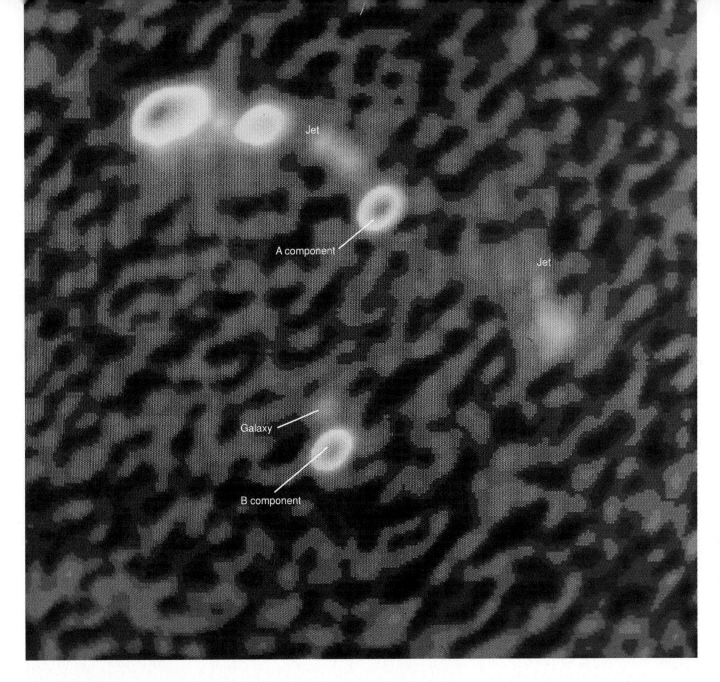

**figure 19.23**
Radio images of Q 0957+561. The A and B components are the twin images of the quasar lying beyond the galaxy.

galaxy. The gravitational field acts like a huge lens to focus the light toward the Earth. To an observer, the light from the quasar is deflected to points *A* and *B* and forms two 17th-magnitude mirages separated by an angle of six arc seconds. The foreground galaxy and the *B* component are barely separated and seem to overlap in visible-light and radio images (fig. 19.23).

Gravitational lensing can provide experimental data in a number of areas of investigation. It can be used as a cosmic telescope to reveal the features of a light source as well as massive objects in the foreground. The lensing effect might be caused by a visible galaxy, as in the case of quasar 0957+561, or by dark matter in intergalactic space.

The formation of multiple images by a foreground galaxy is a strong argument in favor of quasars as distant objects. Moreover, astronomers have suggested that gravitational lensing is responsible for the apparent association of some high-redshift quasars with relatively nearby galaxies (see fig. 19.24).

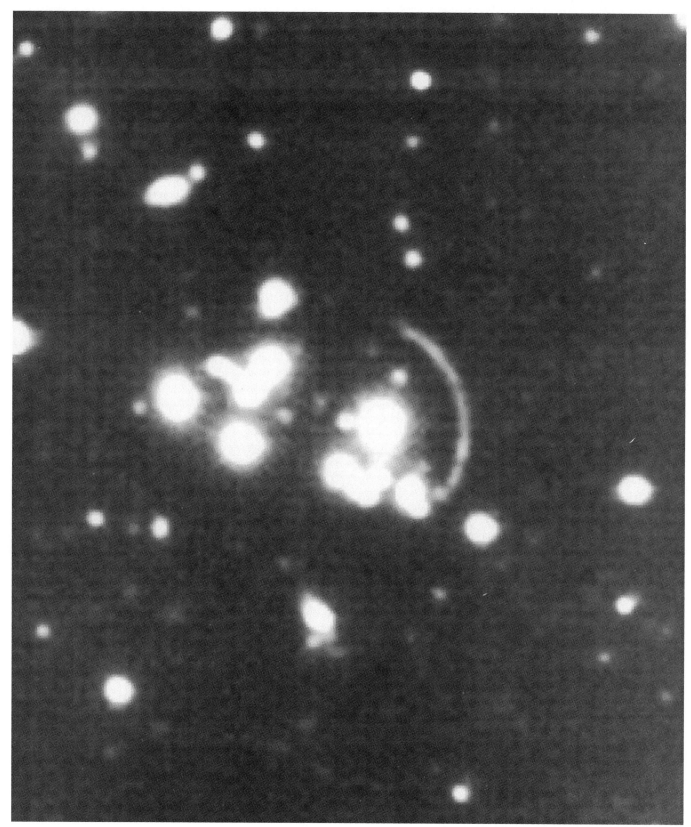

**figure 19.24**

A galactic arc in the galaxy cluster CL 2244-02 may be a lensed image of an object beyond the cluster.

observing quasars and active galaxies

While reading this chapter, you may have gotten the impression that only professional astronomers with extremely advanced telescopes are able to observe distant radio galaxies, Seyfert galaxies, quasars, and BL Lac objects. Fortunately, Sky Watchers can detect such exotic astronomical bodies in tele-

scopes ranging in diameter from 8 to 14 inches. Table 19.1 lists some of the brightest active sources we have discussed in the present chapter. The coordinates of the objects are for the year, or epoch, 2000.0, which corresponds to the positions found in the latest catalogues and star charts. You will need this table and a star chart to identify the active sources against the foreground stars seen in the field of the telescope.

Let us observe two interesting AGNs in the constellation Virgo—a radio galaxy Virgo A and a quasar 3C 273. Virgo A (M87) is the brightest active source in table 19.1 that is visible from the middle latitudes of the northern hemisphere. To find it, locate the bright stars Beta Leonis in the constellation Leo and Epsilon Virginis in Virgo. Aim your telescope between the two stars and locate the center of the Virgo cluster. Find the two

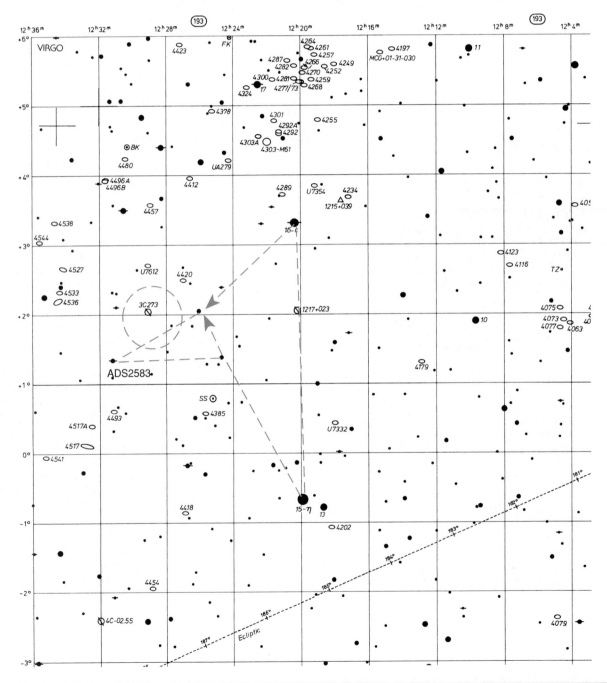

a.

giant elliptical galaxies M84 and M86. The galaxies are separated by an angle of 1/3° and are brighter than other galaxies in your field of view (see the photograph at the beginning of chapter 18). From M86, turn the telescope eastward about 4 times the distance between the galaxies and 1/2° south to M87, the radio galaxy Virgo A. The radio features cannot be detected. Visually, M87 will appear as a bright elliptical galaxy. We can only imagine the accretion disk around a massive black hole and high-speed polar jets that make Virgo A one of the strangest objects in the universe.

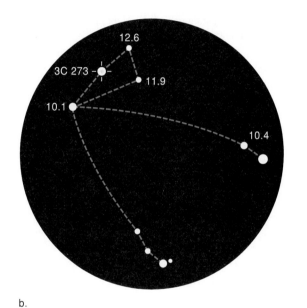

b.

We select 3C 273, the nearest quasar, for our next observing project. As in previous Sky Watchers' exercises, we shall locate the quasar by "star hopping" from the bright stars in the constellation to the fainter stars in the same field as the quasar. It is important to become familiar with star patterns that are easy to recognize. First, plot the quasar on the star chart using the coordinates listed in table 19.1. The star chart illustrated in figure 19.25a is from the sky atlas *Uranometria 2000.0*, which shows where the quasar is found in the constellation Virgo. Virgo is a spring constellation,

### figure 19.25

A *Uranometria 2000.0* star chart of the Virgo region. *a.* Quasar 3C 273 is in the dashed circle. *b.* An enlargement of part of the area within the circle. Magnitudes are given for comparison stars.

so plan your observations during that time of the year.

Select a clear, dark night and set up your telescope at a location with an unobstructed southern horizon. Find the 3.9-magnitude star Eta (η) Virginis, and 16 Virginis, which is a magnitude 5 star about four degrees to the north. Position the stars in the finder telescope. Note that 16 Virginis is a double star, which makes it easy to identify. Next, move the telescope as shown by the arrows in figure 19.25a to the magnitude 8 stars northeast from Eta and southeast from 16 Virginis. The magnitude 8 stars and the double star ADS 2583 form a right triangle. Center the telescope field of view midway between ADS 2583 and the northern magnitude 8 star in the triangle.

Place a low-power eyepiece in the telescope and center the stars to form an inverted V, or arrowhead (see fig. 19.25b). The star marked magnitude 10.1 is the point of the arrowhead, and it along with two stars marked magnitude 11.9 and 12.6 form a triangle that locates the quasar. Move the center of the field to a point midway between the stars 10.1 and 12.6 and your telescope should be centered on the quasar. Repeat the procedure several times each night until you become thoroughly familiar with the star patterns. With practice, you will see 3C 273 stand out among the faint foreground stars.

While observing, let your thoughts carry you back two billion years when the light you see left the quasar. At that time in our planet's history—the Precambrian Era—only soft-bodied creatures such as sponges and worms populated the oceans. The land was barren and devoid of all vegetation. The atmosphere was oxygen-poor and unable to support the many life forms that now populate the Earth.

During the time it took the light to travel from the quasar to the Earth, the greatest events occurred in the history of our planet. In two billion years, the Earth gradually changed into the living planet we know today. Our world became a safe environment for the development of life from the simplest protozoan to the most advanced vertebrates.

## T a b l e  1 9 . 1

### classes of active sources

| Name | R.A. (20000) | dec. (2000) | $m_v$ | z | Type |
|------|------|------|------|------|------|
| 3C 273 | 12h 29.1m | +02° 03′ | 13.0 | 0.158 | Quasar |
| NGC 4151 | 12h 10.1m | +39° 27′ | 10–12 | 0.004 | Seyfert |
| Virgo A | 12h 30.8m | +12° 23′ | 9.6 | 0.004 | Galaxy |
| Cen A | 13h 25.5m | −43° 02′ | 7.5 | 0.002 | Galaxy |
| BL Lac | 22h 02.7m | +39° 41′ | 14.0 | 0.070 | Lacertae |

# SUMMARY

Several types of bodies have active galactic nuclei. A radio galaxy is a system whose radio luminosity ranges from ten to thousands of times greater than its optical luminosity. Such galaxies have a lobed radio source on opposite sides of a compact nucleus. Elongated jets extend from the galactic nucleus to the lobe structure. A radio galaxy has a giant elliptical galaxy at its center. The nucleus may contain a black hole surrounded by an accretion disk formed by turbulent gas from nearby stars.

A Seyfert galaxy is distinguished by its bright, starlike nucleus. The energy output at the center is enormous and must originate from some source other than stars and ionized gas. Seyfert galaxies are variable and change magnitude in periods ranging from months to several hours. Visually, a Seyfert galaxy looks like a blue star. Long-exposure photographs reveal the galaxy's spiral structure and intensely energetic core.

Quasars are the most distant objects observed. They are believed to be the active nuclei of distant galaxies. Quasars are identified by their spectra, which show large displacements of emission lines to longer wavelengths. Most astronomers believe that the redshift is caused by the expansion of the universe. Quasars are detected to distances beyond 14 billion light-years.

Observations reveal that light from many quasars varies in brightness in periods of only a few hours. Such rapid changes can only occur if the source is exceedingly small. The nucleus of a quasar may be no larger than the diameter of the solar system.

The active nucleus of a quasar generates as much energy as hundreds of normal galaxies. How the energy is produced is found by studying the wavelengths in which it is emitted. The process responsible for radio emissions is synchrotron radiation; some quasars have polar jets similar to radio galaxies. Infrared radiation is given off by dust clouds scattered throughout the host galaxy. A large portion of the optical radiation stems from billions of stars that make up the galaxy. Most of the ultraviolet radiation comes from ionized gas clouds. X-rays from a central black hole may be reflected from warm gas spiraling in an accretion disk.

BL Lac objects are distinguished by their unusual radio and optical spectra. Usually, they appear starlike or as a bright nucleus surrounded by a nebulous fuzz. Their spectra show a continuous emission and no distinctive absorption or emission lines that might be used to determine distance.

Gravitational lensing provides astronomers with a way to study distant objects. Light from a remote quasar is bent by the strong gravitational field of a foreground galaxy to produce multiple images such as halos, mirages, and rings. Lensing acts as a cosmic telescope used to investigate distant light sources and possibly dark massive objects in intergalactic space.

# KEY TERMS

| | |
|---|---|
| active galactic nucleus (AGN) | radio galaxy |
| active galaxy | relativistic redshift |
| BL Lacertae object | Seyfert galaxy |
| gravitational lensing | quasar |
| lobed radio source | |

# PROBLEMS

1. Describe the method used by astronomers to map the radio structure of a radio galaxy.

2. What evidence can you give to support the theory that the center of a radio galaxy contains a black hole rather than a massive cluster of stars?

3. Describe the prominent radio feature associated with the giant elliptical galaxy M87, and explain the nature of the emission.

4. Briefly, explain the mechanism that sustains the radio structure found on opposite sides of the center of a radio galaxy.

5. How is synchrotron radiation produced? How does it differ from radiation emitted by ordinary stars?

6. Some active galactic nuclei are variable and change magnitude in short periods of time. How are these rapid pulsations used to estimate the radius of the radiating body?

7. Compare a Seyfert galaxy and a normal galaxy. Describe the identifying features in each galaxy.

8. How do astronomers distinguish radio-quiet quasars from ordinary foreground stars?

9. When first discovered, quasars were believed to contain unknown chemical elements. Why?

10. What evidence can you give in support of the theory that quasars are distant active galaxies?

11. How can the rapid variation in the light of some quasars be used as an argument in favor of the local rather than the cosmological interpretation of distance?

12. Discuss three models that astronomers have proposed to explain how quasars generate energy.

13. Astronomers can construct a model of a quasar by studying its radiation emitted at different wavelengths. Describe the structure of a quasar based upon its radiation in radio, infrared, visible, ultraviolet, and X-ray frequencies.

14. Why is the distance to a BL Lac object difficult to determine?

15. Discuss the following statement: A BL Lac object cannot be a star or an ordinary galaxy.

16. Explain how gravitational lensing is an argument in favor of the cosmological interpretation of the distance to a quasar.

17. A radio galaxy is located 15 million light-years from the Earth. If the visual component is a giant elliptical galaxy with an angular diameter of 413 arc seconds, what is the distance across the galaxy in light-years?

18. The galaxy in question 17 has radio lobes that are 10° apart. How many light-years does the radio structure extend beyond the optical region of the galaxy?

19. Find the recessional velocity of a quasar if the observed wavelength of the Hβ line in the Balmer series is shifted to 6861 angstroms.

20. For a given quasar, what is the observed wavelength of the 21-cm spectral line when $z = 0.2$?

# REFERENCES

Bishop, Roy L., ed. 1991. *Observer's Handbook 1991*. The Royal Astronomical Society of Canada. Toronto: University of Toronto Press.

Burns, Jack O. 1990. Chasing the Monster's Tail: New Views of Cosmic Jets. *Astronomy* 18, no. 8 (August).

Burns, Jack O., and R. Marcus Price. 1983. Centaurus A: The Nearest Active Galaxy. *Scientific American* 249, no. 5 (November).

Courvoisier, Thierry J.-L., and E. Ian Robson. 1991. The Quasar 3C 273. *Scientific American* 264, no. 6 (June).

Disney, Michael J., and Phillippe Verón. 1977. BL Lacertae Objects. *Scientific American* 237, no. 2 (August).

Downes, Ann. 1986. Radio Galaxies. *Mercury* (Astronomical Society of the Pacific) 15, no. 2 (March/April).

Finkbeiner, Ann. 1992. Active Galactic Nuclei: Sorting Out the Mess. *Sky and Telescope* 84, no. 2 (August).

Gregory, Stephen A. 1988. Active Galaxies and Quasars: A Unified View. *Mercury* 17, no. 4 (July/August).

Gregory, Stephen A., and Nancy D. Morrison. 1986. Visible Synchrotron Emission from the Lobes of a Radio Galaxy. *Mercury* 15, no. 4 (July/August).

Harrison, Edward R. 1981. *Cosmology*. Cambridge: Cambridge University Press.

Hodge, Paul W. 1986. *Galaxies*. Cambridge, Mass.: Harvard University Press.

Kanipe, Jeff. 1987. M87: Describing the Indescribable. *Astronomy* 15, no. 5 (May).

———. 1988. Anatomy of a Cosmic Jet. *Astronomy* 16, no. 7 (July).

Lea, Susan M. 1983. M87. *Mercury* 12, no. 1 (January/February).

MacRobert, Alan M. 1988. The Brightest Quasar. *Sky and Telescope* 75, no. 3 (March).

Maran, Stephen P. 1987. Unexplained Blazing Objects. *Natural History* (March).

Mood, John. 1987. Star Hopping to a Quasar. *Astronomy* 15, no. 4 (April).

Morrison, Nancy D., and Stephen A. Gregory. 1984. Centaurus A: The Nearest Active Galaxy. *Mercury* 13, no. 3 (May/June).

Ostriker, Jeremiah P., and Mario Vietri. 1990. Are Some BL Lacs Artifacts of Gravitational Lensing? *Nature* (London) 344, no. 6261 (March 1).

Preston, Richard. 1988. Beacons in Time: Maarten Schmidt and the Discovery of Quasars. *Mercury* 17, no. 1 (January/February).

Rees, Martin J. 1990. Black Holes in Galactic Centers. *Scientific American* 263, no.5 (November).

———. 1990. "Dead Quasars" in Nearby Galaxies? *Science* (American Association for the Advancement of Science) 247, no. 4944 (February 16).

Schild, Rudolph E. 1991. Gravity Is My Telescope. *Sky and Telescope* 81, no. 4 (April).

Schorn, Ronald A. 1988. The Extragalactic Zoo II. *Sky and Telescope* 75, no. 4 (April).

Shlosman, Isaac, Mitchell C. Begelman, and Julian Frank. 1990. The Fuelling of Active Galactic Nuclei. *Nature* 345, no. 6277 (June 21).

Smith, David H. 1988. Arcs Galore. *Sky and Telescope* 76, no. 4 (October).

Tirion, Wil, Barry Rappaport, and George Lovi. 1987. *Uranometria 2000.0*. Vol. I, *The Northern Hemisphere*. Richmond, Va.: Willmann-Bell, Inc.

Weymann, Ray J. 1970. "Seyfert Galaxies." In *Frontiers in Astronomy: Readings from Scientific American*. San Francisco: W. H. Freeman and Company.

Wilkes, Belinda J. 1991. The Emerging Picture of Quasars. *Astronomy* 19, no. 12 (December).

the origin and structure of the universe

A photograph of the Hercules cluster of galaxies
at a distance of more than 500 million light-
years. All hazy objects are galaxies; the circular
images represent foreground stars within
our Galaxy.

I n the sixth century B.C., the Greek philosopher and mathematician Pythagoras was first to use the word *kosmos,* our *cosmos,* to mean the universe as an orderly system. His view was geocentric, and he envisioned concentric spheres carrying the Moon, Sun, planets, and stars around a stationary Earth. Eventually the geocentric universe was displaced by the heliocentric universe during the Copernican revolution. Later, Newton visualized a centerless universe having no limits or bounds.

Our modern view deals with the universe on a more impressive scale. Today the study of the structure of the universe, **cosmology,** includes the curved space-time relationship of general relativity and the universal expansion implied by the redshifts of galaxies. Such investigations lead to **cosmogony,** which is the study of the origin and development of the universe.

We have seen how Hubble and Humason discovered the relationship between the amount of spectral redshift and the distances to the galaxies. Together, the velocity-distance law and general relativity theory have led cosmologists to believe that the universe is expanding and has continued to expand for at least 15 billion years (see chapters 18 and 19). The initial stage describes the universe as a dense concentration of thermal energy. When expansion began, the temperature rapidly decreased and changed a universe of energy into one of stars and galaxies.

## The Dark Night Sky

The geocentric cosmology described by Aristotle and other Greek scientists and philosophers claimed the universe to be finite and bounded by a sphere of fixed stars centered on the Earth. The same idea of an outer limit of stars was adopted by Copernicus in his heliocentric world system, although the Earth was displaced from its position as the center of the universe. Soon afterward, in 1576,

Thomas Digges modified the Copernican universe by scattering the stars to different distances beyond the Sun.

Galileo's telescopic observations in 1609 further dispelled the illusion of a boundary to the stars. He found the Milky Way to be a collection of increasingly fainter stars that seemed to lie at greater distances than naked-eye stars.

Kepler used Galileo's discoveries to argue in favor of a finite universe where the stars were situated in a thick, shell-like structure. The stellar population diminished as the stars' distances increased from the Earth. Kepler envisioned a dark emptiness beyond the stars. He reasoned that if the stars are uniformly scattered throughout endless space in all directions, the combined light of the stars would make the night as bright as the daytime sky. Even if the stars are not evenly distributed, but are grouped in clusters, their overwhelming number would achieve the same result and cause the night sky to be bright.

The apparent paradox between theory and observation was further intensified by Isaac Newton's gravitational law (1687). In accordance with the law, each star would attract every other star with a force that varies inversely as the square of their distances. In those days, the universe was believed to be *static,* or stationary, so the stars remained in their places forever. Thus, in the Newtonian universe, an infinite number of stars extending to vast distances was needed to offset the gravitational attraction and keep the system in equilibrium. At the time, Edmond Halley attempted to bring the Newtonian universe into agreement with the dark-night-sky paradox. He assumed that the most distant stars provided the required gravitational attraction but were too faint to be seen.

The Newtonian concept of a static and infinite universe persisted through the nineteenth century. In 1823, Heinrich Olbers explained the dark night sky as caused by the absorption of starlight by an interstellar medium. Olbers' proposal was incorrect; the absorbing medium would emit as much energy as it acquired from the stars. Later, the contradictory description of the night sky was called **Olbers' paradox,** although the problem

had been recognized by Johannes Kepler two centuries earlier.

In the twentieth century, the cosmological redshift caused by the dilation of space provided another explanation for Olbers' paradox. In 1929, Hubble discovered that the universe is not static as described by Newton, but is in a state of expansion. The infinite number of stars of Newton's universe are replaced by countless galaxies and galaxy clusters receding from each other.

The motion of the galaxies has an effect upon the photons of radiation emitted by the stars. The **cosmological redshift** lowers the frequency and therefore the energy of the photons. As expansion continues, fewer photons per unit time will reach the Earth. These effects combine to make the night sky dark (fig. 20.1a). The receding galaxies cause the brightness of the stars to decrease more rapidly than they would according to the inverse square law. The night sky is dark because the universe is expanding.

Has Olbers' paradox been solved? Not according to Edward R. Harrison and other cosmologists who have shown that the recession of galaxies has only a limited effect. There are two factors to consider: the velocity of light through space, *c,* is constant; and the stars within a visible galaxy are transitory objects that evolved in less time than the age of the **observable universe.**

For our purposes, let the observable universe be represented by a spherical surface about 15 billion light-years in radius centered on the Earth. All galaxies we can see lie within this boundary, called the **particle horizon.** The radius of the particle horizon is limited by the velocity of light; we cannot see objects at distances greater than 15 billion years of light-travel time. When we look out into space and back in time, our view is restricted to a finite distance inside the observable universe. If there are galaxies in the unbounded universe beyond the observable frontier, they cannot contribute to the overall radiation reaching the Earth. The night sky remains dark because we see a finite number of galaxies, filled with evolving stars in an observable universe limited in size by the velocity of light (figs. 20.1b and 20.2).

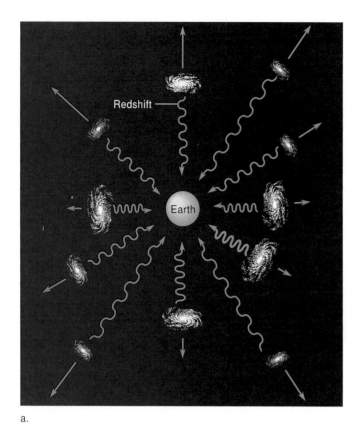

a.

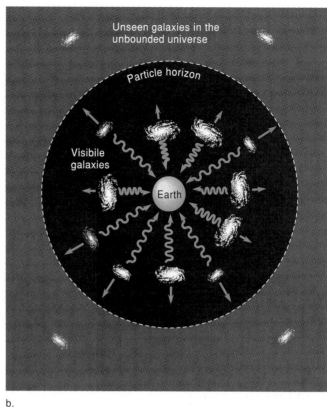

b.

### figure 20.1

Two possible solutions to Olbers' paradox. *a.* The night sky is dark because the universe is expanding. *b.* An observer on Earth can see only a finite number of galaxies inside the particle horizon.

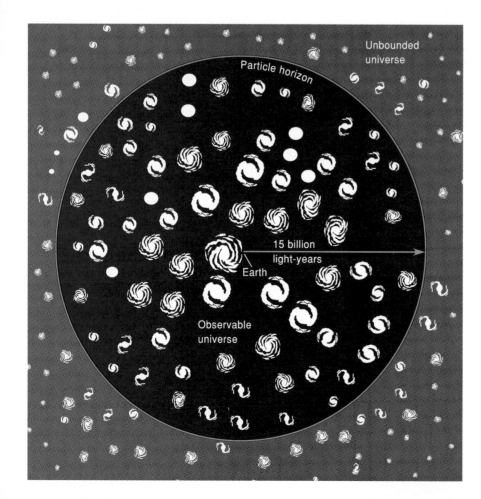

## The Big Bang

The concept of the universe beginning as a hot, dense primordial atom represents one of the most dramatic scientific ideas of the twentieth century. The observable universe erupted in a burst of energy giving the event its popular name—the **big bang.** (Do not think of the beginning as an explosion, which the term *big bang* suggests.) In time, energy was transformed into such particles as quarks, protons, neutrons, and electrons that make up the stars found in galaxies. Cosmologists *assume* the universe began this way by extrapolating back in time. If the universe is expanding and distances between galaxies are increasing, at zero time all matter and energy must have been concentrated in a state of infinite density and temperature.

### figure 20.2

A two-dimensional representation of the observable universe. All visible galaxies and quasars lie within the observable universe, which extends to the particle horizon. The distance to the horizon is limited by the velocity of light.

Of course, the initial event cannot be probed by means of instruments and studied quantitatively. Astronomers detect a 2.7 K background radiation that originated about 300,000 years after the big bang. This afterglow acts as an opaque barrier to the investigation of earlier evolutionary stages. The radiation was predicted and many cosmologists consider its discovery as a triumph for the big bang theory.

There are a number of essential conditions that are taken for granted in the big bang or **standard model.** Let us assume that the universe is steadily expanding and all places are changing in the same way. The physical laws of nature are invariant and remain unchanged during all the epochs of the universe. The general theory of relativity expresses the gravitational curvature of space-time. The self-gravitational effect of component matter gives the universe a smooth general curvature.

The standard model describes the early universe as a plasma of particles in thermal equilibrium that is increasing in volume at a constant rate. In the 1940s, George Gamow proposed that protons and neutrons formed hydrogen, deuterium, and helium through cosmic nucleosynthesis. The predicted ratio of hydrogen to helium formed in the early universe matches that found in the galaxies today. In the big bang theory, the universe evolves according to the expansion law developed by Hubble in 1929. These arguments in support of the model apply to the universe back to within three minutes after the big bang. The predictions are consistent with observations made today, 15 to 20 billion years after the events took place.

## The Cosmological Principle

We have seen how stars and star clusters form galaxies. On a higher level, the galaxies are grouped into galaxy clusters, and there are intricate networks of supergalaxies and voids on the highest level. Any local region of the universe may appear clumpy, but the overall structure is exceedingly smooth.

**figure 20.3**

A universe of clusters and voids. The universe is homogeneous and isotropic. One local region should look the same as another in all directions.

In general, one local region of the universe should look the same as any other. However, the exact distribution of matter and energy is not known. Therefore, cosmologists make certain assumptions when describing the large-scale structure; that the universe is **homogeneous** and **isotropic** (fig. 20.3). The best evidence for isotropy is the background radiation that astronomers believe to be remnant emission from the early universe. The radiation floods the universe from all directions at nearly constant temperature of 2.7 K.

If the universe is homogeneous, on the average, a local region should be the same as any other region. Suppose we could travel to a planet circling a star in another galaxy. The night sky there would appear about the same as the sky seen from Earth. The stars would be arranged in different patterns but, overall, they would appear the same as the stars we see at home. If the galaxy is a spiral, a "milky way" would glow overhead (fig. 20.4).

The several models of the universe to be discussed are based upon the **cosmological principle,** which states that the universe is homogeneous and isotropic. How does the cosmological principle ap-

ply to a distant galaxy billions of light-years away? If we observe a galaxy as it was billions of years ago, how can the universe be homogeneous and isotropic? The reason is that any changes due to expansion will be the same for every local region. For example, an observer in a galaxy one billion light-years from us will see our galaxy as it was one billion years ago. The cosmological principle remains valid because the look-back time is the same between any other galaxy and the Milky Way system.

## The Geometry of Space

In his description of the four-dimensional continuum, Albert Einstein said "the nonmathematician is seized by a mysterious shuddering . . . by a feeling not unlike that awakened by thoughts of the occult." To say the least, the concept of a curved four-dimensional space-time is difficult to perceive. Our world of space is a three-dimensional continuum. We can plot any position we choose using a coordinate system containing three perpendicular axes, $x$, $y$, and $z$. Since a point in space is measured by its distance from

**figure 20.4**

Star clouds in Sagittarius, in the plane of the Milky Way. The night sky from a planet circling a star in a galaxy millions of light-years distant should look essentially the same as the night sky from Earth.

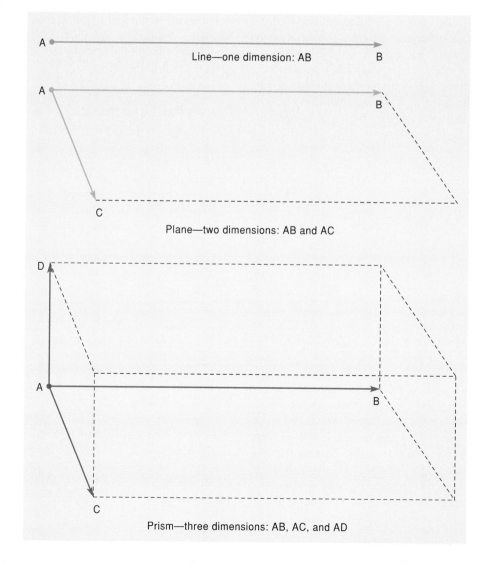

Line—one dimension: AB

Plane—two dimensions: AB and AC

Prism—three dimensions: AB, AC, and AD

the three axes, we say the continuum is three-dimensional.

The universe is described as a four-dimensional continuum. During its history, events have occurred in time as well as in space. For this reason, each event must be represented by four coordinates, three of space and one of time.

It is customary to simply depict the geometry of space-time as a two-dimensional surface. For example, space-time diagrams are two-dimensional representations of an event at a given position in space.

Figure 20.5 illustrates why we see three but have a problem visualizing four dimensions. A line is a one-dimensional space represented by its length. Now suppose the line is extended perpendicular to its length out of its space into a new dimension. The line creates a flat surface that is a two-dimensional space having length and width. If the surface is lifted out of its two-dimensional space, we have a three-dimensional continuum with length, width, and height.

We cannot follow this procedure and create a four-dimensional space any more than a two-dimensional creature can lift itself out of its world into ours. We can only *depict* four-dimensional space-time with a simple two-dimensional model.

## Curved and Euclidean Space

A two-dimensional representation of the universe must be a uniform surface—i.e., homogeneous and isotropic, as required by the cosmological principle. Until the nineteenth century, only the flat surface encountered in plane geometry was known to have such requirements. The *Euclidean surface* is named after the third-century B.C. Greek mathematician who developed the elements of plane geometry.

Two non-Euclidean surfaces were discovered in the nineteenth century. Both surfaces are curved: the first has *negative curvature* that resembles a saddle-shaped surface; the second has the *positive curvature* of a sphere. The three

**figure 20.5**

One-, two-, and three-dimensional continuums.

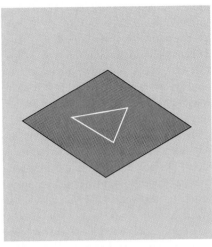
Euclidean surface. Flat—no curvature.

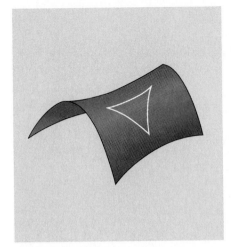
Hyperbolic surface. Negative curvature.

Spherical surface. Positive curvature.

**figure 20.6**

The curvature of space. A simple geometric figure, such as a triangle, will have different properties when constructed on a flat or curved surface.

surfaces—*Euclidean* (flat), *hyperbolic* (negative), and *spherical* (positive)—conform to the cosmological principle and qualify as two-dimensional representations of space-time (fig. 20.6).

Each surface has its own distinctive properties. On a plane surface, a straight line represents the shortest distance between two points. But there are no straight lines on curved surfaces. The straight lines in plane geometry become arc segments called *geodesics* on a curved surface. Euclidean geometry tells us that through a given point, only one line can be constructed parallel to another. On a negative surface, more than one geodesic can be constructed parallel to a given geodesic.

On the surface of a sphere, the shortest distance between two points is an arc segment of a great circle whose center coincides with the center of the sphere. No parallel great circles can be drawn on a positively curved spherical surface.

Simple geometric figures, such as triangles, have different properties when constructed on curved surfaces. The angles of a plane triangle always add up to 180 degrees. The sum of the angles formed by a hyperbolic triangle on a negatively curved surface is always less than 180 degrees. The angles of a spherical triangle on a positively curved surface always add up to more than 180 degrees (fig. 20.6). Therefore, the curvature of a surface can be found from its geometric properties. Likewise, the cur-

vature of four-dimensional space-time can be determined from the self-gravitation of the matter it contains.

The surfaces differ in another way. Euclidean space and hyperbolic space are *open* and without limitation, while spherical space is finite and unbounded. For example, the Earth's surface is finite in size, but one can travel in any direction and return again to the point of departure. Therefore spherical space is said to be *closed*. Cosmologists have yet to determine whether we live in an **open** or **closed universe.**

### The Expanding Universe

The surface analogy is a simple way to illustrate the expansion of the universe and the redshift of receding galaxies. Imagine an invisible flat surface of infinite size. Picture a large number of small disks representing galaxies scattered across the surface. No galaxy occupies a central position; the model universe appears homogeneous and isotropic to every observer at all locations (fig. 20.7).

The surface is elastic and expanding at a constant rate in all directions. Time passes and the galaxies appear to move apart as the space between them increases. The radiation an observer receives from another galaxy travels with the expanding surface. During its passage through space, the wavelength of light will increase by an amount in proportion to the distance travelled. The light

coming from a more distant galaxy will be stretched by the expansion of space for a longer period of time and will show a greater amount of redshift. Thus the cosmological redshift is *not* the familiar Doppler effect caused by luminous objects that move through space. Spectral lines are redshifted because galaxies are carried away from each other by the expansion of the universe.

## General Relativity and Models of the Universe

Modern cosmology began when general relativity theory of curved space-time was applied to models of the universe. One of the predictions of general relativity was the curvature of space surrounding the Sun. The theory states that light will curve during its passage through the Sun's gravitational field. Einstein extended the theory to include the geometry of space-time. The universe has a general curvature due to the self-gravitation of countless masses in space. The curved orbits of moving bodies in Newtonian theory are geodesics in Einsteinian space-time.

Einstein formulated his model of the universe before Edwin Hubble discovered galaxies to be stellar systems. The concept of an expanding universe, exemplified by receding galaxies, had not been established. Therefore, in his early

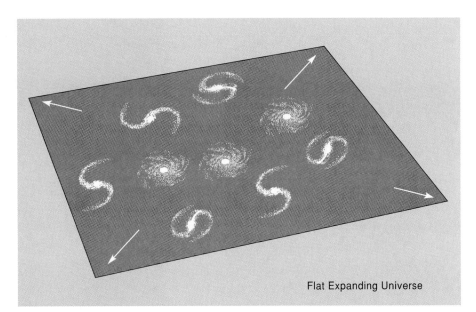

**figure 20.7**

A two-dimensional elastic sheet representing an expanding universe. An observer in any galaxy will see all other galaxies receding in accordance with the Hubble law.

attempts to apply general relativity to cosmology, Einstein pictured a static universe that was neither expanding nor contracting. He based his model upon the Copernican principle that our location is not unique and therefore the universe should appear to be about the same from any direction regardless of the place of observation. Later, these assumptions became the cosmological principle.

In 1922, Alexander Friedmann derived an equation that is fundamental to big bang cosmologies. In **Friedmann models,** the universe cannot be static but is either expanding or contracting. Later, Georges Lemaître proposed that prior to expansion, the universe was a dense "primeval atom." Friedmann's equation contains a term, $k$, that in general relativity can be thought of as representing the curvature of space. The value assigned to $k$, +1, 0, or −1, distinguishes the geometry of a Friedmann universe.

As shown in figure 20.8, a $k = +1$ Friedmann spherical universe is finite and unbounded. The expansion will continue until maximum size has been reached. Then the universe will pause, reverse itself, and collapse to its original state. A $k = 0$ flat Friedmann universe is infinite and unbounded. Expansion and gravitational attraction between galaxies

will continue for an infinite period of time. A $k = -1$ hyperbolic Friedmann universe is also infinite and unbounded. Expansion will continue into the future without limitation.

So far, cosmologists have not determined which of the Friedmann relativistic models is consistent with observation. The question is whether the energy of expansion is greater than, equal to, or less than the self-gravitation produced by the matter contained in the universe. The data required to determine which model agrees with observation are (1) the rate of expansion, and (2) the average density of matter in the universe.

## Critical Density

The average density of matter in the universe is only a few atoms per cubic meter of space. This density is far too low to provide the necessary gravitational energy to prevent expansion from continuing indefinitely. General relativity theory predicts that unless the average density is greater than a critical value, the universe is open and of infinite extent. The **critical density** is related to the Hubble parameter (see Methods and Understandings 18.1). If the Hubble parameter were equal to 50 km/sec/Mpc, the critical den-

sity will be about $4.8 \times 10^{-30}$ gm/cm³. If the Hubble parameter equals 100 km/sec/Mpc, the critical density will be four times greater, or about $1.9 \times 10^{-29}$ gm/cm³. The ratio of the actual average density to the critical density determines whether the universe is open or closed.

## An Open or Closed Universe?

If the average density exceeds the critical density, represented by a $k = +1$ Friedmann closed universe of spherical space, the galaxies are rushing away at less than escape velocity. Eventually the universe will reach a maximum expansion and contract into a singularity. According to the **oscillating-universe hypothesis,** the process begins again with another cycle of expansion and galaxy formation (fig. 20.9).

An open universe can be a $k = -1$ Friedmann model of hyperbolic space in which the critical density is higher than the average density. The universe expands indefinitely; stars continue to form until all available gas and dust in the galaxies are depleted. The galaxies grow increasingly dim as stars enter terminal stages as white dwarfs, neutron stars, and black holes.

In the second open model, a $k = 0$ Friedmann flat universe, the critical density and the average density are equal. The escape velocity and recession velocity have the same value. As shown in figure 20.9, the graph representing a flat universe begins as a steep curve, which indicates that the early expansion rate was greater than now, about 15 billion years later. Gravitation will slow down the rate of expansion but the universe will continue to increase in size for an indefinite period.

In summary, estimates based upon the masses of galaxies in clusters indicate that the actual density is only a fraction of the critical density needed to close the universe. If this is the case, then space is hyperbolic. When the mass of hidden dark matter is added to that of the stars, the density ratio favors the flat $k = 0$ Friedmann model. Cosmologists do not know if "missing mass" exists in sufficient quantity to close the universe.

| Friedmann value | Model of universe | Representation | Average density | Outcome |
|---|---|---|---|---|
| a. $k = +1$ | 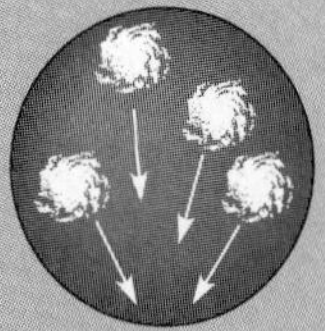 Closed | Spherical | Exceeds critical density | Maximum expansion and contraction singularity |
| b. $k = 0$ | 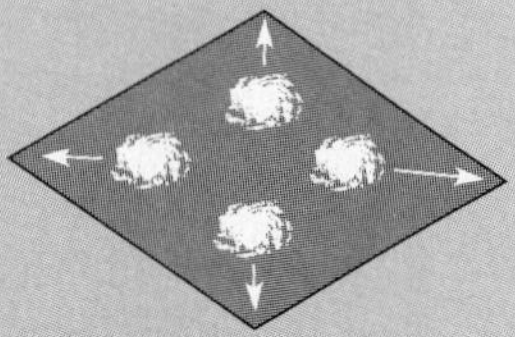 Flat | Flat | Same as critical density | Universe expands indefinitely |
| c. $k = -1$ | 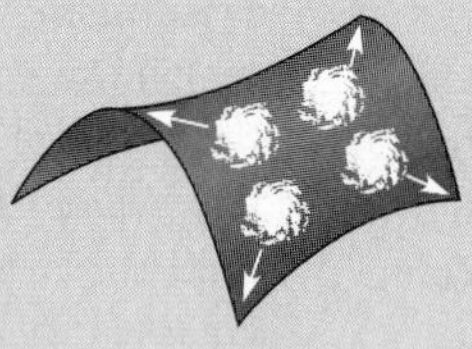 Open | Hyperbolic | Lower than critical density | Universe expands indefinitely |

▲ **figure 20.8**
Friedmann models of the universe.
*a.* $k = +1$; *b.* $k = 0$; *c.* $k = -1$.

**figure 20.9** ▶
Friedmann models of the universe. The scale of the universe—i.e., the distance between galaxies—changes over time. Each model describes various ways in which the universe may evolve at different epochs in its history.

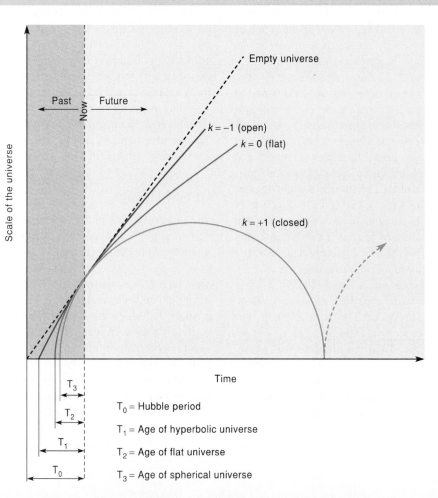

$T_0$ = Hubble period

$T_1$ = Age of hyperbolic universe

$T_2$ = Age of flat universe

$T_3$ = Age of spherical universe

## The Cosmic Background Radiation

The Earth is suffused with puzzling microwave radiation approaching from every direction in space. The intensity of these signals remains fairly constant across the entire sky, and they have been observed at wavelengths from 0.06 cm to 1 m. Observations indicate that the radiation has a redshift of about 1000, which places the source at a distance of at least 15 billion light-years. In that era, less than one million years after the big bang, there were no star-filled galaxies.

## Models of the Expanding Universe

The evolution of Friedmann models of the universe is graphed in figure 20.9. The vertical axis is called the *scale of the universe* and represents the uniform change in distance between objects such as galaxy clusters. The horizontal axis marks the time elapsed since the big bang for each model. A Friedmann universe is subject to deceleration caused by the self-gravitation of clusters of galaxies.

The line tangent to the curves represents the graph of an expanding universe that is completely devoid of matter. The slope of this line is equal to $H_0$, the Hubble parameter for an empty universe. In a Friedmann model, the value of the Hubble parameter will depend upon the slope of each curve at different epochs in the history of the universe. At present, the curves are tangent to the line and have $H_0$ as the rate of expansion. Note that shortly after the big bang, each curve is steeper, giving the Hubble parameter a greater value. In the open $k = 0$ model, its value approaches zero as the universe ages. In the closed model, the Hubble parameter decreases until the universe reaches maximum size. The closed model takes on increasingly negative values as the universe contracts.

The distance between the point of intercept of the line with the time axis and the present is called the **Hubble period,** $T_0$, which represents the age of the universe if the rate of expansion has remained unchanged. $T_0$ is inversely proportional to the Hubble parameter, $H_0$, so that

$$T_0 = \frac{1}{H_0}.$$

$T$ is derived from the Hubble law. If the Hubble parameter is 50 km/sec/Mpc, the maximum age of the observable universe will be 20 billion years.

A universe filled with matter must be younger than the maximum age. If the universe is flat, and $k = 0$, then the age of the universe will be two-thirds $T_0$ before the present, or about 13 billion years. The age of a closed $k = +1$ universe will be less than 13 billion years; the age of an open $k = -1$ universe will be greater than 13 billion years but less than 20 billion years.

Cosmologists using the Hubble Space Telescope have found evidence that might indicate an age for the universe greater than 20 billion years. In 1992, the HST wide-angle camera revealed cepheid variable stars in a faint galaxy found to be more than 15 billion light-years away. Investigators used the cepheids as distance indicators to establish the absolute magnitudes of supernovae discovered in the galaxy. These calculations established the value of the Hubble parameter at 45 km/sec/Mpc, giving a Hubble period $T_0 = 21.7$ billion years, providing the rate of expansion has remained unchanged.

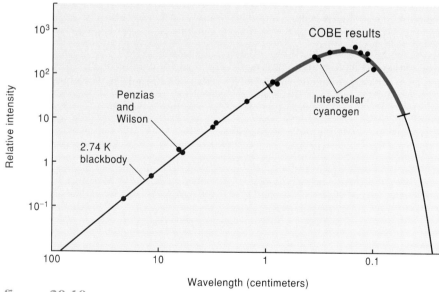

**figure 20.10**

The spectrum of the cosmic background radiation has the characteristics of a blackbody at a temperature of 2.74 K.

Source: Data from Joseph Silk, "Probing the Primeval Fireball" in *Sky and Telescope*, Vol. 79, No. 6, June 1990.

The universe was a hot fireball filled with a hydrogen and helium plasma. Today, the entire physical universe of galaxies serves as a foreground for this distant cosmic glow.

A plot showing the intensity of radiation at radio and near-infrared wavelengths produces a curve corresponding to a blackbody at a temperature of 2.74 K (fig. 20.10). As described in chapter 4, a blackbody is an object in thermal equilibrium that absorbs and emits all radiation. These findings have convinced many astrophysicists that the **cosmic background radiation** is the redshifted echo of a primordial explosion and represents the strongest evidence in support of the big bang theory (fig. 20.11).

The discovery of the cosmic background radiation can be traced back to a series of events that began in the 1930s. At that time, a number of molecules were found in interstellar clouds; in particular, cyanogen, which is made up of carbon and nitrogen atoms. Cyanogen was detected by its telltale absorption line superimposed upon stellar spectra. The cyanogen molecules were at excitation temperature—at energy levels above normal—which astronomers believed was caused by the absorption of microwaves at a temperature of about 2.3 K. In the early 1940s, before development of the big bang theory, astronomers theorized that the excitation resulted from starlight passing through low-temperature gas clouds.

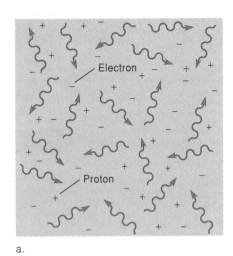
a.

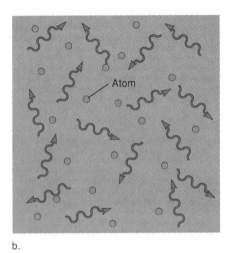
b.

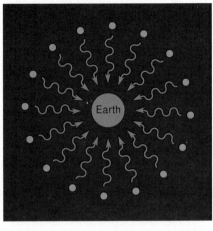
c.

**figure 20.11**

**a.** Shortly after the big bang, the universe contained interacting protons (+) and electrons (−) that absorbed and emitted photons. **b.** When expansion cooled the universe to 3000 K, the protons and electrons combined into atoms. **c.** The last photons to be scattered are observed on Earth as the 2.74 K cosmic background radiation.

By the late 1940s, George Gamow, Ralph A. Alpher, and Robert Herman had described the early universe as a primeval fireball consisting of extremely high-temperature plasma. Thermonuclear reactions took place in the fireball that converted the hydrogen and helium plasma into deuterium and helium nuclei. The rapid expansion of the fireball stopped the conversion at the ratio of hydrogen and helium found in the universe today. Nucleosynthesis of elements shortly after the big bang provided the emission we now detect as the cosmic background radiation.

Gamow predicted that the cosmic radiation should have cooled down to a temperature less than five kelvins. However, he failed to link the predicted background radiation with the excitation temperature of interstellar cyanogen.

In the 1960s, a team of Princeton University scientists, Robert Dicke, P. J. E. Peebles, P. G. Roll, and D. T. Wilkinson, were investigating various models of the universe, including the hot big bang theory proposed by Gamow and his colleagues. Dicke, Roll, and Wilkinson proceeded to construct a radiometer to measure the predicted radiation. Peebles determined that the residual radiation from the big bang would follow the characteristic curve of blackbody radiation. Another clue was provided by Russian astronomers who predicted that the back-ground radiation should be detected in the microwave region of the radio spectrum. Finally, in 1965, the cosmic background radiation was discovered by Arno Penzias and Robert Wilson of Bell Laboratories.

Penzias and Wilson detected unexplained low-intensity thermal radiation while using the sensitive Bell Laboratories horn antenna at Holmdel, New Jersey. The purpose of their investigation was to study the effect that diffuse radio emission would have on data transmission from orbiting communication satellites. After eliminating all possible extraneous radio sources, Penzias and Wilson found a mysterious emission coming from all directions in the sky, which remained unchanged day and night. When the Princeton group headed by Dicke conferred with Penzias and Wilson, Dicke recognized the residual radio hiss as the cosmic background radiation predicted in the big bang theory. In 1978, Arno Penzias and Robert Wilson were awarded the Nobel Prize in physics for their discovery.

Since 1965, astrophysicists have studied the spectrum of the background radiation with ground-based radio telescopes, balloons, rockets, and, more recently, the orbiting *Cosmic Background Explorer* (*COBE*). Observations at millimeter and centimeter wavelengths indicate that the radiation has a wavelength of maximum intensity of about one-tenth of a centimeter, the predicted value for a blackbody at 2.74 K. Rocket-borne helium-cooled radiometers were sent aloft to altitudes of 320 km to study the background radiation at sub-millimeter wavelengths. The purpose was to determine if the intensity of radiation at these wavelengths followed that of a 2.74 K blackbody. Any deviation from the curve would mean that the radiation came from some other source.

COBE laid this matter to rest shortly after its launching on November 18, 1989 (fig. 20.12). The far infrared absolute spectrophotometer (FIRAS) aboard the satellite obtained a spectrum that matched a 2.735 K blackbody to within one percent of its theoretical value. Measurements of the spectrum were made at wavelengths between 0.05 and 1.0 cm.

## Unification Theories and the Early Universe

Let us now consider a time when the observable universe was only a fraction of a second old. Gravitation, electromagnetism, and the strong and weak nuclear forces are believed to have been joined together as one primordial superforce. Moreover, the particles of matter that make up galaxies, stars, the Earth, and ourselves did not exist. In fact, the observable universe was many times

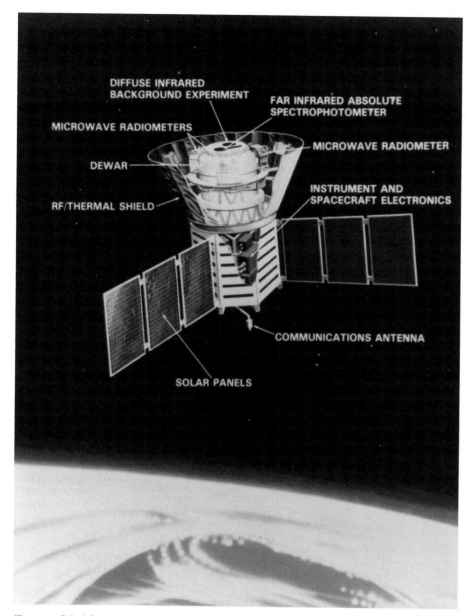

DIFFUSE INFRARED
BACKGROUND EXPERIMENT

FAR INFRARED ABSOLUTE
SPECTROPHOTOMETER

MICROWAVE RADIOMETERS

MICROWAVE RADIOMETER

DEWAR

INSTRUMENT AND
SPACECRAFT ELECTRONICS

RF/THERMAL SHIELD

COMMUNICATIONS ANTENNA

SOLAR PANELS

**figure 20.12**
The Cosmic Background Explorer (COBE) satellite.

smaller than an atom. As predicted by the big bang model, there must have been a moment before fundamental particles emerged out of the expanding primeval fireball. At such an early epoch, the origin and development of the universe are linked to particle physics rather than cosmic structures such as galaxy clusters that extend for billions of light-years. Therefore, we must turn our attention to the microscopic structure of interacting particles and forces that dominated the universe shortly after the big bang. (Before proceeding, you may wish to refer to the sections in chapter 4 describing particles and forces in nature.)

Physicists divide particles into two basic groups called fermions and bosons. The first category contains *quarks* and *leptons.* Quarks combine to form *hadrons* (protons and neutrons); electrons and neutrinos are examples of leptons.

The second group contains *bosons,* "messenger" particles that transmit the fundamental forces. The most familiar carrier particle, the *photon,* is associated with electromagnetism. The gravitational force between two masses is mediated by a theoretical particle called the *graviton.* Three illusive messenger particles called $W^+$, $W^-$, and $Z^0$ carry the weak nuclear force, which is responsible for particle decays, notably the decay of neutrons into protons (fig. 20.13). Carriers of the strong force that binds protons and neutrons together are named *gluons.*

## Unification Theories

One of the most significant developments in cosmology is the combined effort by nuclear physicists and cosmologists to study the microscopic structure of the early universe. Physicists believe that the forces between elementary particles were unified when the universe was in a high-density state. These forces—gravitation, electromagnetism, and the weak and strong nuclear interactions—separated shortly after the big bang. During the earliest epoch, the emerging universe passed through different phase transitions as it expanded and cooled. At each stage, there occurred a physical change analogous to the phase changes that take place as water cools from gaseous water vapor to liquid and finally ice (fig. 20.14).

The first force to separate was gravitation, at only $10^{-43}$ second after the big bang. The other three forces were united until $10^{-33}$ second when the strong force broke away and assumed its present identity. An instant later, the remaining electroweak force separated into the electromagnetic and weak forces.

The idea of unification is not new to science. The classical Greek philosopher Thales proposed a universe of four elements—earth, air, water, and fire—about 600 B.C. Water was the basic substance that condensed into solids and evaporated to produce air, which supported fire, or combustion. In 1687, Isaac Newton was the first modern scientist to link the Earth's gravity with the motion of the Moon. According to the universal law of gravitation, the attractive force embraces *all* bodies in the universe. James Clerk Maxwell, in 1873, established that a relationship exists between the electric and magnetic forces. He unified the forces and described the interactions of varying electric and magnetic

the origin and structure of the universe

397

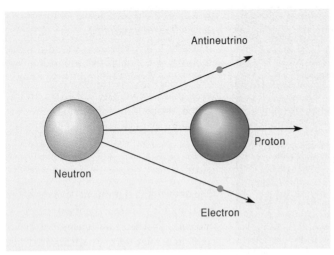

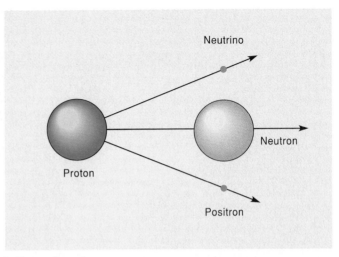

a. Neutron decay

b. Proton decay

**figure 20.13**

Neutron and proton decay. ***a.*** A neutron decays into a proton and releases an antineutrino and an electron. ***b.*** A proton decays into a neutron and releases a neutrino and a positron.

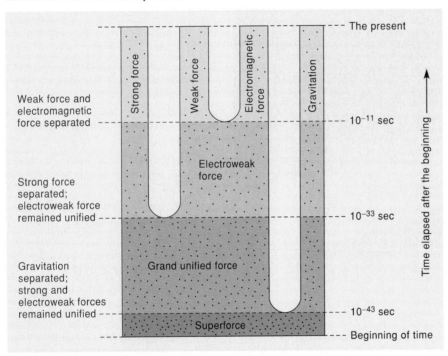

**figure 20.14**

The mutual interactions between elementary particles were unified immediately after the big bang. The universe expanded, cooled, and passed through phase transitions. The forces in nature decoupled and assumed their present identity.

fields as electromagnetic waves. The discovery revealed light, radio, and other forms of radiant energy to be different aspects of the same phenomenon.

## Electroweak Unification

More recently, physicists have shown that there is a connection between the electromagnetic force and the weak nuclear force. Since the 1970s, theoretical and experimental evidence have confirmed the unification of the two forces into the electroweak interaction. Symmetry between the forces existed until about $10^{-10}$ second after the big bang when the temperature was above $10^{15}$ K. Symmetry was broken when the critical temperature was reached.

Four massless particles served as mediators of the electroweak force. Three of the mediating particles became the $W^+$, $W^-$, and $Z^0$ carriers of the weak force. The fourth particle remained massless and serves as the familiar photon, which is the mediator of the electromagnetic force.

## Grand Unification

It is impossible to describe the events that took place from zero time, but quantum theory does provide an interval in which time can be measured. This so-called **Planck time** is equal to an incredibly small unit of $10^{-43}$ second. The theoretical limit to which physicists can probe back in time is $10^{-43}$ second after the big bang. At this mysterious barrier, the temperature was higher than $10^{32}$ K. The fundamental forces were combined into one superforce (fig. 20.15).

Between the earliest Planck time and $10^{-35}$ second, gravitation separated from the superforce so that two forces interacted with matter: gravitation, and the grand unified force representing the strong and electroweak forces. The strong and electroweak forces remained unified at temperatures above $10^{27}$ K.

There are several **grand unified theories** that describe the early universe. In one interpretation, there are 24 massless particles that serve as mediators of the grand unified force. Of this number,

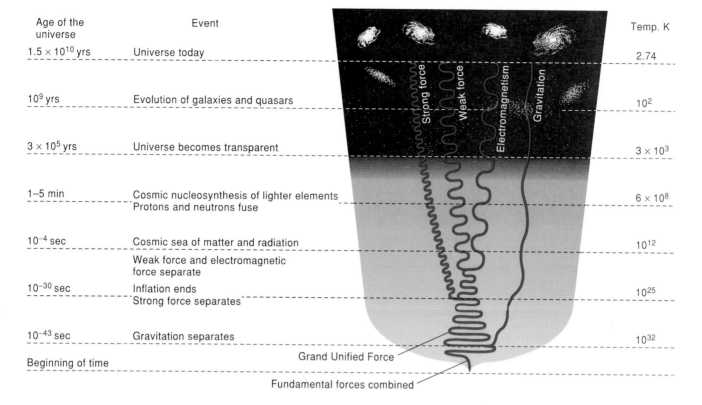

| Age of the universe | Event | | Temp. K |
|---|---|---|---|
| $1.5 \times 10^{10}$ yrs | Universe today | | 2.74 |
| $10^9$ yrs | Evolution of galaxies and quasars | | $10^2$ |
| $3 \times 10^5$ yrs | Universe becomes transparent | | $3 \times 10^3$ |
| 1–5 min | Cosmic nucleosynthesis of lighter elements Protons and neutrons fuse | | $6 \times 10^8$ |
| $10^{-4}$ sec | Cosmic sea of matter and radiation | | $10^{12}$ |
| $10^{-30}$ sec | Weak force and electromagnetic force separate Inflation ends Strong force separates | | $10^{25}$ |
| $10^{-43}$ sec | Gravitation separates | | $10^{32}$ |
| Beginning of time | | | |

Strong force · Weak force · Electromagnetism · Gravitation

Grand Unified Force

Fundamental forces combined

**figure 20.15**

The history of the universe began $10^{-43}$ second after the big bang. At different stages very early in the history of the universe, the forces in nature separated, and elementary particles formed. Later, hydrogen, helium, and other light elements were synthesized. Neutral atoms formed while photons uncoupled from matter to produce the cosmic background radiation.

twelve are known as X-bosons, which decay into quarks or are created through collision. During exchange, X-bosons change quarks into leptons, or leptons into quarks. The two kinds of particles were indistinguishable during the grand unification period.

Of the remaining massless particles, eight are gluons that mediate the strong interaction; three are the $W^+$, $W^-$, and $Z^0$ bosons that are exchanged in the weak force; and one is the photon, mediator of the electromagnetic force.

The rapid creation of quarks, leptons, and X-bosons came to an end as the universe continued to cool. The grand unification period was over when the temperature dropped to $10^{19}$ K, and the strong force decoupled from the electroweak force. The electromagnetic and weak forces separated when the temperature dropped to $10^{16}$ K. The universe entered the next phase in its early history, called the **particle era,** when quarks combined to form protons and neutrons.

## The Particle Era

At a temperature of $10^{15}$ K, about $10^{-10}$ second after the big bang, the universe had cooled sufficiently to permit the electroweak force to decouple. Now the strong, weak, and electromagnetic forces began to interact independently as they do today.

When the temperature dropped below $10^{15}$ K, the strong interaction bound the quarks and antiquarks into protons, antiprotons, neutrons, and antineutrons. Each hadron consisted of three quarks confined by the exchange of gluons. During this so-called *hadron era,* protons and neutrons collided with their respective antiparticles to produce a profusion of electrons and positrons. At the end of the hadron era, only a fraction of the protons and neutrons survived to combine into the atoms that make up the stars and galaxies.

Later, in the *lepton era,* the universe was a cosmic "soup" of photons, electrons, neutrinos, other leptons, and antiparticles. In addition, there were the re-

maining protons and neutrons formed in the hadron era. By now, $10^{-4}$ second after the beginning, the temperature was less than $10^{12}$ K. Protons and neutrons continued to interact with leptons and antileptons.

Neutrinos decoupled as the temperature continued to drop and were free to travel unimpeded through the universe, scarcely interacting with any particles. If the relic neutrinos possess a small mass, as some scientists believe, they may represent the dark matter known to exist by the motions of galaxies in clusters and superclusters.

The big bang theory predicts and observation confirms that the abundance of the lighter elements is roughly 76% hydrogen and 24% helium-4. These ratios were established during the lepton era. When the lepton era began, protons and neutrons transformed freely during high-energy collisions. Later, toward the end of the era, the more massive neutrons continued to change into protons with less difficulty than protons into neutrons. Thus when the **radiation era**

chapter 20
astronomy: through space and time
methods and understandings 20.2

## The Inflationary Universe

The standard model of the universe cannot altogether explain a number of features dealing with the large-scale structure and the initial state of matter and energy. As we know, the large-scale structure of the universe is exceedingly smooth; the entire universe is immersed in the glow of the microwave background radiation. No matter which direction measurements are taken, the temperature remains 2.7 kelvins. The universe must have reached thermal equilibrium a fraction of a second after the big bang in order to maintain nearly constant temperature after 15 billion years of evolution. Such a perfect condition is difficult to explain when even random motions of particles will cause differences in temperature between widely separated regions. The standard model cannot account for this almost perfect regularity.

A comprehensive model must account for the small-scale irregularities that are observed throughout the visible universe. As we have seen, matter is collected in increasingly larger and more complex structures. Planets and satellites revolve around the Sun, stars form binary and multiple systems, stars are grouped into clusters that form galaxies, and galaxies are gathered into galaxy clusters and finally superclusters separated by huge voids. There must have been a countless number of small concentrations of matter that gravitated together a fraction of a second after the beginning. Thus the standard model requires the acceptance of an almost perfectly ordered universe—one with large-scale uniformity and small-scale irregularity.

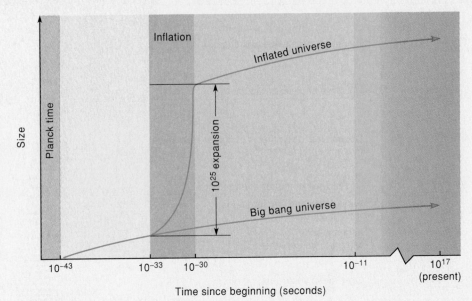

**figure 20.16**

The inflationary model. The period of inflation was very brief, but during this interval the universe expanded from a diameter of $10^{-24}$ cm to a diameter greater than $10^{21}$ km.

The problems inherent in the standard model led to arbitrary assumptions about the characteristics of the early universe. The model describes the initial conditions but fails to explain why they took place. However, the nagging questions posed by the big bang can be answered if space-time had suddenly expanded for a short interval at an enormous rate compared to the standard model.

Such a scenario was originally proposed by Alan H. Guth in 1980 and later modified by A. D. Linde, Andreas Albrecht, and Paul J. Steinhardt. According to the **inflationary theory,** space-time had an extraordinary increase in size about $10^{-33}$ second after the primordial big bang. By $10^{-30}$ second, inflation was over and the universe continued to expand at the rate specified by the standard model (fig. 20.16). It must be understood that the inflationary theory cannot be verified by any high-energy experiment.

---

began about three minutes after the big bang, there were only two neutrons for every ten protons.

## The Radiation Era

Particle production ceased when the temperature dropped to 10 billion kelvins at about age one second. The universe was bathed in an intense glow produced by photons that were constantly scattered by free electrons. Energy and matter were coupled and the action between them prevented the photons from traveling freely through space. The matter-radiation interaction made the universe opaque. This was the beginning of the *radiation era* when the density of radiation surpassed the density of matter.

The idea of radiation density comes from the special theory of relativity. Energy and matter can be measured on a common scale by means of Einstein's equation, $E = mc^2$. Here radiant energy is equivalent to the rest mass of matter multiplied by the square of the velocity of light (see chapter 4).

As the universe expands, radiation density is reduced more rapidly than the density of matter. For example, when the radius of the universe doubles, radiation density is decreased to one-sixteenth its previous value. Meanwhile, the volume of the universe has increased eight-fold, so the density of matter will be reduced to one-eighth its previous value. The density of matter and energy will be equal at the *decoupling epoch* when the temperature has reached 3000 K. The decoupling epoch marks the end of the radiation era when the change from a radiation-dominated to a matter-dominated universe took place.

**figure 20.17**

The inflationary universe. This two-dimensional diagram represents the universe after inflation. If the inflationary theory is correct, the observed universe is insignificant in size compared to the unbounded universe beyond the particle horizon.

15 billion light-years

Accelerator physicists hope to duplicate the conditions of the universe to about $10^{-13}$ second by means of linear colliders. However, inflationary theory is closely linked to grand unified theories, and if the GUTs and the standard model are successfully united, then the inflationary theory can reconstruct the initial events that took place shortly after the big bang.

The period of inflation was exceedingly brief, but during this tiny interval, space-time expanded from an extraordinary small $10^{-24}$ cm to a diameter greater than $10^{26}$ cm. The universe had blown up in size by a factor of $10^{50}$. The region that emerged 15 billion years later as the visible universe was at that time roughly 10 cm across—a minuscule fraction of the universe at large.

How does inflation explain the characteristics of the early universe? According to some grand unified theories, in the be-

ginning the universe was in a chaotic state of seething cosmic foam. Guth assumes that prior to inflation there were regions of hot gas at temperatures above a critical value of $10^{27}$ K. When expansion began in one region, temperatures dropped to below the critical value and the system supercooled. An analogous condition occurs when water remains a liquid although its temperature is less than freezing, zero degrees Celsius.

As the process continued, the expanding gas entered a state called a "false vacuum" in quantum field theory. Think of the false vacuum as a phase transition similar to that which occurs when a liquid crystallizes into a solid. The false vacuum is characterized by a large negative pressure. Gravitation acted as a repulsive force that caused the bubble-like region to double its size every $10^{-34}$ second.

By the end of inflation, the energy density of the false vacuum was released, raising the temperature to roughly $10^{27}$ K. The strong force separated from the unified force, leaving the symmetry reduced. The process of symmetry breaking converted some of the energy into virtually all the particles found in the stars and galaxies we see today (fig. 20.17).

A number of significant events occurred during the radiation era. Among them was the cosmic nucleosynthesis of the lighter elements. Between one minute and five minutes after the big bang, the temperature decreased from about one billion to 600 million K. The reduced temperature was within the range where protons and neutrons can fuse and form nuclei. The process was quite similar to the nuclear reactions that drive the stars.

The first reaction produced deuterium, which consists of one proton and one neutron. Deuterium and another neutron combined to form tritium. Helium-3 con-

sists of two protons and one neutron, which combined to produce helium-4, two protons, and a photon of gamma radiation. In addition, the interactions produced traces of heavier beryllium-7 as well as lithium-7 (fig. 20.18). The cosmic nucleosynthesis that generated these substances ceased when the temperature was reduced and the density of matter was insufficient to continue the process. Virtually all the neutrons produced during the previous era were locked into helium-4 nuclei.

What caused the cosmic background radiation? Let us look back in time to a

period between one million and 300,000 years after the big bang. The universe was a hot, glowing plasma of hydrogen and helium at a temperature of 3000 K. The plasma absorbed and emitted radiation in much the same way as the stars we see today. During this period, the temperature and density of matter had been sufficiently reduced to allow atoms to form. At an earlier period, when temperature and density were much higher, atoms were dissociated into protons, neutrons, and electrons. Photons were continuously scattered by free electrons to make the

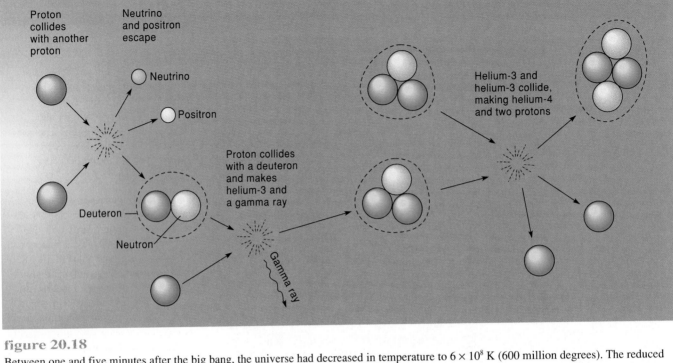

Proton
collides
with another
proton

Neutrino
and positron
escape

Neutrino

Positron

Deuteron

Neutron

Proton collides
with a deuteron
and makes
helium-3 and
a gamma ray

Gamma ray

Helium-3 and
helium-3 collide,
making helium-4
and two protons

**figure 20.18**

Between one and five minutes after the big bang, the universe had decreased in temperature to $6 \times 10^8$ K (600 million degrees). The reduced temperature was within the range to synthesize deuterium and helium as well as traces of other elements.

## methods and understandings 20.3

### *Matter and Antimatter*

We have seen how quantum theory describes the dual nature of particles (chapter 4) and radiation (chapter 3, Albert Einstein's photoelectric effect). Some particles are surrounded by fields that might carry an electric charge. According to theory, such charged fields require a set of two particles that are identical but carry opposite electric charges. For example, the electron has a negative (−) charge while its antiparticle, the positron, has a positive (+) charge. Moreover, theory predicts the existence of the antiquark, antiproton, and antineutron, as well as other particles of antimatter.

If conditions are right, a particle pair (such as an electron-positron) can be annihilated or created. For example, if an electron and positron were to collide, they would be destroyed and produce photons of gamma radiation. Conversely, a particle pair can emerge from the interaction of photons.

The standard model does not account for the lack of antimatter in the universe. Until the grand unified theories were proposed, physicists believed that an absolute symmetry existed between particles and antiparticles. For every proton produced there should be a corresponding antiproton. When a proton and antiproton collide, both particles are annihilated while another

proton-antiproton pair are produced in an unrelated interaction. As expansion continues and temperature drops, at some point the process will not be reversible because of insufficient energy and the particles are not replaced. However, particle pairs continue to annihilate and reduce the number of proton-antiproton pairs.

Why are there so many protons and so few antiprotons today? Before grand unified theories, scientists assumed that matter and antimatter had in some way separated from each other and formed into antigalaxies filled with antistars. Perhaps at one time there was a slight imbalance in number—one billion and one protons for every billion antiprotons. Thus the overwhelming number of protons in the universe today represent the residual one in a billion that remained after countless numbers of particles were annihilated. Why the universe favored matter over antimatter was a mystery.

The combination of grand unified theories and the standard model provides an explanation for the excess of matter over antimatter in the observable universe. Unification theory shows that an excess of matter can be produced immediately after the separation of the strong force. Below $10^{27}$ K, X-bosons carrying "color" charge and electrical charge can interact with quarks and produce electrons, and, conversely, interact with electrons to produce quarks. Such interactions may explain the excess of protons at the beginning of the particle era.

## Wien's Law and the Cosmic Background Radiation

Wien's displacement law states that the wavelength at maximum intensity of radiation is inversely proportional to the absolute temperature of the source (chapter 4). Wien's law can be written

$$\lambda = \frac{2900}{T}$$

where

$\lambda$ = the wavelength measured in micrometers,

and

$T$ = the absolute temperature K.

Let the source of the cosmic background radiation have a temperature equal to 3000 K. What is the peak wavelength of radiation?

$$\lambda = \frac{2900}{3000}$$

$\lambda = 0.967$ micrometers

What is the wavelength of maximum intensity of the cosmic radiation when it reaches the Earth about 15 billion years later?

$$\lambda = \frac{2900}{2.74}$$

$\lambda = 1058$ micrometers, or about one millimeter

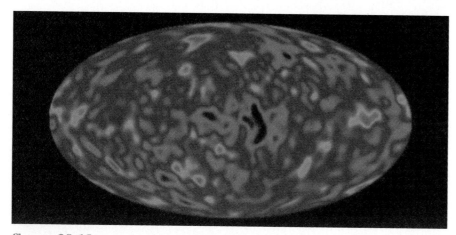

**figure 20.19**
COBE satellite map at 5.7 mm wavelength. The warm (red) and cool (blue) regions represent variations in temperature of the 2.735 K background radiation caused by outside sources such as instrument noise. Only a miniscule variation in temperature of $3 \times 10^{-5}$ K is attributed to density fluctuations connected to the origin of galaxies.

ionized gas opaque. Thus we cannot observe radiation from this period.

Photon-scattering came to an end during the decoupling epoch when protons and electrons combined to form atoms of hydrogen. The universe became transparent and photons were free to carry the image of the glowing plasma through space. Today, astronomers detect this energy as the cosmic background radiation. The radiant energy left the source as visible and infrared radiation. Since then, space between us and the source has expanded so that we observe the wavelength redshifted to a peak of about one millimeter at a temperature of 2.735 K.

## Origin of the Galaxies

The most distant object known (as of 1992) is a quasar named PC 1247+3406. Astronomers estimate that the radiation left the quasar about one billion or more years after the decoupling epoch. In 1992, astronomers discovered a galaxy designated 4C 41.17, which is estimated to be only one billion light-years closer to us than the quasar. At some time during this one- or two-billion-year interval, primordial hydrogen and helium formed into extensive clouds that condensed into galaxies and superclusters.

How did such vast clumps of matter emerge from the smooth plasma that characterized the universe during the radiation era? Several models propose that small density fluctuations developed shortly after the unified forces decoupled. These changes in density were of infinitesimal size, no greater than two-centimeter ripples of water on a one-kilometer lake. Matter and energy were in equilibrium until they separated 300,000 years after the big bang. The cosmic background radiation is convincing proof that matter and energy were at the same temperature. Yet large variations in density and eventual fragmentation of matter must have occurred after the decoupling epoch.

One of the goals of the COBE satellite is the investigation of irregularities in the background radiation. Cosmologists are looking for variations in the microwave emission that may be related to the density fluctuations in the big bang. In 1992, after eliminating all possible extraneous radio emissions, investigators found a slight deviation in the background radiation amounting to only $3.0 \times 10^{-5}$ K (fig. 20.19). Other researchers

the origin and structure of the universe

are studying data from microwave telescopes carried aloft by balloons. In this way, scientists hope to learn if the ripples in the background radiation reveal the predicted precursors of the    galaxies.

## The Matter Era

Expansion continued during the *matter era*. The regions where matter was slightly denser than average were held together by the self-gravitation of the constituent atoms of hydrogen and helium. Gravity was sufficient to counteract the expansion of space and keep clouds of particles together. During random collisions between atoms, bound electrons absorbed energy and jumped into higher (excited) orbits. A pulse of radiant energy was emitted when an electron returned to ground state (see chapter 4). By this process, kinetic energy (collisions of the atoms) was converted to radiant energy. The transfer reduced the temperature and brought the atoms closer together, thereby increasing the density and gravity within the clouds. The result was a continuous growth in the size of the clouds at the expense of nearby formations. Eventually, the clouds collapsed into structures that in time became superclusters and voids.

Despite intensive investigations by cosmologists and particle physicists, how such large-scale structure formed remains obscure. Density fluctuations that emerged after the decoupling epoch would require more time than the age of the universe to grow into the immense superclusters we observe today. Moreover, the primordial clouds of hydrogen and helium did not provide enough matter to account for the observed mass in galaxies and galaxy clusters.

The distribution of hidden mass in the early universe may have been vital to the evolution of galaxies and superclusters. There is evidence that large quantities of dark matter surround our own and other galaxies. The invisible material represents most of a galaxy's mass. On a higher scale, there is unseen mass that provides the necessary gravity to keep galaxy clusters from drifting apart. How much dark matter exists is not known, but it might be more than

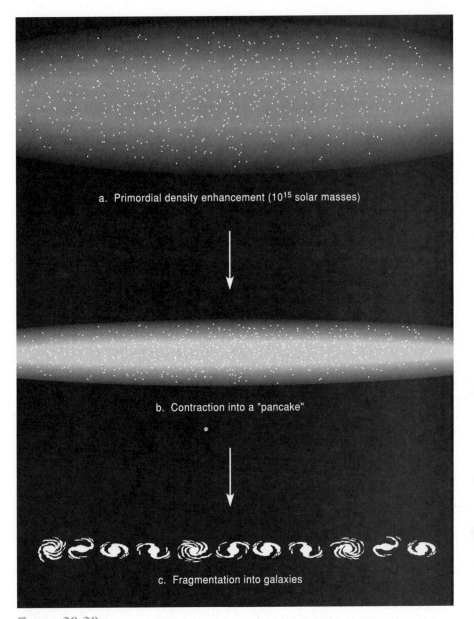

**figure 20.20**

Hot dark matter theory. *a.* Neutrinos mix with atoms of hydrogen and helium. *b.* The cloud contracts into a pancake structure that *c.* fragments into superclusters, and finally, galaxies.

90% of the total mass of the universe (see chapters 17 and 18).

In the 1980s, astronomers proposed two hypotheses to describe dark matter: *hot dark matter* where particles are moving at speeds approaching that of light, and *cold dark matter* where particles move slowly. In either case, they are believed to be weakly interacting particles.

In the hot dark matter scenario, the particles are neutrinos that decoupled during the radiation era when the temperature was approximately $10^{10}$ kelvins, about $10^{-4}$ seconds after the big bang (fig. 20.20). If the neutrinos have mass,

it is less than one ten-thousandth the mass of an electron. Such lightweight particles travel at relativistic speeds. Neutrinos with mass may be created during the spontaneous transformation of electron neutrinos to mu and tau neutrinos (refer to Methods and Understandings 12.2).

The process of galaxy formation began after the decoupling epoch when the universe was dominated by matter. Density fluctuations increased and formed dark clouds of neutrinos intermingled with atoms of hydrogen and helium. The neutrino clouds acted as matrices for the atoms of ordinary matter to form clumps

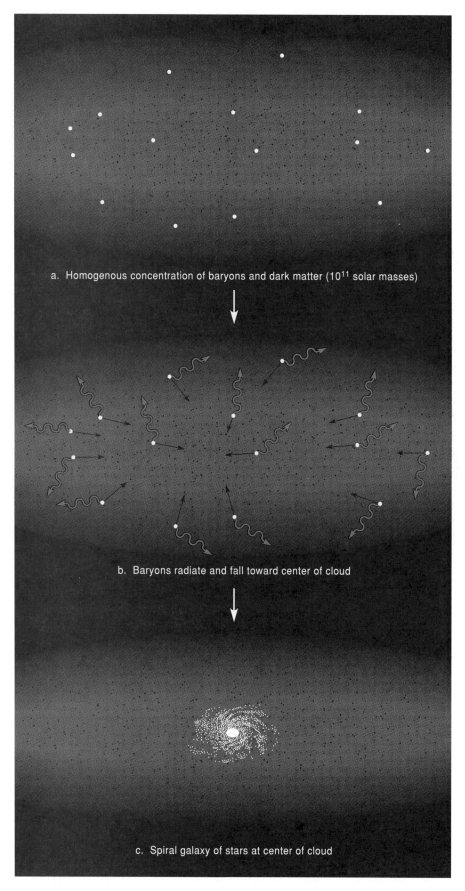

a. Homogenous concentration of baryons and dark matter ($10^{11}$ solar masses)

b. Baryons radiate and fall toward center of cloud

c. Spiral galaxy of stars at center of cloud

**figure 20.21**
Cold dark matter theory. *a.* Slow-moving cold dark matter and baryons are mixed in a huge cloud. *b.* Atoms of hydrogen and helium collide, produce radiant energy, and fall toward the center of the cloud. *c.* Hydrogen and helium form a galaxy of stars at the center of the cloud. Dark matter remains as an extensive halo around the galaxy. Galaxies join into clusters and superclusters.

and voids. The clouds contracted into pancake structures that eventually broke up into thousands of fragments. First to form were superclusters, then rich clusters, and finally galaxies.

Cold dark matter is a general term applied to a hypothetical group of particles predicted by the inflationary theory. They are believed to be weakly interacting, slow-moving particles with masses on the order of protons and neutrons. Dark matter particles "feel" the gravitational force and are readily bound together by their mutual attraction. Moreover, small density fluctuations caused by random motions may have formed during the particle era as early as $10^{-30}$ seconds after the big bang. Such irregularities in the weakly interacting dark matter could have built up without affecting the smoothness of the cosmic background radiation.

At the end of the radiation era, clouds of cold dark exotic particles and ordinary matter formed a homogeneous concentration on the order of $10^{11}$ solar masses (fig. 20.21). During this time, hydrogen and helium atoms collided and produced radiant energy. The transfer of kinetic energy to radiant energy caused the atoms to cool and contract into a massive central nucleus surrounded by a flattened rotating disk. The dark matter remained as an extensive invisible halo about the central structure. The central region of the protogalaxy was made bright by the evolution of first-generation stars. Eventually, protogalaxies joined to form the groups, galaxy clusters, superclusters, and voids that represent the large-scale structure of the visible universe.

the origin and structure of the universe

### the dark night sky

Sky Watchers can take part in a simple investigation of Olbers' paradox, which seems to contradict common sense. Ask a friend why the sky is dark at night. Chances are the answer will be that the bright Sun has set and now illuminates the sky elsewhere about the Earth. This answer may seem satisfactory, but we know the explanation is more profound. People have tried to answer the question long before recorded history, and our current ideas will no doubt be superceded by future theories. Now it's time for you and your friend to ponder the question while you visually observe the bright stars and deep-sky objects with the aid of binoculars and a portable telescope.

Begin your investigation shortly after sunset when the first bright stars and perhaps a planet or two appear in the twilight glow. Soon the sky grows dark and fainter stars come into view. All the stars seem to be at

the same distance from us as though they were attached to a huge vault above the Earth. Like Kepler, we might conclude that a dark emptiness lies beyond a shell of stars that diminishes in population at greater distances from us.

Look carefully at the distribution of stars. Some regions, such as the glowing band of the Milky Way, are teeming with stars. Scan a portion of the Milky Way with binoculars and see how faint stars are resolved. If you view the same part of the sky with a telescope, even fainter stars appear in the field of view. We can appreciate why Isaac Newton and other seventeenth-century scientists believed the universe to be endless and filled with stars at infinite distances. Edmond Halley seems justified in believing that the sky is dark because the remotest stars are too faint to be seen.

Here is the paradox! If the universe is infinite and the stars extend endlessly into space, the night sky should be completely filled with light. An infinite universe filled

with countless stars would cover the sky with overlapping points of light. The sky would be as bright as the face of the Sun.

Is the sky dark because the stars we see are confined to a finite system called the Milky Way Galaxy? Turn your telescope to other galaxies listed in the Messier and NGC catalogues. Look at individual galaxies such as M31 in Andromeda, and galaxy clusters in Virgo and Coma Berenices. Is there sufficient space between galaxies to make the sky dark at night? The paradox is not resolved since there are many millions of galaxies to provide the light to make the sky bright.

In a small telescope, the galaxies in the Virgo cluster appear as fuzzy patches of light. Look back in time further than the faint glow of the galaxies. Picture a wall of darkness at the limit of the visible universe. The paradox extends to the particle horizon. The light from galaxies beyond this barrier has yet to reach the Earth. The night sky is dark because we cannot see the vast, unbounded universe.

## SUMMARY

Cosmology is the study of the structure of the universe, which includes the curved space-time relationship of general relativity and the universal expansion implied by the Hubble law. Cosmogony treats the origin and development of the universe. The velocity-distance law and relativity theory imply that the universe is expanding and has continued to expand for about 15 billion years.

Modern cosmology explains Olbers' paradox in the following way: The night sky is dark because the universe is expanding and the finite velocity of light limits our view to galaxies within the particle horizon.

Cosmologists hypothesize that the observable universe began in a burst of energy called the big bang. Part of the expanding energy eventually converted into the particles of matter that make up the stars and gas clouds found in the galaxies. In addition, there exists dark matter that may make up most of the mass in the universe.

The big bang theory is supported by several predictions verified through observation. Today, the energy emitted during the decoupling epoch is observed as the cosmic background radiation. The ratio of hydrogen to helium predicted by the big bang is about the same as that found in the galaxies.

Cosmologists make certain assumptions that comply with the cosmological principle when describing the large-scale structure of the universe. The universe is homogeneous and isotropic, which means that a local region should be about the same as any other local region and will appear the same in all directions.

Models of the universe are based upon the cosmological principle and the four-dimensional space-time described by general relativity

theory. According to Friedmann models, the universe is either expanding or contracting. Each model is distinguished by its geometry. A closed spherical universe is finite and unbounded. An open flat universe and an open hyperbolic universe are infinite and unbounded.

The critical density of the universe determines whether the universe is opened or closed. If the average density exceeds the critical density, the universe is closed and will reach a maximum expansion and contract. If the average density is equal to the critical density, the universe is open and flat. If the average density is less than the critical density, the universe is hyperbolic.

Unification theories describe the early universe within a fraction of a second after the big bang. During this time, the forces in nature were combined into one superforce. The universe passed through phase transitions as it expanded and cooled. At each stage, the forces separated into the four components known today. Different particles and their antiparticles were produced during each transition.

The inflationary theory is closely linked to grand unification theories (GUTs) and the standard big bang model. According to theory, space-time had an extraordinary increase in size a fraction of a second after the big bang. The inflationary scenario is designed to explain a number of features such as the smooth background radiation and why the average density is close to the critical value.

Cosmologists have proposed two ways in which galaxies may have been formed. In both hypotheses, weakly interacting dark matter serves as a matrix for hydrogen and helium atoms to form extensive gas clouds. If the dark matter is composed of high-velocity neutrinos, the mixture of dark and ordinary matter contract into superclusters, galaxy clusters, and galaxies. If the dark matter is made of slow-moving exotic particles, the cloud fragments into galaxies, which then join to form clusters and superclusters.

# KEY TERMS

big bang

closed universe

cosmic background radiation

cosmogony

cosmological principle

cosmological redshift

cosmology

critical density

Friedmann models

grand unified theories
  (GUTs)

homogeneous

Hubble period

inflationary theory

isotropic

observable universe

Olbers' paradox

open universe

oscillating-universe
hypothesis

particle era

particle horizon

Planck time

radiation era

standard model

# PROBLEMS

1. Describe two hypotheses for the origin of dark matter. What evidence suggests that dark matter was probably involved in the early evolution of galaxies?

2. Explain how unification theories have contributed to the understanding of the events that took place in the early universe.

3. Discuss the significance of the critical density of matter in the universe for a $k = +1$ Friedmann model.

4. If the cosmological principle applies to objects billions of light-years away, why are more quasars located at greater distances from our galaxy?

5. Why is the cosmic background radiation a barrier to the investigation of the earliest stages in the evolution of the universe? Why was the universe opaque before decoupling?

6. How does the inflationary theory explain such features as the isotropic background radiation and the ratio of the average density of the universe to the critical density?

7. When the mass of dark matter is added to the estimated mass of ordinary matter, which Friedmann model best represents the universe?

8. In what significant way does the cosmological redshift differ from the Doppler effect?

9. The universe is homogeneous and isotropic. Explain.

10. Assuming that the maximum age of the observable universe is now 15 billion years, how far away will the particle horizon be five billion years into the future?

11. Why was it impossible for atoms to form prior to the separation of the weak and electromagnetic interactions?

12. Which value for the Hubble parameter, 50 km/sec/Mpc or 100 km/sec/Mpc, requires that the universe have a greater critical density?

13. To what wavelength of electromagnetic radiation did the background emission correspond during the decoupling epoch?

14. Describe two predictions in support of the big bang theory that are consistent with observation.

15. Explain why the radius of the observable universe is limited by the velocity of light.

16. If the cosmic background radiation has a redshift $z = 1000$, what is its distance in light-years? Let the Hubble parameter equal 65 km/sec/Mpc. Hint: Convert one Mpc to light-years and kilometers.

17. A quasar is 3776 Mpc from the Earth. What is its distance in light-years? How long did it take light from the quasar to reach us?

18. In question 17, if the Hubble parameter is 75 km/sec/Mpc, what is the recessional velocity of the quasar?

19. What is the maximum age of the universe when the value of the Hubble parameter is 50 km/sec/Mpc? When it is 100 km/sec/Mpc? Hint: How many seconds are there in one year?

20. Is a Hubble parameter greater than 100 km/sec/Mpc compatible with the evolution and age determination of stars? Why? Base your answer on the maximum age of the universe computed in problem 19.

# REFERENCES

Barrow, John D., and Joseph Silk. 1980. The Structure of the Early Universe. *Scientific American* 242, no. 4 (April).

Bartusiak, Marcia. 1987. The Cosmic Burp: The Genesis of the Inflationary Universe Hypothesis. *Mercury* (Astronomical Society of the Pacific) 16, no. 2 (March/April).

Davies, Paul. 1985. New Physics and the New Big Bang. *Sky and Telescope* 70, no. 5 (November).

———. 1991. Everyone's Guide to Cosmology. *Sky and Telescope* 81, no. 3 (March).

Einstein, Albert. 1931. *Relativity.* Translated by Robert W. Lawson. Reprint of 1920 edition. New York: Peter Smith.

Ferris, Timothy. 1984. The Radio Sky and the Echo of Creation. *Mercury* 13, no. 1 (January/February).

Fienberg, Richard Tresch. 1992. COBE Confronts the Big Bang. *Sky and Telescope* 84, no. 1 (July).

Greenstein, George. 1989. Through the Looking Glass. *Astronomy* 17, no. 10 (October).

Gulkis, Samuel, Philip M. Lubin, Stephan S. Meyer, and Robert F. Silverberg. 1990. The Cosmic Background Explorer. *Scientific American* 262, no. 1 (January).

Guth, Alan H., and Paul J. Steinhardt. 1984. The Inflationary Universe. *Scientific American* 250, no. 5 (May).

Halliwell, Jonathan J. 1991. Quantum Cosmology and the Creation of the Universe. *Scientific American* 265, no. 6 (December).

Harrison, Edward R. 1981. *Cosmology.* Cambridge: Cambridge University Press.

Kanipe, Jeff. 1990. Too Smooth—COBE's Perfect Universe. *Astronomy* 18, no. 6 (June).

Kippenhahn, Rudolf. 1987. Light from the Depths of Time. *Sky and Telescope* 73, no. 2 (February).

Krauss, Lawrence M. 1986. Dark Matter in the Universe. *Scientific American* 255, no. 6 (December).

Kutter, G. Siegfried. 1989. *Origin and Evolution of the Universe.* Boston: Jones and Bartlett Publishers.

Lindley, David. 1990. A Case of Extended Inflation. *Nature* (London) 345, no. 6270 (May 3).

LoPresto, James Charles. 1987. The Geometry of Space and Time. *Astronomy* 15, no. 10 (October).

Maddox, John. 1990. Making the Universe Hang Together. *Nature* 348, no. 6302 (December 13).

Mallove, Eugene F. 1988. The Self-Reproducing Universe. *Sky and Telescope* 76, no. 3 (September).

Melott, Adrian L. 1988. Part Four: Recreating the Universe. *Astronomy* 16, no. 5 (May).

Odenwald, Sten. 1991. Einstein's Fudge Factor. *Sky and Telescope* 81, no. 4 (April).

Page, Don N., and M. Randall McKee. 1983. The Future of the Universe. *Mercury* 12, no. 1 (January/February).

Pagels, Heinz R. 1985. *Perfect Symmetry.* New York: Simon and Schuster, Inc.

Powell, Corey S. 1992. The Golden Age of Cosmology. *Scientific American* 267, no. 1 (July).

Riordan, Michael, and David N. Schramm. 1991. *The Shadows of Creation.* New York: W. H. Freeman and Company.

Schramm, David N., and Gary Steigman. 1988. Particle Accelerators Test Cosmological Theory. *Scientific American* 258, no. 6 (June).

Shu, Frank. 1983. The Expanding Universe and the Large-Scale Geometry of Space-time. *Mercury* 12, no. 6 (November/December).

Silk, Joseph. 1989. *The Big Bang.* Revised and updated edition. New York: W. H. Freeman and Company.

———. 1990. Probing the Primeval Fireball. *Sky and Telescope* 79, no. 6 (June).

Trefil, James S. 1983. *The Moment of Creation.* New York: Charles Scribner's Sons.

Wesson, Paul S. 1989. Olbers' Paradox Solved at Last. *Sky and Telescope* 77, no. 6 (June).

# A

## Table A.1

### physical constants (SI)

| Constant | Symbol | Value |
|----------|--------|-------|
| velocity of light | $c$ | $2.997925 \times 10^8$ m $\cdot$ s$^{-1}$ |
| charge of electron | $e$ | $1.60210 \times 10^{-19}$ C |
| electron rest mass | $m_e$ | $9.1091 \times 10^{-31}$ kg |
| proton rest mass | $m_p$ | $1.67252 \times 10^{-27}$ kg |
| Planck's constant | $h$ | $6.6256 \times 10^{-34}$ J $\cdot$ s |
| Rydberg's constant | $R$ | $1.09737 \times 10^7$ m$^{-1}$ |
| Boltzmann's constant | $k$ | $1.38054 \times 10^{-23}$ J $\cdot$ °K$^{-1}$ |
| Wien displacement constant | $b$ | $2.8978 \times 10^{-3}$ m $\cdot$ °K |
| Stefan-Boltzmann constant | $\sigma$ | $5.6697 \times 10^{-8}$ W $\cdot$ m$^{-2}$ $\cdot$ °K$^{-4}$ |
| Gravitational constant | $G$ | $6.6726 \times 10^{-11}$ N $\cdot$ m$^2$ $\cdot$ kg$^{-2}$ |

Abbreviations: C—coulomb; J—joule; N—newton; W—watt

## Table A.2

### conversion factors

| | |
|---|---|
| standard gravity (g) | $= 9.80665$ m $\cdot$ s$^{-2}$ |
| angstrom unit (A) | $= 10^{-10}$ m |
| nanometer (nm) | $= 10^{-9}$ m |
| astronomical unit (AU) | $= 1.495 \times 10^{11}$ m |
| light year (ly) | $= 9.46 \times 10^{15}$ m |
| parsec (pc) | $= 3.08 \times 10^{16}$ m |
| | $= 3.26$ ly |
| sidereal year | $= 3.155815 \times 10^7$ s |
| statute mile | $= 1609.3472$ m |
| radian (R) | $= 206265$ arc seconds (˝) |

Source: Data from *Handbook of Mathematical Functions*, National Bureau of Standards.

appendix

# B

greek  alphabet

## T a b l e   B . 1

### greek alphabet

| | | | | | | | | | | | |
|---|---|---|---|---|---|---|---|---|---|---|---|
| α | A | alpha | η | H | eta | ν | N | nu | τ | T | tau |
| β | B | beta | θ | Θ | theta | ξ | Ξ | xi | υ | Y | upsilon |
| γ | Γ | gamma | ι | I | iota | o | O | omicron | φ | Φ | phi |
| δ | Δ | delta | κ | K | kappa | π | Π | pi | χ | X | chi |
| ε | E | epsilon | λ | Λ | lambda | ρ | P | rho | ψ | Ψ | psi |
| ζ | Z | zeta | μ | M | mu | σ | Σ | sigma | ω | Ω | omega |

# C

## T a b l e   C . 1

### planets: orbital data (for epoch 2000.0 January 1.5)

| Planet | Mean (AU) | Distance ($10^6$ km) | Sidereal Period (years) | Synodic Period (days) | Orbital Velocity (km/s) | Inclination to Ecliptic (degrees) | Orbital Eccentricity |
|--------|-----------|----------------------|--------------------------|------------------------|--------------------------|-----------------------------------|----------------------|
| Mercury | 0.3871 | 57.9 | 0.2408 | 115.88 | 47.8725 | 7.005 | 0.206 |
| Venus | 0.7233 | 108.2 | 0.6152 | 583.92 | 35.0214 | 3.394 | 0.007 |
| Earth | 1.0000 | 149.6 | 1.0000 | ——— | 29.7859 | 0.000 | 0.017 |
| Mars | 1.5237 | 227.9 | 1.8808 | 779.94 | 24.1309 | 1.850 | 0.093 |
| Jupiter | 5.2026 | 778.0 | 11.8622 | 398.88 | 13.0697 | 1.303 | 0.045 |
| Saturn | 9.5549 | 1429.0 | 29.4577 | 378.09 | 9.6724 | 2.489 | 0.056 |
| Uranus | 19.1839 | 2868.0 | 84.0133 | 369.66 | 6.8352 | 0.773 | 0.046 |
| Neptune | 30.0578 | 4504.0 | 163.7934 | 367.49 | 5.4778 | 1.770 | 0.009 |
| Pluto | 39.4387 | 5896.0 | 247.6760 | 366.72 | 4.7490 | 17.142 | 0.249 |

Source: Data from *Explanatory Supplement to the Astronomical Almanac,* University Science Books, 1992, p. 704.

# T a b l e    C . 2

## planets: physical data

| Planet | Mass (Earth = 1) | Equatorial Radius (km) | Mean Density (g/cm$^3$) | Period of Rotation (days) | Inclination of Equator to Orbit (degrees) | Albedo |
|---|---|---|---|---|---|---|
| Mercury | 0.0553 | 2439.7 | 5.43 | 58.646 | 0.00 | 0.106 |
| Venus | 0.8150 | 6051.9 | 5.24 | −243.01* | 177.30 | 0.65 |
| Earth | 1.0000 | 6378.1 | 5.52 | 0.9973 | 23.45 | 0.367 |
| Mars | 0.1074 | 3397.0 | 3.94 | 1.026 | 25.19 | 0.15 |
| Jupiter | 317.8334 | 71,492.0 | 1.33 | 0.414 | 3.12 | 0.52 |
| Saturn | 95.1592 | 60,268.0 | 0.70 | 0.438 | 26.73 | 0.47 |
| Uranus | 14.4998 | 25,559.0 | 1.30 | − 0.65* | 97.86 | 0.51 |
| Neptune | 17.2040 | 24,764.0 | 1.76 | 0.768 | 29.56 | 0.41 |
| Pluto | 0.0025 | 1151.0 | 1.10 | − 6.387* | 118.0 (est.) | 0.30 |

*Rotation is retrograde with respect to the pole that lies north of, or above, the plane of the solar system.

Source: Data from *Explanatory Supplement to the Astronomical Almanac,* University Science Books, 1992, p. 706.

astronomy: through space and time

# Table C.3

satellites: orbital data

| Planet | | Satellite | Period[1] (days) | Mean Distance from Planet (10³ km) | Orbital Eccentricity | Inclination to Planetory Equator (degrees) |
|---|---|---|---|---|---|---|
| Earth | | Moon | 27.3217 | 384.400 | 0.055 | 18.28–28.58 |
| Mars | I | Phobos | 0.3189 | 9.378 | 0.015 | 1.0 |
| | II | Deimos | 1.2624 | 23.459 | 0.001 | 0.9–2.7 |
| Jupiter | I | Io | 1.7691 | 422.0 | 0.004 | 0.04 |
| | II | Europa | 3.5512 | 671.0 | 0.009 | 0.47 |
| | III | Ganymede | 7.1546 | 1070.0 | 0.002 | 0.21 |
| | IV | Callisto | 16.6890 | 1883.0 | 0.007 | 0.51 |
| | V | Amalthea | 0.4982 | 181.0 | 0.003 | 0.40 |
| | VI | Himalia | 250.5662 | 11,480.0 | 0.158 | 27.63 |
| | VII | Elara | 259.6528 | 11,737.0 | 0.207 | 24.77 |
| | VIII | Pasiphae | 735.0 R | 23,500.0 | 0.378 | 145.0 |
| | IX | Sinope | 758.0 R | 23,700.0 | 0.275 | 153.0 |
| | X | Lysithea | 259.22 | 11,720.0 | 0.107 | 29.02 |
| | XI | Carme | 692.0 R | 22,600.0 | 0.207 | 164.0 |
| | XII | Ananke | 631.0 R | 21,200.0 | 0.169 | 147.0 |
| | XIII | Leda | 238.72 | 11,094.0 | 0.148 | 26.07 |
| | XIV | Thebe | 0.6745 | 222.0 | 0.015 | 0.8 |
| | XV | Adrastea | 0.2983 | 129.0 | | |
| | XVI | Metis | 0.2948 | 128.0 | | |
| Saturn | I | Mimas | 0.9424 | 185.52 | 0.020 | 1.53 |
| | II | Enceladus | 1.3702 | 238.02 | 0.005 | 0.00 |
| | III | Tethys | 1.8878 | 294.66 | 0.000 | 1.86 |
| | IV | Dione | 2.7369 | 377.40 | 0.002 | 0.02 |
| | V | Rhea | 4.5175 | 527.04 | 0.001 | 0.35 |
| | VI | Titan | 15.9454 | 1221.83 | 0.029 | 0.33 |
| | VII | Hyperion | 21.2766 | 1481.1 | 0.104 | 0.43 |
| | VIII | Iapetus | 79.3302 | 3561.3 | 0.028 | 14.72 |
| | IX | Phoebe | 550.48 R | 12,952.0 | 0.163 | 177.0[2] |
| | X | Janus | 0.6945 | 151.472 | 0.007 | 0.14 |
| | XI | Epimetheus | 0.6942 | 151.422 | 0.009 | 0.34 |
| | XII | Helene | 2.7369 | 377.40 | 0.005 | 0.00 |
| | XIII | Telesto | 1.8878 | 294.66 | | |
| | XIV | Calypso | 1.8878 | 294.66 | | |
| | XV | Atlas | 0.6019 | 137.670 | 0.000 | 0.3 |
| | XVI | Prometheus | 0.6130 | 139.353 | 0.003 | 0.0 |
| | XVII | Pandora | 0.6285 | 141.700 | 0.004 | 0.0 |
| | XVIII | Pan | 0.5750 | 133.583 | | |

*Table C.3 continues on next page*

u x i p u e d d e

continued

| Planet | | Satellite | Period[1] (days) | Mean Distance from Planet (10³ km) | Orbital Eccentricity | Inclination to Planetory Equator (degrees) |
|---|---|---|---|---|---|---|
| Uranus | I | Ariel | 2.5204 | 191.02 | 0.003 | 0.3 |
| | II | Umbriel | 4.1442 | 266.30 | 0.005 | 0.36 |
| | III | Titania | 8.7059 | 435.91 | 0.002 | 0.14 |
| | IV | Oberon | 13.4632 | 583.52 | 0.001 | 0.10 |
| | V | Miranda | 1.4135 | 129.39 | 0.003 | 4.2 |
| | VI | Cordelia | 0.3350 | 49.77 | <0.001 | 0.1 |
| | VII | Ophelia | 0.3764 | 53.79 | 0.010 | 0.1 |
| | VIII | Bianca | 0.4346 | 59.17 | <0.001 | 0.2 |
| | IX | Cressida | 0.4636 | 61.78 | <0.001 | 0.0 |
| | X | Desdemona | 0.4737 | 62.68 | <0.001 | 0.2 |
| | XI | Juliet | 0.4931 | 64.35 | <0.001 | 0.1 |
| | XII | Portia | 0.5132 | 66.09 | <0.001 | 0.1 |
| | XIII | Rosalind | 0.5585 | 69.94 | <0.001 | 0.3 |
| | XIV | Belinda | 0.6235 | 75.26 | <0.001 | 0.0 |
| | XV | Puck | 0.7618 | 86.01 | <0.001 | 0.31 |
| Neptune | I | Triton | 5.8769 R | 354.76 | 0.000 | 157.345 |
| | II | Nereid | 360.1362 | 5513.4 | 0.751 | 27.6[3] |
| | III | Naiad | 0.2944 | 48.2 | <0.001 | 4.74 |
| | IV | Thalassa | 0.3115 | 73.6 | <0.001 | 0.21 |
| | V | Despina | 0.3347 | 52.6 | <0.001 | 0.07 |
| | VI | Galatea | 0.4287 | 62.0 | <0.001 | 0.05 |
| | VII | Larissa | 0.5547 | 50.0 | <0.001 | 0.20 |
| | VIII | Proteus | 1.1223 | 117.6 | <0.001 | 0.55 |
| Pluto | I | Charon | 6.3873 | 19.6 | <0.001 | 99.0[3] |

[1]Sidereal periods, except that tropical periods are given for the satellites of Saturn. R = retrograde.
[2]Relative to the ecliptic plane.
[3]Referred to equator of 1950.0.

Source: Data from *Explanatory Supplement to the Astronomical Almanac*, University Science Books, 1992, p. 708.

## satellites: physical and photometric data

| Planet | | Satellite | Radius (km) | Period of Rotation* (days) | Albedo |
|--------|------|-----------|-------------|----------------------------|--------|
| Earth | | Moon | 1738 | S | 0.12 |
| Mars | I | Phobos | 13.5 × 10.8 × 9.4 | S | 0.06 |
| | II | Deimos | 7.5 × 6.1 × 5.5 | S | 0.07 |
| Jupiter | I | Io | 1815 | S | 0.61 |
| | II | Europa | 1569 | S | 0.64 |
| | III | Ganymede | 2631 | S | 0.42 |
| | IV | Callisto | 2400 | S | 0.20 |
| | V | Amalthea | 135 × 83 × 75 | S | 0.05 |
| | VI | Himalia | 93 | 0.4 | 0.03 |
| | VII | Elara | 38 | 0.5 | 0.03 |
| | VIII | Pasiphae | 25 | | |
| | IX | Sinope | 18 | | |
| | X | Lysithea | 18 | | |
| | XI | Carme | 20 | | |
| | XII | Ananke | 15 | | |
| | XIII | Leda | 8 | | |
| | XIV | Thebe | 55 × 45 | S | 0.05 |
| | XV | Adrastea | 12.5 × 10 × 7.5 | | 0.05 |
| | XVI | Metis | 20 | | 0.05 |
| Saturn | I | Mimas | 196 | S | 0.5 |
| | II | Enceladus | 250 | S | 1.0 |
| | III | Tethys | 530 | S | 0.9 |
| | IV | Dione | 560 | S | 0.7 |
| | V | Rhea | 765 | S | 0.7 |
| | VI | Titan | 2575 | S | 0.21 |
| | VII | Hyperion | 205 × 130 × 110 | | 0.3 |
| | VIII | Iapetus | 730 | S | 0.2 |
| | IX | Phoebe | 110 | 0.4 | 0.06 |
| | X | Janus | 110 × 100 × 80 | S | 0.8 |
| | XI | Epimetheus | 70 × 60 × 50 | S | 0.8 |
| | XII | Helene | 18 × 16 × 15 | | 0.7 |
| | XIII | Telesto | 17 × 14 × 13 | | 0.5 |
| | XIV | Calypso | 17 × 11 × 11 | | 0.6 |
| | XV | Atlas | 20 × 10 | | 0.9 |
| | XVI | Prometheus | 70 × 50 × 40 | | 0.6 |
| | XVII | Pandora | 55 × 45 × 35 | | 0.9 |
| | XVIII | Pan | 10 | | 0.5 |

*Table C.4 continues on next page*

| Planet | | Satellite | Radius (km) | Period of Rotation[*] (days) | Albedo |
|---|---|---|---|---|---|
| Uranus | I | Ariel | 579 | S | 0.34 |
| | II | Umbriel | 586 | S | 0.18 |
| | III | Titania | 790 | S | 0.27 |
| | IV | Oberon | 762 | S | 0.24 |
| | V | Miranda | 240 | S | 0.27 |
| | VI | Cordelia | 13 | | 0.07 |
| | VII | Ophelia | 15 | | 0.07 |
| | VIII | Bianca | 21 | | 0.07 |
| | IX | Cressida | 31 | | 0.07 |
| | X | Desdemona | 27 | | 0.07 |
| | XI | Juliet | 42 | | 0.07 |
| | XII | Portia | 54 | | 0.07 |
| | XIII | Rosalind | 27 | | 0.07 |
| | XIV | Belinda | 33 | | 0.07 |
| | XV | Puck | 77 | | 0.07 |
| Neptune | I | Triton | 1353 | S | 0.7 |
| | II | Nereid | 170 | | 0.4 |
| | III | Naiad | 29 | | 0.06 |
| | IV | Thalassa | 40 | | 0.06 |
| | V | Despina | 74 | | 0.06 |
| | VI | Galatea | 79 | | 0.06 |
| | VII | Larissa | $104 \times 89$ | | 0.06 |
| | VIII | Proteus | $218 \times 208 \times 201$ | | 0.06 |
| Pluto | I | Charon | 593 | S | 0.5 |

[*]S = synchronous; rotation period equal to revolution.

Source: Data from *Explanatory Supplement to the Astronomical Almanac,* University Science Books, 1992, pp. 710–711.

astronomy: through space and time

# D

m a j o r   m e t e o r   s h o w e r s

## T a b l e   D . 1

### major meteor showers

| Shower | Maximum Date | Duration (days) | Activity (ZHR)[*] | Radiant | | Geocentric Velocity (km s⁻¹) | Parent Object |
|---|---|---|---|---|---|---|---|
| | | | | R.A. (degrees) | Dec. (degrees) | | |
| Quadrantid | Jan. 3 | 0.4 | 80 | 230 | +49 | 42 | |
| Lyrid | Apr. 22 | 1 | 15 | 272 | +33 | 48 | Comet Thatcher |
| Eta Aquarid | May 4 | 6 | 60 | 336 | 0 | 66 | Comet Halley |
| Arietid (D) | Jun. 7 | 12 | 100 | 45 | +23 | 39 | Asteroid Icarus? |
| Zeta Perseid (D) | Jun. 9 | 8 | 80 | 62 | +24 | 29 | |
| Beta Taurid (D) | Jun. 29 | 5 | 40 | 86 | +19 | 30 | |
| Southern Delta Aquarid | Jul. 29 | 8 | 30 | 331 | −16 | 41 | |
| Northern Delta Aquarid | Aug. 12 | 8 | 20 | 339 | −5 | 41 | |
| Perseid | Aug. 12 | 3 | 100 | 46 | +57 | 60 | Comet Swift-Tuttle |
| Orionid | Oct. 21 | 2 | 30 | 95 | +16 | 66 | Comet Halley |
| Southern Taurid | Nov. 3 | 30 | 15 | 53 | +12 | 29 | Comet Encke |
| Northern Taurid | Nov. 5 | 30 | 15 | 54 | +21 | 30 | Comet Encke |
| Leonid | Nov. 16 | 2 | 20 | 152 | +22 | 72 | Comet Tempel-Tuttle |
| Geminid | Dec. 13 | 3 | 90 | 112 | +32 | 36 | Asteroid Phaethon |
| Ursid | Dec. 22 | 1 | 20 | 217 | +76 | 34 | Comet Tuttle |

[*]Zenithal Hourly Rate

From Robert L. Hawkes, "Meteors, Shower and Sporadic" in *The Astronomy and Astrophysics Encyclopedia*. Copyright © 1992 Van Nostrand Reinhold Company, New York, NY. Reprinted by permission.

## T a b l e   E . 1

### the nearest stars

| Star | Magnitude | | Parallax π (arcsec) | Distance (1y) | Spectral Type |
|------|-----------|-----------|---------------------|---------------|---------------|
|      | $m_v$ | $M_v$ | | | |
| Sun | −26.72 | 4.85 | | | G2V |
| Proxima Cen | 11.05 | 15.49 | 0.767 | 4.2 | M5.5V |
| α Cen A | −0.01 | 4.37 | 0.750 | 4.3 | G2V |
| B | 1.33 | 5.71 | | | K1V |
| Barnard's Star[*] | 9.54 | 13.22 | 0.545 | 6.0 | M3.8V |
| Wolf 359 | 13.53 | 16.65 | 0.421 | 7.7 | M5.8V |
| BD +36° 2147[*] | 7.50 | 10.50 | 0.397 | 8.2 | M2.1V |
| L 726-8 | 12.52 | 15.46 | 0.387 | 8.4 | M5.6V |
| Sirius A | −1.46 | 1.42 | 0.377 | 8.6 | A1V |
| B | 8.3 | 11.2 | | | wd |
| Ross 154 | 10.45 | 13.14 | 0.345 | 9.4 | M3.6V |
| Ross 248 | 12.29 | 14.78 | 0.314 | 10.4 | M4.9V |
| ε Eri | 3.73 | 6.14 | 0.303 | 10.8 | K2V |
| Ross 128 | 11.10 | 13.47 | 0.298 | 10.9 | M4.1V |
| 61 Cyg A | 5.22 | 7.56 | 0.294 | 11.1 | K3.5V |
| B[*] | 6.03 | 8.37 | | | K4.7V |
| ε Ind | 4.68 | 7.00 | 0.291 | 11.2 | K3V |
| BD +43° 44 | 8.08 | 10.39 | 0.290 | 11.2 | M1.3V |
| L 789-6 | 12.18 | 14.49 | 0.290 | 11.2 | M5.3V |
| Procyon A | 0.37 | 2.7 | 0.285 | 11.2 | F5IV-V |
| B | 10.7 | 13.0 | | | wd |
| BD +59° 1915 | 8.90 | 11.15 | 0.282 | 11.6 | M3.0V |
| CD -36° 15693 | 7.35 | 9.58 | 0.279 | 11.7 | M1.3V |
| G 51-15 | 14.81 | 17.03 | 0.278 | 11.7 | M6.6V |
| τ Cet | 3.50 | 5.72 | 0.277 | 11.8 | G8V |
| BD +5° 1668[*] | 9.82 | 11.94 | 0.266 | 12.3 | M3.7V |
| L 725-32 | 12.04 | 14.12 | 0.261 | 12.5 | M4.5V |
| CD −39° 14192 | 6.66 | 8.74 | 0.260 | 12.5 | K5.5V |
| Kapteyn's Star | 8.84 | 10.88 | 0.256 | 12.7 | M0.0V |

continued

| Star | Magnitude | | Parallax π (arcsec) | Distance (1y) | Spectral Type |
|------|-----------|---|---------------------|---------------|---------------|
| | $m_v$ | $M_v$ | | | |
| Kruger 60 A | 9.85 | 11.87 | 0.253 | 12.9 | |
| B | 11.3 | 13.3 | | } | M3.3V |
| BD −12° 4253 | 10.11 | 12.07 | 0.247 | 13.2 | M3.5V |
| Ross 614 A | 11.10 | 13.12 | 0.246 | 13.3 | |
| B | 14.0 | 16.0 | | } | M4.5V |
| Van Maanen's Star | 12.37 | 14.20 | 0.232 | 14.1 | wd |
| Wolf 424 A | 13.16 | 14.97 | 0.230 | 14.2 | |
| B | 13.4 | 15.2 | | } | M5.3V |
| CD −37° 15492 | 8.56 | 10.32 | 0.225 | 14.5 | M2.0V |
| L 1159-16 | 12.26 | 14.01 | 0.224 | 14.6 | M4.5V |
| BD +50° 1725 | 6.59 | 8.32 | 0.222 | 14.7 | K5.0V |
| L 143-23 | 13.92 | 15.64 | 0.221 | 14.8 | |
| LP 731-58 | 15.60 | 17.30 | 0.219 | 14.9 | |
| CD − 46° 11540 | 9.37 | 11.04 | 0.216 | 15.1 | M2.7V |
| G 158-27 | 13.74 | 15.39 | 0.214 | 15.2 | M5.5 |
| CD − 49° 13515 | 8.67 | 10.32 | 0.214 | 15.2 | M1.8V |
| CD − 44° 11909* | 10.96 | 12.60 | 0.213 | 15.3 | M3.9V |
| BD +68° 946* | 9.15 | 10.79 | 0.213 | 15.3 | M3.3V |
| G 208-44 A* | 13.41 | 15.03 | 0.211 | 15.5 | |
| B | 13.99 | 15.61 | | | M5 |
| BD −15° 6290 | 10.17 | 11.77 | 0.209 | 15.6 | M3.9V |
| o² Eri A | 4.43 | 6.01 | 0.207 | 15.7 | K1V |
| B | 9.52 | 11.10 | | | wd |
| C | 11.17 | 12.75 | | | M4.3V |
| BD +20° 2465* | 9.43 | 11.00 | 0.206 | 15.8 | M3.3V |
| L 145-141 | 11.5 | 13.07 | 0.206 | 15.8 | wd |
| 70 Oph A | 4.22 | 5.76 | 0.203 | 16.1 | K0V |
| B | 6.00 | 7.54 | | | K4V |
| BD +43° 4305* | 10.2 | 11.7 | 0.200 | 16.3 | M5 |
| Altair | 0.76 | 2.24 | 0.198 | 16.5 | A7V |

*Suspected unseen companion.
π = Annual Parallax; wd = White Dwarf.

Source: Data from Alan H. Batten, "The Nearest Stars" in *Observer's Handbook*, Royal Astronomical Society of Canada.

## the brightest stars

| Star | Magnitude | | Distance | | Spectral Type |
|------|-----------|---|----------|---|---------------|
| | $m_v$ | $M_v$ | (pc) | (ly) | |
| Sirius | −1.46 | 1.4 | 2.65 | 8.6 | A1V |
| Canopus | −0.72 | −2.5 | 23 | 75 | A9II |
| α Centauri | −0.01 | 4.4 | 1.33 | 4.3 | G2V |
| Arcturus | −0.04 | 0.2 | 10.3 | 33.6 | K1.5III |
| Vega | 0.03 | 0.6 | 7.5 | 24.5 | A0V |
| Capella | 0.08 | 0.4 | 13 | 43 | G6III |
| Rigel | 0.12 | −7.2 | 290 | 945 | B8I |
| Procyon | 0.37 | 2.7 | 3.42 | 11.2 | F5IV-V |
| Achernar | 0.46 | −1.3 | 22 | 72 | B3V |
| Betelgeuse | 0.50 | −5.5 | 160 | 522 | M2Iab |
| β Centauri | 0.61 | −4.4 | 100 | 326 | B1III |
| Altair | 0.76 | 2.2 | 5.1 | 16.5 | A7V |
| Aldebaran | 0.85 | −0.3 | 17 | 55 | K5III |
| Antares | 0.96 | −5.2 | 160 | 522 | M1.5Iab |
| Spica | 0.97 | −3.2 | 70 | 228 | B1V |
| Pollux | 1.14 | 0.7 | 12 | 39.1 | K0IIIb |
| Fomalhaut | 1.16 | 2.0 | 6.9 | 22.5 | A3V |
| Deneb | 1.25 | −7.2 | 490 | 1600 | A2Ia |
| β Crucis | 1.25 | −4.7 | 155 | 506 | B0.5III |
| α Crucis | 1.33 | −4.2 | 130 | 425 | B0.5IV |
| Regulus | 1.35 | −0.3 | 21 | 69 | B7V |

Note: The distances of the remote stars were derived by the relationship between their spectral type, and apparent and absolute magnitudes.

Source: Data from *Observer's Handbook,* Royal Astronomical Society of Canada.

# Table E.3

## constellation names and abbreviations

| Nominative | Abbreviation | Genitive | Nominative | Abbreviation | Genitive |
|---|---|---|---|---|---|
| Andromeda | And | Andromedae | Lacerta | Lac | Lacertae |
| Antlia | Ant | Antliae | Leo | Leo | Leonis |
| Apus | Aps | Apodis | Leo Minor | LMi | Leonis Minoris |
| Aquarius | Aqr | Aquarii | Lepus | Lep | Leporis |
| Aquila | Aql | Aquilae | Libra | Lib | Librae |
| Ara | Ara | Arae | Lupus | Lup | Lupi |
| *Argo | Arg | Argus | Lynx | Lyn | Lyncis |
| Aries | Ari | Arietis | Lyra | Lyr | Lyrae |
| Auriga | Aur | Aurigae | Mensa | Men | Mensae |
| Boötes | Boo | Boötis | Microscopium | Mic | Microscopii |
| Caelum | Cae | Caeli | Monoceros | Mon | Monocerotis |
| Camelopardalis | Cam | Camelopardalis | Musca | Mus | Muscae |
| Cancer | Cnc | Cancri | Norma | Nor | Normae |
| Canes Venatici | CVn | Canum Venaticorum | Octans | Oct | Octantis |
| Canis Major | CMa | Canis Majoris | Ophiuchus | Oph | Ophiuchi |
| Canis Minor | CMi | Canis Minoris | Orion | Ori | Orionis |
| Capricornus | Cap | Capricorni | Pavo | Pav | Pavonis |
| Carina | Car | Carinae | Pegasus | Peg | Pegasi |
| Cassiopeia | Cas | Cassiopeiae | Perseus | Per | Persei |
| Centaurus | Cen | Centauri | Phoenix | Phe | Phoenicis |
| Cepheus | Cep | Cephei | Pictor | Pic | Pictoris |
| Cetus | Cet | Ceti | Pisces | Psc | Piscium |
| Chamaeleon | Cha | Chamaeleontis | Piscis Austrinus | PsA | Piscis Austrini |
| Circinus | Cir | Circini | Puppis | Pup | Puppis |
| Columba | Col | Columbae | Pyxis | Pyx | Pyxidis |
| Coma Berenices | Com | Comae Berenices | Reticulum | Ret | Reticuli |
| Corona Australis | CrA | Coronae Australis | Sagitta | Sge | Sagittae |
| Corona Borealis | CrB | Coronae Borealis | Sagittarius | Sgr | Sagittarii |
| Corvus | Crv | Corvi | Scorpius | Sco | Scorpii |
| Crater | Crt | Crateris | Sculptor | Scl | Sculptoris |
| Crux | Cru | Crucis | Scutum | Sct | Scuti |
| Cygnus | Cyg | Cygni | †Serpens | Ser | Serpentis |
| Delphinus | Del | Delphini | Sextans | Sex | Sextantis |
| Dorado | Dor | Doradus | Taurus | Tau | Tauri |
| Draco | Dra | Draconis | Telescopium | Tel | Telescopii |
| Equuleus | Equ | Equulei | Triangulum | Tri | Trianguli |
| Eridanus | Eri | Eridani | Triangulum Australe | TrA | Trianguli Australis |
| Fornax | For | Fornacis | Tucana | Tuc | Tucanae |
| Gemini | Gem | Geminorum | Ursa Major | UMa | Ursae Majoris |
| Grus | Gru | Gruis | Ursa Minor | UMi | Ursae Minoris |
| Hercules | Her | Herculis | Vela | Vel | Velorum |
| Horologium | Hor | Horologii | Virgo | Vir | Virginis |
| Hydra | Hya | Hydrae | Volans | Vol | Volantis |
| Hydrus | Hyi | Hydri | Vulpecula | Vul | Vulpeculae |
| Indus | Ind | Indi | | | |

* In modern usage, Argo is divided into Carina, Puppis, and Vela.

† Serpens is divided into Serpens Caput and Serpens Cauda.

From *Explanatory Supplement to the Astronomical Almanac.* Copyright © 1992 Her Majesty's Stationery Office, London, England. Reproduced with the permission of the Controller of Her Majesty's Stationery Office.

appendix e

# Table E.4

## the messier catalogue

| M | NGC or IC | R.A. h | m | Dec. ° | ' | Const. | Size | m_v | Type |
|---|---|---|---|---|---|---|---|---|---|
| 1 | 1952 | 5 | 34.5 | +22 | 01 | Tau | 6 × 4 | 8.4 | Di |
| 2 | 7089 | 21 | 33.5 | −0 | 49 | Aqr | 13 | 6.5 | Gb |
| 3 | 5272 | 13 | 42.2 | +28 | 23 | CVn | 16 | 6.4 | Gb |
| 4 | 6121 | 16 | 23.6 | −26 | 32 | Sco | 26 | 5.9 | Gb |
| 5 | 5904 | 15 | 18.6 | +2 | 05 | Ser | 17 | 5.8 | Gb |
| 6 | 6405 | 17 | 40.1 | −32 | 13 | Sco | 15 | 4.2 | OC |
| 7 | 6475 | 17 | 53.9 | −34 | 49 | Sco | 80 | 3.3 | OC |
| 8 | 6523 | 18 | 03.8 | −24 | 23 | Sgr | 90 × 40 | 5.8 | Di |
| 9 | 6333 | 17 | 19.2 | −18 | 31 | Oph | 9 | 7.9 | Gb |
| 10 | 6254 | 16 | 57.1 | −4 | 06 | Oph | 15 | 6.6 | Gb |
| 11 | 6705 | 18 | 51.1 | −6 | 16 | Sct | 14 | 5.8 | OC |
| 12 | 6218 | 16 | 47.2 | −1 | 57 | Oph | 14 | 6.6 | Gb |
| 13 | 6205 | 16 | 41.7 | +36 | 28 | Her | 17 | 5.9 | Gb |
| 14 | 6402 | 17 | 37.6 | −3 | 15 | Oph | 12 | 7.6 | Gb |
| 15 | 7078 | 21 | 30.0 | +12 | 10 | Peg | 12 | 6.4 | Gb |
| 16 | 6611 | 18 | 18.8 | −13 | 47 | Ser | 7 | 6.0 | OC |
| 17 | 6618 | 18 | 20.8 | −16 | 11 | Sgr | 46 × 37 | 7 | Di |
| 18 | 6613 | 18 | 19.9 | −17 | 08 | Sgr | 9 | 6.9 | OC |
| 19 | 6273 | 17 | 02.6 | −26 | 16 | Oph | 14 | 7.2 | Gb |
| 20 | 6514 | 18 | 02.6 | −23 | 02 | Sgr | 29 × 27 | 8.5 | Di |
| 21 | 6531 | 18 | 04.6 | −22 | 30 | Sgr | 13 | 5.9 | OC |
| 22 | 6656 | 18 | 36.4 | −23 | 54 | Sgr | 24 | 5.1 | Gb |
| 23 | 6494 | 17 | 56.8 | −19 | 01 | Sgr | 27 | 5.5 | OC |
| 24 | | 18 | 16.9 | −18 | 29 | Sgr | 90 | 4.5 | |
| 25 | IC 4725 | 18 | 31.6 | −19 | 15 | Sgr | 32 | 4.6 | OC |
| 26 | 6694 | 18 | 45.2 | −9 | 24 | Sct | 15 | 8.0 | OC |
| 27 | 6853 | 19 | 59.6 | +22 | 43 | Vul | 8 × 4 | 8.1 | Pl |
| 28 | 6626 | 18 | 24.5 | −24 | 52 | Sgr | 11 | 6.9 | Gb |
| 29 | 6913 | 20 | 23.9 | +38 | 32 | Cyg | 7 | 6.6 | OC |
| 30 | 7099 | 21 | 40.4 | −23 | 11 | Cap | 11 | 7.5 | Gb |
| 31 | 224 | 0 | 42.7 | +41 | 16 | And | 178 × 63 | 3.4 | S |
| 32 | 221 | 0 | 42.7 | +40 | 52 | And | 8 × 6 | 8.2 | E |
| 33 | 598 | 1 | 33.9 | +30 | 39 | Tri | 62 × 39 | 5.7 | S |
| 34 | 1039 | 2 | 42.0 | +42 | 47 | Per | 35 | 5.2 | OC |
| 35 | 2168 | 6 | 08.9 | +24 | 20 | Gem | 28 | 5.1 | OC |
| 36 | 1960 | 5 | 36.1 | +34 | 08 | Aur | 12 | 6.0 | OC |
| 37 | 2099 | 5 | 52.4 | +32 | 33 | Aur | 24 | 5.6 | OC |
| 38 | 1912 | 5 | 28.7 | +35 | 50 | Aur | 21 | 6.4 | OC |
| 39 | 7092 | 21 | 32.2 | +48 | 26 | Cyg | 32 | 4.6 | OC |
| 40 | | 12 | 22.4 | +58 | 05 | UMa | | 8 | |
| 41 | 2287 | 6 | 47.0 | −20 | 44 | CMa | 38 | 4.5 | OC |
| 42 | 1976 | 5 | 35.4 | −5 | 27 | Ori | 66 × 60 | 4 | Di |
| 43 | 1982 | 5 | 35.6 | −5 | 16 | Ori | 20 × 15 | 9 | Di |
| 44 | 2632 | 8 | 40.1 | +19 | 59 | Cnc | 95 | 3.1 | OC |
| 45 | | 3 | 47.0 | +24 | 07 | Tau | 110 | 1.2 | OC |
| 46 | 2437 | 7 | 41.8 | −14 | 49 | Pup | 27 | 6.1 | OC |
| 47 | 2422 | 7 | 36.6 | −14 | 30 | Pup | 30 | 4.4 | OC |
| 48 | 2548 | 8 | 13.8 | −5 | 48 | Hya | 54 | 5.8 | OC |
| 49 | 4472 | 12 | 29.8 | +8 | 00 | Vir | 9 × 7 | 8.4 | E |
| 50 | 2323 | 7 | 03.2 | −8 | 20 | Mon | 16 | 5.9 | OC |
| 51 | 5194-5 | 13 | 29.9 | +47 | 12 | CVn | 11 × 8 | 8.1 | S |
| 52 | 7654 | 23 | 24.2 | +61 | 35 | Cas | 13 | 6.9 | OC |
| 53 | 5024 | 13 | 12.9 | +18 | 10 | Com | 13 | 7.7 | Gb |
| 54 | 6715 | 18 | 55.1 | −30 | 29 | Sgr | 9 | 7.7 | Gb |
| 55 | 6809 | 19 | 40.0 | −30 | 58 | Sgr | 19 | 7.0 | Gb |
| 56 | 6779 | 19 | 16.6 | +30 | 11 | Lyr | 7 | 8.2 | Gb |
| 57 | 6720 | 18 | 53.6 | +33 | 02 | Lyr | 1 | 9.0 | Pl |
| 58 | 4579 | 12 | 37.7 | +11 | 49 | Vir | 5 × 4 | 9.8 | S |
| 59 | 4621 | 12 | 42.0 | +11 | 39 | Vir | 5 × 3 | 9.8 | E |
| 60 | 4649 | 12 | 43.7 | +11 | 33 | Vir | 7 × 6 | 8.8 | E |
| 61 | 4303 | 12 | 21.9 | +4 | 28 | Vir | 6 × 5 | 9.7 | S |
| 62 | 6266 | 17 | 01.2 | −30 | 07 | Oph | 14 | 6.6 | Gb |
| 63 | 5055 | 13 | 15.8 | +42 | 02 | CVn | 12 × 8 | 8.6 | S |
| 64 | 4826 | 12 | 56.7 | +21 | 41 | Com | 9 × 5 | 8.5 | S |
| 65 | 3623 | 11 | 18.9 | +13 | 05 | Leo | 10 × 3 | 9.3 | S |
| 66 | 3627 | 11 | 20.2 | +12 | 59 | Leo | 9 × 4 | 9.0 | S |
| 67 | 2682 | 8 | 50.4 | +11 | 49 | Cnc | 30 | 6.9 | OC |
| 68 | 4590 | 12 | 39.5 | −26 | 45 | Hya | 12 | 8.2 | Gb |
| 69 | 6637 | 18 | 31.4 | −32 | 21 | Sgr | 7 | 7.7 | Gb |
| 70 | 6681 | 18 | 43.2 | −32 | 18 | Sgr | 8 | 8.1 | Gb |
| 71 | 6838 | 19 | 53.8 | +18 | 47 | Sge | 7 | 8.3 | Gb |
| 72 | 6981 | 20 | 53.5 | −12 | 32 | Aqr | 6 | 9.4 | Gb |
| 73 | 6994 | 20 | 58.9 | −12 | 38 | Aqr | | | OC |
| 74 | 628 | 1 | 36.7 | +15 | 47 | Psc | 10 × 9 | 9.2 | S |
| 75 | 6864 | 20 | 06.1 | −21 | 55 | Sgr | 6 | 8.6 | Gb |
| 76 | 650-1 | 1 | 42.4 | +51 | 34 | Per | 2 × 1 | 11.5 | Pl |
| 77 | 1068 | 2 | 42.7 | −0 | 01 | Cet | 7 × 6 | 8.8 | S |
| 78 | 2068 | 5 | 46.7 | +0 | 03 | Ori | 8 × 6 | 8 | Di |
| 79 | 1904 | 5 | 24.5 | −24 | 33 | Lep | 9 | 8.0 | Gb |
| 80 | 6093 | 16 | 17.0 | −22 | 59 | Sco | 9 | 7.2 | Gb |
| 81 | 3031 | 9 | 55.6 | +69 | 04 | UMa | 26 × 14 | 6.8 | S |
| 82 | 3034 | 9 | 55.8 | +69 | 41 | UMa | 11 × 5 | 8.4 | Ir |
| 83 | 5236 | 13 | 37.0 | −29 | 52 | Hya | 11 × 10 | 7.6 | S |
| 84 | 4374 | 12 | 25.1 | +12 | 53 | Vir | 5 × 4 | 9.3 | E |
| 85 | 4382 | 12 | 25.4 | +18 | 11 | Com | 7 × 5 | 9.2 | E |
| 86 | 4406 | 12 | 26.2 | +12 | 57 | Vir | 7 × 6 | 9.2 | E |
| 87 | 4486 | 12 | 30.8 | +12 | 24 | Vir | 7 | 8.6 | E |
| 88 | 4501 | 12 | 32.0 | +14 | 25 | Com | 7 × 4 | 9.5 | S |
| 89 | 4552 | 12 | 35.7 | +12 | 33 | Vir | 4 | 9.8 | E |
| 90 | 4569 | 12 | 36.8 | +13 | 10 | Vir | 10 × 5 | 9.5 | S |
| 91 | 4548 | 12 | 35.4 | +14 | 30 | Com | 5 × 4 | 10.2 | S |
| 92 | 6341 | 17 | 17.1 | +43 | 08 | Her | 11 | 6.5 | Gb |
| 93 | 2447 | 7 | 44.6 | −23 | 52 | Pup | 22 | 6.2 | OC |
| 94 | 4736 | 12 | 50.9 | +41 | 07 | CVn | 11 × 9 | 8.1 | S |
| 95 | 3351 | 10 | 44.0 | +11 | 42 | Leo | 7 × 5 | 9.7 | S |
| 96 | 3368 | 10 | 46.8 | +11 | 49 | Leo | 7 × 5 | 9.2 | S |
| 97 | 3587 | 11 | 14.8 | +55 | 01 | UMa | 3 | 11.2 | Pl |
| 98 | 4192 | 12 | 13.8 | +14 | 54 | Com | 10 × 3 | 10.1 | S |
| 99 | 4254 | 12 | 18.8 | +14 | 25 | Com | 5 | 9.8 | S |
| 100 | 4321 | 12 | 22.9 | +15 | 49 | Com | 7 × 6 | 9.4 | S |
| 101 | 5457 | 14 | 03.2 | +54 | 21 | UMa | 27 × 26 | 7.7 | S |
| 102 | | | | | | | | | |
| 103 | 581 | 1 | 33.2 | +60 | 42 | Cas | 6 | 7.4 | OC |
| 104 | 4594 | 12 | 40.0 | −11 | 37 | Vir | 9 × 4 | 8.3 | S |
| 105 | 3379 | 10 | 47.8 | +12 | 35 | Leo | 4 × 4 | 9.3 | E |
| 106 | 4258 | 12 | 19.0 | +47 | 18 | CVn | 18 × 8 | 8.3 | S |
| 107 | 6171 | 16 | 32.5 | −13 | 03 | Oph | 10 | 8.1 | Gb |
| 108 | 3556 | 11 | 11.5 | +55 | 40 | UMa | 8 × 2 | 10.0 | S |
| 109 | 3992 | 11 | 57.6 | +53 | 23 | UMa | 8 × 5 | 9.8 | S |
| 110 | 205 | 0 | 40.4 | +41 | 41 | And | 17 × 10 | 8.0 | E |

astronomy: through space and time

## continued

Right ascension (R.A.) and declination (Dec.) are given for equinox 2000.0.

$m_v$ = apparent visual magnitude.

Types: Di, diffuse nebula; Gb, globular cluster; OC, open cluster; Pl, planetary nebula; E, elliptical galaxy; Ir, irregular galaxy; S, spiral galaxy.

M1. Crab nebula. Remnant of the supernova of A.D. 1054.

M8. Lagoon nebula.

M13. Hercules cluster.

M17. Omega nebula.

M20. Trifid nebula.

M24. Messier described the brightening of the Milky Way here; he did not mention the small open cluster NGC 6603.

M27. Dumbbell nebula.

M31. Andromeda galaxy.

M40. The wide double star Winnecke 4; magnitudes 9.0 and 9.6, separation 50 arcsec.

M42. Great Nebula in Orion.

M44. Praesepe, or Beehive cluster.

M45. Pleiades, or Seven Sisters.

M51. Whirlpool galaxy.

M57. Ring nebula in Lyra.

M64. Black-eye galaxy.

M73. An asterism consisting of only four stars.

M76. Little Dumbbell nebula.

M97. Owl nebula.

M102. An accidental reobservation of M101, according to Messier's colleague P. Mechain.

M104. Sombrero galaxy.

Adapted from *Sky Catalogue 2000.0,* Vol. 2, by A. Hirshfeld and R. Sinnott (Sky Publishing Corp., 1985).

appendix e

# g l o s s a r y

### absolute magnitude (M)
A star's apparent magnitude if located at a standard distance of 10 parsecs or 32.6 light-years from the Sun.

### absorption spectrum
A continuous spectrum interlaced by dark lines and bands.

### acceleration
The rate of change in velocity or direction of a body with respect to time; the increase in velocity of falling bodies due to the acceleration of gravity; the change in orbital velocity caused by acceleration of the planets.

### achondrites
Stony meteorites similar in composition to terrestrial basalts and lunar rocks.

### achromatic lens
A double convex lens made of crown glass and a plano-concave lens composed of flint glass to help correct chromatic aberration.

### active galactic nucleus (AGN)
The center of an active galaxy that may generate up to one million times more energy than a normal galaxy.

### active galaxy
A galaxy distinguished by the vast amount of energy released from its nucleus as synchrotron radiation.

### albedo
The ratio between the amount of sunlight reflected and the amount received by a body in the solar system.

### Allende meteorite
A carbonaceous chondrite with a composition believed to be similar to the particles that formed the solar accretion disk.

### altazimuth mount
A telescope mount used to determine positions in the horizon system of coordinates.

### altitude
The angular distance of a body above the horizon measured along the vertical circle passing through the body from 0° at the horizon to 90° at the zenith.

### amplitude
The measure of light variation such as the difference between maximum and minimum brightness in a variable star.

### Andromeda galaxy
The nearest spiral star system at a distance of 2.2 million light-years from our Galaxy.

### annual motion
The apparent eastward drift of the Sun along the ecliptic due to the Earth's revolution.

### aperture
The clear diameter of a telescope's objective lens or primary mirror.

### aphelion
A point in the orbit where a revolving body is at its greatest distance from the Sun.

### apogee
A point in the orbit where the Moon or a satellite is at its greatest distance from the Earth.

### apparent magnitude (m)
A measure of a star's observed brightness.

### apparent relative orbit
The apparent ellipse that results when the true relative orbit of the companion star in a visual binary system is projected to the plane of the sky perpendicular to the observer's line of sight.

### apparent solar day
The time interval between two successive transits of the Sun.

### apparent solar time
Time measurement based upon the angle of the Sun with respect to the meridian.

### asterism
A conspicuous group of stars within a constellation such as the Big Dipper in Ursa Major and the Northern Cross in Cygnus.

### asteroid
One of thousands of small bodies in the solar system that, in general, revolve in orbits between the planets Mars and Jupiter.

### astrometric binary
A binary system where the irregularities in the orbital motion of the visible primary star are used to determine the orbit and mass of an unseen companion star.

### astronomical unit (AU)
The mean distance between the Earth and the Sun, $1.495 \times 10^8$ km or $9.289 \times 10^7$ miles.

### Aten/Apollo/Amor asteroids
A class of minor planets that approach or cross the Earth's orbit.

### atomic number
The number of nuclear protons of an element.

### aurora australis
The southern lights composed of luminous arcs, rays, streamers, and curtains of ionized oxygen and nitrogen atoms in the Earth's upper atmosphere situated near the south magnetic pole.

### aurora borealis
The northern lights composed of ionized particles of oxygen and nitrogen in the Earth's upper atmosphere situated in a plasma ring surrounding the north magnetic pole.

### autumnal equinox
One of the intersections of the ecliptic and the celestial equator; the position of the Sun on the first day of autumn in the northern hemisphere, September 23.

### azimuth
The angular distance of a body measured eastward along the horizon from the north point to the vertical circle passing through the body. Azimuth increases from 0° at the north point through 360°.

### Balmer series
A distinctive series of lines in the spectrum of hydrogen.

### Barringer Crater (Meteor Crater)
A 1260-km depression in Arizona formed by the impact of a huge iron-nickel meteoric body about 25,000 years ago.

### barycenter
The center of mass in the Earth-Moon system.

### basin
A large ringlike depression, up to 300 km in diameter, on the surface of the Moon.

**belts**
Dark rose-colored clouds in the atmosphere of Jupiter.

**big bang theory**
The concept of the expanding universe beginning as a hot, dense primordial atom that erupted in a burst of energy from which all matter formed.

**binary star**
A system of two stars that revolve around a common center of mass.

**blackbody**
An object in thermal equilibrium that absorbs and radiates away all energy without reflection.

**black hole**
An exotic object of such overpowering gravitational attraction that nothing, not even radiation can escape.

**BL Lacertae object**
A point source of visible radiation whose spectrum shows continuous emission and lacks distinctive emission and absorption lines.

**blue giant star**
A high-temperature spectral class O or B main sequence star.

**Bohr atom**
A model of a hydrogen atom proposed by Niels Bohr where an electron can revolve around the proton without the loss of energy.

**bolometric magnitude**
A measurement of a star's total energy emission in all wavelengths.

C

**calendar year**
The chronological division of the year into months, weeks, and days.

**Caloris Basin**
A large multi-ringed impact basin located at one of the hot subsolar points on the surface of Mercury at perihelion.

**carbonaceous chondrites**
A type of stony meteorite composed of millimeter-sized silicate spheres, carbon, carbon compounds, water, and amino acids.

**carbon-nitrogen-oxygen cycle**
A nuclear reaction that occurs in the interior of massive stars where carbon joins with hydrogen to form nitrogen and oxygen. Carbon acts as a catalyst to initiate the process, and nitrogen and hydrogen combine to form helium and carbon as the end product.

**cardinal points**
The directions north, east, south, and west that divide the horizon into equal quadrants.

**Cassegrain focus**
An arrangement of mirrors in a telescope where light from the concave primary mirror is reflected by a convex secondary mirror to the focal point beyond a hole in the primary mirror.

**Cassini division**
A separation 5000 km wide in the ring system of Saturn discovered by Giovanni Cassini in 1675.

**catadioptric telescope**
An instrument consisting of a combination of a correcting lens and a primary mirror.

**celestial equator**
The great circle on the celestial sphere midway between the celestial poles; the extension of the Earth's geographic equator to the celestial sphere.

**celestial meridian**
The vertical reference circle in the horizon system that passes through the north point on the horizon, the north celestial pole, the zenith, the south point, and the nadir.

**celestial poles**
The two points on the sky representing the intersection of the Earth's axis with the celestial sphere.

**celestial sphere**
The inner surface of an imaginary sphere on which celestial bodies, coordinate systems, and reference points are projected.

**central bulge**
A condensation of stars and interstellar matter surrounding the nucleus of a spiral galaxy.

**centripetal force**
A force directed toward the center that impels a body from a straight to a curved path; the Sun's centripetal force causes the planets to accelerate in curved orbits.

**cepheid variable star**
A star that changes periodically in brightness due to rhythmic pulsations of its outer layers. The correlation between the light variation and the luminosity makes the star an important distance indicator.

**Chandrasekar limit**
The theoretical critical value of 1.44 solar masses that represents the limiting mass of a white dwarf star.

**chaotic hummocky terrain**
A surface region of Mars characterized by an agglomerate of isolated blocks and cliffs interlaced with faults and fractures.

**Charon**
Satellite of Pluto, revolving at a distance of about 20,000 km from the planet in a period of 6.39 days.

**chasmate**
Name given to deep channels on the planet Venus.

**charge-coupled device (CCD)**
A detector consisting of many rows of photodiodes capable of producing images on a monitor screen.

**chondrite**
A stony meteorite characterized by chondrules, which are tiny granules of enstatite and olivine.

**chromatic aberration**
The difference in the positions of the focal points for light of different colors passing through a lens.

**chromosphere**
The region of the Sun's atmosphere nearest to the visible photosphere.

**circumpolar stars**
The stars that follow diurnal circles between the horizon and the celestial pole at any given latitude and remain above the horizon during the entire period of the Earth's rotation.

**closed universe**
A universe in which space is finite and unbounded.

**color index (B–V)**
The difference in a star's magnitude measured in two different spectral regions defined by a standard magnitude and color system.

**coma**
A cloud of dust and gas surrounding the nucleus of a comet.

**Coma cluster**
A large cluster of galaxies containing thousands of members located in the constellation Coma Berenices at a distance of about 325 million light-years.

**comet**
One of a multitude of small icy bodies that revolve in orbits around the Sun. When a comet approaches the Sun, its solid nucleus vaporizes to form a cloud or coma. Solar radiation pressure may cause material of the comet to form gaseous and dusty tails.

**Comet Halley**
The most celebrated comet named after Edmond Halley who first determined its orbital elements. At its last appearance in 1986, six international space probes made close-up investigations of the comet's structure and composition.

**companion star**
The secondary star in a binary system.

**conjunction**
The apparent positions of two celestial bodies having the same celestial longitude or right ascension.

**conservation of angular momentum**
The angular momentum of a rotating body about an axis, or the revolution of a body in orbit, is constant in magnitude and direction unless acted upon by an external force or an interaction of components within the system.

**constellation**
A group of stars that portray various people and animals in legend and mythology; or the division of the sky in which the star group may be found.

**continuous spectrum**
An emission spectrum where the colors blend into each other without interruption within the optical region and an unbroken emission band in the radio region.

**co-orbiting satellites**
Two satellites revolving in nearly the same orbit around a planet.

**core**
The central region of a planet, composed of silicates or heavy metals such as iron and nickel.

**corona**
Outermost region of the Sun's atmosphere.

**coronal hole**
A large expanse in the Sun's atmosphere where density and temperature are less than the surrounding region.

**cosmic background radiation**
A microwave radiation corresponding to a blackbody temperature of 2.74 K approaching from every direction in space that represents evidence in support of the big-bang theory.

**cosmogony**
The study of the origin and development of the universe.

**cosmological principle**
A generalization which states that the universe is similar in structure and composition in all directions.

**cosmological redshift**
The lowering of the frequency of radiation emitted by distant galaxies due to the expansion of the universe.

**cosmology**
The study of the spacetime structure of the universe.

**cratered regions**
The areas on the planet Mercury that show evidence of heavy meteoric impact.

**cratered terrain**
The upland regions in the southern hemisphere of Mars representing an ancient surface covered by craters.

**craters**
Bowl-shaped formations on the Moon and other members of the solar system formed by the impact of meteoric bodies.

**critical density**
The minimum average density of matter required to prevent the expansion of the universe to continue indefinitely.

**crust**
The thin, solid layer of the Earth that forms the continents and ocean floors.

**current sheet**
Electrically charged particles confined in the plane of a planet's magnetic equator.

**dark nebulae**
Extensive obscuring clouds of fine-grained dust found in the arms of a spiral galaxy.

**declination, dec.**
The coordinate in the equator system which is the measure of the angular distance of a body north (+) or south (−) from the celestial equator (0°) to the celestial poles (90°).

**deductive reasoning**
Procedure by which ideas are shaped from general principles.

**deferent**
An eccentric circle used in the geocentric Ptolemaic system to explain the variation of the apparent motion of a planet as the distance between the planet and the Earth changes.

**degenerate electron gas**
A high-density substance where ideal gas laws no longer apply; electrons occupy all energy states and none may change energy state until another is vacated.

**degenerate neutron gas**
The degenerate matter contained in a neutron star.

**density wave theory**
An explanation proposed by C. C. Lin and F. H. Shu where spiral arms in a galaxy are formed when complex motions of stars cause compression and rarefaction of material in various regions of the galactic disk.

**detector**
An instrument used to measure and record data.

**direct motion**
The motion of a body on the celestial sphere from west to east with respect to the stars.

**discontinuity**
A boundary marking the interface between two regions of different density and composition.

**dispersion**
The separation of light into its different wave-lengths when passed through a prism or diffraction grating.

**distance modulus (m–M)**
A measurement expressed as the difference between a star's apparent and absolute magnitudes.

**diurnal circle**
The apparent path of a celestial body across the sky caused by the Earth's rotation.

**diurnal motion**
The apparent motion of the sky from east to west caused by the rotation of the Earth from west to east.

**Doppler effect**
The apparent displacement in wavelength of sound and electromagnetic radiation when the source of wave motion approaches or recedes from the observer.

**eastern quadrature**
The position of a celestial body at 90° east of the Sun as measured from the Earth.

**ebb tide**
The gradual fall of the waters to a minimum level at low tide.

**eccentricity**
The elongation of an ellipse. The eccentricity is obtained by dividing the distance between the focal points by the length of the major axis.

**eclipsing variable star**
A binary system where the orbital plane lies in or near the line of sight so that the component stars will eclipse each other and cause variations in the total brightness.

**ecliptic**
The great circle on the celestial sphere representing a complete circuit of the Sun against the stars of the zodiac; the great circle representing the intersection of the Earth's plane and the celestial sphere.

**electromagnetic radiation**
All radiant energy propagated by the oscillations of electric and magnetic fields.

**electromagnetic spectrum**
The complete range of electromagnetic energy from the shortest wavelengths of gamma rays to the longest radio waves.

**electromagnetism**
The magnetic field produced by an electric current.

**electron**
A fundamental particle in an atom having a negative electrical charge.

**elliptical galaxy (dwarf, giant)**
A spherical or ellipsoidal galaxy without spiral arms.

**emission nebula**
A gaseous cloud principally composed of hydrogen ionized by the intense ultraviolet radiation from nearby high-temperature stars.

**emission spectrum**
A bright-line spectrum where the lines are separated by an amount corresponding to their wavelengths and frequencies.

**Encke division**
A gap in the A-ring of Saturn discovered by the nineteenth century astronomer, J. F. Encke.

**epicycle**
A smaller circle whose center revolves in a larger circle, called a deferent used in the Ptolemaic geocentric system to explain the motion of a planet with respect to the stars.

**equator system**
A celestial coordinate system where the celestial equator is the fundamental reference circle.

**equatorial mount**
A telescope mounting which consists of a polar axis pointing toward the celestial pole and a declination axis supporting the telescope at 90° to the polar axis.

**event horizon**
The spherical boundary separating a black hole from the universe at large.

**eyepiece**
A magnifying lens system through which the observer views an image formed by the objective lens or primary mirror of a telescope.

F

**faculae**
Bright, active regions of high temperature in the Sun's photosphere.

**fixed stars**
The name given to the stars by early astronomers who believed the stars to be attached to the celestial sphere.

**flare**
A powerful short-lived eruption on the Sun from a sunspot region.

**flood tide**
The gradual rise in the height of the waters to a maximum level at high tide.

**focal length**
The distance from the objective lens or primary mirror of a telescope to the focal point.

**focal point (focus)**
The point where parallel light rays converge after refraction by a convex lens or reflection by a concave mirror.

**focal plane**
A plane containing the focal points of all parts of the image.

**Fraunhofer lines**
Dark absorption lines observed in solar and stellar spectra.

**frequency**
The number of waves of a wave motion or other period phenomenon that pass a point in one second (cycles per second).

**fretted hummocky terrain**
A rippled surface region of Mars that contains isolated blocks, mesas, and cliffs located at the boundary of the cratered uplands.

**Friedmann models**
Mathematical models derived by Alexander Friedmann in 1922 that describe the geometry of an expanding or contracting universe.

**fusion**
The synthesis of lighter atomic nuclei to form more massive elements accompanied by the release of an enormous amount of energy.

G

**galactic cannibalism**
The absorption of a smaller galaxy by the gravitational attraction of a nearby larger galaxy.

**galactic cluster**
An open cluster. A sparsely populated collection of population I stars of common origin that have the same space motion and are located in or near the plane of the Milky Way.

**galactic corona**
A massive spherical region of unseen matter surrounding a galaxy that extends into intergalactic space.

**galactic nucleus**
The central core of a galaxy that may contain a massive black hole.

**galaxy**
An aggregation of stars, star clusters, and interstellar matter analogous to the Milky Way Galaxy.

**galaxy cluster**
A formation of galaxies ranging in number from a group with only a few members to rich clusters with more than 1000 member galaxies.

**Galaxy (Milky Way)**
The huge star system which contains the Sun. See Milky Way Galaxy.

**Galilean satellites**
The four largest satellites of Jupiter discovered by Galileo in 1610.

**general theory of relativity**
Albert Einstein's treatment of gravitation as an effect of the curvature of space-time rather than an attractive force between masses.

**geocentric world system**
A universe in which the Sun, planets, and stars revolve around a stationary central Earth.

**geographic equator**
The great circle on the Earth's surface midway between the north and south geographic poles.

**giant branch**
The upper right region of the Hertzsprung-Russell diagram representing the giant and supergiant stars that increase in size and luminosity as their temperature decreases.

**giant molecular cloud**
A massive nebula that comprises molecular hydrogen, carbon monoxide, and traces of other molecules and occupies the dark rifts in the Milky Way.

**grand unified theories (GUTs)**
Theories developed to describe the early universe when the forces of nature were combined into one superforce.

**granulation**
The granular structure of the Sun's photosphere caused by the convective transport of hot gas from the interior.

**gravitation**
The attraction between two material bodies or photons of electromagnetic radiation.

**gravitational lensing**
The relativistic bending of light from a distant source while passing through the gravitational field of a massive foreground body. Light will be deflected and form halos and rings about the foreground image.

**Great Dark Spot**
A distinct dark oval in the atmosphere of Neptune believed to be a hole in the cloud layer to expose a darker region in the planet's gaseous envelope.

**greatest elongation (east and west)**
The maximum angular distance of an inferior planet east or west of the Sun as measured from the Earth.

**Great Red Spot**
A 25,000-km anticyclonic disturbance extending several kilometers above the surrounding cloud level in the atmosphere of Jupiter.

**greenhouse effect**
The additional heating of a planet's lower atmosphere by the absorption of infrared energy radiated from the surface.

**Greenwich mean time, GMT**
Mean solar time starting at midnight in Greenwich; universal time, UT.

**Gregorian calendar**
The revised calendar recommended by Pope Gregory XIII in 1582 which remains in use today.

**grooved terrain**
A light-colored region on the surface of Jupiter's satellite Ganymede characterized by complex grooves and ridges.

**ground state**
The normal or lowest energy state of an atom.

H

**halo**
A tenuous spherical region of old stars and globular clusters that surrounds the entire visible structure of a galaxy.

**Hayashi track**
The graph of an almost vertical line on the H-R diagram that represents the evolutionary changes in a contracting protostar.

**heliocentric world system**
A universe in which the planets and the stars revolve around a stationary central Sun.

**helioseismology**
The study of internal oscillations in the Sun.

**heliosphere**
The region surrounding the Sun that extends out to where the solar wind meets the interstellar medium.

**helium flash**
The ignition of the degenerate core of a red giant star as helium transforms into carbon at the start of the triple-alpha process.

**Herbig-Haro object**
A small nebula that is formed when bipolar material ejected from a T Tauri star collides with interstellar gas and dust.

**Hertzsprung-Russell (H-R) diagram**
A graphic representation of stars according to spectral class (or color index and temperature) and absolute magnitude (or luminosity).

**Hirayama families**
Clusters of main-belt asteroids sharing the same orbital elements.

**horizon**
A great circle representing the intersection of the observer's horizontal plane and the celestial sphere.

**horizon system**
A celestial coordinate system where the astronomical horizon serves as the reference circle. The coordinates are called altitude and azimuth.

**hour angle**
The angle between the hour circle of a body and the celestial meridian measured westward from the meridian from 0h to 24h.

**hour circle**
A great circle in the equator system that passes through the celestial poles perpendicular to the celestial equator.

**Hubble constant/parameter**
The ratio between the recession velocity of a remote galaxy and its distance.

**Hubble law**
The radial velocity of a galaxy, observed as a redshift of its spectral lines, increases with respect to the distance of the galaxy from the Earth.

**Hubble period**
The age of the universe if the rate of its expansion remained unchanged.

**hydrostatic equilibrium**
In the Sun and stars, the balance between the outward pressure at any given distance from the center and the inward force of gravity at that point.

**hypothesis**
A proposition or provisional solution to a problem that is consistent with known data and requires further investigation which may strengthen or weaken the original generalization.

**inclination**
The angle formed by the rotational axis of a body and a given reference plane.

**inductive reasoning**
Procedure by which generalizations are formulated after support is obtained through experimentation or observation.

**inertia**
The property of a body to remain at rest or in uniform motion unless acted upon by an external force.

**inferior conjunction**
The apparent position of an inferior planet when it is between the Earth and the Sun.

**inferior planet**
The designation for the planets Mercury and Venus whose orbits are nearer to the Sun than is the orbit of Earth.

**inflationary theory**
A theory proposed by Alan H. Guth in 1980 in which space-time had an extraordinary increase in size a fraction of a second after the big bang. By $10^{-30}$ second, inflation was over and the universe continued to expand at the rate specified by the standard big-bang model.

**instability strip**
An almost vertical region in the H-R diagram occupied by intrinsic variable stars.

**interacting galaxies**
Galaxies in close approach or actual collision with each other.

**intercrater plains**
A terrain peculiar to the planet Mercury that covers about one-third of the planet's surface.

**interference**
A phenomenon that occurs when waves of similar frequency are combined. The waves either reinforce each other and create a pattern of bright fringes, or they interfere with each other and form a pattern of dark fringes.

**interstellar medium**
Material between the stars mainly composed of hydrogen gas and tiny solid grains of uncertain composition.

**intrinsic variable star**
A star that varies from maximum to minimum brightness due to physical changes in its atmosphere.

**inverse square law**
The intensity of radiation decreases inversely as the square of the distance between the source and the observer.

**ionosphere**
The ionized region of the Earth's upper atmosphere.

**iridium**
A silver-white substance, chemical symbol Ir, found in meteorites and as a trace element in the Earth's crust.

**iron meteorites**
A class of meteorites composed of iron and nickel alloys.

**irregular galaxy**
An asymmetrical galaxy, neither elliptical nor spiral in structure.

**isotope**
Atoms of the same chemical element having different atomic mass.

**Jovian planet**
The name of a giant planet derived from the Roman sky god Jupiter (Jove).

**Julian calendar**
The Roman calendar established by Julius Caesar in 46 B.C.

**Kepler's laws**
The three laws of planetary motion formulated by Kepler in the seventeenth century.

**Kirkwood gaps**
Resonance gaps in the asteroid belt discovered by Daniel Kirkwood in 1867. The gaps are caused by the gravitational influence of Jupiter.

**L**

**Lagrangian point**
One of five positions of equilibrium in the gravitational field of two massive bodies revolving around each other where a body of low mass will remain in balance between the two major bodies.

**Large Magellanic Cloud (LMC)**
The larger irregular galaxy associated with the Galaxy observed in the southern hemisphere.

**latitude**
The geographic coordinate that defines the angular distance north and south from 0° at the equator to 90° at the poles along the meridian passing through the position.

**light curve**
A plot of a variable star's change in brightness (or magnitude) with respect to time.

**light-gathering power**
The increase in image brightness in proportion to the square of the diameter of the telescope's objective lens or primary mirror.

**limb darkening**
The gradual decrease in light intensity of the Sun's photosphere from the center of the disk to the limb.

**liquid metallic hydrogen**
A dense fluid of electrically charged atomic hydrogen situated above the core at the center of Jupiter.

**liquid molecular hydrogen**
A shell of molecular hydrogen above the metallic hydrogen layer in the interior of Jupiter.

**lithosphere**
The solid, outer layer of the Earth composed of the crust and a thin portion of the upper mantle.

**lobate scarps**
A distinctive feature of long, curved cliffs that extend several hundred kilometers across the surface of Mercury.

**lobed radio source**
Regions emitting radio radiation of varying intensity situated on each side of the active nucleus of a radio galaxy.

**Local Group**
A small cluster of about thirty stellar systems in which three spirals—the Andromeda galaxy, our Galaxy, and M33—are the principal members.

**longitude**
The geographic coordinate that defines the angular distance from 0° at the prime meridian through 180° east and west along the equator or the parallel circle passing through the position.

**long-period comet**
A comet with an orbital period in excess of 200 years and aphelion equal to thousands of AU.

**luminosity**
The total energy output per unit of time in all directions of the Sun and stars.

**luminosity classes**
A graphic representation of stars according to their luminosities and spectral classes.

**lunar eclipse**
The darkening of the Moon that occurs during full phase when the Moon is immersed in the Earth's shadow.

**Magellanic stream**
A band of neutral hydrogen extending from the Magellanic Clouds to the vicinity of the Andromeda galaxy.

**magnetosphere**
A planet's outermost region that is dominated by high-energy protons and electrons from the Sun.

**magnifying power**
The ratio between the focal lengths of the objective lens or between the primary mirror and the eyepiece.

**magnitude**
A numerical measurement of the brightness of a star or other luminous celestial body.

**main sequence**
The principle series of stars that stretches from the upper left to the lower right region of the H-R diagram.

**major planet**
One of the nine largest planets in the solar system.

**mantle**
The most extensive layer of the Earth that extends from the crust to a narrow boundary above the liquid outer core.

**mare**
A Latin word meaning "sea" used to identify dark, flat plains that cover the lunar surface visible from the Earth.

**mass**
A measure of the material content of a body.

**mass loss**
The vast amount of material ejected by a massive star during later phases of its evolution.

**mass-luminosity relation**
A graphic representation of the relationship between the mass and luminosity of a main sequence or a subgiant star.

**mean solar time**
The time measurement computed from the position of the mean sun.

**mean sun**
A fictitious sun devised to eliminate the variations of apparent solar time. The imaginary mean sun moves with uniform speed along the equator, completing one tropical year in the same interval as the actual Sun.

**meridian**
A great circle on a sphere which passes through both poles and is perpendicular to the equator or reference circle.

**Messier catalogue**
A listing of nebulae, star clusters, and galaxies compiled by the eighteenth century French astronomer, Charles Messier.

**meteor**
A bright streak of light that occurs when cosmic particles of metal and rock vaporize in the Earth's atmosphere.

**meteor shower**
An increase in the number of meteors per hour observed when the Earth encounters a stream of meteoric particles left in the wake of a disintegrated comet.

**meteorite**
A body that does not completely vaporize on entering the atmosphere and falls to the surface of the Earth.

**meteoroid**
One of countless metallic and rocky bodies that permeate the solar system.

**Milky Way**
The glowing band of light spanning the sky consisting of stars, light and dark nebulae, and dust that form the spiral arms in the central plane of our galaxy.

**Milky Way Galaxy**
Another name used to describe our stellar system.

**minor planet**
An asteroid.

**Mira variable star**
A class of long-period variable stars named after the prototype, Mira, Omicron Ceti.

**model**
A mathematical description of phenomena such as the motions of celestial bodies and the behavior of matter and energy.

**mons**
Name used to identify volcanic peaks on Venus and Mars.

**montes**
Mountain ranges on Venus.

**Murchison meteorite**
A carbonaceous chondrite recovered in 1969 that contains extraterrestrial amino acids.

**nadir**
The point on the celestial sphere opposite the zenith.

**neap tide**
An unusually low high tide that occurs when the Moon is at quarter phase and the gravitational attraction of the Moon and Sun counteract each other.

**nebula**
A cloud of dust or gas in interstellar space.

**neutron**
An electrically neutral atomic particle that is bound to the proton in the nucleus of an atom.

**neutron star**
A terminal stage of a dense star composed entirely of neutrons; its mass is greater than 1.4 solar masses and its diameter is between 10 to 30 km.

**New General Catalogue of Nebulae and Clusters of Stars (NGC)**
The compilation of about 8000 star clusters, nebulae, and galaxies by J. L. E. Dreyer in 1888.

**Newtonian focus**
The focus obtained by diverting the converging light from the primary mirror to a prism or diagonal plane mirror, and then to the side of the telescope tube where the eyepiece is attached.

**Newton's laws**
The laws set forth by Isaac Newton that form the basis for classical and celestial mechanics.

**nova**
(Latin for "new star.") A star that explodes or suddenly erupts and increases in brightness.

**nucleus (comet)**
The small, frozen central body of a comet.

## O

**O association**
Sparsely populated aggregation of young O and B spectral class main-sequence stars.

**objective lens**
The lens that forms the image in a refracting telescope.

**obliquity of the ecliptic**
The angle on the celestial sphere formed by the intersection of the ecliptic and the celestial equator.

**observable universe**
The region of the universe that can be detected from the Earth.

**occultation**
An eclipse phenomenon where a star is concealed by a planet or the Moon.

**Olbers' paradox**
A proposal by Heinrich Olbers in 1823 to explain why the night sky is dark.

**Olympus mons**
The largest volcano in the solar system located on the surface of Mars.

**Oort cloud**
A vast spherical cloud containing more than one trillion cometary nuclei extending as far as 200,000 AU from the Sun. The existence of this cloud was proposed by the Dutch astronomer Jan Oort in 1950.

**open universe**
A universe in which space extends indefinitely.

**opposition**
The apparent position of a superior planet situated 180° from the Sun as measured from the Earth.

**Orion arm**
The spiral arm of the Galaxy that contains the Sun and solar system.

**oscillating-universe hypothesis**
A description of a closed Friedmann universe that will reach maximum expansion and contract to a singularity.

## P

**parallax**
The apparent displacement of an object when viewed from two directions.

**parallels (circles)**
Small circles on the surface of a sphere parallel to a reference or great circle.

**parsec**
A contraction of *par*allax and *sec*ond. The distance at which the radius of the Earth's orbit (1 AU) will have an angular displacement of one arc second. One parsec = 3.26 light-years.

**particle era**
The phase in the history of the universe when quarks combined to form protons and neutrons.

**particle horizon**
The boundary of the observable universe which is limited in radius by the light-travel time of radiation from the most distant objects seen from Earth.

**path of totality**
A long, narrow strip of the Earth's surface where a total eclipse of the Sun may be observed.

**Pauli exclusion principle**
In quantum mechanics, a fundamental law that no two free electrons can simultaneously occupy the same energy state.

**peculiar galaxy**
A galaxy with a distorted shape or other unusual feature.

**peculiar terrain**
A chaotic lineated region on the planet Mercury that formed when a meteoric object struck the opposite side of the planet.

**perigee**
The point in the orbit of the Moon or a satellite located nearest to the Earth.

**perihelion**
The point in the orbit of a body in the solar system located nearest to the Sun.

**period-luminosity relation**
The connection between the periods of light variation and luminosities of cepheid variable stars.

**period of revolution**
The time interval required to complete one cycle in a regularly recurring event.

**Perseus arm**
The spiral arm of the Galaxy immediately beyond the spiral arm in which the Sun is located.

**phases (lunar)**
The conspicuous change in the appearance of the illuminated surface of the Moon as seen from Earth: new, first quarter, full, and last quarter.

**photodisintegration**
One of the processes in the core of a massive star whereby high-energy photons break down iron nuclei into alpha particles and neutrons to drive the core to its ultimate collapse.

**photon**
A quantum of electromagnetic radiation.

**photon sphere**
A shell of radiation surrounding a black hole that is formed when photons are deflected into closed orbits by the intense gravitational field.

**photosphere**
The visible layer of the Sun.

**plages**
Bright chromospheric regions that are prominent in monochromatic photographs in the K line of ionized calcium and the red alpha line of hydrogen.

**Planck's law**
The radiation law which describes the relationship between temperature, frequency, and intensity of radiation.

**Planck time**
The theoretical limit to which physicists can probe back in time to a fraction of a second after the big bang.

**planetary nebula**
An extensive shell surrounding a central star that forms when the outer envelope expands and the hot interior region of the star is exposed.

**planetesimal**
One of a countless number of small particles that are believed to have surrounded the evolving Sun at an early period in the history of the solar system.

**planitia**
Name given to a flat lowland region on the surfaces of Venus and Mars.

**plate tectonics**
The theory of the processes that produce movement in the Earth's crust and upper mantle.

**Polaris**
The North Star, Alpha Ursae Minoris, located within one degree of the north celestial pole.

**polarization**
The state in which light or other transverse waves vibrate in only one plane at right angles to the direction of propagation.

**populations I and II stars**
Two general categories of stars grouped according to stage of evolution, location in a galaxy, and chemical composition.

**position angle**
In a binary system, the angle measured from the hour circle of the primary star, from north in an easterly direction, to the great circle connecting the primary and secondary stars.

**precession**
The gradual turning of the Earth's rotational axis around the ecliptic poles in a period of about 26,000 years.

**precession of the equinoxes**
The gradual westward drift of the equinoxes and solstices along the ecliptic due to the precession of the Earth.

**primary eclipse**
The time of minimum light when the brighter star in an eclipsing binary system is concealed.

**primary mirror**
The mirror that forms the image in a reflecting telescope.

**primary star**
Usually the brighter member of a binary system.

**prime meridian**
By international agreement, the meridian through Greenwich, England which is the reference circle for the measurement of geographic longitude.

**Principia**
A short form of *Philosophiae Naturalis Principia Mathematica*, Issac Newton's famous work of 1687 in which the laws of motion and gravitation were formulated.

**principle of equivalence**
A fundamental law of general relativity where the inertial mass and the gravitational mass are equal and the acceleration of a body is independent of its mass.

**prominence**
A gaseous eruption in the Sun's chromosphere.

**proton**
The particle in an atomic nucleus that carries a positive charge.

**proton-proton chain**
Thermonuclear process in the Sun and sunlike stars where four protons are fused into a helium nucleus while a small fraction of the mass is converted to energy.

**protoplanet**
A body that gained mass through gravitational accretion of dust and gas to form into a planet.

**protosun**
A condensation of interstellar dust and gas that contracted to form the Sun.

**pulsar**
A pulsating radio source identified as a neutron star with a period ranging from 0.0015 to 4.0 seconds and a linear diameter between 10 and 30 km.

**quadrature (east and west)**
The apparent position of a planet at 90° east or west of the Sun as measured from the Earth.

**quantum**
A discrete unit of energy at which electromagnetic radiation can be emitted or absorbed.

**quasar**
A distant active galactic nucleus surrounded by faint luminous matter believed to be stars and nebulosity in the host galaxy.

**radial velocity curve**
A graph depicting the change in radial velocity (km/sec) versus the period (days) as stars in a binary system alternately approach and recede, or the change in the rate of expansion and contraction of an intrinsic variable star.

**radiant**
The apparent point in the sky from which a meteor shower seems to emanate.

**radiation**
The process by which electromagnetic energy is transmitted across space without an intervening medium.

**radiation era**
The phase in which the universe became transparent and photons were free to travel through space.

**radio galaxy**
A class of active galaxies that produce more radio emissions than normal galaxies.

**radio interferometer**
Two or more radio telescopes focused on the same object to obtain a higher resolution.

**rays (lunar)**
Bright streaks of pulverized deposits of surface material ejected from more recently formed lunar craters.

**red dwarf star**
A faint spectral type M main sequence star.

**reflecting telescope**
A telescope in which an image is produced when incoming light is focused by a concave mirror.

**reflection**
The return of a wave motion at the interface between two dissimilar media.

**reflection nebula**
A dust cloud that reflects light from nearby stars.

**refracting telescope**
A telescope in which the image is produced when the incoming light is focused by refraction through a lens or lens system.

**refraction**
The bending of radiation at the interface where two transparent substances of different densities are in contact.

**regiones**
Isolated plateaus found on the surface of Venus.

**relativistic redshift**
The value of the redshift (z) of a remote galaxy corrected for the effects of relativity when recession velocity approaches *c*, the velocity of light.

**relativity**
The theories formulated by Albert Einstein dealing with space, time, and the structure of the universe. In the special theory, the measurements of time and distance are dependent upon the relative motion at constant velocity of the observer and source under investigation. The general theory treats the structure of space and gravitation in terms of a four-dimensional continuum.

**resolving power**
The ability of a telescope to separate close binary stars or fine details on the surfaces of extended objects such as the Moon and planets.

**retrograde motion**
The motion of a body on the celestial sphere from east to west with respect to the stars.

**revolution**
The motion of a celestial body in an orbit around a more massive body.

**right ascension, R. A.**
A coordinate in the equator system measured eastward along the celestial equator from the vernal equinox to the hour circle of the celestial body. Right ascension is measured in hours, minutes, and seconds of time.

**ring-arcs**
The partial ring system of Neptune.

**ring system**
A thin disk of particles in orbit around each of the giant planets, Jupiter, Saturn, Uranus, and Neptune.

**Roche lobe**
The limiting volume of space that encloses each member of a binary system, the interior of which is under the gravitational influence of the central star.

**rotation**
The spin of a celestial body about an imaginary axis.

**RR Lyrae variable star**
Class of short-period intrinsic variable stars named after the prototype RR Lyrae.

**Sagittarius A\***
An intense radio source associated with the nucleus of the Galaxy.

**Sagittarius arm**
The spiral arm of the Galaxy between the Orion arm containing the Sun and the galactic center.

**saros**
A cycle marking an interval of 18 years 11 days (6585.5 days) when eclipses of the Sun and Moon will occur again in the same order.

**satellite**
A body that revolves in an orbit around a planet.

**Schmidt telescope**
An optical system invented by Bernhard Schmidt that consists of a spherical mirror corrected for spherical aberration by an aspheric lens placed at the center of curvature.

**Schwarzschild radius**
The distance from the center of a black hole to the event horizon.

**scientific law**
A generalization or mature theory that is supported by experimentation or observation.

**scientific method**
An established procedure used to find solutions to problems. The investigator will define a problem and collect data, make a tentative proposal or hypothesis consistent with known data, test the hypothesis by means of observations, and determine whether or not the hypothesis is supported by established evidence.

**scintillation**
The rapid changes in the brightness and color of stars called "twinkling" which is caused by density variations in the Earth's atmosphere.

**secondary eclipse**
An eclipse showing less reduction of light when the fainter companion star in an eclipsing binary system is concealed.

**secondary mirror**
A plane or curved mirror mounted in the telescope to divert the light cone from the primary mirror to the eyepiece.

**secondary star**
The companion or second brightest star in a binary system.

**seeing**
The condition of the atmosphere in terms of turbulence, haze, transparency, cloud cover, and other effects that limit astronomical observations.

**separation**
The angular distance between the primary and secondary stars in a visual binary system.

**Seyfert galaxy**
An active galaxy with a bright, starlike nucleus, broad emission lines, and large energy output from a compact non-stellar source.

**shepherd satellites**
Satellites of the giant planets that occupy orbits on the inner and outer edges of a ring and keep the ring particles from scattering.

**short-period comet**
A comet in an orbit of small eccentricity and at an aphelion distance near the orbit of Jupiter. Cometary periods average about seven years.

**sidereal day**
The time interval between two successive meridian transits of the vernal equinox.

**sidereal month**
The time required by the Moon to complete one revolution in its orbit with respect to the stars.

**sidereal period**
The time required for a celestial body to complete one revolution with respect to the stars.

**sidereal time**
The measure of the Earth's rotation with respect to the stars. Sidereal time (S. T.) is equal to the hour angle of the vernal equinox, or it is the time elapsed since the vernal equinox crossed the observer's meridian (00h S. T.).

**sidereal year**
The Earth's period of revolution with respect to the stars.

**singularity**
The point mass where all the mass of a black hole is found.

**Small Magellanic Cloud**
A small irregular galaxy associated with the Galaxy and is seen as a patch of light in the southern hemisphere.

**smooth plains**
Flat surface features of the planet Mercury, similar to the maria found on the Moon.

**solar constant**
The measure of the solar energy received at an area of one square centimeter per second outside the Earth's atmosphere in the direction of the Sun's vertical rays.

**solar cosmic radiation**
The corpuscular radiation emitted by the Sun during a flare outburst that ionizes the Earth's atmosphere and produces auroras in the polar regions.

**solar eclipse**
The obscuration of the Sun by the new Moon which can be observed where the Moon's shadow strikes the Earth's surface.

**solar nebula**
The spherical cloud of dust and gas that contracted into a lenticular disk from which the solar system evolved.

**space-time**
In relativity, a four-dimensional continuum consisting of three coordinates of space and one of time in which a physical event can be described.

**spectroscope**
An instrument used to analyze light in different wavelengths.

**spectroscopic binary**
Binary stars with small angular separations that cannot be resolved as individual points of light but are identified by their spectral characteristics.

**spherical aberration**
An image defect caused by the spherical shape of a lens or mirror. Central light rays have a greater focal length than the marginal rays.

**spiral arms**
The spiral structure in a plane that winds around the nucleus of a galaxy and is composed of young stellar associations, emission nebulae, and dust and gas lanes.

**spiral galaxy**
A stellar system with young stars and interstellar matter arranged in spiral arms that extend outward and around the nucleus of the galaxy.

**spiral tracers**
Objects such as stars and nebulae that are used by astronomers to plot the spiral structure of the Galaxy.

**sporadic meteor**
A single or random streak of light that is not associated with a meteor shower.

**spring tide**
The pronounced high tide that occurs when the Moon is at new or full phase and the gravitational attraction of the Moon and Sun are additive.

**standard distance indicators**
Various celestial objects used by astronomers to measure distances to remote galaxies.

**standard model**
The big-bang theory of the universe.

**standard time**
The local mean time of the standard meridian; zone time. Every locale within a zone keeps the same clocktime.

**starburst galaxies**
Interacting galaxies where interstellar matter is squeezed into dense clouds triggering a period of intense star formation.

**Stefan-Boltzmann law**
The equation that expresses how the total radiation emitted by a black body is directly proportional to the fourth power of its absolute temperature.

**stellar parallax**
One-half the apparent parallactic displacement of a relatively nearby star against the background of more distant stars caused by the revolution of the Earth around the Sun. The angle made by the radius of the Earth's orbit observed at the star's distance.

**stony meteorites**
A class of meteorites mainly composed of silicate minerals.

**stony iron meteorites**
A class of iron meteorites containing olivine, a silicate of magnesium.

**stratosphere**
The portion of the Earth's atmosphere that begins at about 12 km above sea level and extends to 50 km.

**strong nuclear force**
The attractive force which holds the constituent protons and neutrons together in the nucleus of an atom.

**subduction**
Geologically, the movement of one tectonic plate beneath another into the partially molten asthenosphere.

**summer solstice**
The northernmost point on the ecliptic; the position of the Sun on June 21, the first day of summer in the northern hemisphere.

**sunspot cycle**
An 11-year fluctuation in the number of sunspots appearing in the Sun's photosphere.

**sunspots**
The bipolar magnetic regions of lower temperature where twisted magnetic field lines from the interior break through the Sun's photosphere.

**supercluster**
A large aggregation of thousands of galaxies that extends for hundreds of millions of light-years.

**supergiant star**
A huge luminous red star located above the red giant stars on the giant branch in the H-R diagram.

**supergranules**
Large convective cells enclosed in a network of small spikelike prominences rising in the Sun's chromosphere.

**superior conjunction**
The apparent position of an inferior planet in which the Sun is between the planet and the Earth.

**superior planet**
A planet revolving in an orbit beyond the Earth's orbit.

**supernova**
A spectacular eruption that occurs in the late evolutionary stages of some massive stars. Current models for a Type I supernova outburst suggest a white dwarf member of a binary system as the progenitor star. A Type II supernova explosion is caused by the core collapse of a red supergiant or blue supergiant star.

**synchrotron radiation**
Electromagnetic radiation emitted by high-speed electrons spiraling around magnetic field lines.

**synodic month**
The interval of time required by the Moon to complete its phases.

**synodic period**
The time between two successive configurations between a planet and the Sun.

## T

**tail (comet)**
An extension of a comet's coma accelerated by the solar-wind plasma and solar radiation pressure to form an ion tail of ionized molecules and a dust tail composed of microscopic particles and grains.

**T associations**
An aggregation of pre-main-sequence T Tauri stars that have unpredictable light variations linked to their interaction with surrounding nebulosity.

**tektites**
Glassy specimens that may represent terrestrial rock fused by meteoric impact or extraterrestrial fragments that ablated during passage through the Earth's atmosphere.

**temperature**
The measure of the average random motion of the molecules in a body.

**terrae**
Regions on Venus that are comparable to continental land masses on Earth.

**terrestrial planet**
One of the Earth-like planets, Mercury, Venus, Earth, and Mars.

**Tharsis bulge**
A large volcanic dome centered on the equator of Mars.

**theory**
An hypothesis that has been verified through observation or experimentation.

**thermal equilibrium**
In the Sun and stars, the balance between the amount of energy generated in the core and the amount radiated into space.

**tidal flexing**
The periodic variation in the tidal bulge raised on the surface of Jupiter's satellite Io, caused by the changes in distance between the planet and satellite.

**transit**
The passage of a star or other body across the observer's celestial meridian.

**triple alpha process**
A nuclear reaction whereby three helium nuclei form a carbon nucleus.

**Trojan asteroids**
A group of asteroids that revolve in Jupiter's orbit and form an equilateral triangle with Jupiter and the Sun. See *Lagrangian point*.

**tropical year**
The year of the seasons or the time interval required by the Earth to make one revolution with respect to the equinoxes.

**troposphere**
The first layer of the Earth's atmosphere above the surface to a height of about 12 km.

**true relative orbit**
In a binary system, the relative orbit of a secondary star in its own plane.

**T Tauri star**
A huge pulsating pre-main-sequence star.

**Tunguska meteorite**
A brilliant fireball of unknown origin that exploded over central Siberia on June 30, 1908.

## U

**UBV system**
A photometric system where stellar magnitudes are determined in ultraviolet (U), blue (B), green-yellow or visual (V).

**undivided plains terrain**
A large flat region covering a large portion of the northern hemisphere of Mars.

**universal time, UT**
Local mean time for a position on the Greenwich meridian.

## V

**Valles Marineris**
An extensive canyon complex that stretches 4000 km across the surface of Mars.

**Van Allen radiation belts**
Two concentric rings of high-energy protons and electrons in the Earth's magnetosphere discovered by James Van Allen.

**vernal equinox**
One of two points of intersection of the ecliptic and the celestial equator; the position of the Sun on about March 21, the first day of spring in the northern hemisphere.

**Virgo cluster**
The nearest supercluster located in the direction of the constellation Virgo.

**visual binary**
A binary system where the stars are resolved in a telescope and can be observed visually.

**voids**
Twisted, interconnected regions of space that form gaps between superclusters.

## W

**walled plains**
The largest lunar craters up to 200 km diameter.

**wavelength**
The distance between two successive points (from crest to crest or trough to trough) of a wave motion.

**weak nuclear force**
The force that is responsible for particle decays, notably the decay of neutrons into protons.

**white dwarf star**
A terminal stage where a star has been compressed to the size of a planet but remains as massive as the Sun.

**Widmanstätten patterns**
Geometric figures that appear in the crystalline structure of iron meteorites when their cut surfaces are polished and etched with acid.

**Wien's displacement law**
The equation that expresses how the wavelength of maximum intensity of radiation emitted by a black body varies inversely with respect to the absolute temperature.

**winter solstice**
The southernmost point on the ecliptic; the position of the Sun on December 22, the first day of winter in the northern hemisphere.

# Z

**Zeeman effect**
The splitting of spectral lines in a magnetic field discovered by the Dutch physicist P. Zeeman in 1896.

**zenith**
The point on the celestial sphere directly above the observer at 90° altitude from the horizon.

**zero-age main-sequence (ZAMS) object**
The stage in a star's evolution when thermal and hydrostatic equilibrium are reached and hydrogen nuclei are converted to helium in a nuclear process that liberates a vast amount of energy.

**zodiac**
A series of twelve constellations along the ecliptic depicting various gods, heroes, and animals.

**zodiacal light**
The glow of sunlight reflected by meteoric dust found in the plane of the ecliptic.

**zones**
Light-colored bands of stratified clouds in the atmosphere of Jupiter.

# c r e d i t s

## ILLUSTRATIONS

### Chapter 1

**Figure 1.16:** From Sune Engelbrektson, *Stars, Planets, and Galaxies.* Copyright © 1975 Ridge Press/Bantam Books. Reprinted by permission of Sune Engelbrektson.

### Chapter 2

**Figure 2.4:** From Sune Engelbrektson, *Stars, Planets, and Galaxies.* Copyright © 1975 Ridge Press/Bantam Books. Reprinted by permission of Sune Engelbrektson; **Map I:** From Wil Tirion, "Sky Almanac" in *Astronomy,* April 1989. Copyright © 1989 Kalmbach Publishing Company, Waukesha, WI. Reprinted by permission; **Map II:** From Wil Tirion, "Sky Almanac" in *Astronomy,* July 1989. Copyright © 1989 Kalmbach Publishing Company, Waukesha, WI. Reprinted by permission; **Map III:** From Wil Tirion, "Sky Almanac" in *Astronomy,* October 1991. Copyright © 1991 Kalmbach Publishing Company, Waukesha, WI. Reprinted by permission; **Map IV:** From Wil Tirion, "Sky Almanac" in *Astronomy,* January 1992. Copyright © 1992 Kalmbach Publishing Company, Waukesha, WI. Reprinted by permission.

### Chapter 5

**Figure 5.23 (top):** Diagram by Steven Simpson, *Sky and Telescope* Magazine. Reprinted by permission.

### Chapter 7

**Figure 7.2:** From Charles C. Plummer and David McGeary, *Physical Geology,* 4th ed. Copyright © 1988 Wm. C. Brown Communications, Inc., Dubuque, Iowa. All Rights Reserved. Reprinted by permission.

### Chapter 9

**Figure 9.12:** Diagram courtesy of *Sky and Telescope* Magazine.

### Chapter 10

**Figure 10.25:** Courtesy *Sky and Telescope* Magazine.

### Chapter 11

**Figure 11.13:** Diagram by Steven Simpson, courtesy of *Sky and Telescope* Magazine.

### Chapter 12

**Figure 12.4:** From *Sun and Earth* by Friedman. Copyright ©1986 by W. H. Freeman and Company. Reprinted by permission; **Figure 12.22:** From *Sun and Earth* by Friedman. Copyright © 1986 by W. H. Freeman and Company. Reprinted by permission.

### Chapter 13

**Figure 13.13:** Diagram by Steven Simpson, courtesy of *Sky and Telescope* Magazine; **Figure 13.15:** Courtesy of *Sky and Telescope* Magazine.

### Chapter 14

**Figure 14.3:** From *Principles of Astrometry* by Peter van de Kamp. Copyright © 1967 by W. H. Freeman and Company. Reprinted with permission; **Figure 14.5:** From *Principles of Astrometry* by Peter van de Kamp. Copyright © 1967 by W. H. Freeman and Company. Reprinted with permission; **Figure 14.14:** From *Astronomical Photometry* by Arne A. Henden and Ronald M. Kaitchuck (Willmann-Bell, 1982). Reprinted by permission.

### Chapter 15

**Figure 15.13:** From *The Youngest Stars in New Frontiers in Astronomy* by George H. Herbig. Copyright © 1990 by W. H. Freeman and Company. Reprinted with permission.

### Chapter 16

**Figure 16.3:** Source: Data from *The H R Diagram,* A. G. Davis Philip and D. S. Hayes (eds.), 1978; **Figure 16.6:** From Michele Gerbaldi, "Binary Stars" in *The Cambridge Atlas of Astronomy,* 2d ed., Jean Audouze and Guy Israel (eds.). Copyright © Cambridge University Press, New York, NY. Reprinted by permission.

### Chapter 17

**Figure 17.11:** From "Updating Galactic Spiral Structure" in *The New Astronomy and Space Science Reader* by Brandt and Maran. Copyright © 1977 by W. H. Freeman and Company. Reprinted with permission; **Figure 17.13:** Courtesy of Patrick Thaddeus; **Figure 17.21:** Source: Dennis Downes, Arthur E. Maxwell, and M. L. Meeks, 36.6-meter radio telescope at Westford, MA.

### Chapter 18

**Figure 18.5:** From Don Mathewson, "Mt. Stromlo and Siding Springs Observatory: The Mini-Magellanic Cloud" in *Mercury,* March/April 1984, p. 57. Reprinted by permission; **Figure 18.20:** *Uranometria 2000.0, Vol. I—The Northern Hemisphere to -6* by Wil Tirion, Barry Rappaport, and George Love, Copyright © 1987, 1988 by Willmann-Bell, Inc. Reprinted by permission.

### Chapter 19

**Figure 19.2:** Copyright © Mullard Radio Observatory, Cambridge, England; Reprinted by permission of J. E. Baldwin. **Figure 19.25A:** *Uranometria 2000.0, Vol. I—The Northern Hemisphere to -6* by Wil Tirion, Barry Rappaport, and George Love, Copyright © 1987, 1988 by Willmann-Bell, Inc. Reprinted by permission.

### Chapter 20

**Figure 20.16:** Courtesy of *Sky and Telescope* Magazine.

credits

## PHOTOGRAPHS

Harvard University; **15.4:** © Royal Observatory, Edinburgh/Anglo-Australian Telescope Board/Photo Researchers, Inc.; **15.5:** © Anglo-Australian Telescope Board; **15.6:** © Royal Observatory, Edinburgh/Anglo-Australian Telescope Board, 1982; **15.7:** © Anglo-Australian Telescope Board, 1981; **15.11B:** Data obtained at the Five College Radio Astronomy Observatory, University of Massachusetts by R. Snell and F. P. Schloerb, *Science* 248: 568, May 4, 1990. © 1990 by the AAAS; **15.12:** The Slide Centre/The Rickitt Encyclopedia of Slides; **15.14:** © Anglo-Australian Telescope Board, 1991; **15.17:** National Optical Astronomy Observatories; **15.18:** Tersch; **15.19:** National Optical Astronomy Observatories; **15.20:** Yerkes Observatory; **15.22:** © Anglo-Australian Telescope Board, 1981; **15.23:** U.S. Naval Observatory

## Chapter 16

**Chapter Opener:** Smithsonian Institution; **Figure 16.5:** © Dr. Hilmar W. Duerbeck/SPL/Photo Researchers, Inc.; **16.7:** Astronomical Society of the Pacific; **16.10A:** Smithsonian Institution; **16.10B:** Courtesy National Radio Astronomy Observatory/AUI; **16.11A,B:** Palomar Observatory/California Institute of Technology; **16.13:** Courtesy of the European Southern Observatory; **16.14:** © Anglo-Australian Telescope Board; **16.15:** © Royal Observatory, Edinburgh/Anglo-Australian Telescope Board/ Photo Researchers, Inc.; **16.16:** National Optical Astronomy Observatories/Dr. Nigel Sharp; **16.20:** Painting by Helmut K. Wimmer; **16.23:** The Slide Centre/The Rickitt Encyclopedia of Slides

## Chapter 17

**Chapter Opener:** © Paul DiMare; **Figure 17.1:** © Anglo-Australian Telescope Board; **17.2:** © Royal Observatory, Edinburgh/Anglo-Australian Telescope Board, 1987; **17.3:** © Dennis di Cicco; **17.7:** Palomar Observatory/California Institute of Technology; **17.8:** © Royal Observatory, Edinburgh/Anglo-Australian Telescope Board, 1979; **17.9:** Anglo-Australian Telescope Board; **17.10:** © Anglo-Australian Telescope Board, 1992; **17.12:** Courtesy Gart Westerhout U. S. Naval Observatory; **17.13A:** Thomas M. Dame, Harvard-Smithsonian Center for Astrophysics; **17.17A,B:** Courtesy Stuart N. Vogel; **17.18:** NASA; **17.20:** National Radio Astronomy Observatory/AUI; **17.21:** National Radio Astronomy Observatory/AUI; **17.22:** NASA

## Chapter 18

**Chapter Opener:** © Royal Observatory, Edinburgh/Anglo-Australian Board, 1987; **Figure 18.1:** U.S. Naval Observatory; **18.3A,B:** Dr. Sune Engelbrektson; **18.4A:** © Anglo-Australian Telescope Board, 1984; **18.4B:** © Royal Observatory, Edinburgh/Anglo-Australian Board, 1984; **18.6, 18.7:** Palomar Observatory/California Institute of Technology; **18.8, 18.9:** Photographs by Halton C. Arp, Max-Planck-Institute for Astrophysics; **18.10:** © Anglo-Australian Telescope Board; **18.11:** Space Telescope Science Institute/NASA; **18.12:** Palomar Observatory/California Institute of Technology; **18.13:** M. J. Geller and J. P. Huchra, Smithsonian Astrophysical Observatory; **18.14:** The Slide Centre/The Rickitt Encyclopedia of Slides; **18.15A–H:** Photograph by Halton C. Arp, Max-Planck-Institute for Astrophysics; **18.16:** © Anglo-Australian Telescope Board, 1992; **18.17:** National Optical Astronomy Observatories; **18.18:** Courtesy Alar Toomre; **18.19A–D:** These images were obtained at the Palomar Observatory, California Institute of Technology, Courtesy of D. Sanders; **18.20A:** Rudy Schild, Smithsonian Astrophysical Observatory; **18.21A,B:** U.S. Naval Observatory; **18.23:** Palomar Observatory/California Institute of Technology

## Chapter 19

**Chapter Opener:** © Paul DiMare; **Figure 19.1:** Palomar Observatory/California Institute of Technology; **19.3 A,B:** National Radio Astronomy Observatory/AUI; **19.4:** © Anglo-Australian Telescope Board; **19.5, 19.6, 19.7:** Smithsonian Institution; **19.8, 19.9:** National Radio Astronomy Observatory; **19.10:** Photograph by Halton C. Arp, Max-Planck-Institute for Astrophysics; **19.11:** Palomar Observatory/California Institute of Technology; **19.12:** National Optical Astronomy Observatories; **19.13:** Courtesy Maarten Schmidt, Caltech; **19.14:** John W. MacKenty, Space Telescope Science Institute and Alan Stockton, University of Hawaii; **19.15:** National Optical Astronomy Observatories; **19.18A,B:** Wise Observatory of Tel Aviv University; **19.18C:** Courtesy of the Observatory of Haute-Provence, France; **19.23:** Courtesy David H. Roberts, Perry Greenfield, Bernard Burke. Photo taken using the Very Large Array of the National Radio Astronomy Observatory; **19.24:** National Optical Astronomy Observatories

## Chapter 20

**Chapter Opener:** © Dr. Rudolph Schild/SPL/Photo Researchers, Inc.; **20.3:** Courtesy Steven Maddox, Royal Greenwich Observatory; **20.4:** © Dennis di Cicco; **20.12:** Cosmic Background Explorer (COBE) Satellite, courtesy of the NASA Goddard Space Flight Center; **20.19:** COBE Differential Microwave Radiometer results as reported by G. Smoot, et al. in *Astrophysical Journal* 396, L1–L5 (1992)

## ILLUSTRATOR CREDITS

**Illustrious, Inc.:** Figures 1.2, 1.4, 1.5, 1.6, 1.7, 1.8, 1.9, 1.11, 1.12, 1.13, 1.14, 1.15, 1.16, 1.17, 1.19, 2.2, 2.3, 2.4, 2.5, 2.6, 2.7, 2.8, 2.16, 2.18, 3.3, 3.4, 3.5, 3.6, 3.9, 3.12, 3.13, 3.14, 3.15, 3.18A, 3.19, 3.21, 4.1, 4.2, 4.3, 4.5, 4.6, 4.7, 4.8, 4.9, 4.10, 4.12, 4.13, 4.14, 4.15, 4.16, 4.17, 4.18, 4.21, 5.1, 5.3, 5.4, 5.5, 5.6, 5.7, 5.10, 5.11B, 5.12, 5.23, 6.2, 6.4, 6.6, 6.8, 6.9, 6.11, 6.12, 6.13, 6.16, 6.20, 6.21, 6.22, 6.24, 7.2, 7.3, 7.4, 7.6, 7.7, 7.9, 7.10, 7.11, 7.13, 7.15, 7.16, 7.18, 7.24, 8.4, 8.6, 8.7, 8.11, 8.15, 8.16, 8.17, 8.26, 9.3, 9.4, 9.7, 9.8, 9.10, 9.13, 9.14, 9.20, 9.21, 10.1, 10.2, 10.4, 10.6, 10.7, 10.8, 10.17, 10.18, 10.21, 10.24, 11.2, 11.3, 11.4, 11.6, 11.7, 11.8B, 11.10, 11.11, 11.13, 12.2, 12.3, 12.4, 12.15, 12.16, 12.22, 12.23, 13.1, 13.2, 13.5, 13.6, 13.9, 13.12, 13.13, 13.14, 13.15, 13.16, 13.18, 14.1, 14.2, 14.3, 14.5, 14.6, 14.8, 14.9, 14.10, 14.11, 14.12, 14.13, 14.14, 14.18, 15.8, 15.9, 15.10, 15.11A, 15.13, 15.15, 15.16, 15.21, 16.1, 16.2, 16.3, 16.4, 16.6, 16.8, 16.9, 16.12, 16.17, 16.18, 16.19, 16.21, 16.24, 17.4, 17.5, 17.6, 17.11, 17.14, 17.15, 17.16, 17.19, 18.2, 18.5, 18.22, 19.2, 19.16, 19.17, 19.19, 19.20, 19.21, 19.22, 19.25B, 20.1, 20.2, 20.5, 20.6, 20.7, 20.8, 20.9, 20.10, 20.11, 20.13, 20.14, 20.15, 20.16, 20.17, 20.18, 20.20, 20.21

**Alice Thiede:** Figure 2.17

# index

index